AN
INTRODUCTION TO
VIROLOGY

CLYDE R. GOODHEART
INSTITUTE FOR BIOMEDICAL RESEARCH, CHICAGO, ILLINOIS

W. B. SAUNDERS COMPANY · PHILADELPHIA · LONDON · TORONTO

1969

W. B. Saunders Company: West Washington Square
Philadelphia, Pa. 19105

12 Dyott Street
London W.C. 1

1835 Yonge Street
Toronto 7, Ontario

An Introduction to Virology

PREFACE

Virology continues its exponential growth. Yet the growth is not uniform: many subdivisions and specialized areas of virology have grown at a much more rapid rate than other areas, resulting in an inevitable fragmentation. This book has attempted to bring some of the fragmented fields back together and to look at viruses as a unified whole, whether they are of bacterial, animal, or plant origin. For this reason the book has been organized on the basis of the molecular interaction of the different viruses with their host cell during the replicative stage, rather than on the basis of a distinction between plant viruses, bacterial viruses, or animal viruses.

It is also for the purposes of unifying the various aspects of virology that the classification chapter was included, although the classification chosen is not universally accepted. The beginning student needs an organizational structure in which to place the various viruses as he becomes acquainted with them. The beauty of the classification proposed by the Provisional Committee for the Nomenclature of Viruses is that it places viruses with similar properties side by side, regardless of their origin.

Advanced students of biology and microbiology attended my course in General Virology at the University of California, Los Angeles, during the spring semesters of 1962, 1963, and 1964. This book is an outgrowth of my experiences in that course, and it is intended as a textbook for students at that level. It presupposes an elementary knowledge of biochemistry, but a formal course in bio-chemistry need not be a prerequisite. It also presupposes a minimal background in mathematics, and for this reason mathematical discussions have been limited whenever possible, and have been derived from only one concept, the Poisson distribution. (Some might argue that mathematical rigor has been stretched a bit in places to achieve this.)

Although practitioners of medicine and virologists working in clinical laboratories may find the book useful, it is primarily intended for the student who is interested in viruses from the basic standpoint and who wants to learn of the contributions made by virologists to the understanding of the molecular basis of genetic expression. For this reason, extensive discussion of mechanisms of viral diseases has been omitted. Likewise, there is minimal discussion of serologic and other techniques of working with viruses.

Many people have helped with the preparation of this text. Drs. Bruce Casto, Tom Benjamin, and John Drake read various parts of the text and offered many useful suggestions; my wife, Barbara, provided editorial help; and many fellow scientists willingly supplied electron micrographs, and in some cases, took special pictures on newly pre-pared material solely for use in this book. For all of these efforts I am especially grateful. I am also thankful to Mrs. Jan Eby for her line drawings and to Mrs. Eby, Mrs. Linda Dema, and Mrs. Linda Tuttle for typing and retyping the many drafts. And last, I would like to thank the publishers for their several years of patience in awaiting the arrival of the manuscript.

C. R. GOODHEART

CONTENTS

1

INTRODUCTION 1

2

SIZE AND MORPHOLOGY OF VIRAL PARTICLES 9

3

CLASSIFICATION 37

4

ASSAY OF VIRUS SUSPENSIONS 60

5

ACTION OF PHYSICAL AND CHEMICAL AGENTS ON VIRIONS 78

6

SEROLOGY OF VIRUSES 99

7

REPLICATION OF BACTERIAL VIRUSES CONTAINING DOUBLE-STRANDED DNA 116

8

BIOCHEMISTRY OF PHAGE-INFECTED CELLS: THE LYTIC CYCLE 136

9

REPLICATION OF ANIMAL VIRUSES CONTAINING DNA 157

10

REPLICATION OF PHAGES CONTAINING SINGLE-STRANDED DNA 187

11

REPLICATION OF VIRUSES THAT CONTAIN RNA 199

12

VIRUSES "PARASITIC" ON OTHER VIRUSES 227

13

INTERFERENCE WITH VIRAL REPLICATION 238

14

VIRAL GENETICS: MUTATION 257

15

VIRAL GENETICS: RECOMBINATION 273

16

LYSOGENY 291

17

TUMOR VIRUSES THAT CONTAIN RNA 315

18

TUMOR VIRUSES THAT CONTAIN DNA 332

19

WHAT IS A VIRUS? 355

REFERENCES 366

INDEX 423

1

INTRODUCTION

A virus, consisting of genetic material enclosed in a protective coating, is one of the simplest entities able to reproduce. Viruses have no metabolic systems, they have no intrinsic motility, they cannot respond to stimuli, and they do not grow in the usual sense. The ability to maintain genetic continuity, with the possibility for mutation, is the only basis for considering viruses to be alive.

Furthermore, the mechanism by which viruses reproduce is unique in biology. This seems to be true whether one is talking about a virus of green plants, bacteria, mushrooms, algae, insects, higher animals, or humans. In all cases, during the reproductive cycle the genetic material of the virus becomes a functional part of the cell it has infected. The genes added to the cell by the virus cause the infected cell either to produce more virus particles, with cell death usually the end result, or to become changed and acquire new characteristics. The interaction of the genetic material of the virus with that of the cell is the main theme of this book.

WHAT IS A VIRUS?

An infectious agent is considered to be a virus if it meets certain criteria. These criteria have changed from time to time as more knowledge has accumulated. Some time ago, an important one was filterability. The experimenter working with an unknown infectious agent used a filter with pores small enough to retain bacteria. If the unknown agent could pass through the pores, it was called a "filterable virus."

Alternatively, a preparation containing the agent was examined with an ordinary optical microscope. If the infectious agent could not be seen, it was submicroscopic and therefore viral. However, filterability and submicroscopic size are no longer valid criteria. We now know that some viruses can be seen with the microscope under certain conditions, whereas some bacteria are difficult to see; and some bacteria pass through filter pores that retain some of the largest viruses.

Culturability was another criterion. Although bacteria usually can grow on artificial media, viruses are obligate intracellular parasites and can replicate only in actively metabolizing cells. Distinguishing viruses from bacteria on this basis is not very reliable either. Because some bacteria are fastidious and require special media, lack of growth of an unknown agent might indicate only that the proper medium was not tried, rather than that the unknown agent was viral.

As more information has been accumulated about viruses, bacteria, and other tiny organisms, the classic criteria have gradually been replaced. Organisms not meeting the new criteria are no longer considered to be "true" viruses. For example, the psittacosis agent, Eaton agent (a pleuropneumonia-like organism), and trachoma agent are no longer viruses.

It is very difficult to define the "true" viruses. Most are submicroscopic and therefore cannot be seen with an ordinary optical microscope. "True" viruses consist of a nucleic acid core enclosed in a protein or protein-lipid shell. The nucleic acid is usually a single molecule of either RNA or DNA, either single- or double-stranded. No "true" virus possesses both RNA and DNA.

The "true" viruses are unique in that they direct an infected cell to make virus parts and then to assemble the parts into finished virus particles. Thus, viruses are made in a cell and do not grow in the sense that bacteria grow larger and divide. At some time in their growth cycle, viruses characteristically become part of the infected cell. Unlike conventional organisms, viruses can be reproduced entirely from their nucleic acid.

Stating some of their characteristics, however, does not answer the question, What are viruses? Lwoff (1957) discussed this problem eloquently and thoroughly. He concluded that "viruses should be considered as viruses because viruses are viruses." There is no completely satisfactory definition of viruses, nor is there agreement as to whether they are organisms. Even the question, Are viruses alive? cannot be answered. This book, however, in part represents an examination of these problems. After we have discussed virus properties, we will consider these questions again; but in the meantime, for the sake of simplicity, we will consider viruses to be living organisms.

WHERE DID VIRUSES ORIGINATE?

Several possibilities have been put forward about the origin of viruses. Perhaps viruses are a degenerate kind of cell — a cell that over a long period of time and by successive mutations lost one enzyme system after another so that now it is completely dependent upon the host cell's enzyme systems. If this is how viruses arose, the process could have happened repeatedly to give rise to each present-day kind of virus, or it could have occurred once, with all viruses evolving from the one ancestral virus.

Another possibility is that viruses could be parts of cells that, through some odd set of circumstances, acquired autonomy in the sense of having an extracellular existence. A mitochondrion, ribosome, or other cell organelle could thus be the forerunner of modern viruses. Each different main group of viruses may have come from a different cell organelle.

It is also possible that viruses represent a primitive form of life — perhaps the first aggregation of nucleic acid and protein with any resemblance of life that gave rise to all higher forms of plants and animals. There is, of course, no way of deciding for or against this or any of the other proposals for the origin of viruses, but the last possibility seems most improbable. Viruses make such extreme demands on their environment for replication that it is difficult to imagine how they could have persisted in the rigors of the primeval world.

HIGHLIGHTS IN THE DEVELOPMENT OF VIROLOGY

Viruses have victimized mankind since the beginning of history. Rameses, an Egyptian king in the period around 1100 B.C., died of an acute illness at the age of 40 years. The skin lesions on his mummified remains resemble very closely those of smallpox. It was not until two or three hundred years ago, however, that medical descriptions of illnesses resembling smallpox began to appear.

In the fifteenth and sixteenth centuries, smallpox was so prevalent that the people of the time accepted it as a part of life and hardly considered smallpox an illness, much as we today are only slightly concerned by colds. Smallpox occurred both as sporadic cases and as epidemics, and vast numbers of people were killed or disfigured by the disease.

Poliomyelitis is another disease dating to antiquity. The skeleton of an Egyptian who lived 5000 years ago has been found with a leg deformity similar to that typically caused by paralytic poliomyelitis. Not until the eighteenth century, however, was poliomyelitis recognized and described as a disease. Epidemics began about 1890 and increased in severity until 1955, when a vaccine became available. It is now a disappearing disease.

Yellow fever has also influenced the course of history. For centuries yellow fever has been widespread in tropical regions and in other parts of the world, including the United States. The prevalence of yellow fever caused severe hardship to African trading ships of the seventeenth and eighteenth centuries; and, according to Burnet (1945), disease of the crews probably accounts for the legends of the "Flying Dutchman" and the "Ancient Mariner."

At the beginning of this century, yellow fever was so common that it slowed construction of the Panama Canal. In 1900 a special investigative team dispatched by the U. S. Army Commission discovered that certain mosquitoes are the vector. It was not possible to complete the Canal until public health measures eradicated mosquitoes from Panama. Further use of these measures also cleared the United States of yellow fever.

People and their domesticated animals have suffered from severe infectious disease for centuries, but the causes did not become known until recently. Preventive measures sometimes became available before the cause of a disease was discovered. It was generally known in the eighteenth century that a person who had had smallpox did not contract the disease when exposed a second time. In fact, people sometimes deliberately exposed themselves or their children to a person with the disease. This was obviously a dangerous way to acquire an immunity; better methods were needed.

Jenner (1798) was the first to record any experiments with viral material. He observed that dairy maids who had acquired cowpox by milking diseased cows were immune to smallpox. He found that he could give cowpox to susceptible people by scratching some material from a cowpox lesion into the skin of their arm. A local reaction occurred and the person developed an immunity to smallpox. Jenner found that a previous case of natural smallpox conferred no greater immunity to smallpox than did a mild cowpox infection.

Jenner's work was noteworthy from several standpoints, not the least of which was the development of the first vaccine. His scientific, experimental approach to the problem was also remarkable, as science was in its infancy and the scientific method was just developing. Nothing was known about either bacteria or viruses, but Jenner deduced that he had a method for causing immunity to natural smallpox. Vaccination has been used for nearly two centuries and is still performed essentially as he developed it. Smallpox is now virtually eliminated from many parts of the earth.

In the late 1800's, Pasteur (1884) turned his attention to rabies, a disease that is common and mild in some mammals, but almost invariably fatal in humans. Pasteur apparently believed that spinal cords of rabid animals contained bacteria that caused the disease. He presumably reasoned that these bacteria could not be cultured because the right medium had not yet been developed. We now know, of course, that rabies is caused by a virus, which cannot be cultured on artificial media.

Unlike Jenner, Pasteur did not have at his disposal a natural mild disease related to rabies with which to create immunity in humans. He therefore took the natural, quite virulent rabies virus from a diseased dog and inoculated it into the brain of a rabbit. When the animal died, he inoculated material from it into another rabbit. With each subsequent passage, the virus caused a more severe disease in rabbits and a less severe disease in dogs.

In this way, Pasteur was able to develop the equivalent of Jenner's cowpox: a virus best adapted to another species, able to produce human immunity without significant disease. This approach to vaccine production has been used successfully for other viruses since Pasteur's time. For instance, there are now "live" virus vaccines for yellow fever, poliomyelitis, and measles.

Jenner and Pasteur developed their vaccines without understanding the nature of the infectious agent involved. The distinction between viruses and other microorganisms began to become apparent by the experiments of Iwanowsky in the early 1890's. He filtered fluids pressed from tobacco plants afflicted with tobacco mosaic disease through porcelain filters to remove bacteria. The fluids so treated still caused the disease in new plants and therefore must have contained the infectious agent responsible for the disease. Because of the novelty of this kind of experiment, however, the scientific community was not convinced that a new kind of infectious agent had been discovered.

Beijerinck (1898) usually receives credit for the convincing demonstration that the fluids that passed through the filters contained a disease-producing agent. He called this material "contagium vivum fluidum", and he showed that the filtered material did not contain bacteria, since repeated attempts to grow aerobic or anaerobic bacteria from the material were unsuccessful. The infectious agent could diffuse through agar and retain the ability to cause infection. Other experiments showed that the infectious agent must actually multiply in the tissues of the plant and must, therefore, have at least some characteristics of life. Finally, he found that many other plant diseases likewise were caused by a filterable agent and not by a parasite or bacterium.

The first animal virus was obtained from animals with foot-and-mouth disease by Loeffler and Frosch (1898). The causative agent for the disease was filterable, so by this criterion it was not a bacterium. It could have been a toxin, but if so, it would have to be many times more powerful than any known toxin. Furthermore, because the disease could be passed from animal to animal with great dilution at each passage, the causative agent would have to be reproducing. They concluded that the agent of foot-and-mouth disease was not a toxin but was a minute organism smaller than any known bacterium.

Viruses of other animals soon were discovered. Ellermann and Bang reported the cell-free transmission of chicken leukemia in 1908. Three years later Rous discovered that solid tumors of chickens could be transmitted by cell-free filtrates. This discovery implied that solid tumors of chickens could be caused by viruses. Thus, not only were chickens added to the list of animals susceptible to viruses, but also the first tumor viruses were discovered.

Several years later, Twort (1915) discovered bacterial viruses. He had been working with micrococci growing on agar and observed that an occasional colony would become clear or "glassy," as he called it. The material from "glassy" colonies could be transferred to new colonies and would cause the new colonies to become "glassy."

A prolonged, heated argument over the nature of this material resulted. Some proclaimed that the bacteriophage, as it had been named by d'Herelle, was in actuality an enzyme produced in bacteria. D'Herelle (1922), however, performed an experiment with bacteria growing in suspension showing that the infectious material must reproduce. He removed a small sample of a culture that had cleared by action of the bacteriophage and added it to a fresh bacterial culture. After the new culture cleared, he repeated the process. Each time he did this, the fresh culture would also become clear. He calculated that after many repetitions the original material had been diluted 10^{3982} times, so there was no possibility that any of the original material was present in the final culture. This reasoning led him to the conclusion that because the activity had not been lost in the great dilution, the agent that caused the clearing must have reproduced and must, therefore, be a living microorganism, but one of unknown taxonomic relation to other organisms. D'Herelle wondered,

Is it a protozoon, a fungus, a bacterium? Does it belong to a kingdom which is neither the vegetable nor the animal—a still simpler form of life than any which we at present know? These are questions which cannot at present be answered. All that we know of it is that it is an ultramicroscopic organism, a filterable being, parasite of bacteria endowed with functions of assimilation and reproduction—functions which characterize the living nature of the being which possess these properties.

Gratia, among many others, was unwilling to accept the notion that there might be some form of life responsible for the clearing action. In 1922 he wrote,

There are no unquestionable proofs that the bacteriophage is a living organism.

The assumption of the bacteriophage being a filtrable virus for bacteria was suggested by two main facts: (a) the power of reproduction possessed by the lytic agent, and (b) the localization of the lysis to certain round spots of clarification when a very diluted lytic agent is poured over the surface of an agar culture of sensitive bacteria. Although easily explained by the virus theory, yet both facts are not unquestionable proofs of the living nature of the bacteriophage, because they are by no means exclusive features of living beings.

Fire is not living, and yet fire is endowed with power of reproduction. When once lighted, thanks to an initial impulsion such as an electric spark or the mere striking of a match, it can be indefinitely reproduced if fuel is provided.

Recent years have witnessed a rapid growth in our knowledge of the biology of viruses. In 1935, Wendell Stanley crystallized tobacco mosaic virus that he had extracted from infected tobacco plants. Before and after repeated crystallization, the virus had the ability to reproduce and cause typical mosaic disease. The crystallization of a biological material thought to be alive raised many philosophical questions about the nature of life. Here was a biological material that could be crystallized and handled in the way that one would treat any pure chemical, and it was able to reproduce. Since that time, many other viruses have been crystallized.

The contributions of Sir Macfarland Burnet of Australia deserve special mention. During his long and productive career he frequently has been the first to observe, study, and explain phenomena in bacterial and animal virology. Other workers, often many years later, study the same phenomena in greater detail, building upon the ideas set forth by Burnet.

The development of ideas in biology, as in other sciences, often occurs in steps of increasing detail. As a phenomenon is seen and understood at one level of sophistication, new techniques are developed that allow the perception of more detail. This usually results in a period of intense activity that lasts until the new level of detail is understood and explained and conflicts are resolved.

Such a period of intense activity began about 1950 with the study of bacterial viruses. Max Delbrück recognized that phage would be a useful tool for studying genetics. He discovered recombination in phage about the same time that Alfred Hershey also discovered it. Many other workers joined in, eventually obtaining sufficient information to explain most of the mechanisms by which genetic information is stored, replicated to be transmitted to offspring, and transcribed to control protein synthesis.

Delbrück also investigated the cycle of infection that begins when a phage enters a bacterial cell and ends when many progeny phages issue from the cell when it lyses. Others then looked at the growth cycle in greater detail. They found that the infected cell has its biochemical machinery diverted to the making of phage particles. A new form of RNA, now called messenger RNA, was discovered in phage-infected cells. Arthur Kornberg, Seymour Cohen, and many others have played major roles in understanding the biochemical changes of infected cells.

Another major kind of genetic interaction of phage and cell was studied by Andre Lwoff and many others. This type of interaction, called lysogeny, has revealed many new details about the control of transcription of genetic information. The study of all aspects of bacteriophage has played a major role in reshaping the foundations of biology, and a new discipline, molecular biology, has evolved.

A major turning point in the field of animal viruses occurred with the widespread development of tissue culture methods. Later, a quantitative assay was developed for animal viruses, putting work with animal viruses on an equal quantitative basis with that of bacteriophages. With the discovery and development of transformation of cells in tissue culture from a nonmalignant to a malignant state, animal viruses became useful for studies of the malignant process.

These recent developments, as well as many others, will be discussed in more detail in the remainder of this book, as the chapters to follow really amount to a recent history of virology as a branch of modern biology.

Further Reading

Cairns, J., G. S. Stent, and J. D. Watson (eds.): Phage and the Origins of Molecular Biology. Cold Spring Harbor Laboratory of Quantitative Biology, 1966.

Lwoff, A.: The Concept of Virus. Journal of General Microbiology, 17:239-253, 1957.

Schrödinger, E.: What Is Life? London, The Cambridge University Press, 1955.

Williams, G.: Virus Hunters. New York, Alfred A. Knopf, Inc., 1959.

2

SIZE AND MORPHOLOGY
OF VIRUS PARTICLES

Constancy of size and form are essential characteristics of a population of organisms. To say that something biological reproduces implies that not only do new generations arise, but that they resemble previous generations in size and form, at least at some point in the organism's life cycle.

Viruses qualify as organisms in this respect. Individual particles of a given kind of virus are quite uniform in size and morphology. Closely related kinds of viruses resemble each other more than they resemble more distantly related viruses. These properties, to be discussed in this chapter, are a direct result of genetic continuity in virus replication.

MEASUREMENT OF SIZE

Size is one of the oldest criteria for classifying an infectious agent as a virus. In the formative period of virology, a virus was simply an infectious something that was too small to be anything else.

One way to judge its size is to attempt to see the infectious agent with a microscope. The wavelength of light that is used determines the minimum size that can be resolved; under usual conditions a particle must be larger than about 200 millimicrons (mμ) to be visible. Most bacteria, but only a few viruses, are larger than this. Some of the largest viruses have been seen and photographed with the light microscope, but details could not be resolved.

Many indirect methods were developed for measuring the size of viruses too small to be seen with the light microscope. For many years the simplest, most practical, and most popular way to measure size was to see whether the unknown infectious agent would pass through a ceramic filter containing pores small enough to retain bacteria. By this method it was not possible to measure a particle, but it was at least possible to set a limit on its size. Because of the widespread use of this technique, viruses were usually specified as "filterable."

Elford (1938) improved the filtration technique by using sieves with known pore diameters. These sieves, called Gradacol membranes, are made by floating a collodion solution on the surface of water. The average pore diameter can be varied by varying the ratio of collodion and solvent and by varying the drying conditions. Recently, filters made from cellulose and having a graded series of pore diameters have become available from commercial sources. The average pore diameter of either kind of filter membrane can be determined by measuring the pressure required to force air or liquid through it.

The experimenter's job, if he wants to measure the diameter of a virus particle by filtration, is to filter some of the virus preparation through each of the filters in the graded series. He assays the filtrate for the amount of virus infectivity that passes through the filter. If successful, he will find one size that retains the virus, whereas the next filter in the series allows the virus to pass through. Elford called this the filtration end point. Because of the Brownian motion of the virus particles, a correction factor must be used to convert the filtration end point to the diameter of the virus particle. A few examples of filtration end points are shown in Figure 2-1.

However, use of such membranes sometimes results in misleading measurements. Some viruses pass through the pores and adsorb to the membrane; when this occurs, the infectivity does not appear in the filtrates. Other viruses require cell material in order to retain infectivity, and a much larger piece than just the virus particle itself has to go through the membrane. Despite the problems involved, membrane filtration was developed to a high degree of perfection. During much of the history of virology it was the only available method for determining the size of virus particles. More recent and more direct methods of measurement have improved the earlier results only slightly.

The electron microscope has also been useful in size determination. The specimen in an electron microscope is in a high vacuum when it is exposed to the electron beam, and therefore it must be in a suitable form so that it is not altered by the extreme conditions. Furthermore, the specimen must be thin so that electrons can pass through it, and there must be differences in the electron scattering power of the parts of the specimen so that contrast results. These ends

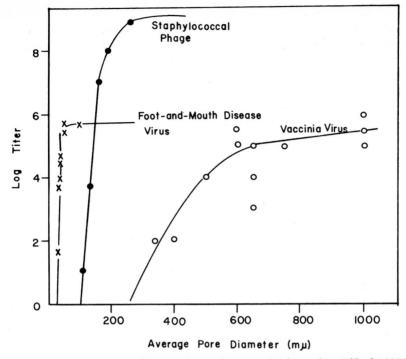

Figure 2-1. Filtration end points of several viruses. (Redrawn from Elford, 1938.)

have been achieved for viruses by three different approaches to specimen preparation.

In one of these methods, a microtome is used to cut exceedingly thin sections. If infected cells are sectioned, the virus particles within the cells can be examined and measured. This method is especially useful in studying the stages of development of a virus; but often shrinkage artifacts or other defects are introduced in steps leading to the sectioning, and the measurements can be misleading. Extracellular virus particles can be sedimented into a pellet and sectioned, but one must be careful about introducing artifacts. Shrinkage can be circumvented to some extent by sectioning crystals of virus particles: Those particles in the center of the crystal are protected somewhat and the measured size is a more accurate reflection of their actual size.

Another approach to preparing specimens was developed by Williams and Wyckoff (1946). Purified virus particles are placed upon an object grid of an electron microscope. The object grid is a thin piece of copper about 2 to 3 mm. in diameter with a meshlike array of holes. It is coated with a thin film of formvar and is used to support the specimen in the way a glass slide is used in a light microscope. The specimen is shadowed with a metal (such as platinum or tungsten), that forms a coating over the particle to increase its contrast. Usually the shadowing is done from an angle; the length of the shadow gives an estimate of the height of the particle over the grid in the same way that the length of the shadow of a tree and the sun's angle can be used to calculate the tree's height. The size of the virus particle can be calculated if the magnification and shadowing angle are known.

Perhaps the best method of determining particle size was developed by Brenner and Horne (1959). In their method, virus particles are mixed with diluted phosphotungstic acid and the mixture is dried on the microscope grid. Phosphotungstic acid is relatively more dense to the electron beam than is the virus particle, which is thus seen in negative contrast. This method yields extremely high resolution so that not only the outline but also many details of the particle's structure can be seen and measured.

Although staining particles by the phosphotungstic acid method is probably the best way to determine the size and structure of virus particles, it too has inaccuracies. Error due to uncertainty in the magnification factor can be eliminated by including as an internal standard some material having known dimensions. However, the particles may be distorted, flattened, or torn apart by surface tension of the drying phosphotungstic acid solution immediately surrounding the particles. Furthermore, because the phosphotungstic acid penetrates some distance into its surface, the particle measures a little smaller than its actual size.

Size alone, however, is no longer an adequate criterion for classifying an infectious agent as a virus. Nevertheless, because of the exceedingly small size of viruses, finding out what they look like has been and still is a most challenging problem for virologists.

STRUCTURE

Initial, relatively crude observations of virus particles with the electron microscope indicated that viruses fall into one of three broad structural groups: roughly spherical, elongated rod-shaped, or tadpole-shaped with head and tail.

In 1956, before the development of high resolution techniques for the electron microscope, Crick and Watson predicted what small plant viruses would look like. Studies by x-ray diffraction had already established that the atoms in a crystal of virus are arranged with great spatial regularity, being packed into repeating units that outline a cube. Thus, the crystallographic symmetry is called cubic.

Because of its small size, the virus can contain only limited genetic information. Therefore, Crick and Watson predicted that the shell of the viral particle must be composed of a small number of different kinds of molecules, perhaps of only one kind. The limited variety of protein molecules would require repeated use of these few as building blocks. Crick and Watson also reasoned that the shell's assembly is based on the principle of minimization of energy, so that the subunits would fall into place spontaneously to form a stable structure, eliminating the necessity for the virus to carry the information for assembly. With these restrictions, there are only a few possible arrangements in which subunits can form a spherical shell. These predictions have been shown to be valid and substantially correct for many viruses by recent high-resolution electron microscope studies.

It is now known that the structure of a virus particle has one of several basic symmetries. The ones discussed by Crick and Watson (1956) have cubic symmetry. Others are helical, and some have either a combination of symmetries (binal symmetry) or no discernible symmetry at all. These last are called complex.

Before looking at a few different kinds of particles in detail, it might be well to define some of the parts of a virus particle. These were named by Lwoff *et al.* (1959) and the definitions were clarified by Caspar *et al.* (1962). The mature virus particle, found extracellularly, is a virion and is not necessarily infectious. A virion may have a membranous envelope such as that possessed by viruses in the herpes group. It has been suggested that the envelope be called a peplos and its subunits peplomers (Lwoff and Tournier, 1966). The virion of most kinds of viruses, however, consists of the capsid (what we have up to now referred to as the protein shell) and the enclosed nucleic acid, together referred to as the nucleocapsid. The structural subunits that form the capsid are called capsomers and are not necessarily equivalent to single protein molecules. Some of the bacterial viruses have additional parts that will be described later.

Viruses With Cubic Symmetry

The regular icosahedron is the geometrical structure underlying the arrangement of capsomers in viruses with cubic symmetry. This was strikingly shown by double-shadowing *Tipula* iridescent virus (Smith and Williams, 1958). The shape of the resulting shadows (Fig. 2-2), with one blunt and one pointed, could occur only if the virus particle was icosahedral.

A regular icosahedron is a solid with 20 faces (each of which is an equilateral triangle), 12 vertexes, and 30 edges. A regular icosahedron, held so that the viewer looks directly at the center of one of the faces, can be rotated into three equivalent positions (Fig. 2-3). This is called a rotational axis of threefold symmetry. Similarly, if an icosahedron is

Figure 2-2. The icosahedral shape of *Tipula* iridescent virus. The virus preparation (*A*) was freeze-dried on the electron microscope grid and metallic shadowed from one direction. The grid was then rotated slightly and shadowed again. The two shadows that resulted are identical to the two shadows in *B*, which were obtained with an icosahedron photographed with light from two angles. (Bar is 100 mμ.) (Smith and Williams, 1958. By permission of the authors and the editor of Endeavor.)

viewed down an axis passing through one of the vertexes, there are five equivalent positions into which it can be rotated. This is called a fivefold symmetry axis. There is a twofold axis passing through the center of the edges. The icosahedron has six fivefold axes, 10 threefold axes, and 15 twofold axes of rotational symmetry.

The arrangement of capsomers on an icosahedron to form the capsid is restricted by geometrical requirements. The same requirements were encountered by Buckminster Fuller, the architect, in his design of geodesic domes. To illustrate the generality of these design principles, Figure 2-4 shows a picture of the dome covering the American Pavilion at the Montreal World's Fair of 1967. Most of the structural units of the dome are hexagons. Some, however, as indicated on the picture, are pentagons; in fact, if the dome were complete, it would have 12 pentagonal units and 2550 hexagonal units.

The theoretically possible number of structural units or cap-

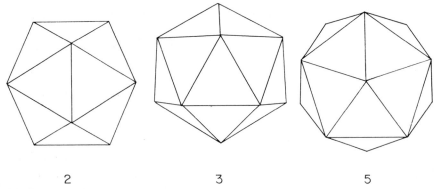

2   3   5

Figure 2-3. The three symmetry axes of the regular icosahedron. The views are along a twofold, a threefold, and a fivefold axis of rotational symmetry.

Figure 2-4. The American Pavilion at the World's Fair, 1967, in Montreal, Canada. The geodesic dome is made mostly of repeating hexagonal units, with some pentagonal units as indicated. (Photo courtesy of the Montreal Gazette.)

somers is given by the formula $10\,x\,(n-1)^2+2$ (Horne and Wildy, 1961). The number of capsomers on an edge is designated by n and includes those at each end of the edge. Two series of possible forms are of interest here: One series is that generated when x (which represents an integer) is equal to one, and the other is that generated when x is equal to three (Table 2-1).

TABLE 2-1. NUMBERS OF STRUCTURAL UNITS IN VIRUS PARTICLES WITH CUBIC SYMMETRY

$x = 1$		$x = 3$	
n	C	n	C
2	12	2	32
3	42	3	122
4	92	4	272
5	162	5	482
6	252	6	752
7	362	7	1082
8	492		
9	642		
10	812		

The two series of numbers are generated by

$$C = 10x(n-1)^2 + 2$$

where C is the number of structural units on the virion, $x = 1$ or 3, and n is the number of units on an edge of the virion.

A diagram is presented in Figure 2-5 to show the arrangement of five-coordinated (pentagonal) and six-coordinated (hexagonal) structural units, as would be found on a virus particle. The pattern in Figure 2-5A is that for $x = 1$, $n = 4$, with 92 subunits making up the particle. In B the pattern is that for $x = 3$, $n = 3$, with 122 units in the particle.

Thus, there is a great variety of virions with cubic symmetry, even though the possibilities are limited by the requirements of geometry. There are some virions with the theoretically minimum number of 12 capsomers and others with 812 capsomers. Of the virions with cubic symmetry that have been photographed using the electron micro-

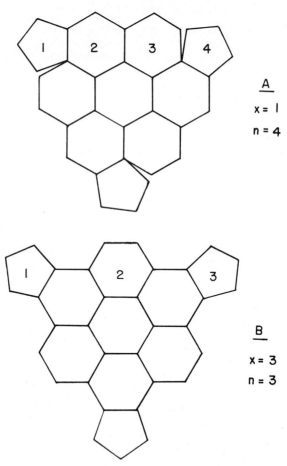

Figure 2-5. Representative arrangements of structural units (hexagons and pentagons) on one of the equilateral triangular facets of a virus particle. The complete particle in **A** would have 92 structural units ($x = 1$, $n = 4$) and that in **B** would have 122 units ($x = 3$, $n = 3$).

scope, several best illustrate the many structural similarities and the variety of structural forms. The following examples have been chosen for the detail with which they are known and for their illustrative value.

Adenoviruses. Adenoviruses constitute a large group, with representatives that infect many species of animals and man. The adenoviruses are by no means the simplest viruses, but their structure, basic to many with cubic symmetry, is clearly evident.

Many excellent electron micrographs of adenoviruses have been prepared. The particles seem to be quite similar, regardless of the species they infect and regardless of their serologic type. Figure 2-6 shows an electron micrograph of a representative adenovirion. The

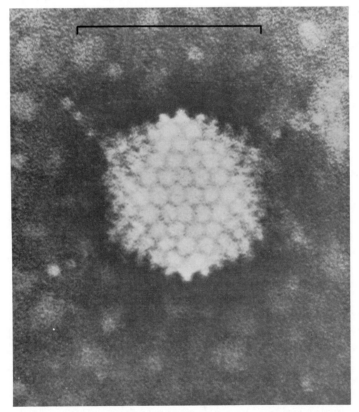

Figure 2-6. A virion of human adenovirus type 5, negatively stained in phosphotungstate, showing the arrangement of capsomers. Five-coordinated capsomers are clearly evident; there are six capsomers on an edge. (Bar is 100 mμ.) (Valentine and Pereira, 1965. By permission of the authors and the editor of the Journal of Molecular Biology.)

first detailed description was by Horne *et al.* (1959), who observed that the virion is about 70 mμ in diameter and has a distinct arrangement of subunits or capsomers. Each capsomer is about 7 mμ in diameter with no discernible substructure; it seems only to be a smooth sphere, although there is some disagreement on this point.

Each of the 20 faces of an adenovirus icosahedron has 21 capsomers with six along each edge. Twelve capsomers are situated at the points of the equilateral triangle and form the vertexes of the icosahedron. Each of these 12 capsomers is surrounded by five neighbors.

The adenovirion has a total of 252 capsomers of two different kinds. Figure 2-7 shows an electron micrograph of human adenovirus type 5 prepared to emphasize the appendages at each vertex as shown in the model. The 12 capsomers with the appendages are serologically distinct from the remaining capsomers and have been named penton antigens (Ginsberg *et al.*, 1966). These antigens can be obtained from infected cells and purified. Such a preparation is shown in Figure 2-8A. The appendages can be removed from the capsomer, such as by treating with trypsin. The isolated appendage is called the fiber antigen and is shown in Figure 2-8B. The majority of the capsomers are hexon antigen, shown in Figure 2-8C. Therefore, an adenovirion has 240 hexon and 12 penton capsomers. The subunits are morphologically similar to the soluble antigens obtained from infected cells (Norrby, 1966; Wilcox *et al.*, 1963). The adenovirion, therefore, probably contains at least two different kinds of protein molecules, and perhaps three (Norrby, 1966; Valentine and Pereira, 1965).

The nucleic acid of an adenovirus particle is a single molecule of double-stranded DNA in linear form (M. Green *et al.*, 1967b). The DNA constitutes about 13 per cent of the dry weight of the virion and has a molecular weight of about 23 million (23×10^6) daltons[*] (Green, 1962a; Green and Piña, 1964; M. Green *et al.*, 1967b). The configuration of the DNA within the adenovirus capsid is unknown. It could be coiled into the hollow interior of the capsid, or it could be interlaced with the capsomers making up the capsid.

Herpesviruses.   Several members of the herpes group of viruses have now been examined in detail with the phosphotungstic acid negative staining method. The viruses of this group have fewer capsomers than the adenoviruses, but they present several new features of interest.

Wildy *et al.* (1960a) made a detailed study of the structure of the herpes simplex virion. The nucleocapsid is about 100 mμ in diameter and has icosahedral symmetry with 5:3:2 symmetry axes. Since the

---

[*]A dalton is the unit of molecular weight equal to the weight of a hydrogen atom.

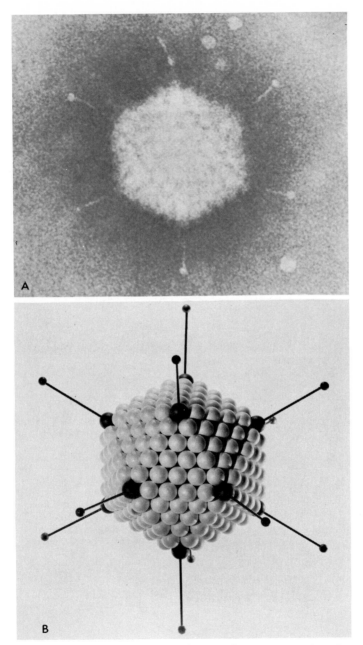

Figure 2-7. *A*, Electron micrograph of human adenovirus type 5 emphasizing the appendages. *B*, A model to demonstrate the structure of the adenovirion. (Valentine and Pereira, 1965. By permission of the authors and the editor of the Journal of Molecular Biology.)

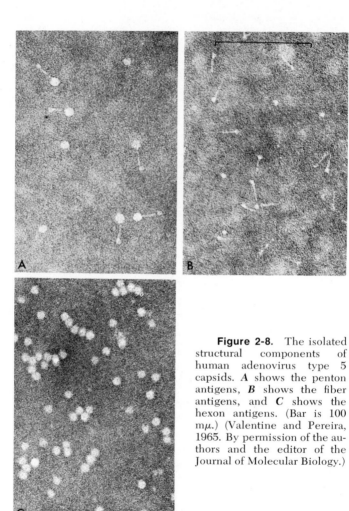

Figure 2-8. The isolated structural components of human adenovirus type 5 capsids. *A* shows the penton antigens, *B* shows the fiber antigens, and *C* shows the hexon antigens. (Bar is 100 mμ.) (Valentine and Pereira, 1965. By permission of the authors and the editor of the Journal of Molecular Biology.)

virion has five capsomers along each edge, 162 capsomers make up the capsid. Figure 2-9 shows an electron micrograph of one of the herpesviruses.

Further detail can be made out in the capsomers. They seem to be hollow, elongated prisms, with either five or six sides. The five-sided prisms occur at the 12 vertexes of the icosahedron, whereas the six-sided ones make up the rest of the capsid. The capsomers measure about 9.5 mμ in width and 12 to 13.5 mμ in length. The axial hole seems to run the length of each capsomer and measures about 4 mμ in diameter. Wildy *et al.* (1960a) estimated the molecular weight of a capsomer to be about 500,000 daltons. The five or six protein subunits comprising the capsomers would thus be 80,000 to 100,000 daltons.

In many electron micrographs of herpesviruses, some particles seem to have empty centers while others seem to have full centers. The center or core region of the so-called "empty" particles is more dense to the electron beam than is the protein capsid. This indicates that the phosphotungstic acid has penetrated through the capsid into the core region. These particles have been called "empty" because they were thought not to possess a DNA core.

Reissig and Kaplan (1962) used 5-fluorouracil to inhibit production of DNA in rabbit kidney cells infected with pseudorabies virus (a member of the herpesvirus group). The cells produced a normal complement of virus capsids, but they were not infectious. Both the infectious form and the noninfectious form were examined in the electron microscope by the use of the phosphotungstic acid tech-

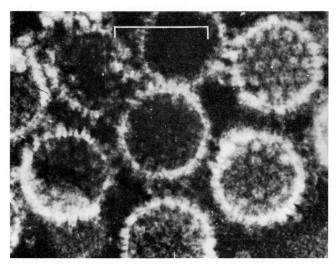

Figure 2-9. Human cytomegalovirus, a member of the herpes group. (Bar is 100 mμ.) (Wright *et al.*, 1964. By permission of the editor of Virology.)

nique and there was no detectable difference in the electron density of the core of the two kinds of particles. Therefore, the presence of phosphotungstic acid in the cores of particles of the herpesvirus group may not indicate the presence or absence of the proper complement of DNA.

The viruses in the herpes group have another characteristic not shared by the adenoviruses: They have an envelope or membrane (peplos) surrounding the nucleocapsid (Wildy *et al.*, 1960a). The composition of the envelope is not known, but possibly it is added to the virus particle as it goes through the cytoplasmic or nuclear membrane during the maturation process.

Experiments performed by D. H. Watson and P. Wildy (1963) are consistent with the idea that the peplos contains cellular material. Antiserum was prepared using either cells or herpesvirions as antigen. Preparations containing both enveloped and naked particles were then treated with the two antiserums. The serum prepared against cells agglutinated the enveloped particles more than it did the particles without envelopes. The serum prepared against herpesvirus agglutinated the particles without membranes more than those with membranes. The membrane surrounding the capsid of the herpes particles therefore probably contains cellular antigens.

Four different kinds of particles have been identified in preparations of herpes simplex virus. There are capsids with electron dense centers ("empty" particles) and without envelopes, similar capsids with envelopes, so-called "full" nucleocapsids with envelopes, and "full" nucleocapsids without envelopes. A similar situation has been reported for varicella (chickenpox) virus by Almeida *et al.* (1962), for cytomegalovirus by Smith and Rasmussen (1963) and Wright *et al.* (1964), and for avian infectious laryngotracheitis virus by Cruickshank *et al.* (1963). These four morphological types are depicted in Figure 2-10.

In any animal virus preparation, not all particles that can be seen in the electron microscope are infectious. With the viruses in the herpes group, the question arises whether infectivity is associated with the presence or absence of a dense core. It has already been noted that Reissig and Kaplan (1962) did not find such a correlation by negative contrast staining.

Holmes and Watson (1963) studied the attachment and penetration of herpesvirus particles into cells. The cells were sectioned at various times after infection and were examined with the electron microscope. Counts were then made of which types of particles had penetrated into the cell. It was found that both the naked and enveloped forms of virion were able to penetrate, but a higher percentage of the enveloped forms were found within the cell than were present in the original virus preparation. The fact that a virus particle was able

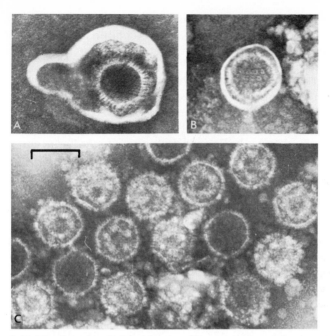

Figure 2-10. The four morphological types of human cytomegalovirus. *A* shows an "empty" enveloped particle, *B* shows a "full" enveloped particle, and *C* has two "empty" and many "full" particles. (Bar is 100 mμ.) (Wright *et al.*, 1964. By permission of the editor of Virology.)

to gain entrance into a cell, however, is not sufficient evidence to establish that the particle actually began a replicative cycle within that cell.

Another attempt to correlate the morphological appearance of herpes simplex virus and its infectivity was made by Watson *et al.* (1963). Differential counts on preparations of herpesvirus were made to determine the relative proportions of each type of virus particle. Infectivity titrations on the same virus preparations were also done in an attempt to show a correlation between infectivity and morphology. It was found that, on the average, one of 10 particles was able to initiate infection. The specific infectivity could be changed, such as by dialyzing the preparation, but this did not change the proportion of morphological types. They were therefore unable to conclude from their study which type of virus particle might be able to initiate infection, or whether all types might be equally infectious.

The herpesviruses contain DNA, amounting to about 6.5 per cent of the particle's weight. The DNA molecule is a double-stranded helix with a molecular weight of about 50 to 80×10^6 daltons (Russell and Crawford, 1963). The particle also contains about 70 per cent protein,

22 per cent phospholipid, and about 1.6 per cent carbohydrate (Wildy and Watson, 1962). There is no detectable RNA (Ben-Porat and Kaplan, 1962).

Polyoma Virus Group.   One of the first attempts to study the structure of polyoma virus was made by Wildy and his colleagues (1960b) using the phosphotungstic acid technique. Highly purified virus was used, yielding excellent electron micrographs. The capsomers seemed to be hollow and elongated, similar to the capsomers occurring in herpes simplex virus. Unlike herpes simplex virus, polyoma virus has no enveloped forms. Some particles were stained in the core, suggesting that perhaps these were "empty" capsids. An electron micrograph of the human wart virus, one of the polyoma-papilloma viruses, is shown in Figure 2-11.

Examination of a large number of particles indicated that there were five-coordinated and six-coordinated capsomers, consistent with 5:3:2 icosahedral symmetry. However, the structure of the virion was not readily apparent, as inspection of Figure 2-11 will show. The triangular facets which are so clearly evident on the adenovirion cannot be seen on virions in this group. The first impressions were that polyoma virus has 42 capsomers, with 12 at the apexes of the icosahedron and the remaining 30 situated over the rest of the capsid.

With 42 capsomers, the structure would fall into the series predicted by the formula with n equal to 3. The next in the series would have four capsomers along each edge and would have a total of 92 subunits. It would seem that the difference between 42 and 92 sub-

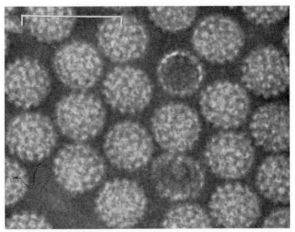

Figure 2-11.   The human papilloma virus. Most of the virions in the picture are "full," but one is "empty." There is one particle (lower center) that seems to be partially disintegrating. (Bar is 100 mμ.) (Courtesy of Dr. A. Klug.)

units should be readily apparent from the electron micrographs; such is not the case, however.

A controversy arose between those in favor of 42 subunits and those in favor of 92 subunits, as is documented in a series of papers (Williams *et al.*, 1960; Melnick, 1962; Mayor and Melnick, 1962; Breedis *et al.*, 1962; Mattern, 1962; Howatson and Crawford, 1963). Excellent electron micrographs have been obtained of many of these viruses, so the problem really is one of interpretation of the micrographs. Neither the 42 nor the 92 capsomer proposal seems to fit the data, but the requirements based on the geometry of how such capsomers could fit together were thought to require one of these arrangements. A compromise solution was needed.

This problem seems to have been resolved by the proposal that the capsomers have a skew arrangement in the shell, an arrangement that does not fall into the theory as originally proposed. Caspar and Klug have been active in developing a new theory of construction of such particles. This aspect is summarized in several papers (Caspar and Klug, 1962; Caspar and Klug, 1963; Caspar, 1965). These workers introduced the triangulation number (Table 2-2), which allows the formation of two series of particles identical to the two series derived from the formula presented before, but it also allows a third series in which the lines connecting the capsomers at the vertexes of the basic icosahedron do not follow a row of capsomers. (The derivation of the triangulation number is given by Caspar, 1965.) The number of morphological subunits on the capsid can be figured as shown in Table 2-2. It should be noted that f in Table 2-2 corresponds to $(n - 1)$ in the formula presented before. The lowest triangulation number for a skew class is 7; such a particle would have 72 subunits.

Another feature of the skew classes of icosahedral particles is that there can be right- and left-handed forms, as is apparent in Figure 2-12. That is, the displacement of the capsomers from a line connect-

TABLE 2-2. THE CLASSES OF ICOSAHEDRAL DELTRAHEDRA*

Class:								
P = 1	1	4	9		16		25	......
P = 3		3		12			27	......
Skew			7	13		19	21	......

Triangulation number:
  $T = Pf^2$ where $P = h^2 + hk + k^2$, h and k are any pair of integers with no common factor, and $f = 1, 2, 3, 4, ...$
Number of structure units:
  $S = 60T$
Number of morphological units:
  $M = 10T + 2 = 10 (T-1)$ hexamers $+ 12$ pentamers

*From Caspar and Klug, 1962.

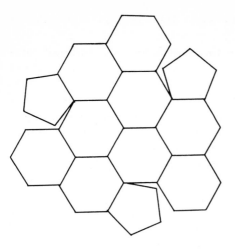

Figure 2-12. The arrangement of structural units on one of the equilateral triangular facets of a virus particle of the skew class; triangulation number, T = 7, of dextro handedness. The complete particle would have 72 structural units.

ing the points of the vertexes of the icosahedron can be either in one direction or the other. The right-handed form is called the dextro or d-form, and the left-handed form is called the levo or l-form. It is possible to determine the handedness of a particle in the electron microscope if the viewer knows the orientation of the object carrier (grid) and whether the near or far surface of the virion is being viewed.

The possibility that the polyoma viruses contain 72 subunits arranged in a skew formation was discussed in a series of three papers (Klug and Finch, 1965; Klug, 1965; Finch and Klug, 1965), which represent perhaps the most careful and thorough studies made of this group of viruses. They concluded that the human wart virus has 72 subunits and is the dextro form. The rabbit, or Shope papilloma virus, also has 72 morphological units, but is of the levo form. An electron micrograph of a rabbit papilloma virion, marked to show the five-coordinated capsomers, is shown in Figure 2-13.

Whether the controversy is settled remains to be seen. It illustrates the difficulty, however, of interpreting what is seen in the electron microscope. What emerges from these various studies is that the viruses of the polyoma and papilloma group are quite similar in their morphology.

Figure 2-13. A rabbit papilloma virion. In **A** the print is marked to show the five-coordinated capsomers. (Courtesy of Dr. A. Klug.)

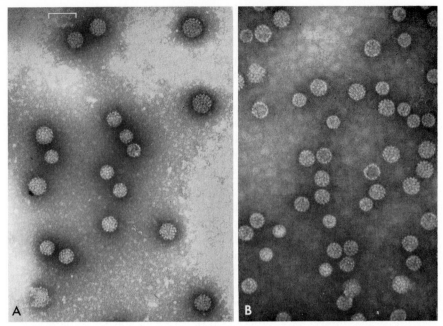

Figure 2-14. Electron micrographs of mixtures of viruses of the polyoma-papilloma group. In *A* are the human papilloma and polyoma viruses and in *B* are the Shope (rabbit) papilloma and polyoma viruses. Polyoma is the smaller of the two kinds of viruses in each mixture. (Bar is 100 mμ.) (Courtesy of Dr. L. V. Crawford.)

They are not, however, identical in size. Crawford and Crawford (1963) showed this by carefully making mixtures of the different viruses on the same electron microscope grid (Fig. 2-14) so that the different virions could be studied in the same view; therefore, variation in magnification factors from one electron microscope to another and from one preparation to another could not account for the slight differences in size, as indicated in Table 2-3.

TABLE 2-3. SIZE COMPARISON OF PAPILLOMA AND
POLYOMA VIRUSES

	PAPILLOMA VIRUS	POLYOMA VIRUS
Shope (rabbit)	53.7	43.5
Bovine	52.0	43.7
Canine	54.7	44.3
Human	52.4	43.0

Each row shows the measurements of virions of a papilloma virus and polyoma virus mixed on the same grid in the electron microscope (see Fig. 2-14). The papilloma viruses, as a group, are larger than polyoma virus (Crawford and Crawford, 1963).

The DNA of the viruses of this group differs slightly in base composition from one to another. All of the viruses that have been studied contain double-stranded DNA in cyclical configuration, in the form of a closed ring, to be discussed in more detail in a later chapter. The DNA constitutes about 13.5 per cent of the particle's weight (Winocour, 1963).

Several of the viruses have been shown to have an elongated form that seems to arise because of an error in virus replication, possibly owing to the skew arrangement of the capsomer. These forms are often quite long, showing very well the helical arrangement of subunits.

The Nucleic Acid.   The arrangement of the nucleic acid in the nucleocapsid is unknown for any of the icosahedral viruses. The presence of nucleic acid is apparently not necessary for capsid formation; or, if the DNA is lost after the capsid is formed, the capsid remains intact, since capsids not containing the DNA appear morphologically normal. In some viruses, such as the polyoma viruses, the particles containing nucleic acid seem to be more stable than those not containing nucleic acid; therefore, the nucleic acid could add some stabilizing influence to the capsid.

It is possible that the nucleic acid could be coiled like a ball of string within the hollow interior of the capsid. It is also possible that the nucleic acid of the icosahedral particles somehow interlaces the capsomers. Such an idea has been proposed for the RNA-containing turnip yellow mosaic virus (Klug and Finch, 1960; Klug *et al.*, 1966; Finch and Klug, 1966). The structure of this icosahedral plant virus has been studied perhaps more intensively than any other single icosahedral virus. Very careful work with x-ray crystallography and electron microscopy suggests that the viral RNA is interlaced with the capsomers, but the exact configuration is not known.

Viruses With Helical Symmetry

Many viruses, especially those infecting plants, are based on helical or screw-type symmetry rather than icosahedral symmetry. One of the best known examples is the rod-shaped tobacco mosaic virus, often referred to by the initials TMV.

Tobacco Mosaic Virus.   Tobacco mosaic virus has been a favorite subject for investigation for many years. It can be isolated in large quantities from infected tobacco plants, and the extracts are relatively free of extraneous materials. Tobacco mosaic virus was the first virus to be crystallized (Stanley, 1935) and was the first virus studied by x-ray diffraction methods (Bernal and Fankuchen, 1941). It has also been studied in the electron microscope by a great variety of techniques. Caspar (1963) published an extensive description of tobacco mosaic virus.

Tobacco mosaic virus (Fig. 2-15) is rod shaped, 300 mμ long, and about 18 or 19 mμ in diameter. A hole measuring about 3.5 to 4 mμ in diameter runs through the axis of the particle and extends the entire length of the rod. This hole is open to the surrounding medium, allowing free exchange of water or other small molecules between the inside of the hole and the outside.

The rod, diagrammed in Figure 2-16, is composed of 2130 subunits. Each subunit is a single protein molecule (it will be recalled that the subunits of the icosahedral viruses may contain several protein molecules) with a molecular weight of 17,530 daltons. The amino acid composition and the sequence of the amino acids in the individual protein molecules comprising the rod have been determined for tobacco mosaic virus and for many of its mutant strains (Wittmann and Wittmann-Liebold, 1963).

The subunits forming the rod are stacked in a helical fashion around the axial hole with 16 1/3 protein subunits in each turn of the

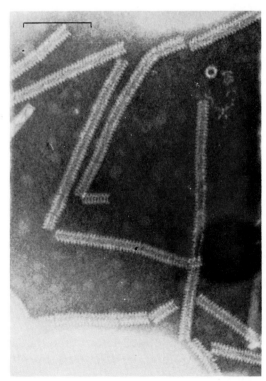

Figure 2-15. Tobacco mosaic virus. Several virions are shown, some of which are broken. One segment of a rod is seen end-on, showing the axial hole. Phosphotungstic acid negative contrast. (Bar is 100 mμ.) (Horne and Wildy, 1961. By permission of the authors and the editor of Virology.)

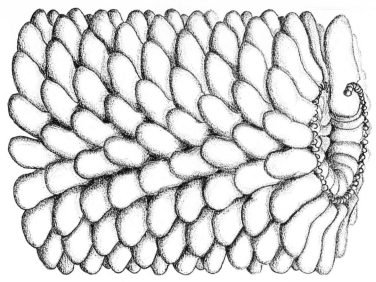

Figure 2-16.   Diagram of the tobacco mosaic virus virion showing the protein subunits and the helical coil of RNA. (Redrawn from Caspar, 1963.)

helix, 49 subunits in three full turns of the helix. The helix has a pitch of 2.3 mμ.

The nucleic acid of tobacco mosaic virus consists of a single molecule of single-stranded RNA with a molecular weight of 2.06×10^6 daltons. There are three nucleotides for each protein subunit, or 6390 nucleotides in the RNA chain. The RNA chain is wound helically around the axial hole at a distance of about 4 mμ from the axis. It passes between successive rows of the protein subunits and seems to add some stability to the rod. Its position in the rod, buried in the protein, protects the RNA from the action of ribonuclease that might be in the environment of the virus particle.

The tobacco mosaic rod can be considered a one-dimensional crystal of protein subunits. The crystal can be dissolved or dissociated in certain media and will recrystallize under appropriate conditions. The dissociated components regain infectivity when reconstituted (Fraenkel-Conrat and Williams, 1955). The presence of nucleic acid is not necessary for crystallization to occur, but if crystallization occurs without an RNA strand, the protein subunits form discs instead of a helix. Sometimes in electron micrographs these discs can be seen to be lying flat and sometimes they stack like coins so that the viewer looks down the axial hole of the disc. Nixon and Woods (1960) and MacLeod *et al.* (1963) determined that a disc had an integral number of subunits; so in three discs there are 48 subunits rather than 49, as in the fully infectious particle.

Myxoviruses. The first electron micrographs of the myxoviruses, such as influenza virus, indicated that the virion was roughly spherical. Therefore, it may seem odd that these viruses are now considered to be helical, similar to tobacco mosaic virus.

By using the negative staining technique, Horne and Waterson (1960) found that the particles of mumps, Newcastle disease, and Sendai viruses were roughly 100 mμ in diameter. In their virus preparations there was an occasional particle (Fig. 2-17) that was disrupted, with the internal structure visible. The component released from the enclosing membrane consisted of a long helical strand resembling that of tobacco mosaic virus, but differing in that it was coiled like a ball of string.

Mumps virus (Cantell, 1961) and influenza virus (Hoyle *et al.*, 1961) also have a helical internal component in a flexible membrane with many spikelike projections on the surface. Hoyle *et al.* (1961) concluded that the external membrane, which gives the virus its ap-

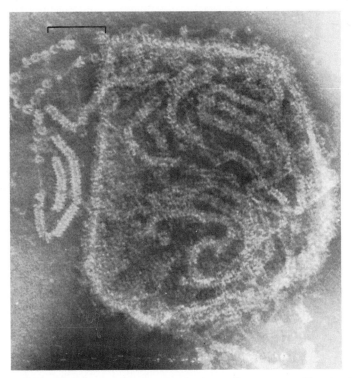

Figure 2-17. A mumps virion showing the internal component. Note its similarity to that of tobacco mosaic virus (Fig. 2-15). The envelope is severely disrupted. (Bar is 100 mμ.) (Horne and Waterson, 1960. By permission of the authors and the editor of the Journal of Molecular Biology.)

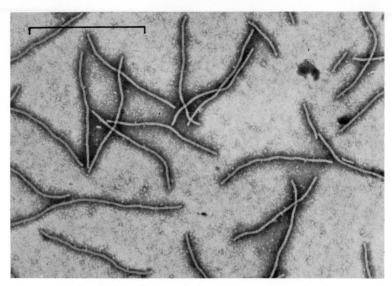

Figure 2-18. Purified nucleocapsids from simian virus 5 (SV5), a parainfluenza virus, negatively stained with phosphotungstate for the electron microscope. The nucleocapsids are about 1 μ long. (Bar is 1 μ.) (Compans and Choppin, 1967. By permission of the authors and the editor of the Proceedings of the National Academy of Sciences.)

parent spherical shape, was composed of cellular material; similar membrane material was found in preparations from normal cells. They thought the internal helical material was the RNA and protein component of the virus.

The RNA of the myxoviruses is difficult to study, and little is known of its properties. A beginning has been made by Compans and Choppin (1967) who obtained the nucleocapsid of SV5, a parainfluenza virus, in pure form (Fig. 2-18). The isolated nucleocapsids averaged slightly over 1 micron in length and contained about 4.1 per cent RNA, corresponding to a molecular weight of an estimated 6.8×10^6 daltons of RNA (in a single molecule) for each nucleocapsid. Apparently some cellular RNA can be included in the capsid of the myxoviruses (Adams, 1966), making it more difficult to study the viral RNA unless purification procedures are used.

Viruses With Complex Symmetry

Several viruses have been studied that do not exhibit any of the recognizable symmetry arrangements just discussed. Still others have a combination of several kinds of symmetry.

Poxviruses.   The poxviruses are the largest and most complex animal viruses. They were first described in 1887 as particles about 0.15 micron in diameter. Many years later, more detailed studies with the electron microscope and metallic shadowing revealed that the poxvirus measured about 240 × 240 × 300 mμ.

Excellent pictures of the poxviruses, orf and vaccinia, were taken by Nagington and Horne (1962). They found that orf virus had a strand, presumably protein, wound around the core very much like bandages wrapped around an Egyptian mummy. These wrappings were not as visible on the vaccinia particle and apparently are not continuous. It is possible that all the viruses of the poxvirus group have a core wrapped with a long protein filament. As shown in Figure 2-19, however, vaccinia virus can take any of several forms, some of which may be artifacts of preparation. There is no evident symmetry arrangement.

The DNA was isolated from cowpox virus and studied in detail by Joklik (1962), who found it to be double stranded. Work by previous authors (Smadel *et al.*, 1939) had indicated that the content per particle was about 160 million daltons. Joklik found the molecular weight of the DNA he isolated to be one half of that, or 80 million daltons. He could not rule out the possibility that one particle contained two molecules of DNA, but it is more likely that the DNA was sheared in half during the isolation. Hyde *et al.* (1967) have measured the length of DNA isolated from fowlpox virus inclusions (see Fig. 9-4); they found its molecular weight to be about 185 × 10^6 daltons.

Vesicular Stomatitis Virus.   Vesicular stomatitis virus has a symmetry all its own, unlike any of the symmetrical viruses that we have

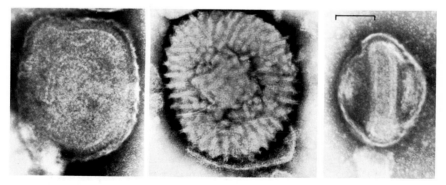

Figure 2-19.   Three particles of vaccinia virus. All three forms are seen in electron micrographs. The one on the left may be artifactual or defective. The other two forms are usually seen. (Bar is 100 mμ.) (Dales, 1965a. By permission of the author and the editor of Progress in Medical Virology.)

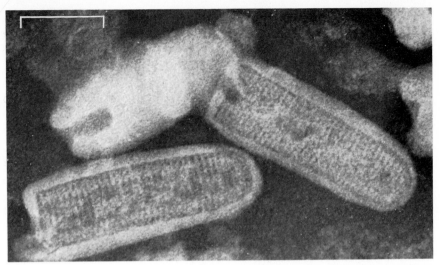

Figure 2-20. Several virions of vesicular stomatitis virus. The bullet shape, with one flat end and one curved end, is evident, as are the cross-striations and the hollow center that opens on the flat end. (Bar is 100 mμ.) (Howatson and Whitmore, 1962. By permission of the authors and the editor of Virology.)

discussed. Howatson and Whitmore (1962) and Hackett (1964) made pictures of this virus showing it to be a cylinder about 68 mμ in diameter and 175 mμ long (Fig. 2-20). The virion is bullet shaped with one hemispherical end and one flat end; it seems to be hollow through part of its length, with a hole extending from the flat end into the hemisphere. Minute striations can be seen running perpendicular to the axis of the particle. Whether these are similar to the discs seen in tobacco mosaic virus is not clear. Vesicular stomatitis virus contains RNA (Chamsy and Cooper, 1963) in unknown configuration.

T-Even Bacterial Viruses.   Many of the bacterial viruses resemble a tadpole with a large head and a tail. Among the tadpole-shaped viruses are the T-even phages (T2, T4, and T6), about which a great deal is known.

The head of a T-even phage particle measures approximately 65 × 95 mμ. In cross section, the head is approximately hexagonal and is capped by a hexagonal pyramid. The head is formed from a large number of subunits, each of which is a single protein of about 80,000 daltons molecular weight.

The head protein forms a semipermeable membrane enclosing the viral DNA. Sudden changes of osmotic pressure rupture the phage head, causing loss of the DNA to the medium. The remaining protein ghost can still attach to bacteria.

The viral DNA is a single molecule with a molecular weight of about 1.30×10^8 daltons (Cairns, 1961; Rubenstein *et al.*, 1961). Also enclosed within the head protein are several other substances. One of these is a low-molecular-weight protein that is antigenically different from other phage proteins (Levine *et al.*, 1958). Putrescine and spermidine (two substances with many amines, and therefore very basic) are also present. It has been postulated that these basic substances neutralize the acidic groups on the DNA so that the DNA can be packed into the small space available to it (Ames and Dubin, 1960).

The tail of the T-even phages is a remarkable organ. It is by the tip of the tail that the phage attaches to a receptor site of the cell wall of a susceptible bacterium. The tail of the phage then injects the DNA from the head of the phage into the interior of the bacterial cell.

Brenner *et al.* (1959) carefully took T-even phage particles apart and obtained some excellent electron micrographs. They found that the phage tail is composed of several parts situated around a central core. The tail core is roughly 95 mμ long and 8 mμ in diameter. It extends from the head of the phage to the tail plate and has a lengthwise axial opening through which the DNA emerges from the head of the phage. Surrounding the core is the tail sheath, composed

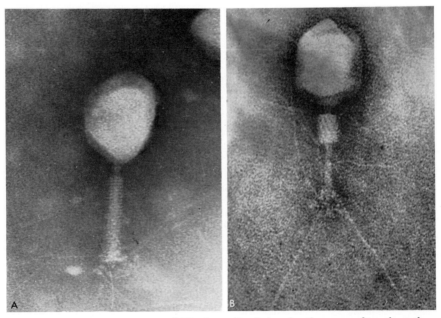

Figure 2-21. Two virions of T2 phage. In *A* the sheath surrounding the tail as rings or a helix is extended. In *B* the phage has been "triggered" with contraction of the sheath. Some of the six fibers attached to the tip of the tail are visible. The tail plate and spikes are not well shown. In *B* the contracted tail sheath has revealed the tail core. (Horne and Wildy, 1961. By permission of the authors and of the editor of Virology.)

of about 200 subunits arranged helically or circularly. Between the sheath and the head of the phage is a small collar which has an unknown function.

In the extracellular phage ready to attach to the bacterial cell, the sheath is extended, as in Fig. 2-21A. Attachment of the tail to a bacterial cell triggers the sheath to contract, as in Fig. 2-21B. This pushes the tail core through the cell wall. The phage DNA then is extruded through the opening of the tail core into the interior of the cell. At the tip of the core, farthest from the head, is a plate with six spikes and six fibers. The fibers are the specific attachment organs. Of the many proteins of the phage particle, it is only the fibers that will adsorb to cells even when isolated from the remainder of the particle. Attachment of phage to bacteria, and the function of the tail parts in initiating infection, will be discussed in more detail in a later chapter.

Kay (1963) discussed the structures of many other phages besides the T-even phage. Here, only the structure of the T-even group has been discussed, as an example of a complex phage that is well known and has a structure that is very closely related to its function.

We have seen in this chapter that viruses come in various sizes, shapes, and structures. There seems to be some homogeneity of structure within groups of viruses possessing similar biological properties, suggesting that morphology might be a basis for classification of viruses. This and other possible means of classifying viruses will be considered in the next chapter.

Further Reading

Bradley, D. E.: Ultrastructure of Bacteriophages and Bacteriocins. Bacteriological Reviews, 31:230-314, 1967.

Caspar, D. L. D.: Design Principles in Virus Particle Construction. *In* Horstall, F. L., Jr., and I. Tamm (eds.): Viral and Rickettsial Infections of Man. Philadelphia, J. B. Lippincott Co., 1965, pp. 51-93.

Horne, R. W.: The Structure of Viruses. Scientific American, 208 (Jan.): 48, 1963.

Klug, A., and D. L. D. Caspar: The Structure of Small Viruses. Advances in Virus Research, 7:225-325, 1960.

3

CLASSIFICATION

Before taking up the classification of viruses, let us consider for a moment the classification of about a million species of plants and about an equal number of species of animals. In the system presently used, introduced by Karl Linnaeus about 230 years ago, all organisms are given a name consisting of two words: the genus name and the species name. In this way, with very little duplication, every species has a unique name, unlike any other species, whether living at present or known only from fossilized remains.

A *genus* consists of a group of similar species possessing common characteristics; the *family* is the next higher group and consists of similar genera; the *order* is a grouping of families; the *class* includes several orders; the *phylum* includes several classes; and finally there are the two great *kingdoms*, one of animals and one of plants. The various groups are thus arranged in a hierarchy of increasing broadness. Each major group is described in terms of the characteristics of all the members of that group or, more commonly, in terms of the characteristics of a prototype of the next less-broad group.

A *species* of a plant or animal is a group of individuals capable of interbreeding under natural conditions. There is, therefore, an objective test of whether a given group of similar animals or plants are members of the same species. The groupings into genera and higher classifications are less objective since they depend upon an opinion about the closeness of the relationship. There is not uniform agreement, in many cases, on how certain groupings should be made.

In addition to providing a catalog by naming and systematically arranging animals and plants, taxonomy serves to show evolutionary relatedness of different organisms. Linnaeus developed his method of classification about 120 years before Darwin proposed his theory of evolution. It is remarkable that the taxonomic system developed by Linnaeus shows the evolutionary relatedness of organisms as seen by Darwin. But Linnaeus developed his system solely for the purpose of producing an orderly catalog of the individual species.

But what about viruses? Can they be classified in Linnean fashion? Several such schemes have been proposed, but they have not been generally accepted. The major reason for the rejection, perhaps, was that the systems were proposed prematurely, before enough was known about viruses, so that the criteria used in the classification proved to be inadequate.

Some of these early systems used a Latin binomial nomenclature, similar to that developed by Linnaeus, implying that species and genera could be defined for viruses. But interbreeding does not occur among even closely related viruses, so such groups cannot be considered species by this definition. (A similar situation exists in defining bacterial species.) It may become necessary to redefine species to include viruses. Lwoff (1967) has suggested that a species is "a collection of viruses with like characters." Unfortunately, such a definition is difficult to apply in a meaningful, objective way.

Problems also arise at the other end of the hierarchy. Should viruses collectively constitute a phylum? If so, are they a phylum of plants or of animals, or should they be intermediate? If the viruses that infect animal cells are to be considered a phylum in the animal kingdom, with a similar phylum of plant viruses, then there is a problem with certain plant viruses: They are transmitted from plant to plant by insects and replicate in the insect as well as in the plant.

Several points could be made in favor of placing viruses in a third kingdom, although there certainly would not be agreement on this among virologists. Viruses are neither plant nor animal, but can infect cells of either type. Characteristics used to distinguish plant cells from animal cells do not apply to viruses, and viruses replicate quite differently from the way that either plant cells or animal cells grow. Defining the viruses as a third kingdom would avoid any implication that they belong to either of the other two kingdoms, and their properties would be clearly delineated.

The only attribute of life possessed by viruses is reproduction with genetic continuity and the possibility of mutation. Evolution can therefore occur. However, the origin of viruses and the evolutionary relatedness, or possible relatedness, of viruses to one another are completely unknown. There is no fossil history that one can examine to look for ancestral viruses. Knowledge about the origin and evolution of viruses would be helpful in classification, as the relationships between them would then be apparent.

FORMER CLASSIFICATION SCHEMES

One of the first systems of classifying viruses was by the diseases they cause. This system, carefully followed, places adenoviruses containing DNA with rhinoviruses containing RNA. Both produce colds in man. At one time, chickenpox was thought to be related to smallpox because of some similarity in the skin lesions. It is now known, however, that the causative viruses are quite different. Conversely, the same virus can frequently cause two or more distinctly different diseases. Plant viruses, too, have been classified by whether they cause leaves to have spots, to roll, or to curl.

Alternatively, viruses have been classified by the organ system they infect. This places polioviruses, containing RNA, with adenoviruses, containing DNA, since both infect the intestinal tract. This also does not seem to be a logical scheme.

The viruses infecting plants, animals, and bacteria sometimes are placed into three separate classification schemes. There are viruses, however, that infect nearly every species of plant or animal, including algae, mushrooms, many different insects, bacteria, and most vertebrates and higher plants. Many of these viruses have great species specificity, so that following this scheme would require a separate classification of viruses for each species of plant or animal.

It no longer seems necessary or advantageous to separate the viruses infecting plants and animals. Viruses infect cells. They interact with the molecular constituents of the cell and, in biochemical and molecular terms, there is little difference between cells of plants and animals. The differences that exist are largely irrelevant to viral replication and have to do primarily with the cell wall, with mechanisms of energy metabolism, and with the ability to synthesize starch. There are greater differences between the various groups of animal viruses than there are between some animal viruses and some viruses of plants or bacteria.

MORE RECENT CLASSIFICATION CRITERIA

There are also other criteria that could be used for grouping viruses. The density (mass per unit volume) has been determined for many viruses quite accurately by methods that will be described later. This is not too useful a criterion, however, because in some cases relatively simple mutations can change the density by a large amount, and many otherwise unrelated viruses have quite similar densities. The base composition of the nucleic acid could be considered as a criterion of relatedness. However, Russell and Crawford (1964) demonstrated that there is a great variability in base composition from one virus in the herpesvirus group to another.

Better, but impractical on a widespread basis, would be to compare base sequences of viruses, as has been done for the T phages (Schildkraut *et al.*, 1962) and for some adenoviruses (Lacy and Green, 1964). The number of homologous genes presumably is an indication of genetic relatedness (Hoyer *et al.*, 1964). Becker (1966) and Bellett (1967) proposed that the molecular weight and other characteristics of the nucleic acid might be suitable criteria for dividing viruses into groups and subgroups. There is, however, considerable variation in these properties among viruses that seem to be closely related in other respects.

Nevertheless, viruses do fall into groups based on biological properties and reactions with antisera. At present, for instance, there are 31 known human adenoviruses; they share a common antigen of the complement fixing type, but each of these adenoviruses can be distinguished from the others by its reaction with specific neutralizing antibody. Each of the 31 is therefore called a different serotype. There are three known serotypes for poliovirus and many other viruses have more than one serotype.

It is clear that the herpesviruses, containing DNA, are different from the adenoviruses, also containing DNA. Most of the bacteriophages are different from animal viruses but have many common properties with them. A satisfactory classification scheme should take all these factors into account. The problem is one of deciding how much importance to give to the various criteria in placing the viruses in a hierarchy. It is generally agreed that the final, most sensitive distinctions between the different viruses should be based on neutralizing antibody. Whether the virus contains RNA or DNA seems to be a suitable characteristic of the broadest scope. Between these clearly defined extremes, however, the various characteristics can be ordered in different ways, resulting in different classification schemes.

Cooper (1961a) originally proposed that viruses might best be classified in terms of their chemical composition. First, he placed all animal viruses into two major divisions, depending on whether they contained RNA or DNA as their nucleic acid. The next subdivision depended on whether they contained lipid. Finally, he considered their size and serological reactions to place them into definitive groups. He intended his classification scheme to apply only to the animal viruses. There is greater diversity in the animal viruses than in either the plant or bacterial viruses, however, so the separation into groups is more easily performed with the animal viruses.

The many recent classification schemes have followed Cooper's lead and divide all viruses into those with RNA and those with DNA (Lwoff *et al.*, 1962; Hamparian *et al.*, 1963; Becker, 1966; and Gibbs *et al.*, 1966). Not only is this division useful, but it could have evolutionary significance. The mutation resulting in this dichotomy must have occurred very early in the evolution of viruses, if they actually have evolved. The extent of mutation that would be required now for a virus to change from one containing RNA to one with DNA or vice versa must be very large.

A great wealth of morphological information has become available largely since the time of Cooper's proposal. In view of the fact that these new pieces of information became available within 5 years of the publication of Cooper's paper, it is probable that a classification proposed now will be substantially changed in the next 5 years.

PROPOSED CLASSIFICATION

There is no generally accepted classification of viruses, but the one proposed by the Provisional Committee for the Nomenclature of Viruses (1965) seems to be the best to date and will be followed here. This classification, based largely on the system proposed by Lwoff *et al.* (1962), groups together the viruses that have similar properties regardless of whether they infect plant, animal, or bacterial cells.

Despite the problems that have been mentioned, the Provisional Committee not only proposed division into a hierarchal classification, defining species and other divisions, but also suggested names, based on Greek or Latin roots, for the divisions. If accepted by virologists, this classification will be in accordance with the systematics of plants and animals. It will then be possible to designate a given virus by its genus and species. In general, existing common names for the viruses will be used in this book.

In this classification, all viruses are placed in a single phylum; subphyla contain the RNA and DNA viruses respectively. Symmetry of the nucleocapsid is used to subdivide into classes, and the presence or absence of an envelope (peplos) subdivides into orders. The order of rod-shaped helical RNA viruses is divided into two suborders for those that are flexible or rigid. Helical viruses are divided into families on the basis of the diameter of the helix, while viruses with cubic symmetry are divided on the basis of the number of capsomers (triangulation number).

The classification of the *Deoxyvira* (DNA-containing viruses), including families and all higher divisions, is shown in Table 3-1. Lower divisions, to the level of species, have also been proposed by the Provisional Committee. There is, however, more room for disagreement at these levels, and the presentation to follow may depart slightly from the proposals.

The families will now be discussed. Emphasis will be placed on

TABLE 3-1. CLASSIFICATION OF THE VIRUSES

Phylum: VIRA
Subphylum: DEOXYVIRA
(DNA-CONTAINING VIRUSES)

CLASSES	ORDERS	FAMILIES
Deoxyhelica (helical symmetry)		
	Chitovirales (Gr: chiton — tunic or envelope)	
		Poxviridae (10 mμ)°
Deoxycubica (cubic symmetry)		
	Haplovirales (Gr: haplos — simple, no envelope)	
		Microviridae (1)+
		Parvoviridae (3)+
		Papilloviridae (7)+
		Adenoviridae (25)+
		Iridoviridae (81)+
		Inoviridae (?)+
	Peplovirales (Gr: peplos — mantle)	
		Herpesviridae (16)+
Deoxybinala (Binal symmetry: cubic + helical)		
	Urovirales (Gr: oura — tail)	
		Phagoviridae

° Diameter (or width) of helical nucleoprotein.
+ Triangulation number.

those viruses that will be important to later portions of this book. Not all kinds of viruses are well known, and at present some are not classifiable. Therefore, the present discussion cannot be complete.

SUBPHYLUM: *Deoxyvira*

Class: *Deoxyhelica*

ORDER: *Chitovirales*

Family: Poxviridae.   Only a few of the poxviruses have been thoroughly studied. They are relatively large, just at the limit of visibility with a light microscope, and are in the size range of 250 to 300 mμ. The structure of a few has been examined with the electron microscope, and a general description was given in Chapter 2. In addition to the vaccinia virus shown in Figure 2-19, others are shown in Figure 3-1.

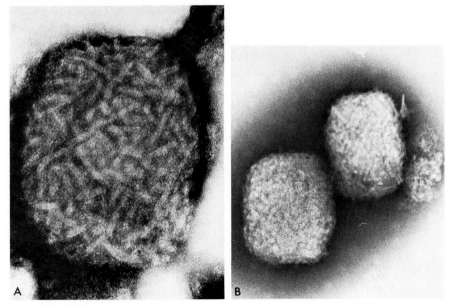

Figure 3-1. Electron micrographs, by negative staining, of fowlpox (**A**) and Yaba monkey tumor virus (**B**), showing different surface patterns. Compare with Figure 2-19. (Fowlpox virus: Hyde *et al.*, 1965, by permission of the authors and the editor of the Journal of Bacteriology. Yaba virus: unpublished micrograph courtesy of R. F. Zeigel and Dr. D. Yohn.)

All poxviruses contain lipid, but in some, the presence of lipid is not essential for infectivity; if the lipid is removed by ether, the poxvirus is still infective. In addition to the nucleic acid and lipid, the poxviruses also, of course, contain protein.

Andrewes (1964a) subdivided the 25 or so known poxviruses into the following six groups, considered to be genera by the Provisional Committee:

GENUS: *Poxvirus.* Includes viruses closely related to variola; all are ether resistant. There are several species: Variola is the causative agent of smallpox and is the type species of the genus; vaccinia is the virus strain used to vaccinate against variola (it was possibly derived from cowpox, but it has been maintained artificially so long and is so genetically stable that it can be considered a distinct strain); cowpox virus is very similar if not identical to vaccinia.

GENUS: *Dermovirus.* These have a woven surface pattern revealed by negative contrast electron microscopy; they are moderately ether sensitive. Two species are contagious pustular dermatitis (orf) and bovine papular dermatitis viruses.

GENUS: *Pustulovirus.* Includes other viruses affecting ungulates; some are slightly ether sensitive. Species are the viruses causing pox diseases of sheep, goats, swine, horses, and camels.

GENUS: *Avipoxvirus.* These ether resistant viruses are transmitted by insects. Species are, for example, fowlpox and canary pox viruses. There are also many other bird poxes.

GENUS: *Fibromavirus.* These are ether sensitive and are transmitted by insects. Species include the rabbit myxoma and rabbit fibroma viruses.

GENUS: *Molluscovirus.* These viruses cause benign tumors. Species include molluscum contagiosum virus, which causes nodular growths on human skin; milkers nodule virus or pseudocowpox, which resembles cowpox infections of humans but has no cross-immunity with cowpox; and Yaba monkey virus which causes subcutaneous tumors in monkeys and is transmissible to humans.

Class: *Deoxycubica*

ORDER: *Haplovirales*

Family: **Microviridae.** There is a small group of bacteriophages, including øX174 and S13, that are among the simplest of all viruses.

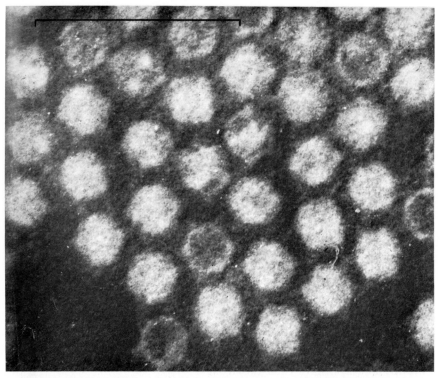

Figure 3-2. Negatively stained electron micrograph of øX174. Several particles are seen with dark centers into which the phosphotungstate has penetrated, presumably "empty" particles. Capsomers are apparent on only some of the virions. (Bar is 100 mμ.) (Unpublished micrograph courtesy of Dr. R. W. Horne.)

øX174 (Fig. 3-2), the best-known member of this group, contains few capsomers, probably 12, in the capsid (Tromans and Horne, 1961) and has a single molecule of single-stranded DNA as the nucleic acid. The DNA has a molecular weight of about 1.6×10^6 daltons (Sinsheimer, 1959b). There are no other constituents in the virion of øX174. Because of its unusual DNA, this virus has been studied in great detail and we will discuss it at length later. It normally infects *Escherichia coli*.

Family: Parvoviridae. The type species of this family is the Kilham rat virus (Kilham and Olivier, 1959). Other members include the H1 and H3 viruses (Moore, 1962) and the X14 virus (Payne *et al.*, 1964), all of which are capable of autonomous replication in appropriate cells. The adeno-associated viruses (Atchison *et al.*, 1965) may also be included in this group; these are of special interest because they apparently can replicate only in the presence of a "helper" adenovirus, not autonomously. The feline panleukopenia virus may also belong in this family (Johnson and Cruickshank, 1966).

The viruses grouped together in this family probably are similar enough to justify this grouping for the present. Further division into genera does not seem warranted now. These viruses appear to be similar in size (all are about 20 to 25 mμ diameter) and seem to have 32 subunits (triangulation number 3). The DNA of the adeno-associated viruses has a molecular weight of about 3×10^6 daltons and is double stranded (Rose *et al.*, 1966). Presumably the others are also double stranded, but the issue is not settled. Mayor and Melnick (1966) proposed to call this group the "picodnaviruses" in parallel with the "picornaviruses," where "pico" means small and "dna" or "rna" denotes the nucleic acid type.

Family: Papilloviridae. The structure of the polyoma and papilloma viruses was described in the previous chapter. These viruses contain a single molecule of double-stranded DNA with an unusual ringlike, or cyclic, structure (Dulbecco and Vogt, 1963; Weil and Vinograd, 1963; Dulbecco, 1963a; Vinograd *et al.*, 1965). The molecular weight is 3 to 5×10^6 daltons.

The Provisional Committee has divided the family into two genera. One contains the larger papilloma viruses, of which there are representatives that infect rabbits (Shope papilloma virus), humans (wart virus), dogs, cattle, swine, horses, and others. The other genus contains the smaller polyoma virus and SV40. (When monkey, or simian, viruses were initially discovered, they were merely given sequential numbers. SV40 is the fortieth virus to be discovered among monkeys.) It is also called the vacuolating agent because in tissue culture (in kidney cells of the African green monkey) it causes the development of very large vacuoles in the cytoplasm of the infected cell.

All the viruses mentioned cause tumors and will be discussed in more detail in a later chapter. Another member, which does not cause tumors, is the K virus. Its relation to the two proposed genera is not clear.

The name "papovavirus" was proposed for this group ("pa" is from papilloma, "po" is from polyoma, and "va" is from vacuolating agent), but the Provisional Committee did not accept it as a family name.

Family: Adenoviridae. The name "adenovirus" was derived from the common occurrence of these viruses in adenoids and tonsils removed surgically from patients with tonsillitis.

There are 31 known serotypes of human adenoviruses, and similar viruses infect dogs, monkeys, mice, chickens, and other species. The structure of the adenoviruses was described in Chapter 2. These viruses do not have an envelope, nor do they contain any other components besides the DNA and proteins. A picture comparing two adenoviruses is shown in Figure 3-3.

Human adenoviruses cause croup in children, sore throats, and other respiratory diseases, as well as keratoconjunctivitis and some forms of gastrointestinal upsets. One kind of adenovirus (infectious canine hepatitis, ICH, virus) causes hepatitis in dogs. Many adenoviruses that have been tested cause cancers in hamsters, but usually only if the hamster is injected with the adenovirus in the first day or two after birth. Study of the adenoviruses has intensified recently because of their ability to cause the inherited cellular changes manifested as malignant growth.

Adenoviruses can be further subclassified on the basis of their hemagglutination properties, but classification into genera and species has not been done.

Family: Iridoviridae. This family includes *Tipula* iridescent virus, depicted in Figure 2-2. It infects the crane fly, *Tipula paludosa,* and thus is one of many insect viruses. It measures 140 mμ in di-

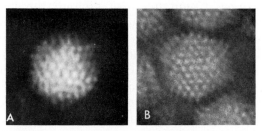

Figure 3-3. Adenoviruses of mouse (*A*) and dog (*B*). Note the similarity of these viruses to each other and to the human adenovirus (see Figs. 2-6 and 2-7). (Mouse adenovirus: Hashimoto *et al.,* 1966, by permission of the authors and the editor of the Japanese Journal of Microbiology. Infectious canine hepatitis virus: Davies *et al.,* 1961, by permission of the authors and the editor of Virology.)

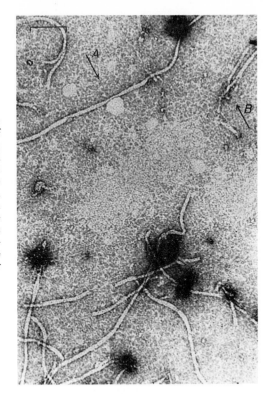

Figure 3-4. The filamentous phage, fd. The filament consists of two tubular structures, side by side; this shows especially well at A, and several other places, where there is a slight twist in the filament. The two sides seem to be separated at B, and the separated filaments from two adjacent virions appear to be twisted around each other. (Bar is 100 mμ.) (Marvin, 1966. By permission of the authors and the editor of the Journal of Molecular Biology.)

ameter and contains DNA. The name of this virus is derived from the crystals that form in an infected insect; because of their number and configuration, they give an iridescent appearance to the insect. Smith (1963) has reviewed this and other insect viruses.

Family: Inoviridae. These bacterial viruses are filamentous; a helical arrangement of subunits has not been demonstrated. The DNA is single stranded and may be cyclic, with the opposite sides of the ring, surrounded by protein, closely applied to each other (Fig. 3-4). It has been determined that one of these phages, fd, contains about 12 per cent DNA with a molecular weight of about 1.3×10^6 daltons. The particle is about 700 mμ long and about 5 mμ in diameter (Marvin and Hoffmann-Berling, 1963). The phage infects only male *E. coli*. Other similar phages are f1 and M13.

ORDER: *Peplovirales*

Family: Herpesviridae. The structure of the herpesviruses was described in detail in Chapter 2. There are many viruses in this family, but all that have been examined by the negative-staining technique are indistinguishable from one another. However, they do have rather marked differences in the base composition of their DNA, as determined in the ultracentrifuge (Russell and Crawford, 1964).

Herpes simplex virus of humans is common; it causes fever blisters or cold sores on the lip margin. It is apparently present in latent form in the skin cells of certain people; in times of stress it becomes active, producing a crop of blisters. Only at this time can the virus be isolated.

Monkey B virus, or simian herpes virus, is latent in monkeys. When transferred to a human by a monkey bite, it produces a disease that is almost invariably fatal.

Pseudorabies virus causes "mad itch" of cattle, sheep, pigs, and other animals; the disease was once thought to be a kind of rabies, but the virus is quite different from that of rabies.

Varicella virus causes either of two diseases: chickenpox or herpes zoster (shingles), a disease of peripheral nerves. Varicella virus is usually transmitted from cell to cell and is usually not infective when extracellular, making study difficult.

Cytomegaloviruses are a large group of viruses occurring in many species. There are probably three human serotypes. The cytomegaloviruses of other mammals are often called salivary gland viruses because of their frequent latency in those glands. The Provisional Committee suggested that the cytomegaloviruses be a separate genus from the herpesviruses.

Many other viruses of the herpes group afflict species of lower animals. See Andrewes (1964a) for a more complete listing.

Class: *Deoxybinala*

ORDER: *Urovirales*

Family: Phagoviridae.   These phages are all similar in that they possess a tail. All contain double-stranded DNA and none contain lipid.

There is a great variety of bacteriophages. They can be isolated very easily from samples of soil or from sewage. Many different species of bacteria serve as hosts, often to more than one kind of phage.

When phages were first studied intensively, they were merely numbered type 1, type 2, and so on. These designations soon were abbreviated to capital T, followed by the number. When numbers got as high as 7, other designations became popular. It turned out later that the even-numbered T phages seemed to be related, and that the odd-numbered phages had certain properties in common. The T-even phages (T2, T4, and T6) have been studied more thoroughly than any other viruses, and much of what we will have to say about phages will refer to the T-even phages.

Phage research has concentrated on only a few phages. These few are known in great detail both for wild-type and for their many mutants. Because of the concentration of interest on only a few types, there has been little or no necessity to develop a classification system for the great variety of phages. The Provisional Committee made no attempt to subclassify the tailed phages further.

However, Kay (1963) proposed classifying phages into four groups on the basis of their morphology. His first three groups constitute this family; each group may be considered a genus by the Committee, but will not be so designated here.

GROUP I: Phages having long tails with contractile sheaths, base plates with prongs, and lateral striations on the sheath (Fig. 3-5).

GROUP IA: The head is longer than it is wide and is a bipyramidal hexagonal prism. This subgroup includes the T-even coliphages. Their structure has already been described.

Figure 3-5. Two phages of Group I. *A* shows coliphage T2, in Group Ia, and *B* shows Pseudomonas phage 12S, in Group Ib. The sheath and base plate are evident on both phages. The regular polygonal head of phage 12S is clearly shown. (Kay, 1963. Electron micrographs courtesy of Dr. D. E. Bradley. *A* is from Kay, Desmond: A Comparative Study of the Structure of a Variety of Bacteriophage Particles with Some Observations on the Mechanism of Nucleic Acid Injection. In *Viruses, Nucleic Acids, and Cancer* [A Collection of Papers Presented at the Seventeenth Annual Symposium on Fundamental Cancer Research, 1963]. Baltimore, Maryland, The Williams and Wilkins Company, 1963.)

GROUP IB: The heads are regular polygons and may be icosahedral or octahedral. This group includes phage P1 and P2
of salmonellae.

GROUP II: Phages having long, narrow, flexible tails with an
axial hole running the length of the tail. The tails are constructed of subunits and have no contractile tail mechanism, but
some have a tail plate (Fig. 3-6).

GROUP IIA: Phages with regular polygonal heads, probably
icosahedral. This group contains coliphages T1, T5, and λ, as
well as other phages of staphylococci and pseudomonads.

GROUP IIB: Phages with heads that are longer than they are
wide. Several lesser-known phages, that we will not have
occasion to discuss, are included in this subgroup.

GROUP III: Phages having short tails and polygonal (probably
icosahedral) heads. The tail is attached to one of the apexes.
Coliphages T3 and T7, as well as others, are included here (Fig.
3-7).

SUBPHYLUM: *Ribovira*

The subphylum *Ribovira* is shown in Table 3-2. It is divided into
two classes. The helical viruses are designated by the diameter of the
nucleocapsid, while the viruses with cubic symmetry are designated
by the triangulation number.

Class: *Ribohelica*

ORDER: *Rhabdovirales*

The viruses that occur as free rods form the order *Rhabdovirales*,
which is in turn subdivided into two suborders containing the rods
that are rigid and those that are flexible, respectively. The suborder
Rigidoviridales includes three families, as shown in Table 3-2. The
common names of the type species are cabbage mosaic virus, tobacco
mosaic virus (Figs. 2-15 and 2-16), and tobacco rattle mosaic virus.
Tobacco rattle virus has a structure like tobacco mosaic virus, but with
76 subunits in three turns of the helix (Offord, 1966). The suborder
Flexiviridales also contains three families; the common names of the
type species are potato virus X, pea mosaic virus, and white clover
mosaic virus. Of the viruses in these six families, tobacco mosaic
virus will be discussed in more detail later.

ORDER: *Sagovirales*

This order includes those helical viruses whose nucleocapsid is
enclosed as a nucleoid within a membrane or peplos.

Family: Myxoviridae. The structure of the myxoviruses has
already been described. They are composed of a helix of RNA and
protein wound tightly into a ball and enclosed in an envelope that is

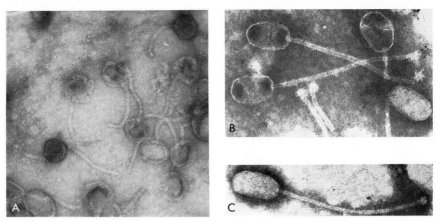

Figure 3-6.   Two phages of Group II. *A* shows coliphage T5, in Group IIa, and *B* and *C* show several views of Staphylococcus phage 594. The phages have long, flexible tails with base plates, as well as differently shaped heads. (Electron micrographs courtesy of Dr. D. E. Bradley. *B* and *C* are from Kay, Desmond: A Comparative Study of the Structures of a Variety of Bacteriophage Particles with Some Observations on the Mechanism of Nucleic Acid Injection. In *Viruses, Nucleic Acids, and Cancer* [a collection of Papers Presented at the Seventeenth Annual Symposium on Fundamental Cancer Research, 1963]. Baltimore, Maryland, The Williams and Wilkins Company, 1963.)

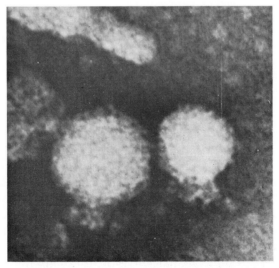

Figure 3-7.   Bacteriophage 12B of Pseudomonas, a phage of Group III. The two phages shown have different size heads. The short tail or base plate can be seen at the lower part of the head. (Bradley, 1963. By permission of the author and the editor of the Journal of Ultrastructure Research.)

TABLE 3-2.   CLASSIFICATION OF THE VIRUSES

Phylum: VIRA
Subphylum: RIBOVIRA
(RNA-CONTAINING VIRUSES)

CLASSES	ORDERS	SUBORDERS	FAMILIES
Ribohelica (helical symmetry)			
	Rhabdovirales (Gr: rhabdos — rod)		
		Rigidoviridales	
			Dolichoviridae (12-13 mμ)* Protoviridae (15 mμ)* Pachyviridae (20 mμ)*
		Flexiviridales	
			Leptoviridae (10-11 mμ)* Mesoviridae (12-13 mμ)* Adroviridae (15 mμ)*
	Sagovirales (L: sago — mantle)		
			Myxoviridae (9 mμ)* Paramyxoviridae (18 mμ)* Stomatoviridae Thylaxoviridae
Ribocubica (cubic symmetry)			
	Gymnovirales (Gr: gymno — naked)		
			Napoviridae (3)+ Reoviridae (9)+
	Togavirales (L: toga — mantle)		
			Arboviridae (?)+

*Diameter (or width) of helical nucleoprotein.
+Triangulation number.

flexible in shape and variable in size (Fig. 3-8). The envelope is sensitive to ether and readily falls apart when its lipid is extracted. The myxoviruses, in general, have the property of hemagglutination and an affinity for certain mucoproteins. In addition, they carry on their surface an enzyme able to break down these mucoproteins.

The internal helix of the influenza and fowl plague viruses has a diameter of about 9 mμ. The particle is 80 to 120 mμ in diameter. (The particle size of the myxoviruses is quite variable because of the method that the cell uses for final assembly, as will be discussed later.) The influenza viruses are called influenza A, B, and C. These and their substrains are frequent causes of respiratory disease epidemics.

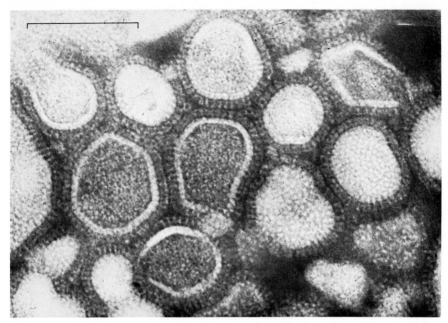

Figure 3-8. Several virions of influenza virus. The flexibility and variability of size of the envelope is quite apparent. Some particles (top center) show a suggestion of subunit (peplomer) structure of the envelope (peplos), and "spikes" can be seen radiating from the surface of all the virions. The internal structure (nucleocapsid) is not readily apparent in this picture (see Figs. 2-17 and 2-18). (Bar is 100 mμ.) (Hoyle *et al.*, 1961. By permission of the authors and the editor of Virology.)

Family: Paramyxoviridae. There are two proposed genera in this family. The genus *Paramyxovirus* includes Newcastle disease virus and parainfluenza types 1 (sometimes called Sendai), 2, 3, and 4. These viruses measure 150 to 250 mμ in diameter, and their internal helix is about 18 mμ in diameter—roughly twice the diameter of the helix of influenza virus. Also included are human mumps virus and measles virus and its close relatives: distemper virus of dogs and rinderpest virus that causes a similar disease of cattle.

The genus *Paramyxovirus* may also include the virus that causes rubella (German measles), which only recently was isolated and grown in tissue culture. The work that has been done so far indicates that rubella virus is about the same size as the parainfluenza viruses. It is sensitive to ether and it probably contains RNA (Parkman *et al.*, 1964). Electron micrographs by the negative staining method reveal particles resembling the myxoviruses (Norrby *et al.*, 1963). Further work will be necessary to make more definite the tentative inclusion of rubella virus in the myxovirus group.

The second genus proposed by the Provisional Committee is

called *Bronchovirus* and includes the respiratory syncytial virus. This virus is one of those that cause common colds. It was only recently described, and its exact position in the paramyxovirus group·is not entirely clear.

Family: Stomatoviridae. This group of viruses has vesicular stomatitis virus (described in Chapter 2) as its type species. All are bullet shaped, and morphologically similar viruses occur in plants as well as in animals. This family probably includes the rabies virus (Hummeler *et al.*, 1967), maize mosaic virus (Herold and Munz, 1967), lettuce necrotic yellows virus (Harrison and Crowley, 1965), and a probable virus of plantain (Hitchborn *et al.*, 1966). Several are shown in Figure 3-9.

Family: Thylaxoviridae. This family was proposed by a group of virologists (Dalton *et al.*, 1966) to include the oncogenic RNA-containing viruses. These are morphologically similar in many respects to the other two families, but morphological information on these viruses is more limited.

It was proposed to have two genera. The first, *Gallivirus*, includes viruses of chickens. These are classified in two subgenera, depending on whether they cause sarcomas or leukemia. The Rous sarcoma virus has been intensively studied and will be discussed in a later chapter. The viruses of the avian leukosis complex cause leukemias and other blood disorders of chickens.

The second genus, *Murivirus*, is also subdivided into subgenera,

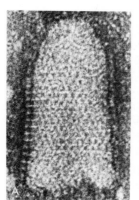  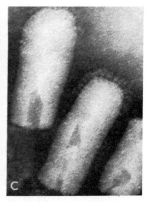

Figure 3-9. Three bullet-shaped viruses: *A* shows the rabies virus; *B*, the virus-like particle of plantain; and *C*, vesicular stomatitis virus (see also Fig. 2-20). The striations and indentation from the flat end are clearly shown, as well as surface projections similar to those of influenza virus (Fig. 3-8). (Rabies virus: Hummeler *et al.*, 1967, by permission of the authors and the editor of the Journal of Virology. Plantain virus-like particle: Hitchborn *et al.*, 1966, by permission of the authors and the editor of Virology. Vesicular stomatitis virus: Howatson and Whitmore, 1962, by permission of the authors and the editor of Virology.)

depending on whether the virus causes sarcomas, leukemia, or carcinomas. All these viruses infect mice. The Moloney sarcoma virus is in the first subgenus. The leukemia viruses of mice include Gross' passage A virus (Gross, 1951a) and the Friend, Graffi, Moloney, and Rauscher leukemia viruses. The Bittner agent, or the mammary tumor agent, causes carcinomas in mice.

Class: *Ribocubica*

ORDER: *Gymnovirales*

Family: Napoviridae. The Provisional Committee has proposed that the members of this family include a rather large group of viruses, subdivided into three subfamilies based on whether their host cells are plant, animal, or bacterial. They also propose that these viruses all have 32 structural units; it should be pointed out that because these viruses are so small, morphological studies have been difficult, especially with the animal virus members. The structure has been shown only for certain of the viruses, such as poliovirus (Mayor, 1964), foot-and-mouth disease virus (Breese *et al.*, 1965), and turnip yellow mosaic virus (Finch and Klug, 1966).

Subfamily: Napovirinae. This subfamily includes one genus, with turnip yellow mosaic virus as its type species.

Subfamily: Picornavirinae. There are six genera, with *Picornavirus* the type genus and foot-and-mouth disease virus the type species; the latter is slightly smaller (20 to 22 mμ) than the other viruses in this subfamily (25 to 30 mμ).

The three genera, *Poliovirus, Coxsackievirus,* and *Echovirus,* are sometimes grouped together and collectively called enteroviruses. There are three known serotypes of polioviruses; about 30 serotypes of coxsackieviruses in two subgroups, A and B; and at least 28 serotypes of echoviruses. (The word *echo* was originally formed from the phrase "enteric cytopathic human orphan." The virus was isolated from the intestinal tract of humans and caused a cytopathic effect by killing cells in tissue culture. When first isolated, the viruses were not associated with any known human disease and therefore were called "orphans." Since then, they have been found to cause enteric infections, such as mild diarrheas; and they can cause more severe disease, such as a self-limited meningitis).

Another genus, *Rhinovirus,* includes a large number of serotypes of viruses that cause common colds. They are distinguishable from the enteroviruses by the fact that they are unstable at acid pH where they lose their infectivity much more rapidly than the enteroviruses (Tyrrell and Chanock, 1963). There are many serotypes of human rhinoviruses, perhaps 40, as well as similar viruses in cattle and horses.

The sixth genus, *Cardiovirus,* consists of a group of viruses that mainly infect mice. It is also called the encephalomyocarditis (EMC) group, including EMC, Columbia SK, MM, and Mengo viruses. Many other closely related viruses occur in various species of mammals.

Subfamily: *Androphagovirinae.*   This subfamily includes the single genus of phages containing RNA, *Androphagovirus*. MS2, for instance, is a coliphage. It has a diameter of 26 mμ and a particle weight of about 3.6×10^6 daltons. Thirty-two per cent of its dry weight

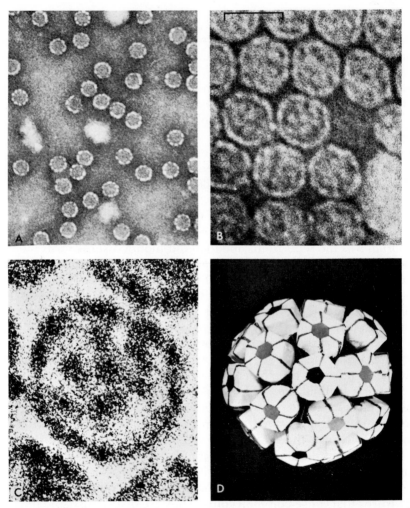

Figure 3-10.   R17, the RNA-containing phage. *A* and *B* are electron micrographs at different magnifications. *C* is an enlarged print of the center particle of *B*, prepared by reversed contrast to emphasize the capsomers. *D* is a model constructed of 32 sub-units, 12 of which are pentagonal and 20 are hexagonal prisms. The central hole of the capsomers shown on the model is not apparent on these electron micrographs. (Bar is 25 mμ.) (Vasquez *et al.*, 1966. By permission of the authors and the editor of the Journal of Bacteriology.)

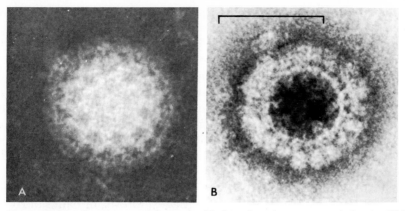

Figure 3-11. Reovirus particles embedded in phosphotungstate. *A* shows a "full" virion; in *B*, the negative contrast material has apparently penetrated the core, suggesting that the particle may be "empty." The contrast material in *B* seems to have outlined an inner structure at the base of the capsomers. (Bar is 60 mμ.) (Dales *et al.*, 1965. By permission of the authors and the editor of Virology.)

is RNA, in a single molecule of single-stranded form, and the remainder is protein (Strauss and Sinsheimer, 1963). Electron micrographs of another RNA coliphage, R17, are shown in Figure 3-10.

Family: Reoviridae. This family is divided into two genera. There are three known serotypes in the genus *Reovirus*; they are numbered 1 to 3. It is not clear what disease, if any, they cause. (The name is derived from respiratory enteric orphan, denoting the sources for isolation of the viruses and the fact that their disease is unknown.) Reoviruses can be isolated from many different mammalian species, and it has been suggested that the virus causing the blue tongue disease of sheep may be a reovirus (Studdert *et al.*, 1966).

The reoviruses are moderately large, about 70 mμ in diameter (Fig. 3-11). The icosahedral capsid is composed of 92 capsomers (Vasquez and Tournier, 1962; Jordan and Mayor, 1962). The nucleic acid of the reoviruses is double stranded (Gomatos and Tamm, 1963; Langridge and Gomatos, 1963). The fact that the RNA is unusual suggests that the reproductive cycle of this virus might also differ from the other RNA-containing viruses. This will be discussed later.

The other genus, *Neovirus*, contains the plant virus called wound tumor virus. It is morphologically identical to the reovirus, showing 92 capsomers by electron microscopy, and has a double-stranded RNA. It also possesses antigens in common with reovirus (Streissle and Maramorosch, 1963).

ORDER: *Togavirales*

Family: Arboviridae. The arthropod-borne viruses not only are carried from animal to animal by insects, but some, at least, replicate in the insect vector as well as in the animal host. The rather cumbersome name "arthropod-borne virus" was shortened to "arborvirus," and more recently the "r" was dropped to avoid the implication that these viruses infect trees.

Arboviruses are isolated in any of several ways, often in tropical regions. They are sometimes isolated from dead or diseased patients or animals, although they can also be found in trapped animals that show no signs of illness. Mosquitos often are found to contain arboviruses. Under these circumstances, unless a known virus has been reisolated, it is difficult to know whether the new virus causes disease. Although there are some exceptions, it has been customary to name arboviruses after the place where they were isolated. These places frequently are small native villages, forests, or banks of rivers; and the virus often acquires an exotic name.

All the arboviruses that have been tested are sensitive to extraction with ether or with detergents that are able to remove lipids. It is thought that the nucleocapsid is icosahedral, enclosed in an envelope. The size of the virion ranges from 20 mμ to more than 100 mμ, possibly reflecting variability in the envelope. It is not certain that all of these viruses contain RNA, but it seems likely. In most cases, the molecular form of the RNA is not known, but it is probably single stranded in at least some.

The arbovirus group is large and possibly heterogenous; these viruses are grouped together because they are carried by insects. As more information is accumulated about the arboviruses, it may very well turn out that this grouping has no biological meaning. As pointed out by Andrewes (1964a), many of these viruses may be shifted into other groups in which their fundamental properties fit more closely. Not many of these viruses have been studied in sufficient detail to know how they should be subdivided further on morphological grounds.

Arboviruses are divided into groups A, B, C, and several smaller groups by their reactions in the hemagglutination-inhibition test. The members of the groups are distinguished from one another by complement-fixation and neutralization tests. (These serologic tests will be described in later chapters.)

Group A arboviruses include 15 members. The Eastern, Western, and Venezuelan equine encephalomyelitis viruses, like most arboviruses, occur naturally in birds or mammals. When these animals are bitten by an insect, in this case a mosquito, the virus is transmitted to a new host. The natural host may have only a minor illness; other hosts may be more severely diseased. Horses and man frequently succumb to infection by the equine encephalomyelitis viruses.

Sindbis virus and Semliki Forest virus are of little or no consequence in causing human disease but are useful in some kinds of experiments. Chikungunya virus is named from the African native expression describing the doubled-up position assumed by a sufferer of the disease. O'nyong-nyong fever virus causes a disease that resembles Chikungunya, but the viruses are different serologically.

There are at least 33 members of the B group of arboviruses. The West Nile, Japanese B, Murray Valley, and St. Louis encephalitis viruses seem to be related in that they cause encephalitis of varying degrees of severity and have some serological cross-reactions. The yellow fever virus is perhaps the best known arbovirus. It is endemic in tropical Africa and South America, but major epidemics have occurred in the United States. Dengue virus is also fairly well known and is in the B group.

About 50 other arboviruses have been described. Most of them have been studied extensively and do not fit into any of the major groups. These and the viruses of group C will not be listed here.

Taxonomy of viruses is in its infancy. The system given here seems to be an important step toward a classification, for not only are there suitable places for known viruses but viruses to be discovered can be added. The present classification also seems to be related to biological properties, as will become apparent in later chapters.

Further Reading

Andrewes, C. H.: Viruses and Noah's Ark. Bacteriological Reviews, 29:1-8, 1965.
Lwoff, A., and P. Tournier: The Classification of Viruses. Annual Review of Microbiology, 20:45-74, 1966.
Pirie, N. W.: Prerequisites for Virus Classification. Symposia of the Society for General Microbiology, 12:374-393, 1962.

4

ASSAY OF VIRUS
SUSPENSIONS

Quantitation is important in all aspects of virology, with the result that many methods have been devised for the measurement of virus activity. Some methods are based on measuring virus material, in terms of either protein or nucleic acid per unit volume of suspension, to yield an estimate of virus concentration. Others are based on counting the number of particles per unit volume. The meaning of the count depends on which of several counting procedures is used. In some cases, the result is a count of physical particles: the concentration of particles without regard to whether they are infectious. In other cases, an infectivity titration is performed, and only particles able to initiate infection are counted.

The choice of method depends upon the use to which the investigator will put the information, upon the particular virus being assayed, upon the purity of the virus suspension, and upon the facilities available to the investigator. Here, we will not consider all the possible methods of assay that have been devised, nor will we give technical details about how to perform the assays (see Adams, 1959 for techniques with phage and Cooper, 1961b for animal viruses). Rather, we will consider the assays in broad terms to see the principles involved.

MEASUREMENT OF CONCENTRATION OF VIRAL CONSTITUENTS

Standard biochemical procedures are available for analyzing a sample for its content of nucleic acid or protein. These procedures sometimes are useful to the virologist, despite some rather stringent requirements that must be met before they are applicable. For one thing, a high concentration of virus must be present to be detectable biochemically, so the sensitivity of this type of assay is not high. A further important restriction is that the sample must be of high purity. If cell debris or other impurity is present, the biochemical procedure may not distinguish between impurity and viral material, giving misleading results. None of the biochemical or biophysical methods indicates whether the virus measured is infective or noninfective.

Radioisotopes are useful if it is possible to incorporate them into the virus. Such methods have been developed for many viruses and usually require the addition of isotope to the medium in which the infected cell is grown. The cell incorporates the isotope into the virus particle, in either the nucleic acid or the protein, depending upon the chemical form of the isotope. Assay for radioactivity then measures viral concentration.

An advantage of using radioisotopes is that assay is much more sensitive and will detect smaller amounts of virus than will biochemical assay. The instrumentation for isotope work has been developed to a high degree of perfection so that the electronic apparatus is available and is easy to use; however, these methods require extremely high purity of the virus preparation, with removal of any extraneous isotopes from the medium before assay.

Optical methods are also sometimes used in determining virus concentration. The simplest and crudest such method for highly concentrated samples is simply to hold the virus suspension, such as one of bacteriophage, up to the light. After some experience, the investigator can obtain a rough estimate of the phage concentration by the amount of light scattering caused by the particles. Depending upon the virus concentration, the suspension will appear bluish or milky. Such estimates of virus concentration are obviously of limited use.

A spectrophotometer is a sensitive optical and electronic instrument for measuring accurately the amount of light of a selected wavelength that passes through a sample. Virus particles have high absorption peaks in the ultraviolet range, usually at a wavelength of about 260 to 280 mμ; therefore, the spectrophotometer can be used to measure the amount of ultraviolet light absorbed by a purified virus suspension. The amount of absorption is proportional to the concentration of virus present. The proportionality between absorption of light and virus concentration must be determined in advance for each kind of virus.

PARTICLE COUNTS NOT BASED ON INFECTIVITY

An absolute titration or physical particle count can be performed by any of several ways. The result is an estimate of the number of particles per unit volume, without regard to which of the particles may be infectious.

The Electron Microscope

Some of the larger viruses, such as vaccinia, can be counted with a light microscope by using special optics and special stains. However, unlike bacteria and blood cells, most viruses are too small to be seen with the light microscope.

Luria *et al.* (1951) developed a method for counting virus particles in the electron microscope. The virus suspension was mixed with a known number (determined by weighing) of latex spheres of about the same size as the virus particles. The mixture was sprayed on the object grid of the electron microscope and examined. The concentration of virus particles was calculated from the ratio of latex spheres to virus particles in the dried droplets. For example, if there were 10^{10} latex spheres per milliliter and the count revealed 50 virus particles for each latex sphere, then the concentration of virus particles in the original suspension would be 50×10^{10} or 5×10^{11} virus particles per milliliter.

This method can be used if the virus is highly concentrated and if the morphologic appearance of the virus particle to be counted is known. Its use has also been extended with herpes simplex virus

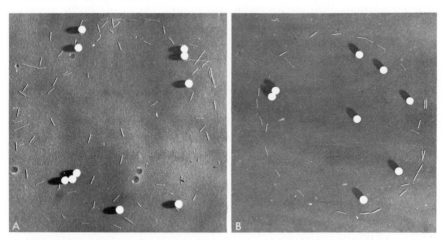

Figure 4-1. Microdroplets containing tobacco mosaic virus rods and latex spheres. Differential counts of rod lengths showed that the standard preparation (**A**) contained rods of many different lengths, whereas a preparation that had been centrifuged through a sucrose gradient (**B**) contained a more homogeneous population of particles. The latex spheres are 264 mμ in diameter. (Symington *et al.*, 1962. By permission of the authors and the editor of the Proceedings of the National Academy of Sciences.)

(Watson *et al.*, 1963) to differential counts of virus particles of different morphologic types and, in the case of tobacco mosaic virus (Fig. 4-1), to counts of particles of different lengths (Symington *et al.*, 1962). There are now many variations of the method for preparing viruses for counting with the electron microscope.

Hemagglutination

Some animal viruses have the property of being able to cause red blood cells of some mammalian species to stick together. This process, discovered by Hirst (1941), can be used for determining the physical particle concentration of some viruses.

When hemagglutination is caused by the virus particle itself, as with influenza virus, a particle joins two red cells together by forming a bridge between them. If there are sufficient hemagglutinating particles present, the red cells form clusters which fall to the bottom of the test tube in a characteristic pattern. Because red cells that are not agglutinated form a different pattern, it is possible to tell quickly whether agglutination has occurred.

To do this test, the virus suspension is diluted serially, usually in twofold steps. Red cells are added in a buffer solution that is appropriate for the virus and red cell system being used, and the mixture is allowed to stand. After an appropriate time, the pattern on the tube bottom is examined; the highest dilution (or its reciprocal) of virus suspension resulting in agglutination is called the hemagglutination titer, sometimes abbreviated to HA titer.

Another method for determining the degree of hemagglutination was devised by Levine *et al.* (1953), who used a spectrophotometer to determine the rate at which red cells sedimented: Cells stuck together as dimers sedimented more rapidly than single cells. The instrument increased the sensitivity of determining the degree of agglutination.

For many viruses causing hemagglutination, the relation between the hemagglutination titer and the electron microscope count indicates that at the end point there probably is one or a few virus particles for every two red blood cells (Tyrrell and Valentine, 1957). Therefore, the number of virus particles in the original suspension can be calculated. Since the hemagglutination test does not depend on infectivity, but only on the number of physical particles, it is a measure of the titer of virus particles, as is the electron microscope count.

INFECTIVITY ASSAYS

In most laboratories, virus concentration is usually determined by some measure of the infectivity possessed by the suspension. There are two major categories of infectivity titrations: the quantal assay, depending on an all-or-none response, and the plaque, pock, or lesion count, in which the effect of a single infectious virus particle is seen as a visible localized change in a background of normal cells.

Quantal Assays

A quantal assay estimates the concentration of infective virus particles by allowing them to multiply in a suitable host so that a single particle can be detected by the amplification effect of the infection.

To do the test, it is necessary to prepare a dilution series of the virus suspension whose concentration is to be determined. The 1:10 dilution series is commonly used, although others, such as 1:2, 1:4, or 1:3.16 (dilution steps such that each is $10^{-0.5}$ of the preceding), are also used. A measured volume of each of several dilutions is inoculated into a group of susceptible hosts. The host or test subject can be an animal, such as a mouse, rat, rabbit, monkey, or human; it can be a plant, an embryonated egg, or a test tube or petri dish containing cultured cells. After enough time has passed to allow any virus present to multiply, each animal, test subject, or culture is scored for whether it shows an effect attributable to the presence of virus.

The characteristic effect scored for depends upon the virus and the host system being used. For instance, with influenza virus inoculated intranasally in mice, a positive response is the development of influenzal pneumonia. With some leukemia viruses of animals, the response is the development of leukemia. Human volunteer subjects have been used in working with hepatitis virus, and they were scored for whether hepatitis developed in them. With tissue culture, the response is the development of cellular changes, called cytopathic effect, characteristic of the virus added to the cells in the tube.

The precision of the estimates is improved by using larger numbers of test subjects. Quantal assays are used, however, either when quick results are needed or when more precise methods cannot be used. Hepatitis virus, for instance, has not yet been grown in tissue culture, and use of human subjects requires that only a few subjects are used at each dilution step. In many laboratories, often two test units are used at each 10-fold dilution step; other laboratories use up to four or six test units routinely.

The data given in Table 4-1 for illustrative purposes are therefore more extensive than commonly occur. This table was prepared by assuming that 0.1 ml. of a dilution of 10^{-6} of a hypothetical virus suspension would cause infection in 50 per cent of the subjects tested. The statistical distribution of virus particles in such samples, as will

TABLE 4-1. HYPOTHETICAL DATA FOR QUANTAL ASSAY

| DILUTION | AVERAGE NUMBER OF INFECTIVE PARTICLES PER 0.1 ML. | RESPONSES | | | |
| | | 10 Subjects Each | | 100 Subjects Each | |
		Positive	Negative	Positive	Negative
10^{-5}	6.93	10	0	100	0
$10^{-5.5}$	2.19	9	1	89	11
10^{-6}	0.693	5	5	50	50
$10^{-6.5}$	0.219	2	8	20	80
10^{-7}	0.069	1	9	7	93
$10^{-7.5}$	0.0219	0	10	2	98
10^{-8}	0.0069	0	10	0	100

To derive the data for this table, it was assumed that at a dilution of 10^{-6}, 0.1 ml. samples would cause a positive response in 50 per cent of test subjects. By the Poisson distribution, such samples contain, on the average, 0.693 infective particles. The number of infective particles and percentage of expected responses was then calculated for the other dilution steps.

be discussed in a later section, allows calculation of the most probable percentage of positive responses at other dilution steps.

The data contained in Table 4-1 are not only more extensive than usually occur, but are exact in the sense that the number of infectious particles in each sample is known and that there is no variability due to such factors as varying susceptibility of hosts or errors in pipetting, which might occur in data from an actual experiment. Different methods of calculating titers will now be used on the data of Table 4-1 to illustrate the different methods and to allow comparison of the precision to be expected.

The percentage of positive responses at each dilution can be plotted as a function of dilution, as shown in Figure 4-2. A character-

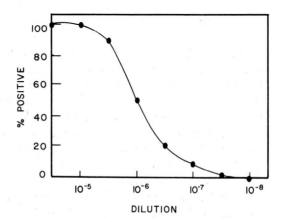

Figure 4-2. Virus dose-response curve, showing the decrease in the percentage of positive responses as the virus sample is made more dilute. (Data for the graph are from Table 4-1.)

istic S-shaped curve results. The 50 per cent end point occurs at the center of the S, where the percentage of positive responses changes most rapidly as the dilution is changed, and it is the most accurately measured part of the curve. Sometimes the infectivity titer is expressed merely as the 50 per cent end point.

More commonly, however, the titer is expressed in terms of the 50 per cent infectious dose, which is the smallest volume capable of producing a positive response in 50 per cent of susceptible subjects tested. The infectious dose is the volume that was inoculated, times the dilution that gave 50 per cent positive responses. The titer is the number of infectious doses in some unit volume, usually 1 ml., and it is therefore the reciprocal of the infectious dose.

Depending upon the expected response, the more common abbreviations for the infectious dose are: ID_{50} (infectious dose for 50 per cent response), $TCID_{50}$ (tissue culture infectious dose for 50 per cent response), ED_{50} (effective dose for 50 per cent response — used when a disease is the response), EID_{50} (egg infectious dose for 50 per cent response), or LD_{50} (lethal dose; that is, fatality occurs in 50 per cent of the hosts tested).

Perhaps the most straightforward way to determine the 50 per cent end point is simply to score the subjects for response or no response and to construct a dose-response curve similar to that of Figure 4-2. The 50 per cent end point can then be read graphically. In the case of the data of Table 4-1, the 50 per cent end point is 10^{-6}, and one ID_{50} is 0.1 ml. of a 10^{-6} dilution. The titer is $\dfrac{1}{0.1 \times 10^{-6}} = 10^{7}\ ID_{50}/ml.$ There is no difference between the titers calculated from the data from 10 or 100 subjects in this example.

Because of statistical variation, especially when small numbers of subjects are used at each dilution, the simple graphic method is not always possible. Other means have been devised for estimating the 50 per cent end point. Some of these methods are relatively simple, but some require rather advanced statistical knowledge. Finney (1952) has summarized these methods.

One method that is sometimes used by virologists was proposed by Reed and Muench (1938). Their method contains two steps. The first step consists of increasing the number of hosts injected with each dilution by "summing-up" and "summing-down." Such a procedure, performed on the data of Table 4-1, resulted in the data in Table 4-2. This "summing-up" and "summing-down" procedure is subject to many criticisms (see Finney, 1952, for example). The summing step was introduced because it was supposed that in this way the number of subjects at each dilution could be increased, but the only way the number of subjects can actually be increased is to inoculate more. To use the summation procedure for this purpose requires the implicit assumption that all individuals tested are equally susceptible. That is,

TABLE 4-2. ACCUMULATED RESPONSES FOR QUANTAL ASSAY

	10 TEST UNITS			100 TEST UNITS		
	Positives	Negatives	% Positive	Positives	Negatives	% Positive
10^{-5}	27	0	100.0	268	0	100.0
$10^{-5.5}$	17	1	94.5	168	11	93.8
10^{-6}	8	6	57.1	79	61	56.4
$10^{-6.5}$	3	14	17.6	29	141	17.1
10^{-7}	1	23	4.2	9	234	3.7
$10^{-7.5}$	0	33	0.0	2	332	0.6
10^{-8}	0	43	0.0	0	432	0.0

Data from Table 4-1 were summed-up (positive responses) or summed-down (negative responses).

a test unit that gives a positive response at one dilution would also be positive at all lower dilutions. This may be valid when using cell cultures as the test units, but it is usually not valid when using complete animals, such as mice or humans, with their varying histories of disease. Further, because the dose-response curve is not symmetrical about the 50 per cent end point, summing causes the end point to shift, as seen in Table 4-2.

Often, when a published report states that the Reed-Muench method was used for calculating end points, what is meant is that the second step of the method was used. This is the interpolation formula that is used when the 50 per cent end point is not exactly at one of the dilution steps. It is written $\dfrac{A-50\%}{A-B} \times \log D = C$, where A is the percentage positive at the next lower dilution than that giving 50 per cent positive responses, B is the percentage positive at the next higher dilution than that giving 50 per cent positive responses, D is the dilution factor, and C is the logarithm to be added to the logarithm of the next lower dilution to give the 50 per cent end point.

Application of the formula to the accumulated responses in Table 4-2 yields an estimate of the 50 per cent end point, for the 10 test units per dilution:

$$\frac{57.1 - 50}{57.1 - 17.6} \times .5 = 0.1$$

50 per cent end point $= 10^{-6} \times 10^{-0.1} = 10^{-6.1}$

Similarly, the 50 per cent end point for the data using 100 test units per dilution is $10^{-6.16}$. The difference arises because of differences in rounding off the percentages in the two sets of data.

With these end points, the titers are $\dfrac{1}{0.1 \times 10^{-6.1}} = 1.3 \times 10^{7}$

ID_{50}/ml., and 1.4×10^7 ID_{50}/ml. for the 10- and 100-test unit data. These titers are too high by about 30 to 40 per cent over the known titer.

By way of experiment, the Reed-Muench method was applied to the data of Tables 4-1 and 4-2 in various ways. It was found that the interpolation formula in effect uses a straight line to connect the two points on either side of the end point; and since the dose-response is not linear in this region, the end point is missed. The interpolation formula introduces an error that partially compensates the error resulting from "summing." There is no apparent advantage in using either the accumulated responses or the interpolation formula with their inherent inaccuracies and invalid assumptions over simply graphing the data and estimating the end point.

Kärber (1931) also devised a procedure for estimating the 50 per cent end point from data such as those in Table 4-2. His procedure (summarized by Lennette and Schmidt, 1964) uses the following formula:

Negative log of ID_{50} = [negative log of highest concentration used] −

$$\left[\left(\frac{\text{Sum of \% positives at each dilution}}{100} - 0.5 \right) (\text{log of dilution factor}) \right].$$

Applying this formula to the data from 10 subjects in Table 4-2 results in:

Negative log of ID_{50}

$$= -5.0 - \left[\left(\frac{100 + 94.5 + 57.1 + 17.6 + 4.2}{100} - 0.5 \right) \times 0.5 \right]$$
$$= -5.0 - [(2.73 - 0.5) \times 0.5]$$
$$= -5.0 - 1.11$$
$$= -6.11$$
$$ID_{50} = 10^{-6.11}$$
$$\text{Titer} = \frac{1}{0.1 \times 10^{-6.11}} = 10^{7.11} = 1.3 \times 10^7 \ ID_{50}/\text{ml.}$$

The same titer is obtained for the data for 100 subjects per sample, about 30 per cent higher than the true titer.

Statisticians have developed methods for calculating titers that are more sound from a statistical and mathematical standpoint, but these methods are usually so much more complicated that their use is often not worth the trouble.

One such method was developed especially for virus titrations (Seligman and Mickey, 1964). In this method, a 50 per cent end point is not estimated first, nor is the doubtful procedure of accumulating responses used. Instead, an estimate is made of the number of infectious particles per sample. Since more than one dilution contains infectious particles, the data from the various dilutions are combined as a weighted average. An advantage is that an estimate of the 95 per cent confidence interval can also be easily obtained (that is, 5 per cent of the time, or one time in 20 trials, because of chance variations the true titer would be outside the confidence interval).

Their method of calculating the titer will not be given in detail here. It was applied to the data of Table 4-1 for the purpose of comparison with the other methods that have been presented. For the data for 10 subjects per dilution, the method yielded a titer of 7.33×10^7 infectious particles per milliliter, an estimate that is too high by $\frac{7.33 \times 6.93}{6.93} \times 100 = 6$ per cent. The 95 per cent confidence interval is 4.25×10^7 to 1.25×10^8 infectious particles per milliliter. A similar calculation for the data using 100 subjects at each dilution gives an estimated titer of 6.98×10^7 infectious particles per milliliter for an error of 0.7 per cent. The 95 per cent confidence interval is 5.89×10^7 to 8.27×10^7 infectious particles per milliliter. The effect of increasing the number of test units at each dilution is quite apparent, both for decreasing the actual error and for narrowing the 95 per cent confidence interval.

Data from an actual experiment using the quantal type assay are presented in Table 4-3. The simplest procedure, graphing, gave a titer of 2.8×10^7 $TCID_{50}/ml$. The titer by the Reed-Muench method is 3.2×10^7 $TCID_{50}/ml$., and by the Kärber method it is 3.7×10^7 $TCID_{50}/ml$.

With these methods for estimating end points, the differences between the estimated and the true titers are usually not important because the percentage error is constant as long as the same method is used consistently. A titer is usually compared with the titer of a control virus preparation, which of course should be assayed under the same conditions. Furthermore, errors due to physiologic variation in the test subjects, even when relatively constant tissue cultures are

TABLE 4-3. EXPERIMENTAL DATA FOR END POINT DILUTION ASSAY

| | RESPONSES | |
DILUTION	Positive	Negative
10^{-5}	12	0
$10^{-5.5}$	12	0
10^{-6}	12	0
$10^{-6.5}$	5	7
10^{-7}	1	11
$10^{-7.5}$	0	12
10^{-8}	1	11

Half-log dilutions were prepared from a stock of virus of unknown concentration, and 0.1 ml. was added to each of 12 tubes containing susceptible cells. After a suitable time, the cells were scored for presence or absence of viral cytopathic effect.

used, are usually greater than the errors in estimating the titer from the responses. As with any infectivity titration, the end point, or quantal, methods detect only those virions able to initiate infection. The titer refers to the concentration of infectious units; it may or may not be the same as the physical particle count.

Statistics of Titration

Consider a volume, say 10 ml., of buffer solution in which there are 10 virus particles randomly distributed. (The discussion will apply equally well to bacteria or other discrete particles; and, as we will see later, it applies to physical damage occurring randomly in a population of virus particles.) Let us divide the suspension into ten 1 ml. parts, as is done when inoculating aliquots or samples of a diluted virus suspension into test subjects.

By chance, a given sample might contain no particles, one or two particles, or even all 10 particles. The statistical distribution of virus particles in such highly diluted samples is called the Poisson distribution and is written

$$P(r) = \frac{\lambda^r e^{-\lambda}}{r!}$$

where $P(r)$ is the fraction of samples containing r particles, λ is the average number of particles per sample, e is the base of natural logarithms numerically equal to 2.718..., and $r!$ is read as "r-factorial," meaning $1 \times 2 \times 3 \times ...r$. For example, 4! means $1 \times 2 \times 3 \times 4$, or 24; $0! = 1$ by definition.

To return to the previous example, with 10 particles distributed among ten 1 ml. samples, there is an average (λ) of one particle per sample. The fraction, P, of samples containing no particles ($r = 0$) is given by $\frac{1^0 e^{-1}}{0!}$ and is 0.37. The fraction of samples containing one particle is also 0.37; the fraction with two particles is $\frac{1^2 e^{-1}}{2!}$, or 0.185; and so forth.

At the 50 per cent end point, one half of the samples contains no infective virus; the other one half contains one or more infective virus particles. It is impossible to tell, in a quantal assay, whether a positive sample contained more than one infective particle because of the amplification effect of viral replication. The response of the host is essentially the same, within rather wide limits, whether it was inoculated with one particle or with many.

The Poisson distribution can be used to calculate the fraction of samples with one, two, or more particles at the 50 per cent point. First, it is necessary to calculate the average number of infective particles per sample. It is easiest to consider the 50 per cent of test subjects that survived the inoculation, as they received n infective particles; therefore, $r = 0$ and $P = 0.5$. Thus, it is necessary to solve $0.5 = e^{-\lambda}$. This can be done by taking the natural logarithms of both sides, $\ln 0.5 = -\lambda$, or $\lambda = \ln 2 = 0.693$. ($e^{-\lambda}$ can also be found in tables of exponential functions.) The average number of infective virus particles at the 50 per cent end point is therefore about 0.693 per sample. The fraction of samples containing one, two, or more infective particles can then be calculated from the Poisson distribution. It was in this way that the "artificial" data of Table 4-1 were obtained and the most probable number of positive responses at each dilution was calculated.

Plaque Titration

With the end point dilution titration, a single virus particle, after multiplication, can make its presence known by a visible or otherwise detectable effect on a susceptible host. Another way to make such an effect visible is by the plaque method. This method is the one used almost exclusively in assaying the concentration of infective phages and is widely used for animal viruses. It is the procedure to be used whenever possible.

Titration of phage by the plaque method was known to d'Herelle (1922). During the ensuing years, changes in the technique have been minor. First, agar plates are prepared. Then, a suspension of bacteria is prepared in dilute, melted agar and a diluted sample of the phage is added. This mixture is spread as a thin film over the surface of the agar plate which is incubated (4 hours to overnight) to allow bacterial growth. The bacteria form a "lawn" with round, bare areas, or plaques, where the bacteria were killed or lysed by the phage. In d'Herelle's method a single virus particle initially infected a single bacterial cell. It went through its cycle of multiplication, and its progeny infected neighboring bacterial cells. The process continued in a widening circle, resulting in the plaque.

A similar assay was devised for animal viruses by Dulbecco (1952). In this case, however, susceptible cells are grown on the bottom of a petri dish or other culture vessel. The liquid medium is removed from over the cells and a suitable dilution of virus is added. After a short period of incubation to allow the virus particles to adsorb to the cells, nutrient agar is placed over the cells. After a few days, or sometimes as long as 2 weeks of incubation, the cells are stained by adding neutral red or some other vital dye to the agar. Living cells take up the stain but dead cells do not. The plaques are seen as unstained circular areas in the stained cell sheet. One example of some animal virus plaques is shown in Figure 4-3.

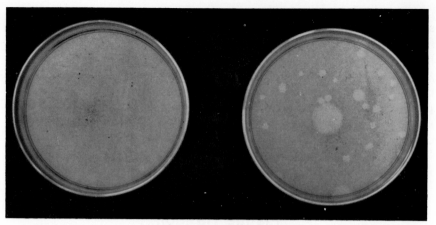

Figure 4-3. Plaques caused by encephalomyocarditis virus (EMC). On the left is a control petri dish of mouse embryo cells. The dish on the right shows several small plaques (wild-type) and two large plaques (mutant). The living cells were stained with the vital dye, neutral red, 2 days after plating the virus. Dead cells in the plaque are unstained.

To obtain the plaque titer, the plaques on the assay dishes are counted. Dilutions are usually necessary, however, to obtain a convenient number of plaques for counting and to prevent overlapping of plaques. The titer of the original suspension is calculated from the plaque count at the dilution that was counted, divided by the volume and the dilution factor. The units usually used for expressing the plaque titer are plaque forming units (PFU) per milliliter. For example, assume that two dishes had received 0.1 ml. each of a 10^{-6} dilution of a virus suspension of unknown concentration, and 68 and 72 plaques appeared on the two dishes. The titer would be calculated from the average number of plaques in 0.1 ml. as:

$$\frac{70}{0.1 \times 10^{-6}} = 70 \times 10^{7} = 7.0 \times 10^{8} \text{ PFU/ml.}$$

The dishes at the next lower dilution, 10^{-5}, would contain about 10 times as many PFU, or about 700 plaques per dish. Since most plaques are 2 mm. in diameter or larger, depending on the virus, such a great number of plaques would be impossible to count because of overlap. The next higher dilution, 10^{-7}, would yield about seven plaques per dish. Although easily counted, the number is too small for good statistical precision.

Other Assays

Many other methods have been developed for assaying the infectivity of a virus preparation. Most are of limited use, applicable only to certain viruses under certain conditions. Some, however, are of more general interest and will be discussed here.

Tobacco mosaic virus is usually assayed by counting local lesions formed on leaves; the assay is therefore somewhat similar to a plaque assay. The virus is rubbed on the leaf of a tobacco plant, and after a suitable period, small lesions appear on the leaf. These can be counted, and clonally derived virus is obtained by extracting the virus from a lesion.

There is much greater variability in the local lesion assay than in a plaque assay. Often there is variability from leaf to leaf with the same virus preparation; more lesions may appear on leaves of one portion of the plant than on other areas of the same plant. For this reason, various procedures have been developed to compare the unknown virus preparation statistically with a standard virus preparation.

One such procedure is to place the standard preparation on one half of a given leaf and the unknown on the other half. The standard then serves as a control for variability from leaf to leaf. Variability also occurs because of differences in how hard the leaf is rubbed after applying the virus preparation and whether the leaf is injured slightly in some way. Often, fine carborundum is added to the virus mixture to scratch the surface of the leaf slightly when the virus preparation is rubbed on the leaf to aid entrance of the virus into the cells. Because of the many variables, a large number of leaves must be inoculated to obtain precision in the assay.

Some animal viruses form local lesions on the chorioallantoic membrane of embryonated eggs. The membrane is exposed by removing part of the shell of the embryonated egg. The air is removed from the air sac, allowing the membrane of the egg to drop, and the diluted virus material is placed upon the membrane. After a suitable period of incubation, local lesions, usually called "pocks," appear on the membrane. The pock count method was used commonly before the plaque method became available but has virtually been replaced by the plaque method, as nearly all animal viruses that cause pocks will also cause plaques.

It is also possible to assay some viruses by the length of the incubation period of the disease they cause. For instance, some of the leukemia viruses of chickens can be assayed by determining the period of time from inoculation to first appearance of the disease. Some of the tumor viruses, in particular the leukemia viruses of mice, have not as yet been induced to cause plaques in cell cultures. One of these leukemia viruses has been assayed by weighing the spleens of infected animals at a given time after inoculation (Rowe and Brodsky, 1959). The weight of the spleen has been shown to be related to the titer of the inoculated virus.

Errors of Infectivity Assays

Measurement of virus concentration, like measurement of anything else, is subject to error. Some errors in virus assay arise by the nature of the sampling process and cannot be avoided. The sampling error of a quantal assay is difficult to estimate, but for plaque assays, the standard deviation is simply the square root of the mean number of plaques counted on a dish. If 36 plaques are counted, the standard deviation is 6; if 100 plaques are counted, it is 10. The coefficient of variation is therefore reduced from 16 per cent to 10 per cent by counting more plaques. In a titration, it is possible to increase the number of plaques counted, and thereby reduce sampling error, by using more closely spaced dilutions or by using more assay plates at each dilution. A detailed analysis of the statistics of plaque assays was presented by Lorenz (1962).

Pipettes, even when carefully calibrated, have inherent error. The error accumulates when a long series of dilutions is made. Because the unavoidable sampling error is generally larger, however, it often is not necessary to attempt to achieve the greatest possible pipetting accuracy.

Plaque assays of bacteriophages or animal viruses have many advantages over other assays that have been developed. The precision is generally higher than with other forms of assay. For instance, if 70 plaques can be counted on one petri dish, that one dish is statistically equivalent to 100 culture tubes used in the quantal assay at the ID_{50}. Usually, the end point assay is used when precision can be sacrificed and only a few cultures are used at each dilution.

The plaque assay has the further possibilities of obtaining mutants able to form different kinds of plaques and of obtaining these mutants in genetically pure form (Dulbecco, 1957). As will be discussed in later chapters, plaque mutants have been very useful in discovering the molecular mechanisms by which genes function.

The Number of Virus Particles Necessary to Form a Plaque

In performing the plaque assay it is important to know whether a plaque could have been caused by a single infectious particle or whether more than one virus particle may have initiated the plaque. The latter situation would require that a cell be infected by more than one virus particle; that is, the virus particles would have to cooperate with one another in order to form the plaque.

It is possible to decide between these two hypotheses by considering the diagram shown in Figure 4-4. The diagram shows that the

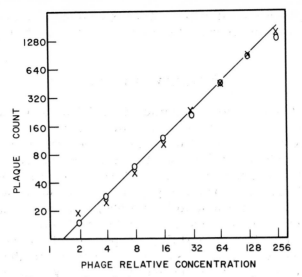

Figure 4-4. Proportionality of phage concentration to plaque count. (Redrawn from Ellis and Delbrück, 1939.)

number of plaques produced on a given dish is proportional to the dilution of the virus suspension applied.

If virus particles had to cooperate to form a plaque, the curve would not be linear. Greater dilution of the virus suspension separates the particles within the suspension, and it is less likely that two or more particles would come in contact with the same cell. At higher concentrations of virus, it is more likely that dual infection could occur; doubling the concentration would more than double the number of plaques. A mathematical demonstration that linearity with dilution implies that one particle is sufficient to initiate a plaque was given by Dulbecco and Vogt (1954). Similar mathematical arguments have been put forward to demonstrate that a single bacteriophage is able to induce a plaque and that a single tobacco mosaic virus particle is able to produce a lesion on a tobacco leaf (Furumoto and Mickey, 1967a, 1967b).

Although a single particle can induce a plaque, a given plaque may have been formed by more than one particle. When too concentrated a virus suspension is used, the chances increase that two particles infect the same cell (or that two plaques are so close together that they look like a single plaque), and there can be mixed virus in a plaque. The important distinction to be made is that one particle is sufficient, although more than one may accidently cause the same plaque. The statistics of overlap of plaques has been thoroughly analyzed (Lorenz and Zoeth, 1966). In a highly dilute suspension so that only a few plaques develop on an assay plate, and under conditions in which plaques are small so that overlap is a minimum, the chances are minute that a double infection has occurred in the area of one plaque.

Efficiency of Plating

To say that a single virus particle is sufficient to initiate a plaque is not the same as to say that every virus particle actually initiates a plaque. A comparison must be made between the plaque or other infectivity titration and the absolute particle count, such as that obtained by the electron microscope. Such a comparison shows that with the bacteriophages, nearly every particle that can be seen in the electron microscope is able to form a plaque (Luria *et al.*, 1951). At worst, one out of two or three phage particles will produce a plaque.

The specific infectivity (PFU/total particles) is not as high with the animal viruses. Sometimes as few as one in several thousand particles, even under the best known conditions, may produce a plaque. For instance, in a survey of all the human adenoviruses, M. Green *et al.* (1967a) found the specific infectivity of the most efficient (type 3) to be 1:11 and that of the least efficient (type 25) to be 1:2300. In other words, many times more physical particles can be detected physically than can initiate plaques in a suitable cell system. It is seldom clear whether only one of many particles is infectious or whether all are equally infectious but with a low probability of causing infection. One of the highest specific infectivities occurs with EMC virus: About one of five particles can initiate infection (Homma and Graham, 1965).

The assay of tobacco mosaic virus by necrotic lesion counts is even less efficient. Only one in a thousand particles, or even one in ten million particles may be able to start a lesion. There are at least three reasons for this low efficiency. Rubbing the tobacco mosaic virus preparation on the leaf scratches the leaf and releases materials able to damage the virus particles and decrease the infectivity. The leaf's surface has a great variety of cells, and these cells may differ in susceptibility to infection by the virus particles; in other words, a lesion might begin only if a virus particle hits a particularly susceptible cell. Also, it is difficult for the virus particle to penetrate the thick wall of a plant cell to gain entrance to the inside of the cell. All of these factors, plus perhaps others, result in an inefficient assay.

The term "efficiency of plating," often abbreviated to EOP, must be defined in terms relative to the particular virus-cell system in question. The absolute efficiency of plating is that obtained by comparing the infectious titer with the electron microscope count. Sometimes, however, the efficiency of plating is compared with infection of some standard cell or under some standard conditions. In any event, in a particular case, the term must be defined.

Despite their small size, viruses replicate rapidly. By killing or by otherwise affecting the cells they infect, their effect is amplified, and their presence becomes visible to the investigator. This fact has resulted in the development of many methods for counting virus particles. Without these tools, virologists would never have been able to determine how viruses react to their external environment and how they increase in number while maintaining constant characteristics. These subjects will be discussed in the following chapters.

Further Reading

Schwerdt, C. E.: Quantitative Relationships Between Virus Particles and Their Fundamental Activity. *In* Burnet, F. M., and W. Stanley (eds.): The Viruses. New York, Academic Press Inc., 1959, Vol. 1, pp. 329-358.

5

ACTION OF PHYSICAL AND CHEMICAL AGENTS ON VIRIONS

During their extracellular existence, viruses are exposed to many chemical and physical agents. Some of these agents are present in the natural environment; others are experimentally introduced by an investigator. Natural agents include temperature and certain enzymes, such as ribonuclease and deoxyribonuclease. Agents not normally present in effective amounts include ultraviolet light, x-rays, radiophosphorus, nitrous acid, and formalin.

Because of their simplicity, viruses react in a limited number of ways to environmental stresses. The most common reaction, and one that is easily measurable, is loss of infectivity. Infectivity can be lost because of extreme disruption of the virion or because of subtle changes in the protein or nucleic acid.

Investigators prefer the term "inactivated" to the lay term "killed." They reason that something cannot logically be "killed" if it is perhaps not alive to begin with. Inactivation can, under certain conditions, be reversible; and although a virus described as "inactivated" can later be "reactivated," once a virus has been described as "killed," "reincarnation" seems to be the only alternative.

Sometimes viruses react to environmental stress by mutating. When this occurs, the next generation of progeny differs from the parent in some detectable way. Because mutations yield valuable information about viral genetics, they are often induced experimentally.

Knowledge of the responses of viruses to environmental agents is important for several reasons. It enables an experimenter to minimize viral losses when it is desirable to have maximum yields. It enables virologists to destroy the infectivity of virus in vaccines without destroying their antigenicity. It also enables investigators to deduce information about viral structure and replication.

Many physical agents were originally used experimentally in studies of viral structure, and some yielded valid conclusions. In many cases, however, similar conclusions have been arrived at more directly; the less direct methods based on inactivation studies often raised more questions than they answered. The principles of viral reactions with chemical and physical agents will be discussed here with respect to extracellular virions, and what is said will also be applicable to intracellular replicating particles. Some of the experiments to be discussed in later chapters will be based on the effect of various physical agents on the viral genome during its stay within the host cell.

LIPID SOLVENTS

Lipids are soluble in many organic solvents, but of chief interest to virologists are chloroform, ether, and detergents (a commonly used detergent is sodium dodecyl sulfate). Many viruses are quite resistant to the effects of these agents. Those that are not resistant include myxoviruses, herpesviruses, arboviruses, and some poxviruses. Adding ether to the aqueous suspension of a sensitive virus and shaking the suspension will cause the virus to lose its infectivity.

The effect of the lipid solvents on the myxoviruses has been studied by electron microscopy. Horne and Waterson (1960) used ether treatment of mumps, Newcastle disease, and Sendai (para-influenza) viruses and found that the ether treatment caused the membrane surrounding the RNA-protein core to fragment or disappear. The RNA-protein core, however, remained relatively intact and was recognizable in the electron microscope; it was similar to that shown in Figure 2-17. Ether treatment now is used often with the myxoviruses to remove the membrane and to expose the core. Apparently the membrane is derived, at least in part, from the cell's cytoplasmic membrane, which contains large amounts of lipid.

THERMAL INACTIVATION

It is impossible for the investigator to avoid exposing viruses to thermal activity because molecules are in constant motion at all temperatures except absolute zero. Virions, therefore, also are subject to thermal agitation. The higher the temperature, the more violent is the motion.

Knowledge about heat inactivation is useful to the virologist who is trying to minimize losses of virus during storage. He usually uses very low temperatures and stabilizing media for long-term storage, but even then some decrease in titer occurs. On other occasions, the investigator desires to destroy viral activity, as, for instance, when he uses an autoclave to sterilize glassware that has been used for handling virus preparations. Gentle heat is sometimes used in vaccine production to inactivate infectivity of virus particles without destroying antigenicity.

The sensitivity of a virus to thermal inactivation is measured as follows: The virus preparation is held at a constant temperature; samples are removed from the preparation periodically and assayed for the concentration of infective particles remaining. When the titer is plotted on a logarithmic scale as a function of time, a curve similar to that shown in Figure 5-1 is usually obtained. This curve is typical in that it is a straight line through the origin with no perceptible lag or "shoulder." It continues as a straight line (exponential decrease, since it is plotted on semilogarithmic axes) over several logarithmic cycles. At a higher temperature, the slope of the curve is greater.

The loss of titer can be explained by the following model: Assume that a virion contains one or more sites that can react in a way that will inactivate the virion. (For the moment, the nature of the site and the reaction will not be specified.) At a given temperature, energy of thermal motion is distributed among the sites. By chance, some sites are at a higher energy level than others; if a given site has energy above a certain threshold, it undergoes a reaction that changes its characteristics. Therefore, raising the temperature increases the average energy per site and also increases the probability that a given site will undergo the reaction.

The linear decrease of the logarithm of the titer at increasing intervals indicates that all critical sites of the virion must be intact (unreacted) for the virion to remain infective. The loss of even one critical site (if there is more than one per virion) will destroy the infectivity of that virion.

This conclusion is based on the following reasoning: Assume that each virion has a certain number of identical, but independent, sites subject to damage. Assume further that random damage occurs in such a way that only a small fraction of sites is damaged. The distribution of damage among the sites is given by the Poisson distribution:

$$P(r) = \frac{\lambda^r e^{-\lambda}}{r!}$$

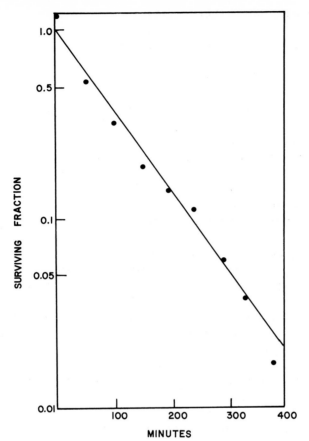

Figure 5-1. Thermal inactivation of the human cytomegalovirus at 37° C. The infectious titer decreases by one half about every 60 minutes, a quite rapid loss for viruses. (Krugman and Goodheart, 1964.)

where $P(r)$ is the fraction of virions with r-damaged sites and λ is the average number of damaged sites per virion.

If damage to only one site is sufficient to inactivate the infectivity of a virion, then the only surviving virions will be those that received no damage, and the equation becomes

$$P(0) = \frac{\lambda^0 e^{-\lambda}}{0!} = e^{-\lambda}$$

For most kinds of damaging agents, the exponent, λ, is a function of time: $\lambda = kt$. Here, k is a proportionality constant, indicating the frequency of occurrence of damage. The longer the time, the higher is λ.

The equation relating the surviving fraction of infective virions to time at a given temperature, under the assumption that a single "hit," or reacted site, is sufficient to inactivate, is therefore

$$P\,(0) = \frac{V}{V_0} = e^{-kt}$$

or, with natural logarithms,

$$\ln \frac{V}{V_0} = -kt$$

This indicates that the natural logarithm of the surviving fraction (V is the titer of virus at some time, t, and V_0 is the titer at the beginning of the experiment) decreases linearly with a slope equal to $-k$. This result seems to fit observed data (see Fig. 5-1). But perhaps some other explanation might also fit.

The next more complicated possibility is that two critical sites must be damaged in order to destroy the infectivity of a virion. In other words, surviving virions would be those with either no damage or at most one damaged site. (In target theory, such as is now under discussion, a damaged site results from a successful "hit" and, therefore is often simply called a "hit." For the sake of simplicity, the customary quotation marks will be omitted from here on.) A single hit is sufficient to cause a given site to react, but at least two sites must be reacted to inactivate the virion.

An expression for survivors under this hypothesis can be derived, assuming that all sites are equivalent and that damage is distributed randomly among them. The proportion of sites that sustain no damage is given by the zero term of the Poisson distribution and is e^{-kt}, which is also the probability that a given site will escape damage. The sum of the probability of an event occurring and the probability of the same event not occurring is equal to 1. Therefore, the probability that a given site will be damaged is $1-e^{-kt}$. The probability that two identical critical sites sustain damage, inactivating the virion, is the product of the individual probabilities, or $(1-e^{-kt})^2$. The probability that a virion survives under the hypothesis of two critical sites, therefore, is $1-(1-e^{-kt})^2$. In general, if there are n critical sites, all of which must be damaged to destroy the particle, the probability of survival is $1-(1-e^{-kt})^n$.

Examples of one-, two-, and three-hit curves are given in Figure 5-2, with the logarithm of the surviving fraction plotted against the dose. The one-hit curve is linear (logarithmic) through the origin. Higher-hit curves have a shoulder at the beginning, then become linear. The reason for this is that at low doses the likelihood that a virion will receive two or three hits and become inactivated is less. At higher doses, most of the population of virions has received one hit; so in essence the original population of virions has been changed into one that requires only one further hit to be inactivated. From that

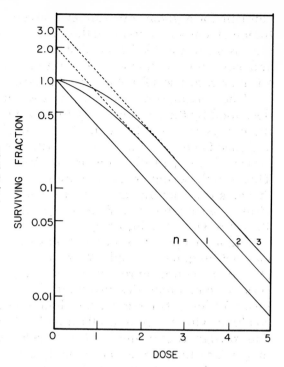

Figure 5-2. Theoretical curves showing the decrease in titer to be expected under the hypotheses that one, two, or three hits are required to inactivate a virion.

point, the inactivation becomes linear. The hit number of an inactivation curve is determined by extrapolating from the linear part back to the ordinate; the intercept of the extrapolated line is the hit number. More detailed discussion of the "target theory" may be found in Lea (1947), Powers (1962), and Hiatt (1964).

In practice, it is often relatively simple to distinguish between a one-hit curve and a multihit curve if the experiment is done carefully and the data are good. With most viruses tested, the experimental data most closely fit the hypothesis that thermal inactivation is a one-hit process.

Where might this single bit of damage occur? The information presented thus far offers no clue. We have referred to "sites" without specifying what a "site" might be: A "site" could be equivalent to a protein molecule of which the virion is composed or to one of the capsomers. If so, can inactivation be explained as a change in one of the proteins or capsomers? It is known that heat denatures proteins and causes loss of the intricate foldings that give a protein its functional properties. Perhaps a similar phenomenon happens with heat-inactivation of a virion.

Evidence on this point has been obtained primarily by two types of experiments. In one type of experiment, the inactivation constant k is measured at different temperatures. As already mentioned, k is constant for a given virus under a given set of conditions (concentration of ions and proteins in the medium, pH, and kinds of salts). It is a measure of the likelihood that a given virion will be inactivated; and, since this likelihood becomes greater at increased temperatures, k is therefore also a function of temperature.

The relationship between inactivation rate and temperature is described by the Arrhenius equation, which allows the calculation of the energy required to excite the essential "sites" so that they react and inactivate the virion. This energy has been measured for many viruses (Woese, 1960) and is usually 50 to 100 kilocalories per mole. This is in the energy range required to denature proteins. In line with this idea is the finding that heat can inactivate foot-and-mouth disease virus, releasing the viral RNA which retains its infectivity (Bachrach, 1961; Brown and Wild, 1966).

Another type of experiment, however, suggests that the picture may not be quite so simple. With many viruses, the loss of infectivity at a given temperature occurs more rapidly than does the loss of certain other properties involving the viral proteins. For instance, phage T1 loses its infectivity at a higher rate than it loses its ability to combine with antibody (Pollard and Setlow, 1953). This perhaps is due to triggering of the particle to release its DNA so that it is no longer infective, but at the same time leaving the protein shell unchanged. In many cases, perhaps also in T1, a slight change in the protein affects infectivity, while a more drastic change is required to affect the ability to combine with antibody. This possibility is consistent with the observation that a virion must be uninjured if it is to possess infectivity. If the virion is changed even slightly, infectivity, the most crucial property, is lost first. The loss of other, less sensitive properties follows.

X-RAY INACTIVATION

To understand how x-rays inactivate the infectivity of virus particles, it is first necessary to understand the action of x-rays on matter. When a liquid is irradiated with x-rays, energy is added to the liquid and ionization of the molecules results. The absorption of energy by the medium results in the formation of secondary electrons. These electrons dissipate the energy by colliding with surrounding molecules. The ionizations are localized around the molecule that absorbs the x-ray quantum.

The high absorption of energy causes the production of peroxides, free radicals, and other toxic materials. The toxic materials accumulate as irradiation is continued, and the level can become toxic for viruses. The inactivation of viruses by toxins is therefore an indirect effect of x-rays. It is possible to prevent or suppress the accumulation of toxic materials by adding certain substances, such as proteins or nucleic acids, to the medium. These substances react with the toxic materials as they form.

The removal of toxic materials, however, does not completely eliminate the effect of x-rays; the remaining effect must be due to a direct effect of the x-ray on the virion. The primary ionization, or the cluster of secondary ionizations, occurs within the virion, or close to it, and results in the inactivation.

When indirect effects are prevented, the inactivation curve shows a linear decrease of the logarithm of the titer as the x-ray dose increases, as shown in Figure 5-3. It is therefore considered to be a single-hit process.

If the primary ionizations are assumed to be randomly distributed, it is possible to calculate from the Poisson distribution and the x-ray dose the average number of ionizations that occurred in a given volume of suspending medium. If 37 per cent ($e^{-1} \times 100$ per cent) of the original infectious virions are still present after irradiation, on the average there has been one hit per particle. Therefore, it is possible to calculate the volume occupied by the sensitive part of the virion. This method was used to obtain an estimate of the volume of virus particles before better methods became available. Many of the measurements obtained in this way are remarkably close to those obtained more recently by other methods.

It has been found that in some of the larger viruses, such as vac-

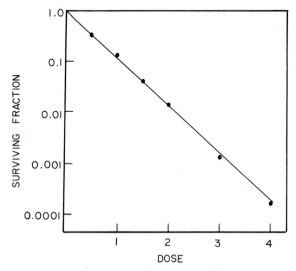

Figure 5-3. Inactivation of phage T2 by the direct effect of x-rays. X-ray dose is in arbitrary units. (Redrawn from Watson, 1950.)

cinia, the target volume is only a small portion of the total volume of the virus particle. This has been interpreted to mean that it is the viral nucleic acid that is sensitive to x-ray inactivation. Watson (1950) found that T2 phages that had been x-ray inactivated were able to adsorb to susceptible bacteria and to kill them. The adsorptive ability was lost as a single-hit process at a lower rate than the loss of infectivity. The bacteria did not produce infectious phage. This means that the target volumes were different for the two functions.

More definitive evidence that the nucleic acid of a virion is the primary site of action of x-rays has come from physical measurements on irradiated nucleic acids. Alexander and Stacey (1956) subjected isolated DNA to varying amounts of x-irradiation and found that the molecular weight of the isolated DNA decreased after exposure to x-rays, but only in high-molarity urea solution. The high-molarity urea breaks the hydrogen bonds holding the two strands together. If one strand is broken by an x-ray hit, the molecule does not break cleanly, as the remaining intact strand is sufficient to maintain the integrity of the molecule (Fig. 5-4).

Using the ultracentrifuge to separate intact from broken DNA strands and to measure their relative numbers, Freifelder (1965, 1966) and Summers and Szybalski (1967) demonstrated convincingly that x-irradiation breaks one or both strands of a DNA molecule. Double-strand breaks inactivate a phage particle; a single-strand break is not lethal.

The effect of x-rays on tobacco mosaic virus, containing RNA, has

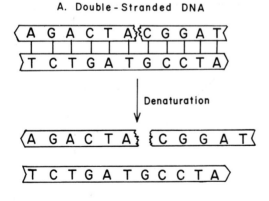

A. Double-Stranded DNA

Figure 5-4. Damage to double-stranded and single-stranded nucleic acids by x-rays. Even though one strand of a double-stranded molecule is broken, the molecule remains intact unless the hydrogen bonding between strands is broken by agents such as heat, urea, or high pH.

B. Single-Stranded RNA

also been studied (Lauffer *et al.*, 1956). The virus was irradiated in suspension, the RNA was isolated, and the viscosity of the RNA solution was measured as an index of the length of the molecules. It was found that viscosity decreased as the x-ray dose increased. In the case of tobacco mosaic virus RNA, however, it was not necessary to use urea to detect the breaks. Since the RNA is single stranded, a single scission of the molecule, produced by a single x-ray hit, will break the molecule into two pieces (Fig. 5-4).

Lauffer and his colleagues found that the virus particle itself was not broken by the irradiation; the break in the nucleic acid showed up only after the nucleic acid was extracted from the virion and no longer supported by the protein. Therefore, the retention of infectivity by tobacco mosaic virus requires that the RNA molecule be unbroken. (It is not necessary that the viral protein be intact to retain infectivity, as will be discussed later.) Furthermore, calculation of the size of the sensitive target from the x-ray data yielded a particle size that was compatible with the size determined in other ways.

ULTRAVIOLET LIGHT INACTIVATION

Ultraviolet light consists of radiations with wavelengths less than about 3000 Å and usually greater than 2000 Å. Unlike irradiation with x-rays, irradiation with ultraviolet light does not produce ionizations; therefore, the biological effect is only by direct effect, due to mechanisms different from those of x-rays.

The survival curve for viruses irradiated with ultraviolet light can be determined by exposing the virus suspension to ultraviolet light in increasing doses and assaying the titer of survivors. Many viruses have been studied in this way. Usually, the survival curve (Fig. 5-5) is exponential (one-hit), but sometimes there is a slight initial shoulder, in which case the straight portion usually extrapolates back to about 1.6 on the ordinate. The meaning of the shoulder has not been adequately explained; it is often ignored, assuming instead that ultraviolet inactivation is one-hit.

The single-hit kinetics indicates that absorption of a single quantum of ultraviolet light is sufficient to inactivate. It is not, however, the same as saying that every absorbed quantum inactivates; and actually, most absorbed quanta are ineffective. It is possible to calculate the quantum yield, or the efficiency of inactivation. Such calculation reveals that for T2 about 1 of 3000 absorbed quanta results in inactivation (Zelle and Hollaender, 1954). The efficiency, therefore, is quite low.

A next question is whether the action of the ultraviolet light takes place in the nucleic acid or in the protein of the virion. The action

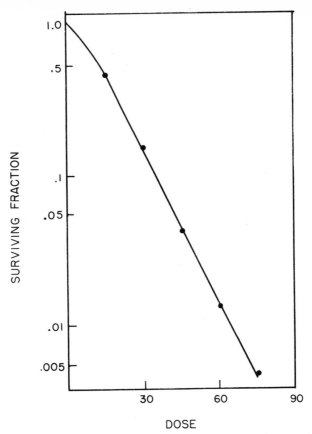

Figure 5-5. Inactivation of a strain of phage T4 by ultraviolet light. The dose is in ergs/mm². (Redrawn from Wulff, 1963.)

spectrum is one way of gaining information on this question (Fig. 5-6). In this procedure, the inactivation curve for a virus is determined for ultraviolet of selected wavelengths, and the efficiency for each wavelength is plotted. The resulting curve shows the wavelength that is most efficient for inactivation.

Proteins and nucleic acids have different absorption spectra. DNA has an absorption peak around 2600 Å, whereas proteins have an absorption minimum at this wavelength and an absorption peak around 2800 Å. The action spectra for many viruses reveal that the most efficient wavelength for inactivation is about 2600 Å (Zelle and Hollaender, 1954; Winkler *et al.*, 1962). Therefore, the viral nucleic acid seems to be the part of the virus that is vulnerable to inactivation by ultraviolet light.

Other mechanisms of inactivation are also operative, however. Winkler *et al.* (1962) found that the action spectrum for the inacti-

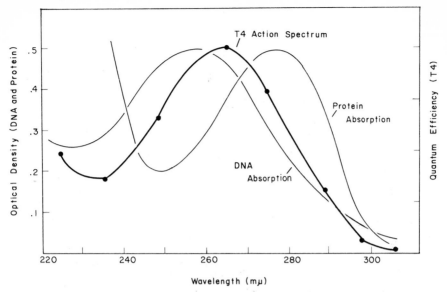

Figure 5-6. Action spectrum for the ultraviolet inactivation of T4 phage. The quantum efficiency of different wavelengths for inactivation of the phage is plotted as arbitrary units. Also shown are absorption spectra for DNA and for protein. The action spectrum more closely resembles the absorption spectrum for DNA than it resembles the absorption spectrum for protein. (Redrawn from Winkler *et al.*, 1962.)

vation of infectivity of T4 coincided with the absorption spectrum of DNA (see Fig. 5-6). In addition, however, electron microscopic examination of virions exposed to ultraviolet light at 2350 Å revealed that many phages had head and tail damage: Some were triggered to release their DNA, some had contracted sheaths, and others had various kinds of tail breaks (Fig. 5-7). All these forms of damage, attributable to effects on protein, occurred at lower efficiency than DNA damage. The most efficient wavelength for inactivation, 2650 Å, resulted in no visible damage, and probably the action at that wavelength is directly on the DNA.

Irradiation of DNA or of pyrimidine nucleotides with ultraviolet light results in the formation of photoproducts (Weinblum, 1967; S. Y. Wang *et al.*, 1967). Dimers are formed either between two free nucleotides (Fig. 5-8), or, when DNA is irradiated, between two adjacent nucleotides on the same strand. The chemistry of these photoproducts was reviewed extensively by Setlow (1966).

One of the more common dimers occurs between adjacent thymines in the same DNA strand; dimerization between two thymines from one strand of DNA to the opposite strand is relatively rare. The thymine dimer twists the DNA chain out of shape, resulting in a spot that is difficult to copy during DNA replication. Wulff (1963) thought

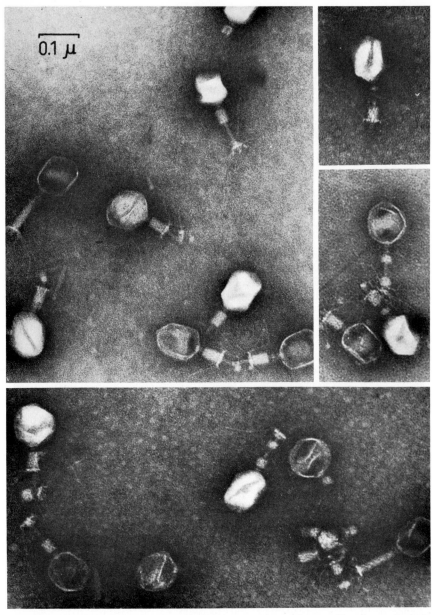

Figure 5-7.   Electron micrograph showing T4 phages damaged by ultraviolet light of 235 mμ wavelength. Some normal phages are visible as well as some showing contracted sheaths—sheaths that are separated into several sections and sheaths that have contracted but left the base plate in place. (Winkler *et al.*, 1962. By permission of the authors and the editor of Virology.)

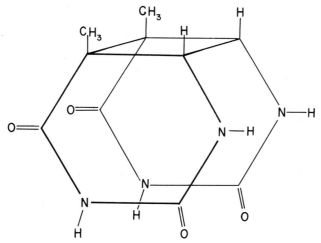

Figure 5-8. Thymine-thymine dimer formed by ultraviolet light irradiation.

that the formation of this dimer might be the lethal event. Careful isolations of the dimers from irradiated phage showed, however, that there were about 4.8 thymine dimers for each phage lethal hit. Therefore, most dimers do not affect the plaque-forming ability of the phage.

Other evidence, however, strongly suggests that the formation of the dimers in the nucleic acid is the biologically important event. Some cells can repair irradiated DNA by removing the thymine dimers, restoring the functional capacity of the DNA. There are several mechanisms for restoration of DNA to a normal state for replication.

Photoreactivation

Dulbecco (1949, 1950) discovered that if he irradiated T phages with ultraviolet light and used these irradiated phages to infect susceptible cells, more plaques appeared if the cultures were incubated in the light than if they were kept in the dark. He called the phenomenon photoreactivation, and it is one mechanism for repair of DNA of inactivated phages. He also found that the action spectrum for the photoreactivating light had a peak at about 4000 Å, which is in the near ultraviolet.

Subsequent work has revealed that photoreactivation is the result of a cellular enzyme or the enzyme-DNA complex that is activated by light, especially light of about 4000 Å wavelength. Photoreactivating enzyme splits thymine dimers, restoring the original configuration (Wulff and Rupert, 1962).

Photoreactivation normally can occur only in infected cells; intense visible light does not reactivate extracellular ultraviolet-inactivated phage. This is easily understandable since the breaking of the dimer is an enzymatic reaction. The enzyme can be isolated from cells, however, and can be used in vitro to break the thymine dimers in isolated DNA. Many, but not all, cells contain photoreactivating enzyme; usually either *E. coli* or yeast are used as an enzyme source for experiments on the enzyme.

Photoreactivation has also been reported to occur in cells infected with ultraviolet-irradiated tobacco mosaic virus (Merriam and Gordon, 1965) and in cells infected with ultraviolet-irradiated pseudorabies virus (Pfefferkorn *et al.*, 1966).

Dark Repair

Damage in ultraviolet-irradiated bacteria can also be corrected by dark repair (Setlow and Carrier, 1964; Boyce and Howard-Flanders, 1964). Like photoreactivation, dark repair is an enzymatic process. Unlike the photoreactivating enzyme, however, the enzyme system that results in dark repair, besides not being light-activated, actually removes the dimer and a few nucleotides from the DNA strand; therefore, it is called an excision enzyme. Removal of the short segment containing the dimer leaves an opening in the DNA strand (Fig. 5-9); other enzymes, the repair enzymes, replace the missing nucleotides,

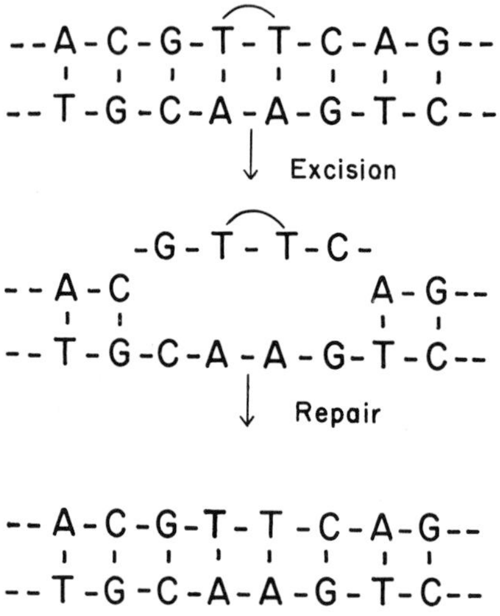

```
  --A-C-G-T̑-T-C-A-G--
    ı  ı  ı  ı  ı  ı  ı  ı
  --T-G-C-A-A-G-T-C--
            ↓ Excision

        -G-T̑-T-C-
  --A-C              A-G--
    ı  ı              ı  ı
  --T-G-C-A-A-G-T-C--
            ↓ Repair


  --A-C-G-T-T-C-A-G--
    ı  ı  ı  ı  ı  ı  ı  ı
  --T-G-C-A-A-G-T-C--
```

Figure 5-9. Removal of thymine-dimer photoproduct from ultraviolet-irradiated DNA by the excision-and-repair enzyme system.

using the remaining intact strand as a template (Pettijohn and Hana-walt, 1964; Strauss *et al.*, 1966).

Excision-and-repair enzymes may also be important to other bio-logical functions, such as recombination (Clark and Margulies, 1965), mutagenesis (Witkin, 1966), prophage incorporation into host-cell DNA, and even normal transcription of DNA (Pauling and Hanawalt, 1965). Many of these phenomena will be considered in more detail in later chapters.

Crossreactivation and Multiplicity Reactivation

Although enzyme systems can erase ultraviolet-light damage and allow phage replication, there are also ways that ultraviolet-inacti-vated phage can replicate without prior repair of the lethal damage.

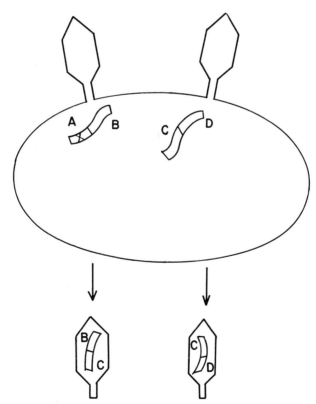

Figure 5-10. Crossreactivation: A bacterial cell infected by an inactive phage car-rying markers *A* and *B*, as well as a second, fully active phage with markers *C* and *D*, yields some particles that contain marker *B*, "rescued" from the inactivated phage.

One way is by crossreactivation, or marker rescue. This occurs in a cell infected with both an inactivated phage and a fully active phage. To detect crossreactivation experimentally, the irradiated phage has to carry distinctive genetic markers; some of the markers of the irradiated phage then are functional (the markers are "rescued") in the progeny virus (Fig. 5-10). Further experiments have shown that it is only the remaining, active genes that are rescued, and not the entire genome of the irradiated phage. The interpretation is that during the intracellular growth cycle, the DNA of the active phage recombines with the active portions of the DNA of the irradiated phage, resulting in a new DNA molecule containing some genes of each parent. The mechanism of recombination will be discussed at greater length in later chapters.

Active phage can be recovered even if none of the infecting phages is fully active. Under certain circumstances, if a bacterial cell

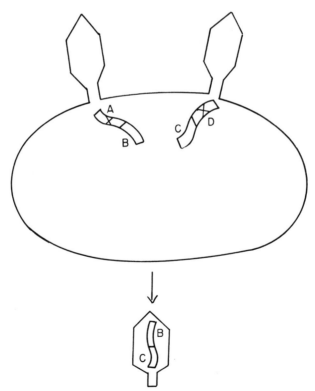

Figure 5-11. Multiplicity reactivation: Double infection of a bacterial cell with phages inactivated by ultraviolet light in different parts of the DNA molecule can result in an active phage containing copies of the remaining active genes of both phages. Phages with the genetic complement of the active parent also result.

is infected with more than one phage, none of which is infective by itself, the bacteria are able to produce perfectly normal infective virions. This phenomenon is called multiplicity reactivation (Fig. 5-11). It was discovered by Luria (1947) and was further elucidated by Luria and Dulbecco (1949) in bacterial virus systems. Multiplicity reactivation has also been reported to occur in ultraviolet-irradiated influenza virus (Barry, 1961) and in reovirus (McClain and Spendlove, 1966).

Since the ultraviolet damage occurs to the viral nucleic acid, it is thought that the only requirement for phage replication is that one complete viral nucleic acid molecule be present. If two molecules are present, each with damage at a different position, then the remaining portions can act together. There is a limitation, however. If the damage occurs in certain critical areas, then some of the enzymes needed early in infection and directed by the viral nucleic acid cannot be made. Further steps in viral replication cannot then take place.

Some viruses, for instance Semliki Forest viruses, are inactivated by visible light in the wavelength range 3300 to 4700 Å. Others are rendered sensitive to visible light when grown in the presence of certain dyes, such as the flavins. It is thought that the inactivation, called photodynamic inactivation, is due to photo-oxidation of the viral nucleic acid (Appleyard, 1967). This kind of inactivation can be important, because neutral red (the vital dye commonly used to stain cells in animal virus plaque assay) can be incorporated in the virions, rendering them susceptible to inactivation by ordinary room light (Tomita and Prince, 1963).

INACTIVATION BY DECAY OF INCORPORATED RADIOPHOSPHORUS

Phosphorus is an important component of nucleic acids. Radioactive phosphorus, P^{32}, can be substituted for regular, nonradioactive phosphorus in phages simply by adding the P^{32} to the medium in which the phage-infected bacteria are grown. Hershey et al. (1951) discovered that preparations of T2 and T4 phages lost their infectivity at a rate dependent on the amount of P^{32} they had incorporated. The kinetics of the inactivation, shown in Figure 5-12, indicates that the inactivation is a single-hit process.

Stent and Fuerst (1955) performed similar studies on several kinds of phages. They, too, found that in all cases the inactivation followed a single-hit kinetics, but with differences in rates for different phages. Calculations showed that only about one of 10 disintegrations resulted in inactivation.

A comparison was also made between the effect of ultraviolet

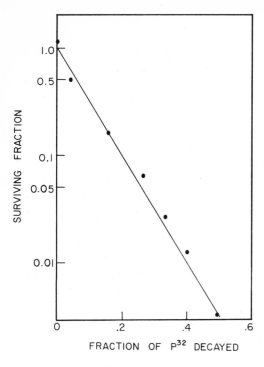

Figure 5-12. Kinetics of inactivation of phage T2 by decay of incorporated P^{32}. (Redrawn from Stent and Fuerst, 1955.)

light and P^{32} decay on viral infectivity. Photoreactivation does not occur with phages that have undergone P^{32} decay inactivation. Further, if the P^{32} is allowed to inactivate the phages extracellularly, the DNA is broken and injection is not complete. Multiplicity reactivation, therefore, does not occur. If the labeled phages are allowed to inject their DNA before decay takes place and the cells are frozen while P^{32} decay occurs, then the entire but broken DNA molecule is present in the cell and multiplicity reactivation can result. Crossreactivation also takes place with P^{32}-labeled phages.

What is the mechanism by which the decay of a P^{32} atom causes inactivation of a virus particle? When a P^{32} atom undergoes decay by ejecting a β particle, it transmutes to an atom of S^{32}. The motion of the ejected β particle results in equal recoil energy imparted to the S^{32} atom. In addition, the sulfur atom is left with excitation energy; these energies are dissipated to the DNA strand by thermal motion of the sulfur atom.

Apelgot and Latarjet (1966) compared the effects of two radioactive isotopes of phosphorus, P^{32} and P^{33}, by experiments with bacteria. The two isotopes were chosen because they have similar excitation energies but different recoil energies. Because the efficiency of inactivation turned out to be the same for the two isotopes, it was concluded that the excitation energy is more important than the recoil energy for the biological effects. Sulfur is not as stable as phosphorus

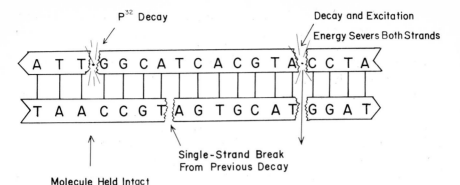

Figure 5-13. Damage to DNA molecule by decay of incorporated P^{32}. Breaks of one strand are not sufficient to sever the whole molecule. About one of five to one of 10 decays breaks both strands with a resulting loss of biological activity.

in its ester linkage; so one of the linkages of the nucleic acid chain becomes greatly weakened when the phosphorus atom suddenly becomes a sulfur atom instead. The excitation energy is then sufficient to cause scission of the strand containing the newly formed sulfur atom.

It might be expected that every disintegration would result in inactivation, rather than only one in 10. The reason for the lower efficiency is that the complementary DNA strand maintains the integrity of the molecule: In only the minority (10 per cent) of disintegrations does the ejected β particle, or the sudden addition of the large excitation energy, also cut the opposite chain resulting in the complete scission of the molecule and loss of infectivity (Fig. 5-13).

This explanation was reinforced by the discovery that the single-stranded DNA phage, ϕX174, was inactivated with an efficiency of 1.0 by P^{32} decay (Sinsheimer, 1959b).

Inactivation by P^{32}, appropriately termed "P^{32} suicide," has turned out to be a useful experimental tool. Such inactivation also occurs in poliovirus (Henry and Youngner, 1963) and polyoma virus (Benjamin, 1965). Its use will come up again in later chapters.

OTHER INACTIVATING AGENTS

Of the many chemical and physical agents known to cause inactivation, only a few more will be discussed here. One of these is nitrous acid, which causes a linear decrease of the logarithm of the virus titer as a function of time. The nitrous acid chemically alters some of the bases in the nucleic acid and changes the manner in which they pair with other nucleic acids. Most of the changes result in inactivation, but some result in the formation of a mutant virus; nitrous acid has been used successfully to produce mutants for genetic studies. There is no apparent effect on the protein of the virus.

Formaldehyde, on the other hand, acts primarily on the protein coat of the virus. Its use is of practical importance in the preparation of vaccines. Formaldehyde was used in the preparation of inactivated poliovirus vaccine, commonly called Salk vaccine in honor of the man who developed it. During the development of the vaccine there were many arguments about the nature of the inactivation curve, which eventually was shown to be exponential only for the initial part of the curve, with a decreasing rate of inactivation as exposure to formaldehyde progressed. The possibility thus arose that some infectious virus could appear in the vaccine and cause illness.

One further kind of chemical agent will be mentioned: the various lytic enzymes to which viruses are exposed during their existence in the extracellular fluids of animals and plants. These include nucleases, ribonuclease and deoxyribonuclease, that break RNA and DNA into small pieces. Virions, whether they contain one or the other nucleic acid, are quite resistant to the action of the nucleases, presumably because the protein capsid serves as a barrier and protects the viral nucleic acid contained within. If the capsid is altered or damaged, however, the nucleases may inactivate the virion by attacking the nucleic acid.

Proteolytic enzymes also exist freely in the environment, and intact virions seem relatively resistant to their action. The reason for the resistance must lie in the configuration of the proteins in the capsid, because once the capsid is broken apart, the viral proteins usually become sensitive to the lytic action of the enzymes.

Many other physical and chemical agents have an effect on virions. In addition, many act in combination to produce an effect, whereas either agent alone would be ineffective. Many substances protect virions against inactivation. Gard and Maaløe (1959) have given a comprehensive summary of the possible combinations and permutations.

There is another important type of viral inactivation that results from the interaction of a virion with a specific antibody molecule. Serologic reactions will be the subject of the next chapter.

Further Reading

Gard, S., and O. Maaløe: Inactivation of Viruses. *In* Burnet, F. M., and W. M. Stanley (eds.): The Viruses. New York, Academic Press Inc., 1959, Vol. 1, pp. 359-427.
Hanawalt, P. C., and R. H. Haynes: The Repair of DNA. Scientific American, 216(Feb.):36, 1967.
Stent, G. S., and C. R. Fuerst: Genetic and Physiological Effects of the Decay of Incorporated Radioactive Phosphorus in Bacterial Viruses and Bacteria. Advances in Biological and Medical Physics, 7:1-75, 1960.
Woese, C.: Thermal Inactivation of Animal Viruses. Annals of the New York Academy of Sciences, 83:741-751, 1960.

6

SEROLOGY OF VIRUSES

Viral nucleic acid maintains genetic continuity of viral replication, insuring that new viral nucleic acid and protein resemble those of preceding generations of virus. Viral protein is not necessary for viral replication; it aids attachment and penetration of the virus into a cell and serves as a protective shell. Viral protein also confers specificity on the virus for the cell types that the virus can infect. The structural differences in viral proteins that result in the specificities have not yet been thoroughly analyzed. That there are differences, however, is clear from the results of many serological studies on viruses.

VIRAL ANTIGENS

The viral protein coat, like other proteins, is antigenic in an immunologically competent host. An animal's immunologic system recognizes as foreign the protein of an invading virus and develops antibodies to it. The kinds of antibodies produced depend upon the method of inoculation and the purity of the inoculated material. Whether the virus multiplies in the inoculated animal also helps determine the antibody response.

Consider an animal inoculated with a highly purified preparation of virions that cannot multiply in that animal. In this case, the viral capsid protein (which may include more than one antigen) is the only protein present, so the only antibodies produced are those specifically active against the capsid protein. This highly simplified, hypothetical situation seldom occurs.

Even in the purest preparations, there is often some cellular protein that acts as antigen. If the virus multiplies in the host animal, the infected cells may form by-products such as enzyme proteins that are released upon death of the infected cells and may be antigenic (Hirst, 1965). These by-products are often induced by the virus (and consequently "foreign" to the organism) and are concerned with virus replication but are not incorporated into the virion. Usually, therefore, the antiserum produced in response to a virus inoculation contains a mixture of antibody molecules.

Studies of antigen development have been useful in understanding the intracellular course of events during infection for many viruses. Examples of different antigens and their relation to infection will be brought up in later chapters. Serologic methods are also useful in studying the structure of virions. Some of the different antigenic components of the T-even phages have already been discussed. The head protein and the various parts of the tail, the sheath, the tail plate, and the fibers are all antigenically different proteins. Serologic methods have been useful in studying the function of the phage tail (Franklin, 1961), as will be discussed. The adenovirus is another example for which there is information about how different antigens correspond to viral structural elements (see Chapter 2). It has also been shown that serologically different strains of foot-and-mouth disease virus have different amino acid compositions (Bachrach and Polatnick, 1967).

TYPES OF ANTIBODIES

Antibodies are often defined operationally. By this we mean that they are named by the process or operation used to detect them. Precipitating antibodies, complement-fixing antibodies, hemagglutination-inhibiting antibodies, and neutralizing antibodies are usually of interest to virologists.

Precipitating Antibodies. Precipitating antibodies cause a visible precipitate, often seen as diffuse cloudiness, when they are mixed with the antigen. The antibody molecules must be bivalent, with at least two combining sites that can attach two virions together. The visible precipitate thus consists of a network or lattice of virus particles interconnected by the antibody molecules. It is perhaps true that most, if not all, viruses stimulate the formation of precipitating antibodies. However, it is not always possible to detect precipitating antibodies because it takes rather large amounts of reagents to produce a visible precipitate; and the smaller the particles, the higher the required concentration. Although the electron microscope has been used to identify small precipitates (Hummeler *et al.*, 1962), this method is most useful when large quantities of virions are available, such as with the plant viruses.

Complement-Fixing   Antibodies. Complement-fixing   anti-bodies are produced in response to many kinds of viruses. When this type of antibody combines with its antigen, which may be the virus particle or any of a number of by-products of cell infection, it removes from the serum a heat-labile serum component called complement that is added to the mixture. The complement is then said to be fixed and is not available for other reactions.

To determine if the complement has been removed from the reaction mixture, an indicator is added. Sheep red blood cells and antisheep-cell antibody (hemolysin) usually constitute the indicator system. The demonstration of the reaction between the cells and he-molysin is a complement-dependent reaction. If the complement has been fixed by the first reaction, that is, by the virus and the antibody, it is not available for a second reaction. The hemolysin cannot then lyse the sheep cells, and they remain intact. If the complement has not been fixed and is available for the second reaction, the sheep cells lyse   and   the   suspension   turns   red   because   of   the   released hemoglobin.

The complement-fixation test is one of the simplest serologic tests to perform and one of the more reliable. Its specificity depends partly upon the purity of the antigen: If purified virus is inoculated into a host in which it cannot multiply, the antibody produced can be quite specific. Often, however, the complement-fixation test is used for diagnostic work where group specificity rather than type or strain specificity is desired. Many closely related viruses have common an-tigens, called group-specific antigens, in their capsids; so an an-tiserum may have a broad reaction.

Hemagglutination-Inhibiting Antibodies. Antibody   produced by some viruses suppresses hemagglutination. This also is a relatively easy antibody to detect, because a hemagglutination test is simple and rapid. The antihemagglutinin can be type specific or group specific, depending on the virus in question.

Neutralizing Antibodies. The fourth   common method of de-tecting antibodies detects neutralizing antibody, which blocks the in-fectivity of a virus particle. This is the most specific reaction with any of the antibodies produced against viruses. Standard reference anti-sera, prepared against prototype strains of known viruses, are used in neutralization tests to identify unknown viruses. Because neutralizing antibodies have great specificity and infective viruses can be detected in very low concentration, neutralization tests are useful in immuno-logical studies of the development of antibodies and of the mechanism of the antigen-antibody reaction.

The potency of an antiserum in the neutralizing reaction can be measured by any of several ways. In the end point dilution assay, a twofold dilution series of the antiserum is set up, and to each dilution is added a standard amount of virus, usually 100 $TCID_{50}$. In one com-monly used procedure, the mixtures are incubated 1 hour at room temperature, although other conditions are sometimes used. Each mixture is then placed in culture tubes containing susceptible cells to determine whether infectious virus is present. The titer of the an-tiserum is the dilution at which half the cultures show viral effect. It should be noted that the antiserum is carried over into the assay system so that neutralization continues. If the assay or indicator system requires inoculation into an animal rather than a culture, the host can respond with its own immune mechanism, which sometimes confuses the results.

The plaque reduction test is also used by animal virologists. Many variations have been developed; but in general, the procedure is that of mixing antiserum dilutions with known amounts of virus, such as 100 PFU. The mixtures are incubated; the reaction between virus and antibody takes place, and the mixtures are placed on tissue culture cells for plaque assay. The antiserum titer is the dilution re-sulting in a 50 per cent reduction of plaques (or some other standard-ized reduction), as compared with a control.

The most sensitive test for neutralization is to measure the rate at which the antiserum inactivates the virus. This is done by incubating a mixture of virus and antiserum at a controlled temperature. The mixture is sampled periodically and assayed for surviving virus. When the assay is performed, dilutions of the mixture are used so that very little antiserum is introduced into the assay system. Thus, the neutrali-zation reaction does not continue past the incubation time. The po-tency of a given antiserum in neutralizing the infectivity of a given virus is expressed as the value of k, the rate constant for the inacti-vation reaction.

The neutralization kinetics test, developed for use with bacterio-phages (Delbrück, 1945), is virtually the only test for neutralization used in phage work. Dulbecco et al. (1956) applied it to animal viruses and began developing a detailed explanation for the mechanism of virus neutralization. This will be discussed in more detail later.

ANTIBODY SYNTHESIS

One of the intriguing questions of biology concerns antibody synthesis. There seem to be an endless number of substances that can act as antigens; many are not natural products and thus could not have been present to influence the course of evolution. An animal, however, can synthesize antibody molecules that specifically interact with a foreign substance. How this is accomplished is unkown, since the information for forming the myriads of possible antibody proteins is not necessarily present as such in the DNA.

No one has yet proposed a completely satisfactory explanation, although many have tried. We will not review the different theories of antibody formation; many good reviews and recent papers with references to the extensive literature are available (Fischer, 1964; Brenner and Milstein, 1966; Burnet, 1966; Smithies, 1967; Whitehouse, 1967; Edelman and Gally, 1967).

In simplest terms, most theories fall into two categories. In some it is proposed that a given cell of the immune system synthesizes antibodies for any (or at least many) antigens that might come along. The antigen somehow induces the formation of the specific antibody protein that can react with it. The antigen is thus pictured as a template against which the antibody is constructed. However, current concepts of protein synthesis include the notion that the amino acid sequence of a protein is determined by the order of bases in the cell's DNA and that this order is changed only by mutation, ordinarily a rare event occurring only at the time of DNA replication.

The other main type of theory of antibody synthesis is that during embryonic development, many clones, or families of cells, arise and that these clones differ in the antibodies they can produce. When confronted with an antigen, the cell that can make the proper antibody proliferates, and the antibody production of the clone becomes sufficient to meet the immune needs. The clonal selection theory, as it is called, has been developed and modified largely by Burnet (a recent reference: Burnet, 1966). A high mutability of the gene controlling antibody production, as discussed by Brenner and Milstein (1966), could accelerate the development of a great variety of clones, as could a high degree of recombination between reduplicated genes (Smithies, 1967; Edelman and Gally, 1967).

NATURE OF ANTIBODY MOLECULES

Operationally, four kinds of antibodies are of chief interest in virology, but these are not necessarily separate molecules. For instance, some neutralizing antibody molecules may also be detected as complement-fixing antibodies or as hemagglutination-inhibiting antibodies.

Neutralizing antibodies can be separated into two groups in the ultracentrifuge: the larger 19S antibodies, which sediment more rap-

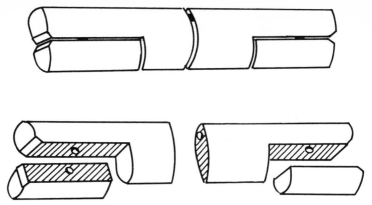

Figure 6-1. The Edelman-Gally model of a 7S antibody molecule. The upper diagram shows the intact molecule, consisting of two larger portions (the heavy chains) and two smaller portions (the light chains). The lower diagram shows the molecule broken into its four components. The S-S bonds that bind the components together are indicated as small circles. (Redrawn from Edelman and Gally, 1964.)

idly than the other group, the smaller 7S antibodies. The two groups also differ in other respects, as will be discussed in a later section.

The 7S molecule has been studied extensively (Cohen and Milstein, 1967). Edelman and Gally (1964) proposed the following description of its structure: Each 7S molecule consists of two light (L) chains, with a molecular weight of 20,000 to 24,000 daltons each, and two heavy (H) chains, with a molecular weight of 55,000 to 60,000 daltons each. These four units are arranged as shown in Figure 6-1.

The complete 7S antibody molecule is about $19 \times 57 \times 240$ Å. The molecule has a combining site at either end and can form bridges between antigens, resulting in lattices or precipitates. These have been seen in striking electron micrographs of polyoma and human wart viruses that had been reacted with their respective antibodies (Almeida *et al.*, 1963, 1967).

DEVELOPMENT OF ANTIBODIES

The use of viruses has facilitated studies of the immune response. Even with dilute virus suspensions, it is possible to measure minute changes in the fraction of infective particles. Much higher concentrations of proteins are necessary if conventional biochemical assays are to be used. When viruses are used, the loss of infectivity in the neutralization kinetics test is easily measured and high purification is not usually necessary. It is possible to measure small amounts of antibody and to determine reversibility of the reaction.

ϕX174 has been used to study the early antibody response in guinea pigs (Uhr *et al.*, 1962b; Uhr and Finkelstein, 1963) and in human infants born prematurely (Uhr *et al.*, 1962a) because it is an excellent antigen and does not replicate in a mammalian host.

The earliest response to primary immunization was the synthesis of 19S antibodies. This type antibody was first detected a few days after inoculation with ϕX174 and continued to be formed for about 10 days (Fig. 6-2). After 10 days, the level of 19S antibody decreased at the same rate as passively injected antibody (half life, 26 hours).

The 7S antibodies formed in the primary response first became detectable about 7 days after inoculation of the antigen and approached peak levels at 10 to 20 days (Fig. 6-2). In contrast to 19S antibody, the 7S did not decline, even over a period of many months. This indicated continued synthesis, since passively inoculated 7S antibody had a half life of about 5.5 days.

This type of response was also seen in lymph node cells in culture (Tao and Uhr, 1966). ϕX174 was added to the cultures, and starting 2 days later the medium was assayed for its content of 19S and 7S antibody. The time course of the development of the antibodies was very similar to the response in the animal (Fig. 6-3).

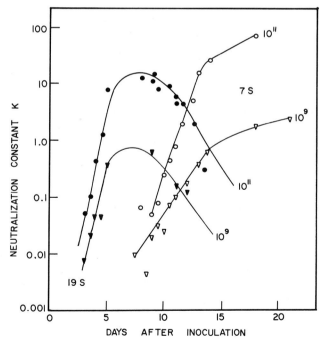

Figure 6-2. Primary antibody response in guinea pigs. Development of 19S and 7S antibodies following inoculation of a high dose (10^{11}) or a low dose (10^9) of ϕX174 bacteriophage. (Redrawn from Uhr and Finkelstein, 1963.)

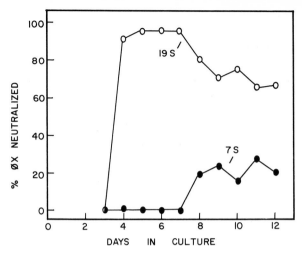

Figure 6-3.   Antibody response in cell culture. ϕX174 was present for the first 2 days that normal lymph node cells were in culture. The medium was assayed daily for antibody. (Redrawn from Tao and Uhr, 1966.)

The results with ϕX174 were confirmed and extended in a series of reports by Svehag and Mandel (1964a). They found that when poliovirus was injected into rabbits, an animal in which it does not grow, rapid production of 19S antibodies resulted. These antibodies were first detectable within a few hours after injection of the virus, and the time course of the response with 19S antibody was about the same as that found for ϕX174. An animal injected with poliovirus produced 7S antibody over an extended period of time; there was very little decrease in nearly a year of observation.

To test the possibility that small amounts of virus might be multiplying within the rabbit and giving a continual antigenic stimulus, Svehag and Mandel injected poliovirus that had been inactivated by ultraviolet light. Under these conditions, 7S antibody production still persisted, but passively transferred antibody was rapidly eliminated from the rabbit.

In addition, they found that the production of 19S antibody was independent of the dose of poliovirus given; however, 7S antibody was produced only when a certain minimum amount of virus was injected. With less than the minimum dosage, the 19S response occurred, but the 7S response did not. When the amount of virus given exceeded a certain threshold amount, all animals responded with the production of 7S antibodies. There was an intermediate dose range, however, in which some rabbits produced 7S antibody and some did not; of those rabbits that did produce 7S antibody, the antibody persisted at the same high level as in those rabbits receiving a larger dose.

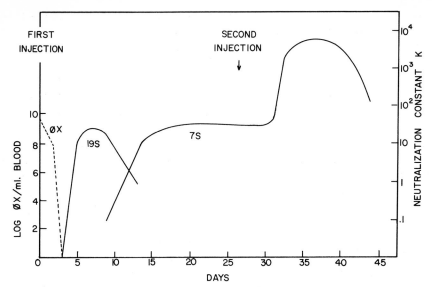

Figure 6-4. Pattern of antibody response in the guinea pig. Two intravenous injections of ϕX174 (10^{11} PFU) were given 1 month apart. (Redrawn from Uhr, 1964.)

It is evident that antibody could play an important role in the host's defense against disease. In guinea pigs, 2 to 3 days after injection the primary immune response began eliminating ϕX174 (Fig. 6-4). Perhaps the major contribution of antibody, however, is the prevention of disease when a host is exposed to a pathogenic organism for the second time. The fact that in these animals the 7S antibody persisted for extended periods suggests that this might be the responsible antibody. In the secondary response (occurring in animals that already had a full primary response), it rose an order of magnitude higher than the primary.

Svehag and Mandel (1964b) obtained similar results on the secondary response by injecting poliovirus into an immunized rabbit. They found several additional facts. The 7S secondary response occurred only if it had occurred previously; if the only previous exposure was a low dose of antigen that had evoked only the 19S response, the 7S response to the second injection was a typical primary response.

The 19S antibody response always was the primary kind; immunologic memory therefore exists only for the 7S antibody. The continued presence of antigen seems to be necessary for 19S antibody synthesis, but 7S antibody synthesis can persist in the absence of antigen.

The immune reaction can also be considered in terms of the complement-fixing antibodies discussed earlier. Both 19S and 7S antibodies are measured by a neutralization reaction. It is possible that the reaction between some neutralizing antibodies and their antigen is complement dependent, and therefore they may be the same as the complement-fixing antibody in some instances.

However, the clinical observation has often been made that during the course of an illness complement-fixing antibodies appear a week or so after the neutralizing antibodies. Complement-fixing antibodies do not persist for extended periods of time, as do the neutralizing antibodies. The tests are of clinical significance: Because of the relatively rapid decline of antibody, a positive complement-fixation test is taken as evidence of recent infection, and the presence of neutralizing antibodies can indicate that an infection took place at some earlier time, not necessarily recently.

IMMUNOLOGICAL COMPETENCE AND TOLERANCE

An animal's ability to respond to an antigenic stimulus (reviewed recently by Miller, 1964, and by Silverstein, 1964) develops during the animal's intrauterine life and shortly after birth. For reasons that are not well understood, the competence to deal with some antigens develops in early gestational life, and the competence to deal with others develops later.

The development of the ability to synthesize antibodies depends on the growth and development of the thymus. The thymus apparently populates the lymph nodes with cells and is therefore the primary source of the cells responsible for the immune response. In most species, immunological competence is fully developed within a few days after birth, and the animal will respond normally to any antigenic stimulation.

Closely related to immunological competence is the concept of tolerance. If an animal is exposed to an antigen while it is still immunologically immature or incompetent to that antigen, it accepts the antigenic protein as its own, not recognizing it as foreign; therefore, it does not develop antibody to it. Tolerance has been demonstrated in many systems but has particular relevance to virology.

The chicken leukosis viruses, studied by Rubin (1962a), are transmitted to the young through the egg. The virus grows after the chick hatches, and the chick does not develop an antibody response. An animal that is tolerant to such an infection usually shows no signs of being infected, and there is no disease. The development of a disease in response to some virus infections is dependent, at least in part, on an antibody response.

If a tolerant state is to develop, the virus must be introduced while the host is still immunologically incompetent to that antigen.

The amount of antigen, in this case virus, must exceed a certain threshold value. In the chickens studied by Rubin (1962a), the tolerant state was established when virus multiplication had caused a high concentration in the blood of the infected chicken, and the state was maintained as long as the virus concentration remained high. The chickens did not develop neutralizing antibody against the virus; so immunity, in the usual sense, did not occur. Immunological tolerance is important in the establishment of viral cancers in susceptible animals, as will be discussed in a later chapter.

THE NEUTRALIZATION OF VIRUSES BY ANTISERUM

The neutralization reaction is generally believed to be responsible for acquired immunity to viral disease. After surviving an infection with a viral agent, the host develops antibody to that virus; the antibody combines with the virus particles and prevents further cellular infection.

The neutralization reaction is of interest to immunologists because the mechanisms of the antibody-antigen reaction can be studied using minute amounts of reagents. Further, the range of concentration can vary a millionfold or more, whereas with most reactions followed chemically the possible range is much less, usually not more than a hundredfold. With virions as antigen, it is possible to have the antibody molecules in great excess and still measure the decrease in infective titer of the population of virus particles.

Combination of Antibody Molecules With Virions

Antiserum causes a logarithmic decrease in the titer of virus when the mixture is incubated at a constant temperature. The results of such an experiment are shown in Figure 6-5. The decrease is exponential (logarithmic) over a ten- to thousandfold range, depending upon the virus and antiserum used. There is no perceptible lag period at the beginning of the reaction for the many virus-antibody systems that have been studied. The interpretation is that one antibody molecule is sufficient to inactivate the infectivity of a single virus particle.

Within limits, the rate at which the infective titer decreases is not dependent on the initial concentration of virus. However, it is a function of certain other variables. For instance, if the serum is diluted before it is mixed with the virus, the slope of the line is less; in other words, the titer does not decrease as rapidly.

The rate of the reaction is also a function of the temperature at which the antiserum-virus mixture is incubated. At lower tempera-

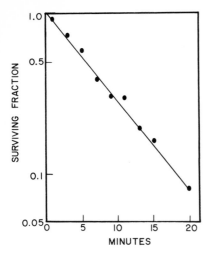

Figure 6-5. Virus neutralization as a function of time. Western equine encephalitis virus (5 × 10⁵ PFU/ml.) was mixed with horse antiserum (3.15 × 10⁻⁴ dilution) at 37° C. (Redrawn from Dulbecco *et al.*, 1956.)

tures, the reaction rate is less. The rate constant for the reaction is changed by a factor of 1.4 for each 10 degrees of change in temperature. The conclusion is that the reaction rate is controlled by the diffusion rates of the virus and antibody molecules; diffusion rates determine how many collisions occur between antibody molecules and virus particles.

The initial logarithmic part of the curve, as shown in Figure 6-5, can be used as a measure of the potency of the antiserum. The equation for survivors, derived from the Poisson distribution as in Chapter 5, yields the expression

$$\frac{V}{V_0} = e^{-kt/D}$$

where V is the titer of virus after a certain time, t; V_0 is the initial titer of the virus; e is the base of natural logarithms; k is the inactivation rate constant; and D is the dilution of antiserum. This equation can be solved for k:

$$K = 2.3 \frac{D}{t} \times \log \frac{V_0}{V}$$

The value for k expresses the potency of an antiserum toward a given virus. It should be remembered that k is a constant only at a given temperature and under the standard conditions of the test.

The measurement of the k value of an antiserum is perhaps the most sensitive way of detecting the antiserum-virus reaction. It is the standard test used with bacteriophages (Adams, 1959), and it has been shown by Ozaki *et al.* (1963) to distinguish the vaccine strain of attenuated poliovirus from the virulent strains occurring in the general population. These two virus strains are so closely related antigenically that it is difficult to tell them apart by any other test. Similarly, Ashe and Scherp (1963) resolved herpes simplex into serotypes by neutralization kinetics tests. As was discussed in an earlier section, the neutralization kinetics test has also been used to detect small amounts of antibody formed soon after the injection of virus into an animal.

Reversibility of the Inactivation Reaction

Dulbecco *et al.*(1956) studied the inactivation kinetics of poliovirus and of Western equine encephalitis virus. They found that after the initial logarithmic phase there was a pronounced flattening of the curve (Fig. 6-6) with a resultant fraction of virus that seemed resistant to inactivation by the antiserum. This fraction they called the "persistent fraction."

The persistent fraction was not composed of virus particles that were genetically resistant to antibody. When the virus particles that survived inactivation in high concentrations of antibody were grown into new stocks, it was found that the progeny were as susceptible to antibody as were the original virus populations. Also ruled out were the possible influences of unspecified cofactors in the serum and inhibitory substances that might have been present.

A more important possibility was that the reaction between antibody and virus particle might be reversible as Burnet originally had suggested many years previously. To test this, Dulbecco and his associates performed a series of experiments to see whether dilutions of the persistent fraction in buffer might cause a dissociation, as would

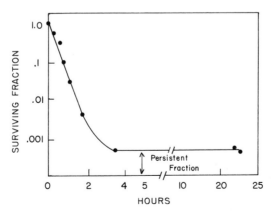

Figure 6-6. Neutralization of poliovirus by rabbit immune serum as a function of time. The "persistent fraction" is evident as a flattening of the curve at extended times. (Redrawn from Mandel, 1960.)

be expected if the reaction were reversible. The results indicated that the poliovirus reaction was not reversible, and that the Western equine encephalitis virus reaction was only slightly reversible.

The report of Dulbecco *et al.* (1956) was thoroughly criticized by Fazekas de St. Groth *et al.* (1958) and by Fazekas de St. Groth and Reid (1958). It was their opinion that the experiments done by Dulbecco *et al.* had been misinterpreted. They theorized instead that the inactivation reaction was reversible, and they postulated that after inactivation occurs upon effective collision of an antibody molecule with a critical site on the virus particle, the antibody molecule might become unattached again, thus reactivating the virus particle.

Crucial tests of the reversibility of the reaction have been made since the initial theoretical treatments. These tests have demonstrated with some degree of certainty that the antibody-virus reaction is reversible. Mandel (1960) reviewed the dissociation reaction and presented evidence that some reactivation can be obtained by simple dilution of the inactivated virus.

More definite reversibility of the reaction was obtained by lowering the pH to between 2.0 and 2.5 (Mandel, 1961). The dependence of the dissociation on pH is shown in Figure 6-7. When poliovirus-antibody complex was held at neutral pH for several months and the pH was then dropped, dissociating the complex, full recovery of

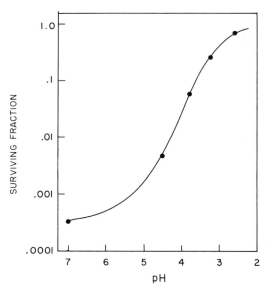

Figure 6-7. Dissociation of poliovirus-antibody complexes as a function of pH. Shown is the increase in titer of a sample of virus that had reacted with neutralizing antibody for 18 hours at pH 7. The pH was then lowered as indicated, and the surviving fraction was measured. (Redrawn from Mandel, 1961.)

the infective poliovirus occurred. Therefore, the antibody does not cause any permanent change in the virion. Furthermore, lowering the pH does not damage the antibody; when the pH is raised again to neutrality, the antibody can recombine with the poliovirus, again neutralizing its infectivity.

Antibody formed early during immunization differs from antibody formed later in the ease with which the complex may be dissociated. Jerne and Avegno (1956) observed that T4 phage inactivated by horse antiserum was reactivated simply by dilution; the reactivation occurred much more easily with early antiserum than with later serum.

Brunner and Ward (1959) found a difference between early and late sera obtained from patients who had been naturally infected by poliovirus. Many sera were studied; those obtained early in the acute phase of the disease were more easily dissociated by decreasing the pH than were the later sera obtained during the patient's convalescence.

The late antisera may have contained greater proportions of 7S antibody and less 19S antibody. For whatever reason, early and late sera have different avidities for the virus.

Mechanism of Inactivation

It is still a mystery in most cases how an antibody molecule blocks the infectivity of a virus particle. The virion is much larger than the antibody molecule, so that one antibody molecule could not form a coat around a virion. Evidence has already been presented that inactivation is not a cooperative effort in which many antibody molecules coat the virion. Nor does the antibody cause a permanent, irreversible change in the virion.

Information on the mechanism of inactivation has been obtained for some bacteriophages. First, an antiserum was prepared against whole T2 or T4 bacteriophage particles. Absorption of the antiserum with various parts of virus particles removed antibodies against those specific parts of the phage. The residual activity for inactivating the infectivity of the phage was then determined. This kind of study was done by Jerne and Avegno (1956) and more recently and in more detail by Franklin (1961). These studies showed that the antibodies that prevent a virus particle from being infective are directed against either the fiber or sheath proteins.

At least two or three antigens on the fibers and on the sheath are able to react with the antiserum. Some of these antigens are common to both T2 and T4, while others are unique to each kind of virus. Reaction with the antibody does not prevent adsorption of the virus to a susceptible cell, but it does prevent the progression of the infection, perhaps by blocking the injection of DNA into the cell. Antibody to other parts of phage particles, even though causing agglutination of particles, will not destroy infectivity.

Particles of phage T4 are active in the presence of tryptophan and lose their activity in its absence. In studies of this tryptophan sensitization, Jerne (1956) obtained other evidence that antibodies block infectivity by acting on the tail fibers. He discovered a third kind of antibody molecule in the serum of a normal horse. The new antibody was present early in the process of immunization against T4, before neutralizing antibody appeared. If tryptophan was added to the medium to activate the phage, and this third kind of antibody was added, removal of the tryptophan no longer inactivated the particle. Jerne postulated that the antiserum somehow interfered with the collapse of the fibers back onto the sheath where they would be no longer available for adsorption.

What has been said about reactions of phage particles with antiserum does not apply to animal virus particles. With animal viruses, it was shown by Dulbecco *et al.* (1956) that there are approximately 15 critical sites for combination of the particle and its antibody. The nature of these critical sites has not been determined, but the number does not correspond to the number of capsomers on the virion. However, it is perhaps possible that the critical sites could be the apexes of the basic icosahedron. The capsomers at the apexes may be somehow different from the remaining capsomers. They are, for instance, known to be 5-coordinated rather than 6-coordinated and they are 12 in number, approximately equal to the 15 critical sites found by Dulbecco *et al.* (1956). Further work, however, is necessary to determine whether combination of an antibody molecule with one of the apical capsomers results in blocking a site that is necessary for infection.

Whatever the neutralization reaction may be, it apparently is not a blocking of adsorption of virus to cell. Dales and Kajioka (1964) found by electron microscopy that antiserum-neutralized vaccinia virus entered cells but that the virion was degraded. Similarly, neutralized poliovirus adsorbs to cells but its nucleic acid is apparently hydrolyzed (Mandel, 1967a, 1967b). The antiserum may therefore be carried into the cell with the virion and may interfere with some intracellular process so that viral synthesis does not occur.

The biology of viruses — their growth cycles, interaction with host cells, interactions with other viruses, and production of alterations of their host cells—illustrates some of the most fundamental cellular molecular processes. It is at the level of these processes that viruses act to subvert the metabolic machinery of the infected cell to the manufacture of more virions. Let us now begin to discuss how these events occur.

Further Reading

Burnet, F. M.: Principles of Animal Virology. New York, Academic Press Inc., 1960, pp. 293-329.

Burnet, F. M.: The Scope and Limitations of Immunological Methods in the Characterization and Functional Study of Viruses. *In* Burnet, F. M., and W. M. Stanley (eds.): The Viruses. New York, Academic Press Inc., 1959, Vol. 1, pp. 525-548.

Fazekas de St. Groth, S.: The Neutralization of Viruses and Evaluation of Quantal Neutralization Tests. Advances in Virus Research, 9:1-125, 1962.

Fenner, F.: Immune Mechanisms in Viral Infections. *In* Horsfall, F. L., Jr., and I. Tamm (eds.): Viral and Rickettsial Infections of Man. Philadelphia, J. B. Lippincott Co., 1965, pp. 356-384.

7

REPLICATION OF BACTERIAL VIRUSES CONTAINING DOUBLE-STRANDED DNA

The phenomenon of the clearing of a bacterial culture by a "lytic principle" had been seen and studied by numerous investigators, and there was much debate about what the "lytic principle" or bacteriophage might be. D'Herelle (1922), in a classic paper, presented experiments showing that this "lytic principle" multiplied, that the clearing effect could be initiated by a single discrete particle because it formed plaques under certain conditions, and that its action could be blocked by specific antibody.

Basing an explanation on sharp reasoning and his well-performed experiments, d'Herelle arrived at the conclusion that the clearing of a culture of bacteria must be caused by an organism parasitic on the bacteria. This explanation, however, was not readily accepted and many years elapsed before it was substantiated.

ONE-STEP GROWTH

D'Herelle's experiments also led him to other important conclusions: A period of time was required for the clearing of the suspension, and there was an increase in the concentration of his bacteriophage. To study this in greater detail, Ellis and Delbrück (1939) and Delbrück (1940) developed a new experimental technique, marking a major turning point in the study of viruses. This technique enabled these investigators to dissect in great detail the viral growth cycle that had been observed by d'Herelle. The growth cycle of viruses, like their size and morphology, is inherited. Thus, another characteristic is added to those that justify inclusion of viruses in biology.

Delbrück performed the one-step growth experiment as follows: A known quantity of T-even phage was mixed with a known number of bacterial cells. The mixture was incubated a short period of time, called the adsorption period, during which the virus became attached to the cells. The mixture was then diluted so that no further adsorption could take place; synchronized infection resulted. Samples taken at intervals after infection were assayed for virus content.

The concentration of virus remained constant for a period of time, then suddenly increased to a new level and remained constant. If no more bacteria were available, or if readsorption could not take place, no further development occurred.

Based on these experiments, the growth cycle, which lasts about 45 minutes at 37° C., is divided into several stages (Fig. 7-1). The first stage, lasting about 17 to 19 minutes, follows the addition of phage to the bacterial culture. This first stage is called the latent period be-

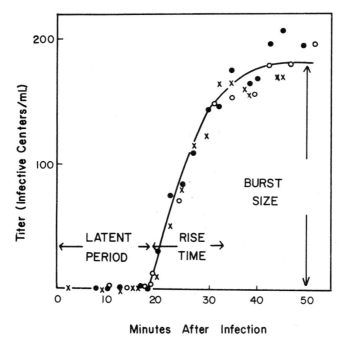

Figure 7-1. The one-step growth curve. At zero time, phages were added to a bacterial culture (5 × 10⁷ bacteria/ml., 10⁷ phages/ml.), rapidly growing in broth at 37° C. After 5 minutes, the culture was diluted at least a thousandfold to prevent further adsorption. Samples taken every 1 or 2 minutes were assayed for infectious centers. The data are from three separate experiments. The burst size under these conditions is about 180 phage/cell. (Delbrück, 1940).

cause there is no increase in titer. The latent period ends when the titer begins to rise. The second period, the time of rising titer, lasts about 15 minutes. The one-step growth period then ends and the phage titer is at a constant new level that is higher than the initial titer. The ratio of final titer to initial titer is called the burst size, and it represents the average number of phage particles produced by each infected cell.

In performing his one-step growth curve, Delbrück periodically assayed the suspension for infectivity. During the latent period the suspension contained bacteria that had been infected; when placed on the assay plate, the infected bacteria registered as single plaques, regardless of whether they contained one or many phage particles. This type of assay is called an infective center assay. It does not distinguish between plaques produced by free phage particles and bacteria containing, intracellularly, one or more phage particles.

Delbrück performed further experiments to determine the factors affecting the shape and duration of the one-step growth curve. He found, for example, that if the temperature of incubation was lowered to 30° instead of the usual 37°, the latent period was greatly lengthened. Other physiological conditions also affected the length of the cycle and the burst size of the infected bacteria. Furthermore, as will become apparent, the parameters of the cycle are different for different cell-virus systems.

Experiments using single infected cells, rather than mass cultures of populations of cells, have yielded a few additional facts. Chiefly, the one-step growth curve of phages in individual cells shows a great deal of variation. The burst size, that is, the number of phages released from an infected cell at the time of lysis, varies greatly from cell to cell; so does the length of the cycle — it is much longer in some cells than in others. A growth curve performed on a population of infected cells yields an average for the burst size and cycle length of the population.

Because the growth cycle of the T-group of phages is known in considerable detail, it will be examined here as a model. Later, the growth cycle of other viruses will be compared with it.

ADSORPTION

The infective cycle begins with the coming together of a phage particle and a susceptible bacterial cell. This union could require active participation by either the cell or the phage particle or both, as would occur if either sought out the other. Alternatively, the process could occur by simple diffusion, since particles the size of bacteria and viruses are in constant Brownian motion when they are suspended in a liquid.

One of the first phage workers to apply quantitative methods to problems of phage growth was Schlesinger (1932). Assuming that collisions between phage and cell occurred only by chance (by diffusion), and using a limited set of basic assumptions about the size of phage particles (their size was not very accurately known then) and their diffusibility, he derived an expression for the rate at which phage would adsorb. Measurements of the rate agreed very closely with his calculation, indicating that a more complicated hypothesis, such as active participation, was not necessary. The rate of adsorption for a phage at a given temperature is simply a function of the concentration of phage and bacterial cells in the suspension.

Schlesinger's experiments really measured only phage particles that were irreversibly bound to bacteria. Phage particles can also be reversibly adsorbed. This can be detected by adsorbing phage to cells in suspension and centrifuging the complexes into a pellet. When the pellet is resuspended in fresh medium and the phage-cell complexes are again centrifuged down, many infective phages are left in the supernatant. These infective phages, initially reversibly bound to the cells, were released from the cells when the fresh medium was added.

It has been postulated that reversible adsorption, due to electrostatic forces, initially binds the phage particle to the cell so that processes making the bond a permanent one can take place. With some phages, adsorption may be favored or inhibited by the concentration of certain ions in the medium — calcium and magnesium, in particular. Other phages are insensitive to their ionic environment.

Reversible attachment does not last long. The phages soon become adsorbed in such a way that removal, with retention of infectivity, becomes impossible. Some doubt exists whether the reversible stage is necessary to virus adsorption. Instead, it is possible that reversible attachment may occur but is not relevant. Nevertheless, the first step in the fixation of phages to bacteria occurs with a collision between the two.

The fact that the phage typically attaches to a bacterium by the tip of its tail is also a result of random diffusion. Because the phage particle has a massive head and a small tail, diffusion tends to cause the tail to move about more than the head. It is more likely, therefore, that the tail will collide first with the cell (Markham, 1962).

Schlesinger (1932) was interested also in how many phage particles could adsorb to a single bacterial cell. He calculated that the surface area of the cell was sufficient to allow adsorption of a few hundred phages if they were closely packed in a single layer. Testing this calculation, he added phages to a bacterial culture until the cells could adsorb no more. He found that the saturation number for his phage, a close relative of the T-even phages, was about 300 phage particles per bacterial cell. This figure agreed with his calculations. Space, then, is the limiting factor that results in the saturation of a cell by phage particles.

It is now customary to express the ratio of phage to cell as the multiplicity of infection. This can be calculated in either of two ways. One is simply as the input multiplicity, or the ratio of infective particles added to a culture to the number of cells in the culture. The second way, a better procedure, is to find the adsorbed multiplicity by determining the number of infective particles that actually adsorbed to the cells. Then the fraction of cells in a culture that are uninfected, the fraction that are infected by one phage, and the fraction that are infected by more than one can be calculated.

This is possible because, to a very good approximation, the phages are distributed among the cells according to the Poisson distribution,

$$C(r) = \frac{m^r \, e^{-m}}{r!}$$

where $C(r)$ is the fraction of cells infected by r particles. The adsorbed multiplicity, m, is determined most easily from the zero term of the Poisson distribution:

$$C(0) = e^{-m}$$

where $C(0)$ is the fraction of cells that are uninfected. It is measured by plating aliquots of the suspension before and after infection to make colony counts of viable bacteria, which, of course, arise only from uninfected cells. Once $C(0)$ is known, m is calculated.

Several lines of evidence indicate that bacterial cell walls have specific receptor sites for the attachment of phages. For instance, by mutating, a cell can gain or lose the ability to adsorb a given type of phage. The composition of the cell wall, and the kind of receptors it contains, is under the genetic control of the cell's chromosome. Mutants with altered receptors for phages have been useful in studies of phage genetics and will be discussed again later.

The cell's surface has different receptors for different phages. A mutation causing the gain or loss of receptor activity for one phage does not necessarily result in gain or loss of receptors for another phage. Furthermore, it is possible to remove the outer two cell membranes by lysozyme, an enzyme prepared from egg white. Phages cannot adsorb to such cells because the receptors are removed along with the cell wall. However, if the cells are infected before the enzyme treatment, they are perfectly capable of forming phage particles.

After the tip of the phage's tail has collided successfully with an appropriate receptor, events begin that make the union irreversible. The tail fibers are important for irreversible attachment. For instance, the fibers must be freely movable, as shown by experiments (Brenner *et al.*, 1962) with phages that require cofactors, such as tryptophan, for attachment. If antibody prepared against sheath protein is added to the medium, and phages are diluted into tryptophan-free medium, infectivity is retained. Without the antibody, infectivity is lost under these conditions. The interpretation of these experiments is that in the presence of cofactor, the fibers are freely movable. When the cofactors are removed, the fibers wrap around the sheath and the phage loses its infectivity. However, when antibody against the sheath is present, it coats the sheath; and then when the cofactors are removed, the fibers cannot adhere to the sheath. They are thus still freely movable and infectivity is retained. In Figure 7-2 tail fibers of a T4 virion are shown apparently attached to an *E. coli* cell wall.

An important enzyme is carried on the phage tail. It resembles the lysozyme of egg white in its action and has amino acid sequences comparable to those of egg white lysozyme (Dunnill, 1967). It is therefore also called lysozyme (Koch and Dreyer, 1958). The enzyme is thought by some workers to be present as a contaminant. Nevertheless, in the usual course of a phage infective cycle, the enzyme

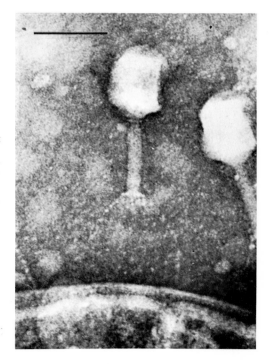

Figure 7-2. Early attachment of a T4 virion to an *E. coli* cell wall. It appears that the tail fibers have made contact with the cell but the base has not done so as yet. (Bar is 100 mμ.) (Simon and Anderson, 1967. By permission of the authors and the editor of Virology.)

comes into contact with the bacterial cell wall and erodes a hole
through it. Constituents of the cell wall can be recovered in the
medium after the phage enzyme has acted on the cell wall (Barrington
and Kozloff, 1954) and some cytoplasmic materials from the cell's interior leak out.

Evidence for cell-wall damage comes mainly from two results.
Doermann (1948) infected *E. coli* with T4 phages and repeatedly measured the turbidity of the culture. Immediately following addition of
the phage there was a brief, but distinct, decrease in the turbidity,
with prompt recovery to preinfection levels (Fig. 7-3). The interpretation is that some contents leaked from the cell with a resulting decrease in turbidity of the culture. The cell quickly repaired the damage
and the turbidity was restored. It decreased again, of course, when
cell lysis occurred.

The second indication of cell-wall damage goes back to observations made very early in the history of phage research. It had been
observed repeatedly that if a high concentration of phage was added
to a culture, almost immediate lysis of the cells occurred. Not only was
there no increase in the infective titer following lysis, but also the titer

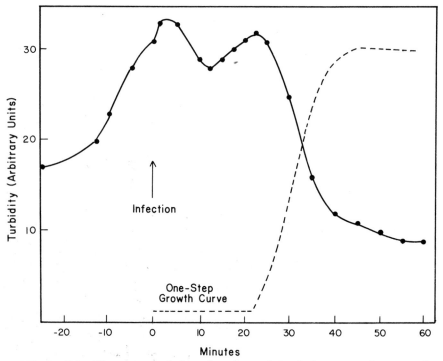

Figure 7-3. Changes in turbidity of a culture of *E. coli* during a replicative cycle
of T4 phage. (Redrawn from Doermann, 1948.)

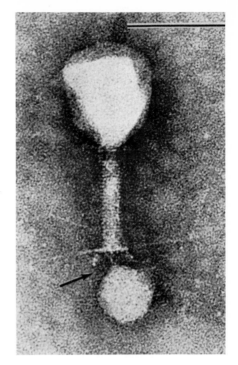

Figure 7-4. A T4 virion attached to an isolated *E. coli* receptor. Contact is shown between the base plate and the receptor. (Bar is 100 mμ.) (Simon and Anderson, 1967. By permission of the authors and the editor of Virology.)

attributable to the infecting phage was lost. This phenomenon was finally explained by Delbrück (1940) who named it "lysis-from-without." The large number of phage particles produce so many holes in the cell wall that the cell, unable to repair them, soon dies. Infection under these conditions does not proceed to the making of new particles, so there is no increase in titer.

It is not necessary for either the phage particles or the bacterial cells to be alive for attachment to occur. The phage particles can be inactivated by ultraviolet light or they can be empty of DNA (Herriott, 1951). Preparations of isolated phage tails will attach to susceptible bacteria. The bacteria can be heat inactivated or can be broken by sonication, by freezing and thawing, or by other means. Preparations have been made of isolated bacterial receptors that can unite with the phage tail as shown in Figure 7-4 (Weidel and Kellenberger, 1955; Simon and Anderson, 1967).

PENETRATION

An experiment performed by Hershey and Chase (1952) demonstrated that only the DNA of a phage is necessary to initiate a cycle of infection in a cell. Other minor protein components contained in the phage head also enter the cell, but the major portion of the phage protein, the shell, remains outside. It has no further function once the DNA is injected.

It had already become clear that phage DNA could be separated from phage protein simply by rapidly changing the osmotic strength of the medium. (This can be done by suspending the phage in high salt solution and rapidly diluting with distilled water.) Thus, perhaps, they separate at the time of infection. Anderson (1951) had also shown, by electron microscopy, that phages attach to cells by the tip of the tail, and therefore the protein shell cannot be too firmly attached. Hershey and Chase (1952) reasoned that,

If this precarious attachment is preserved during the progress of the infection, and if the conclusions reached above are correct, it ought to be a simple matter to break the empty phage membranes off the infected bacteria, leaving the phage DNA inside the cells.

They achieved the separation of phage ghosts from infected cells by using a Waring blender.

Radioactive tracers were used to identify phage protein and DNA. Phages for the experiment were grown in media containing radioactive isotopes instead of nonradioactive isotopes. Thus, P^{32} was incorporated into phage DNA and S^{35} into phage protein.

Hershey and Chase then infected bacteria with purified stocks of phage labeled with S^{35} or P^{32} and placed the culture in the blender. They ran the blender for a short period, sampled the suspension, and repeated the process. Each sample was centrifuged and the supernatant and pellet were assayed for isotope content.

The results (Fig. 7-5) show that the majority of S^{35} is sheared off the cells, but only a small portion of the P^{32} becomes extracellular. Further experiments showed that the S^{35} was in viral protein material: It could be sedimented, could be precipitated with antiphage serum, and could again adsorb to bacteria (but could not initiate infection). The 20 per cent of S^{35} that was not recovered probably was in sheared tails; only about 3 per cent of the isotope entered the cells along with the DNA. The latter has an unknown function, but does not become incorporated into progeny phage.

Hershey and Chase concluded from their experiments that viral DNA enters the cell during infection but that viral protein largely remains extracellular and serves no further function once the DNA is released into the cell.

The contraction of the sheath is part of the mechanism for injection of the DNA into the cell. Sheath contraction is perhaps the only example in all of virology of any intrinsic movement of a virus or any of its parts. The sheath contracts when stimulated by certain chemicals, such as peroxides, cadmium cyanide, and zinc complexes

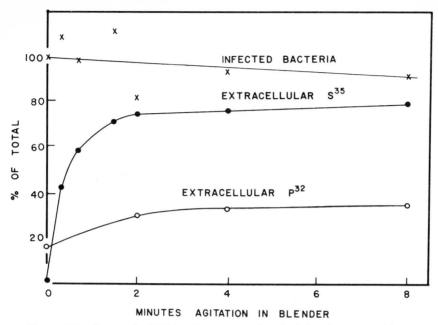

Figure 7-5. Removal of S[35] (in phage protein) and P[32] (in phage DNA) from bacteria infected with radioactive phage, and survival of infected bacteria. (Redrawn from Hershey and Chase, 1952.)

(Kozloff *et al.*, 1957), and sometimes the sheath contracts without any stimulus. Contraction is thought to be triggered by the breaking of thiol ester bonds in the tail protein. In the natural course of events, it is probably the small amount of cellular material leaking from the hole in the cell wall made by the phage lysozyme that triggers the sheath to contract.

The mechanism of contraction of the sheath is closely related to its structure. Moody (1967a, 1967b) examined many contracted and extended sheaths by electron microscopy. His detailed studies led him to conclude that the extended sheath has 24 rings surrounding the tail core, each ring containing six subunits of one size and six of a larger size. During contraction, the subunits move and the small ones merge into the large such that the contracted sheath has 12 rings of 12 subunits. After contraction, the sheath is slightly more than one and a half times its original diameter and is shorter by approximately half. The volume of the sheath is therefore conserved during contraction. The contraction of the sheath pushes the tail core into the bacterium with a slight twisting motion. A similar conclusion about the mechanism of sheath contraction has been reached by Krimm and Anderson (1967).

Energy for contraction is furnished by 144 molecules of adenosine triphosphate contained in the sheath (Wahl and Kozloff, 1962). Apparently there is one molecule of adenosine triphosphate for each subunit in the sheath. At the time of contraction, these molecules of adenosine triphosphate are converted into a similar number of molecules of adenosine diphosphate with the release of inorganic phosphorus.

The tail core is hollow, like a hypodermic needle, and connects the head of the phage to the interior of the bacterial cell. The viral DNA, coiled in the phage head, is extruded through the opening of the tail core into the cell. This is shown in the striking electron micrograph obtained by Simon and Anderson (1967) (see Fig. 7-6). Also extruded with the DNA are several proteins contained within the phage head. These proteins formed part of the 3 per cent of the S^{35} that entered the cells in the experiments of Hershey and Chase (1952) that were discussed before. The function of these proteins is unknown, but it has been suggested that they (together with some polyamines) serve to neutralize the highly acid DNA so that it can fit into its close quarters in the phage head. Entry of phage DNA into the bacterial cell initiates the next stage of the replicative cycle.

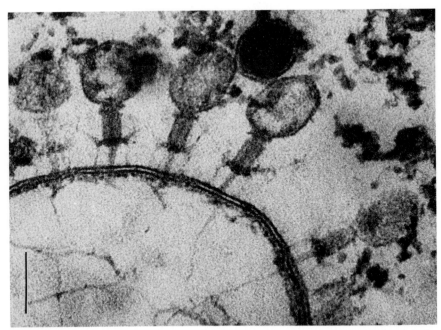

Figure 7-6. Several T4 phages attached to an *E. coli* cell wall. The cell wall is the circular double-membrane. The base plate, tail core, contracted sheath, and head of the virions are clearly visible. Inside the cell are strands that appear to be the DNA molecules being injected. (Bar is 100 mμ.) (Simon and Anderson, 1967. By permission of the authors and the editor of Virology.)

LATENT PERIOD

Doermann (1952) took a closer look at the events in infected cells during the latent period. He devised a method for breaking open infected bacteria and assaying their content of phage particles. The surprising result of his experiments was that the latent period could be divided into two periods (Fig. 7-7). For approximately the first half of the latent period, infected bacterial cells contained no detectable phage. This period is called the eclipse. During the second half of the latent period, called the maturation period, completed infective phage accumulated within the infected cells before being detectable by the one-step growth experiment.

As mentioned before, events in a single infected cell follow the same pattern as events in a population of infected cells. In addition, however, experiments with single cells demonstrate that the intracel-

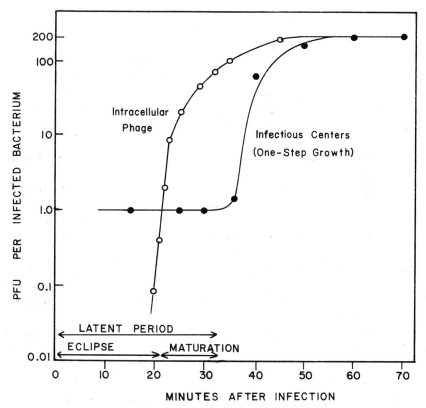

Figure 7-7.   Growth cycle of T-even phage. By lysing cells artificially before natural lysis, it was found that phage briefly loses its identity as an infectious entity during eclipse. New infectious phage begins to mature at the end of the eclipse and accumulates intracellularly until lysis. (Redrawn from Doermann, 1953.)

lular increase of the number of phage particles is linear from the beginning of maturation to the time the cell bursts. The question then concerns what is happening within the cell during eclipse and maturation. If phages grew like ordinary intracellular parasites, dividing by binary fission, their numbers would increase exponentially with time during the maturation period. The eclipse period could then be thought of as a preparatory time. The infecting phage would be truly latent, but changed into some undetectable form, and the cell would perhaps be preparing in some way for the phage to grow and divide.

Alternatively, as was pointed out by Doermann (1952), the eclipse period could represent a time of synthesis of viral parts that will be assembled into finished phage particles later during the maturation stage. Measurements of various phage precursors during eclipse and maturation have confirmed that this is the case. Other materials are formed that are related to phage but are not destined to become a part of the finished phage particle.

Eclipse

Proteins made in cells infected by phages have been studied several different ways. Cohen (1947) simply analyzed infected cells for their content of protein nitrogen and found that there was little or no change in the rate of protein synthesis during the infective cycle. Similar results were obtained by Koch and Hershey (1959) who used radioactive precursors to label the proteins of infected cells. Koch and Hershey also found that the majority of labeled protein was not sedimented with bacterial debris.

Proteins that are directly related to the phage particles were identified by any of several methods. Complete, infective phage particles were sedimented in the centrifuge and their radioactivity was measured. Other phage proteins, not in complete phage, were precipitated by antiphage serum. In this way, Koch and Hershey found that protein synthesis attributable to phage protein shells begins about 15 minutes after infection. The nature of the proteins synthesized during the early part of the cycle, before viral shell proteins are formed, will be discussed in the next chapter.

Another approach to the problem of identifying phage precursor proteins was made possible by a discovery of Burnet (1933). He found substances produced by infected bacteria that inhibit antiserum from neutralizing phage infectivity. Based on Burnet's discovery, De Mars (1955) developed a test for the serum blocking power (SBP) of a lysate. He found that when bacteria were prematurely lysed, SBP resulted even though infectious phage were not produced. SBP appeared at about the same time as the infectious phage but in greater amount. For instance, at the time of spontaneous lysis, 80 to 100 infectious phage particles per cell were released and there was additional SBP equivalent to the protein in about 40 more phage particles. When the synthesis of phage DNA was blocked by the addition of proflavine to the medium, a greater amount of SBP resulted and little or no complete phage was formed.

From these experiments, it can be postulated that the infected cell makes protein coats, ready for assembly into complete phage when the phage DNA is also ready. If no phage DNA is synthesized, more phage coats could be left over. It can also be postulated, however, that the phage proteins detectable as SBP might represent by-products not destined for incorporation in phage particles. Therefore, it is essential to determine if the SBP represents precursor protein. This can be done experimentally by radioactive labeling experiments. If radioactivity exists in phage proteins at one stage of the cycle and appears in finished phage particles later in the cycle, a precursor relationship is established.

This type of experiment was performed by Koch and Hershey (1959) and is called a "flow-through" or "pulse-chase" experiment. The infected cells are in contact with the radioactive protein precursor for a short period or pulse. Proteins being synthesized by the cell during the pulse incorporate the isotope. Labeling is then stopped by diluting the radioactive material with excess nonradioactive isotope and incubation is continued (the chase). Koch and Hershey found that the radioactivity "flowed through" the phage precursor proteins and finally appeared in the completed phage particles during the maturation period. Labeling of proteins by adding radioactive tracers (Kozloff et al., 1951; Siddiqi et al., 1952) demonstrated that little of the virus protein came from preexisting bacterial protein but instead that the virus protein was synthesized from materials assimilated from the medium after infection. The protein precursors accumulate as an intracellular pool from which parts are withdrawn to be assembled into phage particles.

Figure 7-8 shows that, whereas protein synthetic activity of the cell proceeds without detectable delay after infection, DNA synthesis ceases for the first 7 or 8 minutes of the eclipse period before resuming. (An uninfected growing bacterial culture would have an exponential increase of DNA without interruption.) The amount of DNA synthesized during the first 25 minutes would yield about 20 to 25 phage particles per cell, about equal to the burst size under the conditions of this experiment.

Cohen (1948b) performed experiments to determine the source of the phosphorus in T2 and T4 DNA. Since DNA is a stable molecule, its phosphorus can be followed by incorporated radiophosphorus. It is possible to show whether the bacterial DNA, for instance, is incorpo-

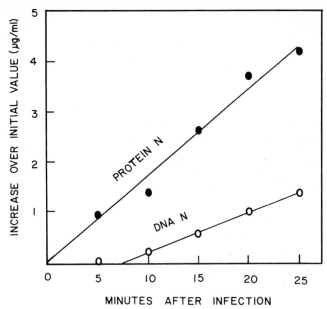

Figure 7-8. Synthesis of DNA and protein in *E. coli* B cells infected with phage T2r⁺. (Cohen, 1948a.)

rated into the phage DNA. Cohen did this in two types of experiment. In one, the DNA of bacterial cells was labeled with radiophosphorus prior to infection. The cells were then incubated in a nonradioactive medium after infection. Under these conditions the amount of label in the phage DNA measures the contribution of the bacterial DNA to the phage. The cell's DNA accounted for about 14 to 18 per cent of the phage DNA. In a converse experiment, cells that had been grown in a nonradioactive medium were infected and then incubated in a radioactive medium. In this way, it was found that the medium contributed between 69 and 75 per cent of the phosphorus of the phage's DNA.

A third source of phage DNA is the DNA of the infecting or parental phage. Putnam and Kozloff (1950) devised a transfer experiment to determine how much of the phosphorus in parental particles reappears at lysis in the progeny particles. They found that 20 to 30 per cent of the radiophosphorus of parental phage was transferred. Improved technical facility in performing the experiment raised the estimate to about 50 per cent (Watson and Maaløe, 1953). That is, about half the parental phage phosphorus is reutilized in the progeny phage. This, of course, represents only a small contribution to the entire output of progeny DNA.

Rapid progress in understanding DNA metabolism of infected cells came when Wyatt and Cohen (1953) analyzed the DNA of a number of viruses to determine the types of bases present. Of the viruses they analyzed, all had the usual four bases (adenine, thymine, guanine, and cytosine), except the T-even phages, which had no cytosine. Instead, a new base, 5-hydroxymethylcytosine (Fig. 7-9), was found. This base, usually called HMC, has been utilized as a tool for distinguishing host-cell DNA from the DNA of infecting T-even phages.

Analyzed in this way, DNA in infected cells was found to be of two kinds: bacterial and viral. The increasing amount of DNA shown in Figure 7-8 was therefore the sum of the two kinds of DNA. The bacterial DNA actually decreased while the phage DNA increased, as shown in Figure 7-10. The number of phage equivalents of DNA was greater than the burst size; here, as was also true for phage proteins, more phage DNA was made by the cell than was incorporated into phage particles.

Further experiments (Hershey, 1953) yielded a much clearer picture of the events concerning DNA in infected cells. Radiophosphorus was used in different labeling regimens to establish precursor-product relationships. In the early period of the replicative cycle, a pool of DNA is built up. This pool is the direct precursor of the DNA in completed phage. The pool receives its phosphorus from three sources: degraded bacterial DNA, newly synthesized materials from the medium, and the DNA of the phage particle, or particles, that initiated the infection.

The pool increases for a short while and then becomes constant at about 50 to 100 phage equivalent units per cell. Once incorporated

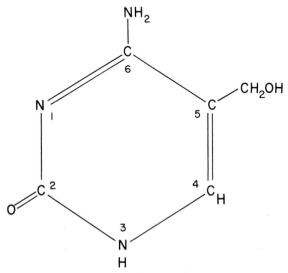

Figure 7-9. 5-Hydroxymethylcytosine.

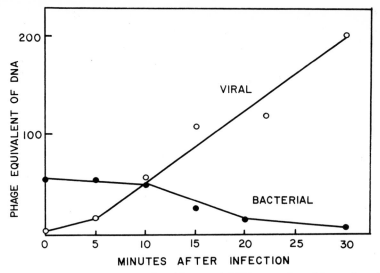

Figure 7-10. Amounts of viral and bacterial DNA per infected bacterium during the phage replicative cycle. Quantities of DNA are measured as the amount of hydroxy-methylcytosine (phage DNA) or cytosine (cell DNA). (Redrawn from Hershey *et al.*, 1953a.)

into finished phage, the phosphorus in the DNA no longer exchanges with the pool or with the external medium. Other experiments have shown that the pool of phage DNA serves as a bank from which DNA molecules are withdrawn randomly and incorporated into phage particles. At the time of lysis, unused DNA is simply released to the medium.

During the eclipse stage phage parts are synthesized and accumulate in pools. When phage parts are assembled into the first complete phage particle, the eclipse stage gives way to the maturation period. During maturation, synthesis of phage protein and DNA continue. The precursor pools are maintained at an approximately constant level; new synthesis adds parts to the pools at about the rate they are withdrawn for assembly. Assembled phages accumulate in the cell until lysis occurs.

Maturation

Kellenberger has used sophisticated electron microscopic techniques to study the maturation of phage particles. He recently summarized these studies in an extensive review (1961).

One of the first steps in phage maturation is condensation of the DNA. While phage DNA is replicating, it is in an extended form. But in the phage head, DNA is tightly packed (condensed) into a ball-like form. It is possible, as Kellenberger speculates, that the internal head proteins are responsible for the condensation, because it occurs before the protein shell is assembled.

The extended and condensed forms of the phage DNA have some analogy with forms of DNA in higher organisms. In the interphase period of cells, the DNA is extended and is not visible as chromosomes. Apparently, DNA can replicate new DNA or transcribe its information into the various kinds of RNA only while it is in the extended form. At prophase, however, in preparation for mitosis, the DNA condenses into chromosomes. Following division, the DNA again takes the extended form and resumes its metabolic functions.

The condensed phage DNA forms a framework or scaffolding, and the head protein precursors become arranged on this scaffolding. The process is somewhat like crystallization, presumably taking place without action by the cell. Although empty heads have been seen by electron microscopy, Kellenberger considers the DNA to be essential for the formation of the head. Heads without DNA are possibly artifacts from which the DNA has been lost during preparative procedures.

One of the first indications that the protein parts of phage particles are assembled randomly from available materials came from the phenomenon called phenotypic mixing. When bacteria were infected simultaneously with both T2 and T4 phages, Delbrück and Bailey (1946) observed some strange particles, which later were shown to contain the genetic material of T2 and the adsorption specificities of T4 (Novick and Szilard, 1951). Streisinger (1956) studied the phenomenon further and demonstrated that materials responsible for the specificities, that is, the phage tail proteins, accumulate in the infected cell and are withdrawn randomly from the pool during assembly. A phage head containing T2 DNA therefore could be assembled with T4 tail parts or vice versa. After one replicative cycle in which only one phage is allowed to infect a bacterium (low multiplicity), the phage phenotype again matches its genotype (Fig. 7-11).

More recent experiments have shown even more convincingly that assembly is largely a spontaneous process. Edgar and Wood (1966) made use of T4 mutants that are unable to direct synthesis of complete particles. Some mutants cause the cell to make complete phage heads, but no tail parts, while others cause the formation of tails but no heads. These abnormal progeny, of course, are not infectious. However, if extracts of cells infected with appropriate mutants are mixed together so that some parts are supplied by one extract and other parts by another extract, complete, infectious phage particles result.

A kind of phenotypic mixing was achieved if the two extracts were from different phages. One extract was from cells infected by a

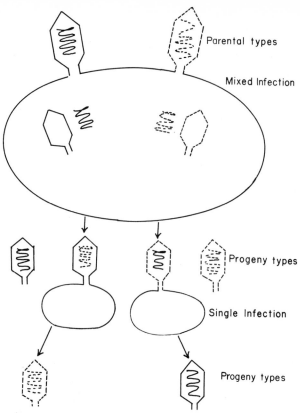

Figure 7-11. Phenotypic mixing. When a cell is simultaneously infected with two different phages, some of the progeny phages are like the parents but the capsid of some may have some or all of the protein of the opposite parent. If such progeny infect a new cell under conditions of single infection, the capsid proteins are in accord with the genetic content of the phage. This test distinguishes phenotypic mixing, which is a nongenetic change of phages issuing from a mixedly infected cell, from recombination (see Chapter 15), which is a genetic change that results from intracellular interaction between two distinguishable phages. Phenotypic mixing also occurs with animal viruses.

T2 mutant that contained T2 tail parts but no complete heads, and the other was from cells infected with a T4 mutant that contained heads but no tails. The resulting phages were genotypically T4 but had the adsorptive characteristics of T2. However, the extracts used had not been purified. Although it was demonstrated that intact cells were not required, enzymes present could have completed the assembly of the parts.

Similar experiments were performed with phage P22 (Israel *et al.*, 1967) and λ (Weigle, 1966) in which the phage parts had been purified to remove enzymes. Thus, it appears that in vitro assembly is not an enzymatic process, and therefore, assembly in the cell probably also occurs spontaneously.

LYSIS

During maturation, completed phages accumulate within the infected cell until the cell lyses. Lysis-from-without, one mechanism by which phages cause lysis of bacterial cells, has already been discussed. Lysis-from-within normally terminates the infective cycle by releasing the phage particles to the external medium.

Bayne-Jones and Sandholzer (1933) made time-lapse movies of infected bacterial cells during entire infective cycles. Observation and measurement of the cells revealed that they begin to swell about midway through the latent period. The swelling continues at an increasing rate, and finally the cells literally explode. Osmotic forces cause rapid uptake of water from the medium, which results in the swelling and bursting. Thus, cell lysis is a dramatic event, presumably the result of alteration of cell membrane permeability.

The cause of the changes in the cell membrane is an enzyme synthesized within the cell. Apparently the enzyme is the same lysozyme that is carried on the tip of the phage's tail. Its synthesis is directed by the phage DNA. This is known because phage mutants that cause the production of lysozymes having different properties have been isolated (Streisinger *et al.*, 1961). Which lysozyme is produced by a given cell depends on the phage mutant that infects the cell.

The phage thus uses an enzyme to gain entry into a cell. It also causes the cell to synthesize the same enzyme, providing a means of escape when sufficient progeny phage have been replicated. The growth cycle can then begin anew.

The stages in the life cycle of a T-even phage are known in great detail. They usually serve as a model for comparison with the growth cycles of other viruses. The replicative cycle for other phages that contain double-stranded DNA, such as λ, closely resembles that of the T-even phages.

In the next chapter, the events that occur during eclipse and maturation, and that result in the synthesis of the phage materials described here, will be discussed from the biochemical point of view.

Further Reading

Cohen, J. A.: Chemistry and Structure of Nucleic Acids of Bacteriophages. Science, 158:343-351, 1967.
Kellenberger, E.: The Genetic Control of the Shape of a Virus. Scientific American, 215 (Dec.):32, 1966.
Wood, B., and R. S. Edgar: Building a Bacterial Virus. Scientific American, 217(July):61, 1967.

8

BIOCHEMISTRY OF PHAGE-INFECTED CELLS: THE LYTIC CYCLE

When phage DNA enters a bacterial cell, the cell embarks on a new set of biosynthetic processes. In the preceding chapter, it was explained how these processes result in the synthesis of phage parts and finally in the assemblage of the parts into finished phage particles. In this chapter, the biochemical mechanisms by which the parts are synthesized will be described.

The mechanisms involved are those concerned with storage, transcription, and translation of genetic information and with protein synthesis. These mechanisms are in full operation in the cell prior to infection. After infection, some of the cell's processes are turned off, others are accelerated, and others are unaltered. In addition, some new ones are introduced. The changes in these activities favor virus production at the expense of the activities of the host cell.

First, the RNA changes will be discussed. These must take place before protein changes, which in turn precede DNA changes. The time relationships among some of the biosynthetic processes are summarized in Figure 8-1.

RNA

Some early concepts of DNA synthesis included the notion that RNA was a precursor to DNA. The two kinds of molecules were known to be similar and it was not inconceivable that RNA could be

136

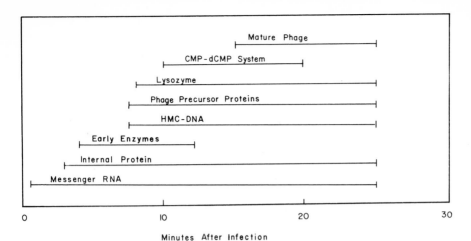

Figure 8-1. Synthesis of phage-related components during the latent period of a T-even phage in *E. coli* incubated at 37° C. (Champe, 1963.)

converted to DNA. Further, some results had been reported that indicated the T-even phages contained small amounts of RNA as well as DNA. Cohen (1948b) investigated these questions using radiophosphorus to label the nucleic acids. He found that RNA was not a precursor to DNA and that RNA synthesis in infected cells was quite minimal. Lack of new RNA synthesis in infected cells was also shown by Manson (1953). These results were difficult to reconcile with the idea that RNA was involved in protein synthesis because when protein synthesis continues after infection, net RNA synthesis should also continue.

Hershey (1953) performed similar experiments with infected bacteria but found that RNA was metabolically quite active, becoming labeled within 5 minutes after infection. Volkin and Astrachan (1956) found that a small fraction of bacterial RNA was labeled with radiophosphorus shortly after infection and that this RNA had a very high rate of turnover; that is, it was rapidly synthesized and rapidly broken down. Consequently, there was no net increase. Furthermore, the base composition of this RNA fraction differed from the base composition of the bulk of the cell's RNA. In fact, its base composition closely resembled that of the phage DNA (using uracil in place of thymine and cytosine in place of hydroxymethylcytosine) (Volkin and Astrachan 1957; Astrachan and Volkin, 1958).

It is important to bear in mind the concept of protein synthesis that was popular at that time. It was known that RNA was somehow involved in protein synthesis because labeled amino acids "flow through" the ribosomes during their incorporation into peptide chains.

The scheme was that ribosomes carried the genetic information from the DNA for translation into the amino acid sequence of proteins. If so, there should be a kind of ribosome for each kind of protein the cell was synthesizing, and the population of ribosomes should be heterogeneous. Their average base composition should match that of the DNA, which, however, it did not. Furthermore, in order for a cell to stop making one kind of protein in favor of another, such as occurs after phage infection, the ribosomal RNA should have a high rate of turnover, which was not the case.

These considerations led Jacob and Monod (1961) to predict that cells must contain another kind of RNA, which they called messenger RNA. They postulated that messenger RNA would be the intermediate that carries genetic information from the DNA to the ribosomes where it would be translated into a specific amino acid sequence of protein. Messenger RNA, therefore, would have a high rate of turnover, while ribosomal RNA would be relatively stable. Could the RNA fraction detected by Volkin and Astrachan in phage-infected cells be the postulated messenger RNA? Many experiments done since overwhelming answer "yes" to this question.

Nomura et al. (1960) found that after infection, radioactive label incorporated into newly synthesized RNA was inseparable from the cell's ribosomes. Because the label was so closely associated, the newly synthesized RNA could represent a new class of ribosomes that were specific for making T2 proteins.

On the other hand, this newly synthesized RNA could be the postulated messenger RNA, specific for T2. In this case, the label would be in RNA attached to nonspecific, nonlabeled, preëxisting ribosomes. In order to determine whether the label was in a new RNA attached to ribosomes or whether it was in new ribosomes, it was necessary to separate newly synthesized RNA and ribosomes from those in the cell prior to infection.

Brenner et al. (1961b) performed the following experiment: First, they increased the density of ribosomes by growing the cells in a medium containing N^{15} and C^{13}, the heavy but nonradioactive isotopes of nitrogen and carbon. After several generations, all the ribosomes had a great enough density increase to be separable from ordinary ribosomes by equilibrium density gradient centrifugation.

In a density gradient analysis, the material to be analyzed is mixed with a concentrated solution of a salt, such as cesium chloride. The mixture is centrifuged at high speed for 1 day or more in the ultracentrifuge. The centrifugal field causes the salt solution to become redistributed with a change in salt concentration from the bottom to the top of the tube, giving a linear density gradient. Particles or macromolecules in the tube redistribute until their density matches that of the surrounding medium. A population of particles that is homogeneous in density forms a band; if the original population also contained particles with a different density, they form a second band at another position in the tube. After equilibrium is reached, the centrifuge is stopped; the bottom of the tube is punctured with a pin; and successive drops, each representing a successive layer in the tube, are collected. These can be analyzed for their content of ribosomes or other particles.

In principle, then, to determine whether the RNA newly synthesized after phage infection was in ribosomes or whether it was messenger RNA attached to ribosomes, cells containing "heavy" (old) ribosomes were infected with T4 and transferred into medium containing isotopes of ordinary density. Radiophosphorus was also added. Under these conditions, ribosomes made before infection were heavy and nonradioactive, while RNA made after infection was light and radioactive. It was found that the radioactive RNA was associated with the heavy ribosomes. This is as would be expected if the newly synthesized RNA was messenger.

Messenger RNA meets the requirement that its overall base composition must resemble that of the phage DNA. But if genetic information is encoded as a definite base sequence, then a further requirement is that the base sequence of the phage-induced messenger RNA must resemble that of the phage DNA. Base composition is relatively easy to determine, but it is very difficult to analyze directly the base sequence of a nucleic acid. Instead, the sequence in one nucleic acid is compared with that in another by seeing whether a hybrid can form between the two (Doty *et al.*, 1960; Marmur and Lane, 1960; McCarthy and Bolton, 1964). Such a hybrid results from specific hydrogen bonding between two molecular strands, which can occur only if the bases are in proper register. Experimentally, this determination is done by incubating a mixture of the two molecules at an elevated temperature (50 to 60° C.). Thus, it was shown for T2 (Hall and Spiegelman, 1961) and for T4 (Bautz and Hall, 1962) that the messenger RNA made after phage infection not only was similar in overall base composition to that of phage DNA but also had a complementary base sequence.

Phage-specific RNA functions as messenger in a cell-free system. For this kind of experiment, Bautz (1962) first prepared a purified sample of T4-specific RNA. Then he added this RNA to a purified preparation of *E. coli* ribosomes in a reaction mixture containing amino acids and other materials that would allow protein synthesis. He found that the messenger was able to direct synthesis of protein in those conditions. His experiments, like those of many other workers, also confirmed that the ribosomes are nonspecific and merely synthesize protein according to the kind of messenger RNA present.

If this new RNA is really a messenger, its function would be demonstrable in the infected cell. To state the problem differently, is it a requirement that the new RNA be synthesized for phage synthesis to occur? An affirmative answer was obtained by Volkin (1960), who demonstrated that if messenger RNA synthesis was restricted, then protein synthesis did not occur, nor were any phage particles subsequently produced.

His observation that messenger RNA seemed to be short-lived was studied further by Bose and Warren (1967) in T4 phage-infected cells. They chose the messenger responsible for directing the synthesis of a specific "early" enzyme, thymidylate synthetase. Synthesis of new messenger RNA molecules was stopped by the addition of actinomycin D, and the activity of existing messenger RNA molecules was determined by enzyme assay. It was found that the messenger RNA molecules were active for 5 to 6 minutes. Enzyme activity then ceased if synthesis of a fresh supply of messenger RNA was prevented by the addition of the drug.

The fact that the proteins that become incorporated into finished phage particles are synthesized late in the infective cycle and that other proteins, synthesized early in the cycle, are not incorporated into phage particles (Hershey *et al.*, 1953b) has already been discussed. To account for this, either different messenger RNA molecules would have to be synthesized at the early and late periods or all would have to be synthesized simultaneously, but only certain ones could be translated into proteins.

To test which of these possibilities is responsible for differential protein synthesis, Kano-Sueoka and Spiegelman (1962) made mixtures of RNA preparations from cells that had been exposed briefly to either H^3-labeled precursors or to C^{14}-labeled precursors early and late in the infective cycle. The RNA mixtures were chromatographed, resolving the differently labeled RNA molecules into two separate fractions. This experiment showed that extracts made early and late in the infective cycle differed with respect to the messenger RNA molecules they contained.

The difference between "early" and "late" messenger RNA molecules was further clarified by Hall *et al.* (1964). They hybridized "early" and "late" messenger RNA with phage DNA, testing for whether the two kinds of RNA competed for the same binding sites on the DNA. They demonstrated in this way that both the "early" and "late" RNA molecules can hybridize with the phage DNA without appreciable competition. Therefore, there are complementary regions where base pairing can take place, but "early" messenger RNA does not take up the binding spots for "late" messenger and vice versa.

Chromatography based on the hybridization procedure was used by Bautz *et al.* (1966) to study messenger RNA synthesis in cells infected with T4. They compared the output of messengers by the *r*II region (an early function) with the output of messengers for lysozyme (a late function). These experiments were in an effort to determine the mechanism by which some genes are operative while others are quiescent. Their results confirmed the previous findings (Kano-Sueoka and Spiegelman, 1962) that the population of RNA molecules from "early" cells differed from that of "late" cells. In addition, it was found that early in the cycle the rII region is active for at least 20 minutes.

The production of the "late" messengers for lysozyme increased at about the time the enzyme was made, that is, 10 minutes and more after infection. This finding is consistent with the idea that the control of whether an enzyme is synthesized occurs when the genetic information of the base sequence of DNA is transcribed into messenger RNA, rather than when the information carried by messenger is translated into the amino acid sequence of a protein. However, it was found that the "late" gene was also transcribed early after infection. It then became relatively inactive before becoming active again. One interpretation of these results is that all genes are transcribed once as soon as the phage DNA is free in the cytoplasm. Some of the messenger molecules are then translated into protein and degraded in the process. Only these molecules are replaced. Regulation of protein synthesis thus would be at the translation level. However, much more work needs to be done before this interpretation, or any other, can be accepted.

In the discussion of RNA metabolism, emphasis has been on messenger RNA. The reason for this is that very few changes occur in the metabolism of ribosomal and transfer RNA. After infection, the cell's production of ribosomes comes to a prompt halt (Brenner *et al.*, 1961b), largely due to degradation of the cell's DNA by mechanisms that will be described in the next section. Since the viral DNA does not code for ribosomal RNA, this type of RNA is not synthesized at all after infection. Apparently, there are sufficient ribosomes in the cell at the time of infection to take care of the requirements for synthesis of viral proteins.

An extensive examination of the transfer RNA in infected cells has revealed only one that changes after infection (Sueoka and Kano-Sueoka, 1964). The transfer RNA concerned with leucine is altered following infection by any of the T-even phages (Kano-Sueoka and Sueoka, 1966) and may actually consist of changes in more than one molecular species of leucine-transfer RNA (Waters and Novelli, 1967). Whether the changes are viral coded or merely alteration in existing transfer RNA is yet to be determined.

Studies on synthesis of RNA in phage-infected cells have contributed to our understanding of the mechanisms of genetic expression and protein synthesis. Work from many other lines of investigation,

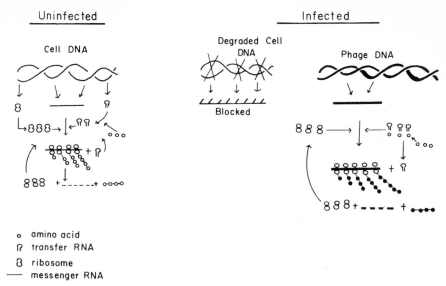

Figure 8-2. Scheme of DNA function in uninfected and infected cells. The DNA in uninfected cells directs the synthesis of three kinds of RNA: ribosomal, messenger, and transfer. The ribosomes and messenger RNA form polysomes. Transfer RNA brings an attached amino acid to the polysome where the amino acids are joined by peptide bonds in the order specified by the messenger RNA. The ribosomes and transfer RNA are released and recycle, and the messenger RNA is degraded. In the infected cell, viral-induced functions degrade the cell's DNA, preventing it from further synthesis of cellular messenger RNA. Messenger RNA directed by the phage DNA functions with preëxisting ribosomes and transfer RNA to form proteins specific for the phage. (Modified from Brenner *et al.*, 1961b.)

not using viruses, has also aided the development of the current concepts. It may be summarized that the DNA acts as a template for the polymerization of a polyribonucleotide chain. The order in which the four bases are linked is established by the sequence of the bases in the DNA. Each gene acts as template for a single kind of messenger RNA, which in turn is translated at the ribosome into the sequence of amino acids that forms the polypeptide chain of a protein. In Figure 8-2 this process is summarized diagrammatically for uninfected and infected cells.

The two major kinds of proteins involved in phage replication are the "late" proteins, chiefly phage components and lysozyme that were discussed in previous chapters, and the "early" proteins, whose nature will now be discussed.

EARLY PROTEINS

It was mentioned before that some of the first experiments using isotope incorporation to study protein synthesis of infected cells re-

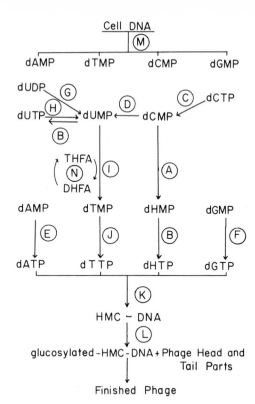

Figure 8-3. The enzymes of phage synthesis. Letters indicate enzymes described in the text: A, Deoxycytidylate hydroxymethylase. B, Hydroxymethyldeoxycytidylic kinase. C, Deoxycytidine triphosphatase. D, Deoxycytidylic deaminase. E, Adenylic kinase. F, Deoxyguanylic kinase. G, Deoxyuridine diphosphatase. H, Deoxyuridine triphosphatase. I, Thymidylate synthetase. J, Deoxythymidylate kinase. K, DNA polymerase. L, Glucosyl transferase.

vealed that more proteins were synthesized than could be found in finished phage particles. The proteins that were not utilized were synthesized early in the infective cycle and were antigenically unrelated to the proteins in mature phage particles.

Progress in understanding the nature of the early proteins began with the discovery that *E. coli* cells infected with T6 phage acquire a new enzyme function not present in uninfected cells (Flaks and Cohen, 1957). This enzyme (designated *A* in Figure 8-3) converts deoxycytidylate (dCMP) to 5-hydroxymethyldeoxycytidylate (dHMP). Flaks and Cohen (1959a) found that the new enzyme, deoxycytidylate hydroxymethylase, occurs in cells infected with any T-even phage. Its substrate is the monophosphate derivative of deoxycytidylate that arises chiefly from degradation of the host-cell's DNA. Further work showed that the enzyme was detectable very early after infection (Flaks *et al.*, 1959).

Polymerization of DNA, however, requires the triphosphate form (dHTP) rather than the monophosphate that results from the reaction catalyzed by deoxycytidylate hydroxymethylase. It was therefore predictable that another enzyme must also exist in infected cells: a kinase that would add two phosphates to the monophosphate. Such an

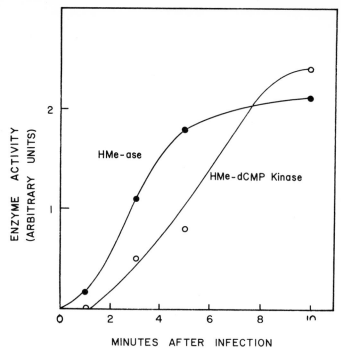

Figure 8-4. Development of hydroxymethylase (HMe-ase) and deoxycytidylate hydroxymethyl kinase (HMe-dCMP kinase) activities in *E. coli* infected with T2 phage. (Somerville *et al.*, 1959.)

enzyme (*B* in Figure 8-3) was found (Kornberg *et al.*, 1959; Somerville *et al.*, 1959). The time course of synthesis of these two enzymes after infection is summarized in Figure 8-4.

Infection of cells by a T-even phage, therefore, introduces a new metabolic pathway into the cell that replaces the preëxisting analogous pathway of synthesis of the phosphorylated derivatives of deoxycytidine. Since the latter pathway is no longer necessary because the phage DNA contains only the hydroxymethyl form of deoxycytidine, what becomes of the cell's enzymes for the deoxycytidylate pathway?

The kinase that phosphorylates deoxycytidine monophosphate (deoxycytidylate kinase) in uninfected cells does not increase after infection (Kornberg *et al.*, 1959). Its residual action is nullified by an opposing enzyme that appears shortly after infection, deoxycytidine triphosphatase (*C* in Figure 8-3). This latter enzyme removes the terminal phosphate groups of deoxycytidine triphosphate (dCTP) that was present in the cell, changing it to deoxycytidine monophosphate, which in turn enters the new pathway already described (Kornberg *et al.*, 1959; Koerner *et al.*, 1959; Koerner *et al.*, 1960; Zimmerman and Kornberg, 1961; Warner and Barnes, 1966).

In addition to its being removed by being hydroxymethylated, deoxycytidine monophosphate is removed from the available pool by another enzyme (*D* in Figure 8-3) that arises shortly after infection. This enzyme (deoxycytidylic deaminase) catalyzes the removal of the amino group from the cytosine, converting the base to uracil. The product of the reaction is deoxyuridine monophosphate (dUMP), which becomes the substrate of a reaction to be discussed (Keck *et al.*, 1960; Maley and Maley, 1966).

After infection, the net effects on the preëxisting deoxycytidylate pathway are to stop production of new deoxycytidine triphosphate that would be a precursor to cell DNA as well as to phage DNA, to destroy deoxycytidine triphosphate that might be present, and to convert the resulting deoxycytidine monophosphate to other reactions. The time course of the development of these enzyme activities is shown in Figure 8-5.

The kinase that phosphorylates deoxyadenosine monophosphate (dAMP) to the triphosphate (dATP), the direct precursor to DNA, is

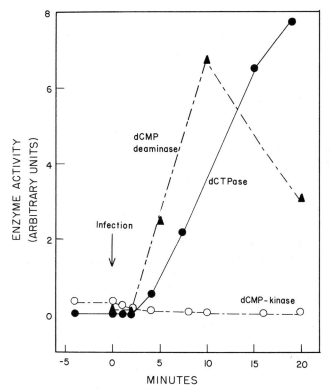

Figure 8-5.   Activity of deoxycytidylate kinase, deoxycytidine triphosphatase, and deoxycytidylate deaminase after infection of *E. coli* by T2. (Redrawn from Kornberg *et al.*, 1959; Keck *et al.*, 1960).

called adenylic kinase (*E* in Figure 8-3). It normally has a higher activity in uninfected *E. coli* than the other kinases and does not undergo any essential change following infection (Kornberg *et al.*, 1959; Bessman, 1959).

Another kinase that increases following infection by T2 is in the pathway of deoxyguanylate metabolism. Deoxyguanylic kinase (*F* in Figure 8-3), normally present in uninfected cells, was found to increase 20- to 45-fold after infection (Kornberg *et al.*, 1959; Bessman, 1959). That the increase represented a different enzyme but with the same function, rather than greater synthesis of the enzyme that is normally present, was suggested by the finding that the concentration of potassium ion acted differently on enzyme preparations from infected and from uninfected cells (Bessman and Van Bibber, 1959). Better evidence, obtained by chromatographing the enzymes from infected and uninfected cells, indicated that the deoxyguanylic kinase of infected cells was a different protein from that in uninfected cells and that the new enzyme was not detectable in uninfected cells (Bello *et al.*, 1961).

Several new enzymes involved in the deoxyuridylate pathway arise in cells infected by T-even phages. Because of reactions that occur in uninfected cells and apparently are not related to phage synthesis, various deoxyuridylate derivatives are synthesized (Bertani *et al.*, 1963). Uracil, however, is not normally present in DNA. The new enzymes that occur after phage infection all act to convert the deoxyuridylate derivatives to the monophosphate to feed into the thymidylate pathway.

One of these enzymes, deoxyuridine diphosphatase (*G* in Figure 8-3), removes one phosphate group, and another, deoxyuridine triphosphatase (*H* in Figure 8-3), removes two phosphate groups (Greenberg, 1966; Warner and Barnes, 1966). There is also a new kinase activity that catalyzes the production of deoxyuridine triphosphate, but it seems likely that this is due to a lack of specificity of hydroxymethyldeoxycytidylate kinase, which can also phosphorylate deoxyuridylate (Greenberg and Somerville, 1962). Since the deoxyuridine triphosphatase activity is much greater than the kinase activity, there is little or no accumulation of the triphosphate derivative of uridylate; therefore, it is not incorporated into DNA.

The last pathway to be discussed is concerned with thymidylate derivatives. New enzymes occur in this pathway following infection with T-even phages. Flaks and Cohen (1959b) reported an increase in activity of thymidylate synthetase (*I* in Figure 8-3) to levels about sevenfold higher than prior to infection. This enzyme catalytically converts deoxyuridylate to thymidylate by a one-carbon addition at the 5'-position on the uracil ring.

With the discovery of thymidylate synthetase and its increase after infection, it became possible to explain the earlier finding (Barner and Cohen, 1954) that a mutant of *E. coli* that required thymine in the medium lost that requirement after infection. Later work revealed that the mutant bacterium lacked thymidylate synthetase (Barner and Cohen, 1959). After infection, however, this enzyme function became quite active in the cells. Since there was no detectable enzyme activity in the virus itself, the viral DNA must have induced the synthesis of this enzyme in the cell.

The new enzyme activity could represent enzyme molecules coded for by the phage, and therefore a kind of protein not present in uninfected cells. Alternatively, it could result from the induction or derepression of transcription of the normal host gene coding for this enzyme. Induction, by phage infection, of this function in mutant bacteria unable to synthesize the enzyme certainly favors the conclusion that the phage DNA codes for the new thymidylate synthetase.

Further evidence, although still not conclusive, was obtained by Greenberg *et al.* (1962), who used column chromatography (Fig. 8-6) to study these enzymes in infected and uninfected cells. In the normal uninfected cell, all the thymidylate synthetase activity was confined to a single peak in the effluent from the column. In normal infected cells, however, there were two peaks of activity. Mutant bacterial cells that require exogenous thymine and uracil to be added to the medium were also infected. In these cells there appeared a peak of enzyme activity at the position corresponding to the viral-induced enzyme in normal infected cells.

Thymidylate synthetase effectively removes the deoxyuridine monophosphate that has already been discussed as being the end product of several other pathways. Deoxythymidylate kinase (*J* in Figure 8-3) is another new kinase that arises in cells infected by T-even phages (Kornberg *et al.*, 1959; Bessman, 1959). The kinase phosphorylates the monophosphate product of thymidylate synthetase, forming the triphosphate derivative that is the direct precursor to DNA synthesis.

To summarize, in the early stages of infection by T-even phages a number of new metabolic pathways appear in the infected cell. Some of these pathways and enzymes do not preëxist, indicating that the information for their synthesis is contained in the phage DNA. The net effect of the new enzyme systems is to divert the synthetic processes of the cell to the making of precursors for phage DNA.

Synthesis of DNA from its precursors is also catalyzed by an enzyme. The triphosphate forms of the base derivatives are polymerized by DNA polymerase (*K* in Figure 8-3), the sequence of the polymerization being determined by the template or "primer" DNA present (Kornberg, 1960; Aposhian and Kornberg, 1962). Shortly after phage infection the activity of DNA polymerase increases 10- to 20-

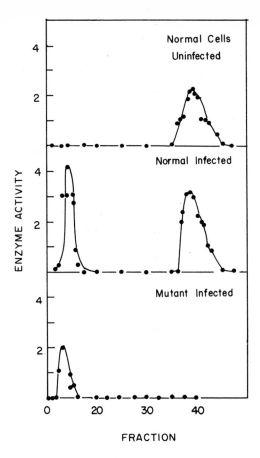

Figure 8-6. Column chromatography (DEAE-cellulose) of thymidylate synthetase from normal cells, normal infected cells, and mutant infected cells. Uninfected mutant cells have no detectable enzyme activity in the position of either peak, and they are unable to synthesize either thymine or uracil, which must therefore be added to the growth medium. (Redrawn from Greenberg *et al.*, 1962.)

fold over the activity in uninfected cells (Kornberg *et al.*, 1959). The newly synthesized enzyme does not specifically require hydroxymethyldeoxycytidine triphosphate, but it can use deoxycytidine triphosphate equally well when deoxycytidine triphosphatase activity is inhibited (Koerner *et al.*, 1959, 1960; Kornberg *et al.*, 1959).

The hydroxymethyl groups of hydroxymethylcytosine have glucose attached. Each of the T-even phages has its pattern of glucosylation: There are three types of glucosyl linkages and the ratio of the three types is characteristic (Lehman and Pratt, 1960), as shown in Table 8-1. The glucosylation occurs after the DNA is polymerized, as the DNA polymerase will utilize only the unglucosylated triphosphate forms of the nucleotide for the polymerization (Kornberg *et al.*, 1959). As might be expected, there is a glucosyl transferase (*L* in Figure 8-3) produced in the infected cell that catalyzes the formation of each type of glucosyl linkage. These enzymes have been isolated and have been shown to have different chromatographic properties,

TABLE 8-1. GLUCOSYLATION OF T-EVEN PHAGE DNA*

| | % OF GLUCOSYLATED dHMP RESIDUES IN PHAGE DNA | | |
TYPE OF LINKAGE	T2	T4	T6
Unglucosylated	25	0	25
α-glucosyl	70	70	3
β-glucosyl	0	30	0
β-glucosyl-α-glucosyl	5	0	72

*From Kornberg *et al.,* 1961.

confirming the idea that they are separate, distinct proteins. The α-glucosyl transferases differ from the β-glucosyl transferase, and the enzymes induced by the three T-even phages differ from each other (Kornberg *et al.,* 1961).

Another important new enzyme in cells infected by T-even phages is a deoxyribonuclease (Pardee and Williams, 1952). Before the deoxyribonuclease can increase, the phage DNA must be injected into the cell, and the cells must be able to metabolize (Kunkee and Pardee, 1956). This new enzyme degrades the DNA of the host cell (Stone and Burton, 1962), ensuring that its genes will not function in the production of messenger RNA for synthesis of host-cell proteins.

Another phenomenon can now be explained. After a certain critical period following the onset of the infective cycle of T-even phages, if the same cell is superinfected by a T-odd phage, the DNA of the latter is degraded, resulting in superinfection exclusion. Presumably, the deoxyribonuclease induced by the first phage degrades the DNA of the second phage. The degradation products resulting from the breakdown of DNA by this enzyme are utilized in the production of phage DNA. They reënter the various pathways already discussed.

Phage infection also results in a two- or threefold increase in activity of dihydrofolate reductase, an enzyme that catalyzes the regeneration of tetrahydrofolate. The last compound is involved in the methylation of deoxyuridylic acid to form deoxythymidylic acid; the carbon atom for the methyl group is from formaldehyde. After being added to the uracil ring, it is reduced by the tetrahydrofolate to a methyl group. Dihydrofolate reductase is present in uninfected cells; and although its activity is augmented after infection, the increase does not seem to be a requirement for phage replication. The precise role of this enzyme is still not completely clear (Mathews, 1966).

When the enzymes induced by the T-even phages were discussed, it was repeatedly pointed out that whenever suitable procedures had been used for testing whether the new enzyme was coded for by the phage DNA or whether the cell's DNA had been released from some inhibition, it was found that the new enzyme seemed to represent a new protein. The new protein was not detectable in the uninfected cell. Further, it seemed to be a new protein, even when the enzyme activity was an augmentation of activity already present. The evidence certainly is in favor of coding by phage DNA; but, as pointed out by Champe (1963), definitive proof will have to await the demonstration that a viral mutation in a gene coding for a new enzyme results in an altered amino acid sequence of the enzyme.

The T-even group of phages has been emphasized here because more is known about these phages than any other group of viruses. Nevertheless, care should be taken in generalizing from these results. For instance, another T-phage, T5, also contains double-stranded DNA and has *E. coli* as its host, but it does not contain hydroxymethyl-cytosine. The new enzymes that T5 induces are therefore different from the ones induced by the T-even phages (Kornberg *et al.*, 1959). Furthermore, to generalize that the enzyme changes are always to the disadvantage of the host cell is not valid, as will be seen in later chapters.

The point to be made is that the phage introduces into the infected cell a new set of instructions that directs the cell to set up a new array of metabolic processes. It is best, therefore, to consider the infected cell as a new complex possessing functions that did not exist before infection. The nature of the changes and their effect on the new complex vary from one system to another.

DNA

In general, DNA has three functions in a cell: to store genetic information as a sequence of bases; to transmit genetic information to the next generation; and to transcribe particular genes, when appropriate, into messenger RNA, with the information finally translated into an amino acid sequence of a polypeptide. Phage DNA does not differ from cellular DNA in these respects. It also stores information as a base sequence. As has been discussed, phage DNA transcribes various messenger RNA molecules that code for specific proteins, such as enzymes for phage synthesis and phage structural components. The "reading out" of the different messages is under regulatory control, as early enzymes are made before lysozyme or other late proteins such as phage parts.

The transcription of DNA into messenger RNA is catalyzed by an RNA polymerase that is dependent upon the presence of a DNA template. Phage DNA utilizes cellular DNA-dependent RNA polymerase for directing messenger RNA synthesis, at least for the early enzymes, since messenger RNA synthesis precedes protein synthesis.

Phage DNA, like cellular DNA, serves to maintain genetic continuity. As was discussed in a previous chapter, the experiments of Hershey and Chase (1952) gave the first clear indication that the phage DNA was completely sufficient for this purpose. The preceding section covered the many metabolic alterations that occur in infected cells to shut off the activities of the host cell's DNA and to synthesize precursors for phage DNA synthesis.

The mechanism by which phage DNA replicates has been examined by many different methods. Luria (1951) used the genetic approach: Analysis of the occurrence of mutants in phage-infected cells led him to the conclusion that phages replicate exponentially. Not only did the parental phage replicate in the infected cell, but its progeny did also. He was aware that it was not whole phage that replicated inside the bacterial cell, although Hershey and Chase (1952) had not yet shown that only phage DNA enters the cell. As Luria (1951) pointed out, "reproduction of the genetic material of phage, therefore, takes place mainly by reduplication of elements that are not yet in the form of mature phage particles." These elements are now known to be the phage DNA replicating to form the DNA pool.

In attempting to understand the mechanism of replication of phage DNA, one could ask about the participation of the initiating DNA in the process. For example, once the process begins, is the initial DNA degraded or changed into some form that distinguishes it from newly synthesized DNA? If so, it would not be expected to reappear in the progeny resulting from the infection. On the other hand, if the initiating DNA were indistinguishable by the cell from the newly synthesized DNA molecules, it would reappear in the progeny. Transfer experiments designed to measure the amount of parental DNA material in the progeny phage indicate that about one half of the DNA phosphorus of the initiating phage reappears in the progeny (Putnam and Kozloff, 1950; Watson and Maaløe, 1953).

This form of transfer raises the question whether certain portions of phage DNA are preferentially transferred while other portions are perhaps degraded. If certain portions have a high likelihood of transfer, performing a transfer experiment with the progeny resulting from one transfer should yield a higher rate of transfer. For instance, if 50 per cent transfer occurred and these progeny were used to reinfect new cells, a portion larger than 50 per cent of the phage DNA would be transferred. On the other hand, if the parts of the viral DNA transferred were incorporated randomly, then there would again be 50 per cent transfer, yielding 25 per cent of the P^{32} in the parental phage used in the first experiment. Another repetition would result in a yield of about 13 per cent of the original (Stent et al., 1959).

Such an experiment demonstrated that transfer is random; that is, parts of the phage DNA are not preferentially transferred (Maaløe and Watson, 1951).

At about the same time, Watson and Crick (1953c) proposed their double-helical model for the structure of DNA. Not only did their proposed structure make sense of previously unexplained experimental data on DNA, but it also suggested a mechanism by which DNA could replicate. During replication the two strands could disintwine, exposing a nucleotide residue on each strand. Each residue, with catalytic aid of DNA polymerase, could then hydrogen bond its complementary nucleotide into place. Polymerization would then result in a new, complementary strand. The suggested mode of replication was called *semiconservative.*

There was, however, an alternate possibility for replication, also consistent with the double-helical structure. The double-stranded structure could remain intact during replication, acting as a template to form a completely new, double-helical structure. This mode of replication was called *conservative* because the integrity of the entire DNA double-helical molecule would be conserved during replication. A third form of replication, in which the template molecules would be completely degraded and the parts reutilized, was called *dispersive.*

The first experiments performed to test which of these mechanisms actually occurred (Meselson and Stahl, 1958) made use of the predicted distribution of parental DNA molecules of the bacterium *E. coli* among the descendent DNA molecules as shown in Figure 8-7. *E. coli* cells were grown in a medium containing heavy

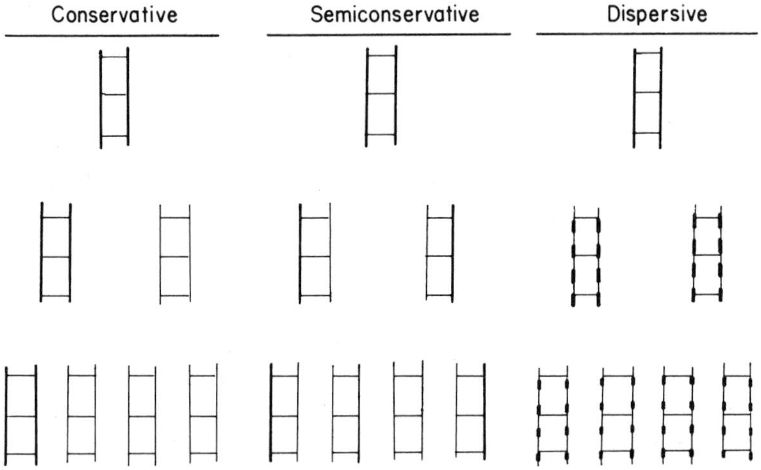

Figure 8-7.   A diagram showing conservative, semiconservative, and dispersive modes of replication of DNA. In each, the original DNA is indicated by heavy lines and DNA synthesized at the first and second replication is indicated by the lighter lines.

N^{15}. In this way, after several generations, the *E. coli* DNA was of greater density than normal DNA. The bacteria were then transferred to medium containing normal nitrogen, and growth continued. Samples were taken periodically and the DNA was extracted. The density distribution of the DNA molecules was determined by centrifuging to equilibrium in CsCl density gradients.

Meselson and Stahl made predictions of the expected distribution under each possible mode of replication. With the conservative model they predicted that there would be two bands after the first DNA replication: one at the density of the DNA containing N^{15} and one at the density of N^{14}, with no DNA of intermediate density. They predicted that under the semiconservative model three bands should arise, and these would change as division progressed. The band of DNA containing N^{15} should give way to one of lesser density when one of the two strands contained N^{15} and the other N^{14}. Later, some molecules would contain exclusively N^{14}. The hybrid band would be midway between the bands of completely N^{14} and completely N^{15} DNA. Under the dispersive model, there would be one broad band, demonstrating the presence of DNA molecules of heterogeneous density.

The test (Fig. 8-8) demonstrated that the Watson-Crick prediction of semiconservative replication of DNA holds for bacterial DNA. But is it also true for phage DNA replication? Since it has already been shown that about half the phage DNA that enters a cell can be recovered in progeny phage, it would seem appropriate to perform a transfer experiment with phage DNA that is increased in density.

Kozinski (1961a) performed such an experiment. He used 5-bromodeoxyuridine to increase the density of the phage DNA. (5-bromodeoxyuridine differs from thymidine only in that the methyl group of the thymine residue is replaced by a bromine atom. Because bromine is about the same size as a methyl group, the analog is incorporated into DNA in place of thymine and thereby increases the density of the DNA.) Phages labeled with radiophosphorus were used to infect cells growing in medium containing 5-bromodeoxyuridine. The CsCl density gradient was fractionated after it had been centrifuged to equilibrium, and each fraction was assayed for radiophosphorus and for the concentration of unlabeled DNA (which was in great excess) by determining the absorbancy of light at a wavelength of 260 mμ.

The results of the experiment are shown in Figure 8-9A. Radiophosphorus was associated with both the parental DNA, of lighter density, and the progeny DNA; the latter contained 5-bromouracil and therefore had an increased density. There was no DNA of hybrid density. Another aliquot of the DNA was treated extensively with high-frequency oscillation, breaking it into small pieces. Density gradient analysis of this sample revealed a peak of hybrid density (Fig. 8-9B). Kozinski interpreted this result to mean that transfer of parental

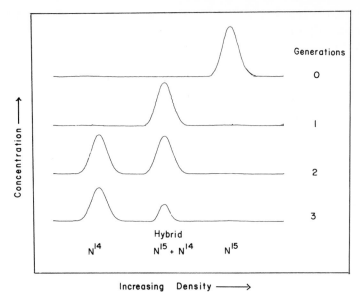

Figure 8-8. Diagram demonstrating the experimental test of the Watson-Crick prediction that double-stranded DNA replicates semiconservatively. *E. coli* cells were grown in N^{15} to increase the density of the DNA; after such growth, the experiment was begun (generation 0) and DNA at that time banded at the dense position. After one generation in N^{14} medium, the DNA banded at a less dense position, demonstrating that each molecule contained some N^{14} and some N^{15}. No DNA molecules contained exclusively either N^{14} or N^{15}. At the end of two generations in N^{14} medium, one half of the molecules still contained an equal mixture of heavy and light isotope, and the other one half of the molecules contained only N^{14}. After three generations, the ratio of DNA with normal density increased relative to that with hybrid density. (Redrawn from Meselson and Stahl, 1958.)

DNA to progeny did occur, but in a fragmentary way. That is, replication was not dispersive in the sense that the parental DNA was completely degraded and uniformly distributed among the progeny molecules. If it had been, breakage of the DNA into small pieces would yield a single population of fragments that would form a single band of increased density. Instead, some fragments were found to be of higher density and some of hybrid density.

Phage DNA, therefore, seems to replicate in a Watson-Crick semiconservative fashion, but there is evidence that additional factors are operative. These result in a wide distribution of fragments of the parental phage DNA among the progeny (Kozinski and Kozinski, 1963). The mechanism by which this probably occurs will be reserved for discussion in a later chapter.

The picture that emerges of the latent period shows it to be a time of great activity. It is not a time of disappearance of the virus, but

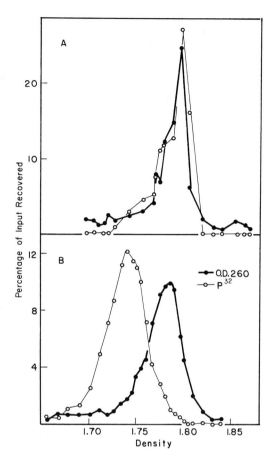

Figure 8-9. Fragmentary transfer of DNA from parent to progeny phage. A phage preparation labeled with P^{32} was used to infect cells grown in the presence of 5-bromo-deoxyuridine. DNA extracted from the parental phage formed a band at a density of 1.700 g./ml. (not shown). DNA extracted from progeny phage (diagram **A**) contains transferred P^{32} and is of increased density (about 1.800 g./ml.) because of the incorporated halogenated analog. Sonication of another aliquot of the same sample of progeny phage DNA is shown in diagram **B**. The bands are broader than in **A** because the smaller molecular weight of the sonicated fragments allows them to diffuse more from the midpoint of the band. The majority of the progeny DNA, shown by its absorption of ultraviolet (O.D. 260), has the same density as unsonicated progeny DNA. A small amount of progeny DNA, not detectable by ultraviolet absorption, contains the transferred P^{32}. The transfer must have been as short stretches of parental DNA; if the parental DNA had been transferred completely intact, it would have banded at the intermediate density without sonication. If the transfer had been due to complete degradation of the parental DNA to the nucleotides which were then rebuilt into progeny DNA, sonication would not have produced fragments with intermediate density. (Redrawn from Kozinski, 1961a).

rather one of loss of viral identity. It is the part of the replicative cycle of viruses—the only part—during which they undergo biological activity.

The replicative cycles of most viruses are quite similar, but differ in important details, as will become apparent in the following chapters.

Further Reading

Cohen, S. S.: The Biochemistry of Viruses. Annual Review of Biochemistry, 32:83-154, 1963.

Cohen, S. S.: Virus-Induced Acquisition of Metabolic Function. Federation Proceedings, 20:641-649, 1961.

Jacob, F., and E. L. Wollman: Viruses and Genes. Scientific American, 204(June):93, 1961.

Luria, S. E.: Bacteriophage Genes and Bacterial Functions. Science, 136:685-692, 1962.

Sinsheimer, R. L.: The Nucleic Acids of the Bacterial Viruses. In Chargaff, E., and J. N. Davidson (eds.): The Nucleic Acids. New York, Academic Press Inc., 1960, pp. 187-224.

9

REPLICATION OF ANIMAL VIRUSES CONTAINING DNA

The growth cycle of the T-even phages is often taken as the model of growth of all viruses. It is true that the growth cycle of all viruses resembles in broad outline the growth cycle of the T-even phages, but it is also true that there are differences. It is of interest, therefore, to examine in some detail the growth cycles of other viruses.

Of the animal viruses that contain DNA, the following have been studied the most thoroughly and will be the main topics of this chapter: Vaccinia, adenovirus, herpesvirus, and polyoma virus. Some of the viruses have at least two possible modes of interacting with a cell. The cytolytic or productive mode will be discussed here. Some of the adenoviruses and most members of the polyoma group can also interact in a nonproductive way, causing malignant change. Discussion of the latter kind of interaction will be deferred to a later chapter.

VIRAL DNA

It will be recalled that vaccinia, adenovirus, herpesvirus, and polyoma virus contain double-stranded DNA. In fact, the only known animal virus that might contain single-stranded DNA is the so-called minute virus of mice (Crawford, 1966). Other animal viruses have, at one time or another, been thought to contain single-stranded DNA, but these reports have not been substantiated.

Polyoma viral DNA has been studied in great detail (Vinograd *et al.*, 1965). Its ring-shaped molecule sediments at any of several different rates, depending on its configuration. The intact molecule, called component I, has a sedimentation constant of 20S; in addition to its right-handed Watson-Crick helix, the molecule has superimposed a left-handed helical twisting, called a supercoil (Follett and Crawford, 1967a, 1967b). The rate at which the DNA molecule sediments is related to the number of twists (Bloomfield, 1966). If a phosphodiester bond in one of the two strands breaks, the molecule is said to be "nicked"; the resulting component II has a sedimentation rate of 16S. The reason for this is that the nick allows the supercoil, which is under some tension, to untwist, leaving an open ring that still retains the Watson-Crick helix. Because the open ring presents a less compact structure, it has increased friction and its sedimentation rate decreases. If both strands break at or near the same site, the ring opens and the molecules become the linear component III with a sedimentation constant of 14S.

Denaturation of the DNA results in strand separation due to breakage of the hydrogen bonds between the two strands. Denaturation of component I results in a random coil, consisting of two interlocked rings. Because the random coil is more compact than the supercoiled form, but has the same mass, its sedimentation rate increases (to 53S). Denaturation of component II results in separation into one random-coiled circular strand (18S) and one linear strand (16S), unless the component II molecule had a nick in each strand at separate locations, in which case two linear strands result. Component III yields two

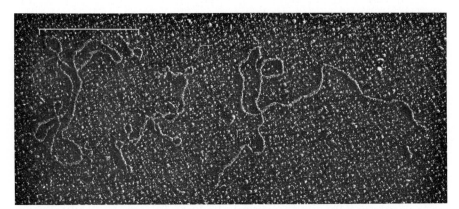

Figure 9-1. An electron micrograph of three forms of bovine papilloma virus DNA. The DNA was extracted from purified virus and prepared for electron microscopy by shadowing. From left to right, the three DNA molecules are the open ring (component II), the supercoiled ring (component I), and the linear form (component III). The bar represents 0.5 μ. The contour length of bovine papilloma virus DNA is 2.54 μ, corresponding to a molecular weight of 4.9×10^6 daltons. (Bujard, 1967. Electron micrograph courtesy of Dr. H. Bujard.)

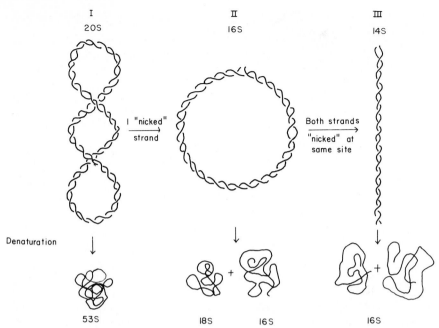

Figure 9-2. The various forms of polyoma-papilloma virus DNA and the effect on configuration that results from denaturation (such as by heating at 100° C. and cooling rapidly). (Modified from Vinograd *et al.*, 1965.)

linear strands (16S) on denaturation (Vinograd *et al.*, 1965). An electron micrograph of these forms of bovine papilloma virus DNA is shown in Figure 9-1; a diagram of their interrelationship is shown in Figure 9-2. A similar situation exists for Shope papilloma virus (Crawford, 1964a; Crawford and Waring, 1967).

The molecular weight of polyoma viral DNA was determined by ultracentrifugation (Crawford, 1964b) and by measuring the length of the molecules (Weil and Vinograd, 1963). These molecules averaged 1.55 μ long, which corresponds to 3.0×10^6 daltons. (Double-stranded DNA, with the bases in the B-configuration, has a molecular weight of 1.92×10^6 daltons per micron.) Assuming 300 as the average molecular weight of a nucleotide residue, calculations reveal that polyoma viral DNA has about 10,000 residues or about 5000 base pairs. An average polypeptide chain has perhaps 200 to 250 amino acid residues; a coding ratio of 3:1 means that 600 to 750 base pairs are required to code for such polypeptide chains. Therefore, polyoma viral DNA could contain about six to eight genes. The number corresponds roughly to the number of binding sites for RNA polymerase, so each gene may bind a molecule of the enzyme (Crawford *et al.*, 1965; Pettijohn and Kamiya, 1967). At least one gene undoubtedly codes for

Figure 9-3.   An electron micrograph of equine abortion virus DNA. Both ends of the molecule are present, showing that it is not cyclic. The contour length is 48 μ. (Soehner *et al.*, 1965. By permission of the authors and the editor of Virology.)

capsid protein, but possibly only one, since electrophoresis detects only one species of capsid protein (Thorne and Warden, 1967). The function of the other genes will be discussed.

The DNA of the adenoviruses is somewhat larger. Measurements of electron micrographic pictures of six human adenoviruses revealed an average length of about 12 μ, corresponding to a molecular weight of about 23×10^6 daltons (Van der Eb and Van Kesteren, 1966; Green *et al.*, 1967b). There are therefore about 50 genes. No circular forms of adenoviral DNA were observed.

Herpes simplex virus DNA has a molecular weight of about 75×10^6 daltons, determined in the ultracentrifuge (Russell and Crawford, 1964). Electron microscopy of the related equine abortion virus DNA (Fig. 9-3) revealed only linear molecules about 48 μ long, corresponding to a molecular weight of about 92×10^6 daltons (Soehner *et al.*, 1965).

Figure 9-4 shows a fowlpox virion that has discharged its DNA with only minimal chance of breakage. Both ends of the molecule can be found in the picture. Measurement of such DNA molecules revealed an average length of about 100 μ or 190×10^6 daltons (Hyde *et al.*, 1967; Gafford and Randall, 1967). This value, although slightly higher, is in the same range as the molecular weight of rabbitpox DNA

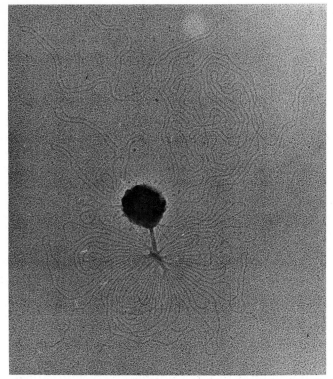

Figure 9-4. An electron micrograph of a fowlpox virion that has discharged its DNA. Two ends of the DNA molecule are visible in the lower part of the picture; no other ends can be seen, indicating that the molecule probably consists of a single piece. The DNA appears to have been extruded from a tail-like appendage. (Magnification ×85,000.) (Hyde and Randall, 1966. By permission of the authors and the editor of the Journal of Bacteriology.)

(Joklik, 1962) and vaccinia virus DNA (Easterbrook, 1967; Sarov and Becker, 1967; McCrea and Lipman, 1967), each with about 160×10^6 daltons.

It is difficult to measure the molecular weight of such long molecules because breakage during preparation is almost unavoidable and there is no simple way of calibrating the methods used for measurement. Measuring DNA molecules by electron microscopy is probably the best method, as the amount of manipulation can be kept to a minimum. It is also possible to select and measure only the longest molecules, as they are the least likely to have been broken.

ONE-STEP GROWTH

The cells in which animal viruses replicate are usually grown in a single layer on the bottom of a culture vessel and covered with liquid nutrient medium, or they may be grown in suspension. Cells can be maintained in continuous propagation, or they can be freshly established from animals. In the latter case, the cells that grow in the culture often are a heterogeneous mixture with different capabilities of sustaining a viral infection.

Growth curves for animal viruses are obtained in essentially the same way as for bacterial viruses. The virus suspension is added to the culture and a time period is allowed for virus particles to adsorb to the cells. After the time allowed for the adsorption, the cells are rinsed with buffer to remove unadsorbed virus. Then nutrient medium is added and the cultures are incubated. The supernatant medium is assayed periodically for released virus. The cells are removed from the culture and plated to determine how many are infectious centers. The content of intracellular virus during the cycle is measured by disrupting the cells and assaying the released virus.

Because of several problems, it is more difficult to perform growth curve experiments with animal viruses than with bacterial viruses. Sometimes only a small proportion of cells in the culture are productively infected. Often a substantial quantity of unadsorbed virus remains loosely attached to the cells and it is difficult to delineate the eclipse phase. Another problem is that some of the released virus adsorbs to cellular debris and does not register as a plaque when assayed. Consequently, careful experimental technique and care in interpreting results are as necessary with animal viruses as with bacterial viruses.

Examples of some growth curves are shown in Figure 9-5. An eclipse period is not so obvious in these experiments as it was in the case of the T-even phages. Presumably, this is because of the unavoidably large residual of unadsorbed virus, rather than because of the lack of an eclipse period. After a latent period, there is a rise period, followed by a plateau reached when the infected cells have died and released their virus.

Several features distinguish these growth curves from those of the T-even phages. The most obvious is that the time scale is in hours, rather than minutes. Vaccinia virus has one of the shortest growth cycles of any animal DNA-containing virus. Polyoma virus and adenovirus have much longer cycles. Perhaps the longest occurs with the human cytomegalovirus (McAllister *et al.*, 1963); the latent period ends about 50 hours after infection and the rise time ends about 80 hours after the beginning of the cycle.

Another difference is the extended rise period. This is due not only to heterogeneity of cycle length but also to the fact that virus is released from the cell gradually rather than in a burst as with the phages.

The yield of infectious particles per cell is quite variable from one

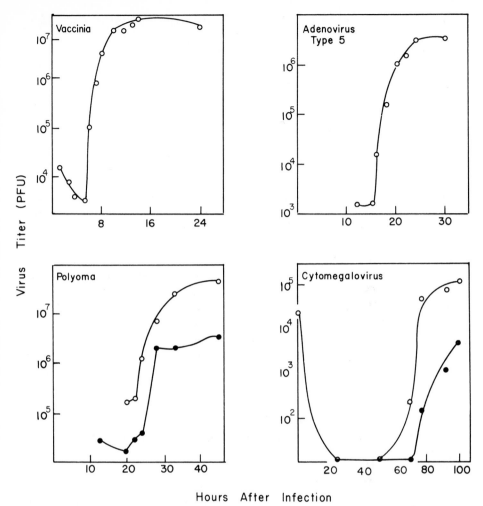

Figure 9-5. Growth curves of representative DNA-containing animal viruses in cultured cells. The curves for vaccinia and adenovirus type 5 show total virus yield from intracellular and extracellular virus. For polyoma virus, the upper curve (open circles) is total virus and the lower curve (filled circles) is extracellular virus. For human cytomegalovirus, the upper curve (open circles) is cell-associated virus and the lower curve (filled circles) is extracellular virus. (Vaccinia: Salzman *et al.*, 1964. Adenovirus type 5: Flanagan and Ginsberg, 1964. Polyoma: Winocour and Sachs, 1960. Cytomegalovirus: McAllister *et al.*, 1963.)

system to another. Since most virions are not infectious, the number of virions produced by each cell may be quite high. It has been estimated, for example, that a cell infected with an adenovirus may produce 10^5 to 2×10^5 virions (Green, 1962b). A bacterial cell is smaller than an animal cell, and the T-even phage it produces is larger than the adenoviruses. When adjusted for these differences, the amount of viral material produced in each case is about the same for equivalent volumes of cell.

A further difference is that a high proportion of the virions is intracellular. This is shown by the growth curves, since the "total virus" curve is higher than the "released virus" curve.

It will be useful to follow the growth cycle through to examine the events that occur at each stage.

ADSORPTION, PENETRATION, AND UNCOATING

The first stage of infection by animal viruses occurs by the same process as with bacteriophages: Virus and cell come together by the forces of simple diffusion. Initial attachment of virus to cell (reviewed by A. Cohen, 1963; Dales, 1965a; and Philipson, 1963) probably involves reversible electrostatic forces.

Receptors on the cell surface to which the virus attaches have been studied chiefly for the myxovirus group. These RNA-containing viruses will be discussed in a later chapter. Receptor activity of cells for the DNA viruses under discussion in this chapter has been studied chiefly for polyoma virus. The cell receptors for polyoma virus seem to be closely related to those for influenza virus, whether the receptors are on host cells or on red blood cells that can be agglutinated by either virus. This is known because neuraminidase (an enzyme occurring in extracts of *Vibrio cholera*) will remove receptors for either virus, rendering the cells immune to virus infection (Rowe, 1961; Helgeland, 1966). Crawford (1962) found that treatment of infected cell debris with neuraminidase released polyoma virus, suggesting that it had been adsorbed to receptors in the debris.

Animal viruses are not known to have any special attachment organs or systems for entering the cell. Instead, animal viruses are actively engulfed by the cell by a process called *viropexis* (Fazekas de St. Groth, 1948). This process is similar or identical to pinocytosis, the mechanism by which a cell "drinks" many of its nutrients, and viral entry may be an accident. In any event, during pinocytosis, or viropexis, the cytoplasmic membrane folds inward into the cell, forming a vacuole containing the virus particles (Dales, 1963a; Dales and Kajioka, 1964). A vaccinia virion is shown in such a vacuole in Figure 9-6; another virion is still outside the cytoplasmic membrane.

That the nucleic acid of animal viruses is sufficient for replication of complete virus was shown by the following type of experiment, done, for instance, with polyoma virus (Di Mayorca *et al.*, 1959; Weil, 1961): The viral protein coat is removed from the nucleic acid by treating a virus preparation with phenol. If the extracted, purified DNA is added to mouse embryo cell cultures under conditions that ordi-

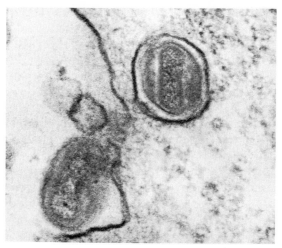

Figure 9-6.   Two vaccinia virions entering a cell. The vertical line in the center of the picture is the cytoplasmic membrane. To the left of the membrane, outside the cell, is a virion becoming attached. The virion to the right of the membrane has been enveloped by the cell in a vesicle, as evidenced by the cytoplasmic membrane that surrounds it. Strictly speaking, the virion still lies outside the cell. (Dales, 1963a. By permission of the author and the editor of the Journal of Cell Biology.)

narily would enable infection to take place with whole virus, the cells are not infected. But if the viral DNA is added to the cells after they are rinsed with hypertonic saline, they undergo a normal infective cycle and produce complete infectious virus particles (with a protein coat). This experiment shows that the DNA of the virus is sufficient to cause the infection of a cell with the production of complete infectious virions. Similar experiments using SV40 and monkey cells gave similar results (Gerber, 1962).

Under ordinary conditions, the protein coat as well as the nucleic acid of the virus enters the cell. As will be discussed later, this seems to be true for all animal viruses. However, once the virion is within the cell, the protein moiety seems to play no further role in the infection.

The process by which the coat is removed from the virion, releasing the DNA into the cytoplasm where it begins its functional role, has been studied in most detail with the poxviruses.

The poxviruses are structurally relatively complex, consisting of the nucleic acid core surrounded by at least two layers of protein and lipid. Careful treatment of extracellular virions has resulted in removal of the coat, layer by layer (Easterbrook, 1966). The DNA was not, however, set free in these studies. In other experiments, with fowlpox virus, when detergent was used to remove the outer lipid-containing layer, the remaining virions were weakened so that dialysis against distilled water released the DNA (Hyde and Randall, 1966). When supported in a protein film and shadowed from all directions, the DNA from this virus appeared as shown in the electron micrograph in Figure 9-4. Not only is the DNA molecule spread, but it seems to have come from one part of the particle, perhaps corresponding to the tail of the phages. If so, it is the only known example of this among the animal viruses.

However, what is accomplished extracellularly, by experimental manipulation, is not necessarily what happens intracellularly. Some of the most extensive work on the uncoating process was done by Joklik (1964a, 1964b). He used highly purified rabbitpox virus that had been labeled in the nucleic acid by C^{14}-thymidine or in the nucleic acid and phospholipid by P^{32}. The susceptibility of the labeled DNA to the action of deoxyribonuclease was used as an index of uncoating. This is a valid test, since the DNA in extracellular, coated virus is not susceptible to the action of the enzyme.

The plan in his experiments was to infect cells with the labeled virus and to disrupt the cells at various times after infection. Aliquots were then assayed for radioactivity in DNA and for susceptibility of DNA to the action of deoxyribonuclease. The results are summarized in Figure 9-7. Under the conditions of this experiment, phospholipid is released from the virions without appreciable delay after infection. There is, however, an appreciable delay in the release of the DNA. Virtually 100 per cent of the phospholipid is released, but at most only about 60 per cent of the viral DNA molecules become susceptible to deoxyribonuclease. Thus, uncoating with this virus occurs in two stages.

Joklik also found that increasing the multiplicity of infection shortened the lag in uncoating. In fact, when he infected cells with unlabeled virus before adding labeled virus, the lag was abolished completely. Inhibition of the second stage of uncoating resulted when puromycin and fluorophenylalanine (inhibitors of protein synthesis) or actinomycin D (an inhibitor of messenger RNA synthesis) was added to the medium.

At the time, the best explanation for Joklik's experiments was that a protein released from the virion in the first stage of uncoating derepressed a host-cell gene; the gene then directed the synthesis of a messenger RNA, and the synthesis of an uncoating enzyme resulted. Such a scheme would explain the lag in uncoating and the shortening of the lag by preinfection, since the cell would then already be synthesizing the uncoating enzyme. The inhibition of the second stage of uncoating by inhibitors of protein or messenger RNA synthesis would also be explained, since synthesis of both these macromolecules would be necessary for the expression of the cell's derepressed gene.

An alternate explanation, however, was made possible by experi-

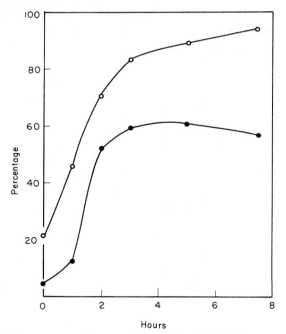

Figure 9-7. Two stages of uncoating poxvirus DNA. The upper curve (open circles) shows release of P^{32} in viral phospholipid, and the lower curve (filled circles) shows sensitization of viral DNA to deoxyribonuclease. The release of phospholipid proceeds without delay, whereas there is a 1 to 2 hour lag in sensitization of viral DNA to deoxyribonuclease. (Joklik, 1964a.)

ments reported by Woodson (1967). His experiments indicated that the viral DNA, while still coated and not susceptible to deoxyribonuclease, began directing the synthesis of messenger RNA. Woodson infected cells with vaccinia virus that had been inactivated with ultraviolet light; such virus does not undergo the second stage of uncoating (Joklik, 1964c). A burst of messenger RNA activity occurred in the first hour after infection with inactivated vaccinia virus. The messenger RNA had the base composition that would be expected if it had been coded for by the vaccinia DNA. Thus, it is not necessary to postulate the derepression of a host-cell gene, since the synthesis of the uncoating enzyme could be entirely coded for by the virus. Similar results, reported by Kates and McAuslan (1967b) and Munyon *et al.* (1967), showed that intact vaccinia virions can synthesize RNA in an in vitro test reaction.

Furthermore, Woodson (1967) also showed that the synthesis of the messenger RNA did not depend on protein synthesis: The messenger RNA was synthesized in cells whose protein synthesis had been shut off by metabolic inhibitors. Therefore, synthesis of early messenger RNA must use preëxisting DNA-dependent RNA polymerase.

The stages of poxvirus uncoating have been seen in the electron microscope (Fig. 9-8). First the outer coat of the virus and the vacuolar membrane disappear. Later, the particle ejects its DNA, leaving an empty shell.

Another of the poxviruses, fowlpox, has also been seen in electron micrographs where the fixation procedure has "frozen" a virion as it was being engulfed into a cell in vacuoles (Arhelger and Randall, 1964). Human adenovirus type 7 (Dales, 1962a, 1962b) and herpes simplex virus (Epstein *et al.*, 1964; Holmes and Watson, 1963) apparently enter cells by the same mechanism, and early stages of the removal of virus capsid material have been photographed. The adeno-virion seems to be only partially opened by removal of some protein before the DNA begins to function (Philipson, 1967; Sussenbach, 1967).

Comparison shows a great similarity in entry and uncoating with these different virus systems. Only with viruses of the pox group, however, has evidence been obtained that a special enzyme may be involved in uncoating. Uncoating of adenovirus occurs in cells in which protein synthesis is blocked (Lawrence and Ginsberg, 1967), showing that new enzyme synthesis is not required. Protein capsids of the polyoma and herpes groups of viruses may also be removed by proteolytic enzymes present in the cell prior to infection. This seems

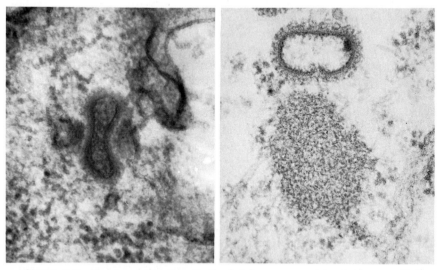

Figure 9-8. Poxvirus uncoating. In the left frame, a poxvirion is shown with the outer layer removed. In the right frame, the poxvirus appears to have ejected its DNA (the large mass below the empty shell) through the pore into the cytoplasm of the cells. (Dales, 1965a, 1965b. By permission of the author and the editors of Progress in Medical Virology and the Proceedings of the National Academy of Sciences.)

especially likely to be the case with polyoma, a virus that has a small amount of genetic material and therefore can code for only a few proteins. It would seem most economical for the virus not to carry the gene for this enzyme if it could survive by using a host-cell enzyme.

After being uncoated, the viral genetic material is transported to the intracellular site where it will multiply. The poxviruses have no problem in this regard, as their site of replication seems to be entirely confined to cytoplasmic "factories." At least, both DNA synthesis and viral antigen occur in the same well-localized area of the cytoplasm, and there is one such area for each infectious particle that enters the cell (Cairns, 1960). Herpes simplex virus, polyoma virus, adenovirus, and presumably all their related viruses replicate in the nucleus of the cell. How the incoming viral particle or its nucleic acid is transported to the nucleus of the cell is not known.

THE LATENT PERIOD

The major difference between the latent period for animal viruses and for bacteriophages lies in the time scale. This is not surprising, perhaps, because the generation time is much longer for animal cells (12 to 36 hours for cells in cultures) than for bacterial cells (20 to 60 minutes). Perhaps some of the factors that cause animal cells to divide more slowly than bacterial cells may also influence the replicative cycle of their respective viruses. In any event, during the replicative cycle, animal viruses cause the production of new kinds of RNA in the infected cell, new enzymes and other proteins, such as viral capsid proteins, are synthesized, and the DNA of the virus replicates in a semiconservative fashion. The experimental evidence supporting these statements will now be discussed.

RNA

As is true with phage, DNA-containing animal viruses cannot replicate until RNA synthesis occurs. This was shown, for instance, by Flanagan and Ginsberg (1964) for human adenovirus type 5. It is also true for vaccinia (Shatkin, 1963a).

It is interesting to compare the postinfection time course of viral-specific RNA production of animal viruses with that in phage-infected bacteria. It will be recalled that within 2 minutes after infection with the T-even phages, it is possible to detect the viral-specific messenger RNA. Vaccinia virus is a relatively rapid animal virus in this regard, as the new viral-specific RNA is detectable within an hour after infection (Loh, 1964; Woodson, 1967; Oda and Joklik, 1967). It was not detectable until about 8 hours after infection of cells with human adeno-

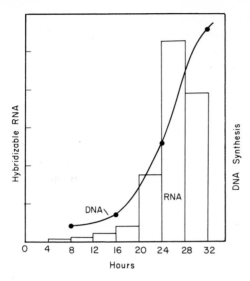

Figure 9-9. Synthesis of viral-specific RNA in polyoma-infected cells. Shown are the relative amounts of pulse-labeled RNA hybridized to polyoma DNA after infection of mouse kidney cells by polyoma virus. Also shown is DNA synthesis, measured by uptake of C^{14}-thymidine in similarly infected cells. Both ordinate scales are in arbitrary units. (Redrawn from Benjamin, 1966.)

virus type 5 (Flanagan and Ginsberg, 1964), about 5 hours after infection with herpes simplex virus (Hay *et al.*, 1966; Flanagan, 1967), and about 4 hours after infection with polyoma virus (Benjamin, 1966). In some cases, the messenger RNA was detected by hybridizing to viral DNA; the amount that was present correlates well with the amount of viral DNA that had been synthesized in the infected cells (Fig. 9-9). Thus, the promptness of onset of messenger RNA synthesis seems to be correlated with the duration of the replicative cycle. There is a demonstrable difference between "early" and "late" messenger RNA (Sebring and Salzman, 1967).

Of interest is the possibility that herpes simplex virus may induce the synthesis of a transfer RNA as well as the messenger RNA required for virus-specific protein synthesis (Subak-Sharpe and Hay, 1965). Thus, not all viral genes need be accounted for by the new proteins synthesized.

The new RNA in vaccinia-infected cells has a rapid turnover (Salzman *et al.*, 1964; Shatkin *et al.*, 1965) and a base composition resembling that of viral DNA rather than that of cellular DNA (Salzman *et al.*, 1964). That the base sequence of the new RNA, as well as the base composition, resembles viral DNA has been shown for polyoma virus (Benjamin, 1966) and herpes simplex virus (Hay *et al.*, 1966) because specific hybridization is demonstrable between the RNA and viral DNA.

Messenger RNA is known to string ribosomes together to form a polysome, which is the actual protein synthesizing complex (Warner *et al.*, 1962; Scharff *et al.*, 1963). The length of a polysome is directly related to the length of the messenger RNA: The longer the message, the larger the polysome and the larger the protein. Polysomes can be sorted out by length (or by number of ribosomes making up the polysome) by centrifuging a cytoplasmic extract of the cells through a solution of sucrose that increases in concentration toward the bottom of the centrifuge tube. Scharff *et al.* (1963) analyzed cytoplasmic extracts of vaccinia-infected cells in this way and found that several kinds of messenger RNA molecules were present; these polysomes synthesized protein antigenically similar to the protein of vaccinia particles. Thus, it is concluded that the various genes of vaccinia virus are expressed in the infected cell and that these associate with ribosomes to form polysomes that synthesize viral proteins.

The nature of the messenger RNA specified by vaccinia virus changes through the course of infection (Becker and Joklik, 1964). Soon after infection, the first new messenger RNA molecules appear. These are shorter than messenger RNA molecules synthesized later in the cycle. Presumably, the change in size of the messenger reflects some mechanism by which synthesis of messenger RNA is regulated. Such regulation would seem to be necessary, since not all proteins are needed for virus synthesis at the same time.

Proteins

In phage-infected cells, two main classes of viral specific proteins arise: enzyme proteins that are concerned with phage replication ("early" proteins) and phage structural proteins that become parts of the completed phage particle ("late" proteins).

A similar situation exists for the four DNA-containing animal viruses described here. For instance, Loh and Riggs (1961) made antisera against different antigenic components of vaccinia virus and demonstrated that each component appeared in the infected cell at a different time after infection. Similarly, Wilcox and Cohen (1967) made antisera against soluble (small) and viral (large) antigens from infected cells. The soluble antigens precede the viral antigens in time of appearance (Fig. 9-10). That some of the first proteins to appear in infected cells are enzymes has also been well documented.

As in phage-infected cells, most of the new enzymes to appear in cells infected by DNA-containing animal viruses are those concerned with DNA synthesis.

Thymidine kinase has been extensively studied. The activity of this enzyme increases following infection with viruses of the pox group (Kit *et al.*, 1962; Kit *et al.*, 1963b; McAuslan, 1963a, 1963b; Green *et al.*, 1964). The increase reaches a maximum at about 6 hours after infection, when the enzyme is "repressed" and no longer in-

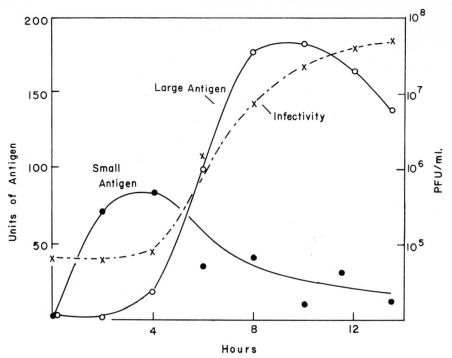

Figure 9-10. Synthesis of large and small antigens in vaccinia virus-infected cells. Each was measured as the amount of C¹⁴-labeled antigen from infected cells that was precipitated by antisera prepared against low molecular weight (small) antigens or high molecular weight (large) antigens. Also shown is the vaccinia virus growth curve in these cells. (Wilcox and Cohen, 1967.)

creases in activity. The repression does not occur if the virus has been inactivated by ultraviolet light (McAuslan, 1963a, 1963b).

Increased thymidine kinase activity in vaccinia-infected cells is inhibited by chemicals that block protein synthesis, suggesting that increased activity requires synthesis of new enzyme molecules (Kit *et al.*, 1963a). DNA synthesis is not required, but the DNA must be able to transcribe messenger RNA for the enzyme activity to appear (Kit *et al.*, 1963c).

Further work (Kit and Dubbs, 1965) has provided more convincing evidence that vaccinia virus induces an enzyme not present in uninfected cells. Thymidine kinase was obtained in partially purified form from uninfected cells and vaccinia virus-infected cells. The enzyme from infected cells was much more stable to thermal inactivation, lasting about 10 times as long as the enzyme from uninfected cells. The enzymes from the two sources also differed in their substrate specificity.

Perhaps the best experiment showing that the vaccinia-induced enzyme is actually a new protein was serologic in nature (Kit and Dubbs, 1965). Antiserum was prepared against partially purified enzyme preparations from uninfected cells and from vaccinia virus-infected cells. Antiserum against enzyme from uninfected cells inhibited that enzyme activity but not the activity of enzyme from infected cells, whereas antiserum prepared using infected-cell enzyme as antigen had the opposite specificity. Furthermore, mutants of vaccinia have been isolated that are unable to induce the synthesis of thymidine kinase (Dubbs and Kit, 1964a). The bulk of the evidence, therefore, is consistent with the conclusion that the increase of thymidine kinase activity in vaccinia-infected cells is due to synthesis of a new enzyme protein not present in the uninfected cell.

A similar situation seems to occur with herpes simplex virus and other viruses of its group. Thymidine kinase is induced by herpes simplex virus in mutant cells that lack the enzyme (Kit and Dubbs, 1963a). Increase in this enzyme is prevented by compounds that block transcription of DNA into messenger RNA (Borman and Roizman, 1965; Kit and Dubbs, 1963b) or that block protein synthesis, and mutants of the virus have been isolated that are unable to cause the increase of enzyme activity (Kit and Dubbs, 1963b; Dubbs and Kit, 1964b).

It is of interest that the mutant viruses fell into three classes, based on the properties of the enzymes induced; in one case, the induction of the enzyme was shown to differ in its temperature dependence from the induction by the other classes of mutants (Dubbs and Kit, 1965).

Thymidine kinase from herpesvirus-infected cells resembled enzyme from noninfected cells in temperature stability (Kit and Dubbs, 1965) but differed in interaction with its substrate and with its products (Klemperer et al., 1967). Enzyme from infected cells differs serologically from that of uninfected cells; the serologic difference has been shown for herpes simplex virus (Klemperer et al., 1967) and for a close relative, pseudorabies virus (Hamada et al., 1966).

Infection of monkey kidney cells by human adenovirus type 2 (Ledinko, 1966) or by simian adenoviruses (Kit et al., 1965a) results in an increase in thymidine kinase activity. The enzyme reaches peak levels about 50 hours after infection (multiplication of human adenovirus is greatly slowed in monkey kidney cells) and differs slightly biochemically from the enzyme in noninfected cells. Furthermore, blockage of protein synthesis prevented the increase in enzyme activity (Ledinko, 1966). A similar stimulation of thymidine kinase occurs in human cells infected with adenoviruses (Ledinko, 1967).

These results differ from those previously reported (Green et al., 1964) in that Green and his associates found no increase in thymidine kinase. The difference in results may be a result of the fact that the negative results were obtained in KB cells. These cells were originally derived from a human carcinoma and are quite abnormal in many of their properties; for example, they have a higher normal background of enzyme activity. In contrast, synthesis of cellular thymidine kinase is repressed in fully grown cultures of monkey kidney cells (Ledinko, 1966).

Thymidine kinase activity also decreases when mouse fibroblast cultures become fully grown and cease dividing (Kit *et al.*, 1965b; Dulbecco *et al.*, 1965). In such cultures, enzyme activity is enhanced about 5- to 20-fold by infection with polyoma virus (Dulbecco *et al.*, 1965; Kit *et al.*, 1966a; Frearson *et al.*, 1965; Kára and Weil, 1967; Hartwell *et al.*, 1965). Thymidine kinase activity does not increase by infection with polyoma virus in mutant cells that lack the enzyme (Littlefield and Basilico, 1966).

Limited study of its properties indicated that thymidine kinase from polyoma-infected cells did not differ from that of uninfected cells (Kit *et al.*, 1966a). More extensive study, however, showed some slight differences in biochemical properties between enzymes from infected and from uninfected cells (Sheinin, 1966), so it is probably a new enzyme. The closely related virus SV40 also causes an increase of thymidine kinase in infected cells (Kit *et al.*, 1966a, 1966c), and there is a significant difference in its biochemical properties from the enzyme in uninfected cells and from the enzyme induced by polyoma virus (Hatanaka and Dulbecco, 1967).

Thus, it appears that the viruses of the four groups discussed here cause an increase in thymidine kinase activity because of the synthesis of a new enzyme. It will be recalled that, although some kinases increase in bacterial cells infected by T-even phages, thymidine kinase is not one of these. The difference in metabolism between animal and bacterial cells that is reflected in these different enzyme inductions is obscure.

Thymidylate is formed both by phosphorylation of thymidine (catalyzed by thymidine kinase) and by methylation of deoxyuridylate monophosphate (catalyzed by thymidylate synthetase). Cells infected with either vaccinia virus or herpes simplex virus do not have an increase in thymidylate synthetase activity. Polyoma virus-infected cells, on the other hand, have about a twofold increase in enzyme activity (Frearson *et al.*, 1965), as do SV40-infected cells (Kit *et al.*, 1966c).

Other kinases have also been studied. Deoxyuridine kinase activity increases following infection by herpes simplex and vaccinia viruses, but this enzyme activity is probably due to nonspecificity of thymidine kinase action (Kit and Dubbs, 1963b). Thymidylate kinase increases in stationary-phase mouse kidney cells after infection with

SV40 (Kit *et al.*, 1966c) and polyoma virus (Kit *et al.*, 1966a; Kára and Weil, 1967). SV40 also causes a slight increase in thymidylate kinase activity in kidney cells from the African green monkey (Kit *et al.*, 1966b). Green *et al.* (1964) reported that vaccinia and adenoviruses do not cause an increase in thymidylate kinase, but Magee (1962) found that vaccinia virus did cause an increase. (The different results are probably due to the type of cell used.) Pseudorabies virus causes an increase in thymidylate kinase (Nohara and Kaplan, 1963) that has been shown clearly, by serologic tests, to be a new protein (Hamada *et al.*, 1966).

It seems well established that deoxyguanylate kinase, deoxycytidylate kinase, and deoxyadenylate kinase do not increase after infection with adenovirus (Green *et al.*, 1964), with vaccinia virus (Green *et al.*, 1964; Magee, 1962), or with pseudorabies virus (Hamada *et al.*, 1966). Polyoma virus, on the other hand, causes a slight increase in deoxycytidylate kinase activity but no increase in deoxyadenylate or deoxyguanylate kinase activities (Kára and Weil, 1967).

Polyoma virus and SV40 also increase the activity of deoxycytidylate deaminase (which catalyzes the conversion of deoxycytidylate to deoxyuridylate, which in turn becomes the substrate for thymidylate synthetase) (Kára and Weil, 1967; Dulbecco *et al.*, 1965; Hartwell *et al.*, 1965; Kit *et al.*, 1967a) and cytidine diphosphate reductase (which catalyzes the conversion of ribose to deoxyribose of cytidine diphosphate) (Kára and Weil, 1967). Dihydrofolate reductase activity is induced by both polyoma virus and SV40 (Frearson *et al.*, 1966). The function of nucleases induced in infected cells is not clear (McAuslan *et al.*, 1965; McAuslan and Kates, 1966, 1967).

A key enzyme concerned with DNA synthesis, DNA polymerase is also increased following infection. (Polyoma virus—Dulbecco *et al.*, 1965; Hartwell *et al.*, 1965. SV40—Kit *et al.*, 1966c; Chang and Hodes, 1967. Vaccinia virus—Hanafusa, 1961; Green and Piña, 1962; Green *et al.*, 1964; Kates and McAuslan, 1967a. Herpes simplex virus—Keir and Gold, 1963.) DNA polymerase was reported not to increase in activity in adenovirus-infected KB cells (Green *et al.*, 1964).

It has been demonstrated biochemically and serologically that the increase in DNA polymerase activity caused by some viruses is due to a new enzyme rather than to an increase of cellular enzyme. (Vaccinia virus—Magee and Miller, 1967. Herpes simplex virus—Keir *et al.*, 1966a, 1966b. Pseudorabies virus—Hamada *et al.*, 1966. SV40—Kit *et al.*, 1967c.) Of particular interest will be the determination of whether these new DNA polymerases have greater specificity for the viral DNA that induced them than for other kinds of DNA, such as that of the cell.

The end result of the increased activity of the enzymes concerned with DNA synthesis is an increase in DNA synthesis itself. This is the result that might be predicted if changes are to be to the advantage of the virus. Many of the enzymes, however, are not specific, in the sense that the product of the reaction they catalyze can be used in the synthesis of any kind of DNA. If the amount of thymidine kinase activity is a regulator of the rate of DNA synthesis, its increase would be expected to increase cellular as well as viral DNA synthesis. An increase in cellular DNA synthesis occurs in stationary phase cells infected with polyoma virus, SV40, pseudorabies virus, vaccinia virus, and adenoviruses; but the DNA synthesized may not be normal (Ben-Porat et al., 1966). (References to the extensive literature are given by Kit et al., 1966a). Suppression of DNA synthesis in stationary cells could be due to repression of synthesis of thymidine kinase; viral-induced enzyme could thus release the DNA synthetic mechanism. It is of interest that the polyoma viral genome must be intact for the induction of host-cell DNA synthesis (Basilico et al., 1966). In actively growing cultures, there is no stimulation of cellular DNA synthesis by viral infection (see Kit et al., 1966a, for references).

It is obvious that there is much more to be learned about the enzymes induced in cells by the DNA-containing animal viruses. For example, polyoma virus, a virus with a limited number of genes, causes detectable changes in infected cells. Some of the enhanced enzymes seem to be new proteins and are therefore probably coded by polyoma DNA; others may be derepressed host-cell enzymes. By the latter mechanism, a single viral gene could alter the function of more than one host-cell gene. Some such mechanism may be operative when polyoma virus undergoes a malignant interaction with its host cell, rather than the productive interaction discussed here.

DNA

Because it is possible to extract, from infected cells, RNA that is homologous in base composition to viral DNA, and because new enzyme proteins appear in infected cells during the latent period, it seems reasonable to conclude that viral DNA performs a template function for transcribing the genetic information it contains. In this regard, the DNA of these viruses does not appear to differ from that of the double-stranded DNA of the T-even phages.

Furthermore, it has been shown for vaccinia virus that the messenger RNA is transcribed directly from the incoming viral DNA without requiring synthesis of some kind of intermediate (Shatkin, 1963b). Apparently, the entire infective cycle of vaccinia virus can take place in the presence of fluorodeoxyuridine, which blocks DNA synthesis. The only virions to reappear in the progeny issuing from the cells presumably contain the genome of the infecting virus particles (Easterbrook, 1963), although a few genomes may be synthesized despite the inhibitor. Vaccinia viral DNA, probably even without extensive replication, can therefore transcribe sufficient information for synthesis of enzymes and proteins to result in recoating.

This experiment is similar in some regards to the transfer experiment done with bacteriophages. It will be recalled that about 50 per cent of the label in the phage DNA that enters a cell reappears in the progeny virus. Such direct experiments have been difficult to perform with the animal viruses because of technical difficulties, largely owing to the fact that a small fraction of all particles present actually result in successful infection. Here, however, under the abnormal circumstances of blocked DNA synthesis, transfer has apparently occurred. Whether transfer occurs under normal circumstances in any of the DNA-containing animal viruses is not yet known.

Semiconservative replication has been demonstrated, however, for polyoma virus (Hirt, 1966) and for pseudorabies virus (Kaplan and Ben-Porat, 1964). In both cases bromodeoxyuridine was used to increase the density of newly synthesized DNA strands. DNA of an infected cell could, therefore, be separated by density gradient analysis in the ultracentrifuge into light parental molecules containing no bromodeoxyuridine, hybrid molecules with one light and one heavy strand, and molecules with both strands of increased density. It may, perhaps, be premature to generalize from these limited experiments, but it appears that the replication of the DNA of the animal viruses will not present any new features not already known for other kinds of DNA.

EFFECTS OF INFECTION ON THE HOST CELL

During the time that synthesis of viral components is proceeding in the infected cell, the cell undergoes characteristic changes. These changes are usually observed in tissue culture where infection of the cells is more easily synchronized and where the cells can be observed repeatedly during the course of infection.

In unstained, living cultures, infected cells often become rounded and develop an increased refractility. This cytopathic effect (CPE) is used as an index of the state of infection of a culture. With some viruses, the morphologic changes in the infected cells are of diagnostic importance because they are so characteristic. Cytopathic effect usually occurs as an infected cell enters the last stages of the infective cycle, although there are instances in which it occurs very soon after infection, before any virus has been replicated.

Fixing and staining the cells for observation with either the light microscope or the electron microscope allows more detailed observation of the morphological changes a cell undergoes during infection. Many such studies have been made; the literature on the cytology of virus-infected cells is quite voluminous. Most such studies have been descriptive. Little effort has been made to relate the morphological changes to the events in the viral replicative cycle and to the molecular mechanisms for the changes.

One kind of morphological change occurring in infected cells is the formation of inclusion bodies. These take various forms depending on the kind of virus that infects the cell rather than on the cell type that is infected. Inclusions formed in cells in living animals are usually morphologically the same as those that occur in cells in culture.

The poxviruses produce cytoplasmic inclusions in infected cells. These inclusions are the site of viral DNA synthesis and the site of viral antigen (presumably coat protein) accumulation (Cairns, 1960). Because the inclusions of poxviruses are the site of synthesis of at least some virus parts and of assembly of virions, they are called "factories." There is one such factory for each virion that successfully initiates infection.

The inclusions induced by fowlpox virus have been isolated and examined by electron microscopy (Randall *et al.*, 1961). The inclusions consist of a matrix material containing randomly scattered virus particles. The inclusion is not surrounded by a detectable membrane structure. Inclusions have also been separated from cells infected with vaccinia virus (Joklik and Becker, 1964), and their development has been studied biochemically. The inclusions begin to be of significant size about 1.5 hours after infection, but their major increase in size occurs in the period 2 to 4 hours after infection.

The morphological changes due to infection by adenoviruses, on the other hand, occur chiefly in the nucleus. Extensive studies of the development of inclusions produced in cells infected by types 1 through 7 have indicated that two kinds of inclusions may form (Boyer *et al.*, 1957; Boyer *et al.*, 1959). Those formed by types 1, 2, 5, and 6 are distinctly different from those formed by types 3, 4, and 7.

From 14 to 16 hours after infection by adenovirus types 1, 2, 5, or 6, multiple, separate, eosinophilic bodies appear in the nucleus. At first these bodies contain no DNA (they do not stain by the Feulgen reaction, a specific cytochemical stain for DNA). Later, they develop Feulgen-positive cores; the bodies merge into a dense mass, leaving the remainder of the nucleus (also Feulgen positive) glassy in appearance. A picture of a human fetal fibroblast cell infected with adenovirus type 1 is shown in Figure 9-11. Crystals that sometimes form in the nucleus of cells infected with type 5 virus contain an unusual protein but no virus particles (Morgan *et al.*, 1957); crystals formed by

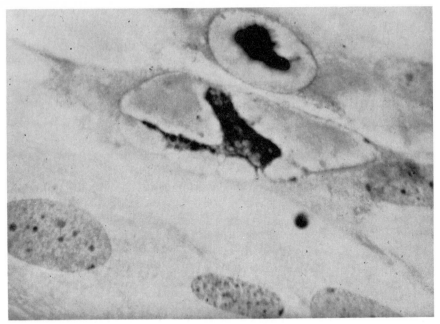

Figure 9-11. Human embryonic fibroblasts infected with human adenovirus type 1. Intranuclear inclusions are visible in the upper two cells as the darkly staining, irregularly shaped bodies. Several nuclei of normal cells are seen in the lower part of the picture. The cytoplasm is faintly stained in these cells. (Magnification ×1200.) (McAllister *et al.*, 1964a. By permission of the editor of Laboratory Investigation.)

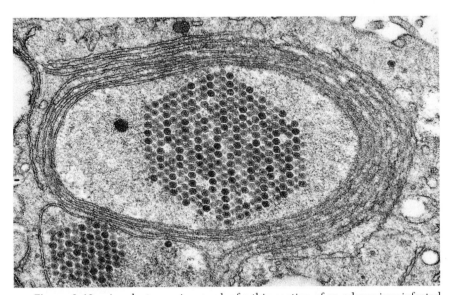

Figure 9-12. An electron micrograph of a thin section of an adenovirus-infected cell showing a crystalline array of virions surrounded by multiple layers of nuclear membrane. (Magnification ×45,000.) (Courtesy of Dr. C. Morgan.)

other adenoviruses, as shown in Figure 9-12, do contain virus particles (Morgan *et al.*, 1956).

Viruses of the herpes group will serve as a third example. All of these viruses produce intranuclear inclusions that differ somewhat from each other and differ distinctively from those produced by the adenoviruses. The inclusion, which begins developing about a third of the way through the infective cycle, is seen as an eosinophilic mass surrounded by a halo or clear space within the nucleus. The chromatin of a herpesvirus-infected cell becomes marginated or pushed to the periphery of the nucleus. Studies by autoradiography of herpes simplex virus-infected HeLa cells (Munk and Sauer, 1964) have shown that DNA synthesis occurs in the intranuclear inclusion when the tritiated thymidine is added after infection. When the tritiated thymidine is added prior to infection, the marginated chromatin is labeled but the label does not shift into the inclusion, suggesting the cellular DNA does not break down and reincorporate into virus.

Human cytomegalovirus, one of the herpes group, has been shown to form an intracytoplasmic inclusion in addition to an intranuclear inclusion (Fig. 9-13) (McAllister *et al.*, 1963). It is unusual for a single virus to form both intranuclear and intracytoplasmic inclusions in the same infected cell. Therefore, the inclusions in cells infected with the human cytomegalovirus were examined in detail. The intracytoplasmic inclusion was shown to contain DNA late in the infective cycle, after it had appeared in the intranuclear inclusion, and fluorescent-labeled antibody indicated that viral antigen was present in both inclusions. Autoradiographic studies (Goodheart *et al.*, 1964) showed that the viral DNA was synthesized in the nucleus and migrated to the cytoplasmic inclusion; no DNA synthesis was detectable in the intracytoplasmic inclusion.

Limited attempts (reviewed by Ginsberg, 1961) have been made to determine the molecular mechanism responsible for the development of cytopathic effect in infected cells. The fact that the changes observed are typical of the virus rather than the cell indicates that the effect probably is coded for by the virus. A less likely possibility is that the viral genetic material alters the function of the cellular genome in such a way that the observed changes result. One such alteration is the disaggregation of host-cell polysomes induced by herpes simplex virus (Sydiskis and Roizman, 1966, 1967), although the mechanism is still not clear. Synthesis of several host cell enzymes is inhibited by adenovirus infection; the inhibition occurs about when viral antigen is synthesized (Bello and Ginsberg, 1967), but whether this inhibition causes cytopathic effect is unknown.

In attempts to determine the mechanism by which human cytomegalovirus causes cytopathic effect and intracellular inclusions, it was found that the morphological changes could occur without the

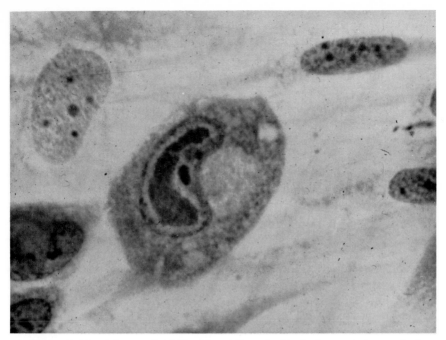

Figure 9-13. A human fetal fibroblast infected with the human cytomegalovirus. The infected cell in the center shows several features characteristic of infection with this virus: The cell seems enlarged and rounded; the cytoplasm is more darkly stained than in the uninfected neighboring cells; and the nucleus is somewhat kidney shaped, with marginated chromatin separated from the intranuclear inclusion by a pale-staining halo. The dark bodies lying in the halo are the nucleoli, and the cytoplasmic inclusion appears as a pale-staining area adjacent to the nucleus. (Magnification ×1000.) (From McAllister *et al.*: The Journal of Pediatrics, 64:278-281, 1964, The C. V. Mosby Company, St. Louis, Missouri.)

formation of infectious virus. Compounds were used that would specifically block the synthesis of certain molecules, and cytopathology occurred in cells unable to synthesize DNA or infectious virus. In other words, it was not necessary for the viral DNA to replicate for cytopathology to occur (Goodheart *et al.*, 1963; Henson and Pinkerton, 1964). However, prevention of transcription of the viral DNA by the addition of actinomycin D did prevent the formation of cytopathology. However, it was not possible in these experiments to block protein synthesis completely (McAllister *et al.*, 1967), and it is unclear whether protein synthesis is required for development of cytopathic effect.

Another kind of morphological change that occurs in viral-infected cells is the formation of giant cells or polykaryocytes; the myxoviruses commonly produce this change. Roizman, who has made an extensive study of viral-induced giant cell formation, has reviewed the subject (1962). In cell culture, giant cells usually arise by fusion of adjacent cells rather than by division of the nucleus without division of the cytoplasm. According to Roizman, a cell infected by herpes simplex virus, for instance, "recruits" neighboring cells into a polykaryocyte. The process continues in an ever-widening circle and ultimately results in a giant cell that may be visible without a microscope. Counts of such cells can serve as an assay method, similar to a plaque assay.

The formation of a giant cell after infection seems to depend on the virus rather than the cell. A given cell type will form giant cells after infection by one kind of virus but not another. As pointed out by Roizman, the viruses that are the chief causes of giant cell formation are in either the herpes group or the myxovirus group. These viruses have in common the acquisition of an envelope that consists partly of cellular material. Some viruses in the herpes group, however, do not cause polykaryocytes. Although the mechanism for giant cell formation is not known, presumably it is related somehow to alterations in the cell membrane caused by viral replication.

Another effect on the host cell occurs with viruses that can cause a cell to become malignant. The many morphological, biochemical, and growth changes in malignant cells that occur as a direct result of viral infection will be discussed in a later chapter.

MATURATION

As in phage-infected bacterial cells, the synthesis of vaccinia virus components precedes assembly of complete particles (Fig. 9-14). In the experiment shown, inhibitors of DNA or protein synthesis were added to the cultures at various intervals after infection so that no further synthesis of these components could occur. Therefore, virus yield in effect measured the amount of material that had been synthesized prior to the addition of inhibitor (Salzman *et al.*, 1963).

In other studies of poxvirus maturation, infected cells have been examined by electron microscopy. In this way it has been possible to find various forms of vaccinia (Kajioka *et al.*, 1964; Dales and Siminovitch, 1961) or Yaba (de Harven and Yohn, 1966) poxvirus particles in the cytoplasmic factories. The various particles can be arranged in an ordered sequence that probably represents the developmental stages of the virions. Some of these forms of Yaba virus are shown in the factory in Figure 9-15. Many of the presumed immature forms appear as circles. Some of the circles are incomplete; others have an outer membrane and have begun to acquire a more dense core, which later condenses. There are also several relatively mature particles containing a dumbbell-shaped core.

The poxviruses contain sufficient genetic information to code for the synthesis of many proteins. Only a few of the proteins are ac-

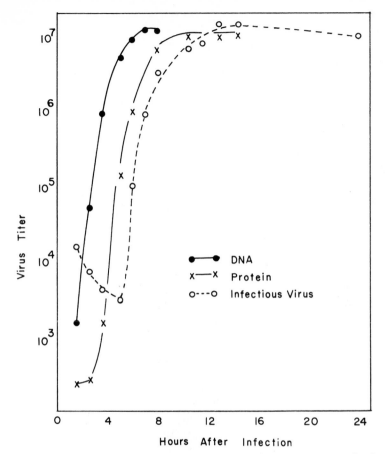

Figure 9-14. The rates of formation of vaccinia viral DNA, protein, and infectious virus. Rates of synthesis of DNA and protein were measured by adding FUdR (to block DNA synthesis) or *p*-fluorophenylalanine (to block protein synthesis) at the indicated times, and virus was harvested at 22 hours after infection. The yield of virus at each time, therefore, represents that which was made prior to the time of addition of the inhibitor. (Redrawn from Salzman *et al.*, 1963.)

counted for in the complete virions. Because of the great complexity of this virus, it is interesting to speculate that assembly may be under control of the viral genome and might require one or more specific assembly enzymes. Synthesis of the many proteins involved in vaccinia virus replication may be under genetic control, as they do not all appear to be synthesized at the same rate (Holowczak and Joklik, 1967a, 1967b).

The viruses of the polyoma-papilloma group, with their limited supply of genetic information, might be expected to rely on spontaneous processes for virion assembly. Incomplete virions lacking DNA are assembled in large quantities (Crawford *et al.*, 1962; Winocour,

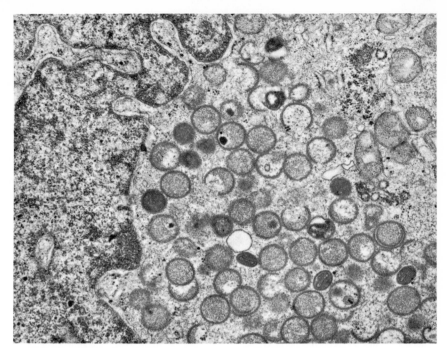

Figure 9-15. Electron micrograph of a thin section of a cell infected with Yaba virus. The cytoplasmic "factory" in the right side of the picture contains a number of virions in various stages of assembly. The circular ones are immature; some of the circles are incomplete. The center, presumably the DNA-protein core, has begun to condense in some; others have beginnings of an outer layer. Several more mature forms, with a core shaped like a dumbbell (compare with Figure 9-6), are also visible. (De Harven and Yohn, 1966. By permission of the authors and the editor of Cancer Research.)

1963). It has been shown (Gershon and Sachs, 1964) that puromycin, an inhibitor of protein synthesis, interferes with viral replication; there is a critical period about 8 or 9 hours after infection. When added 14 hours or later after infection, puromycin has less effect, indicating that the essential proteins have already been synthesized by that time. Mechanisms of assembly have not been adequately studied, and it is unknown whether an "assembly enzyme" is required.

An interesting electron microscopic study of the development of herpes simplex virus (Watson *et al.*, 1964) revealed that virions made at different times after infection differed morphologically. First, naked particles appear, then infectious particles, and finally enveloped particles. Further, these authors were unable to find any correlation between morphology and infectivity.

Roizman (1963), Roizman *et al.* (1963), and Roizman and Roane (1964) studied the time course of herpes simplex virus development and found that the various proteins are synthesized in the infected cells at different times during the cycle. Synthesis of the "early" proteins, probably enzymes, ceases when replication of viral DNA begins. This implies that a mechanism exists for determining which viral genes are to be transcribed. The nature of this mechanism, if it actually does exist, is not known. The mechanism for final assembly of the components into the finished virion is also unknown. Electron microscopy reveals that the herpes virion acquires its envelope at the nuclear membrane by a "budding" process (Darlington and Moss, 1968).

Arginine is required for maturation of both herpes simplex virus (Y. Becker *et al.*, 1967) and adenovirus type 2 (Rouse and Schlesinger, 1967). In arginine-deficient medium, viral DNA is synthesized but no virions are assembled. When arginine is added, assembly begins without delay. The role of arginine is not clear, but it is apparently required for some essential step.

RELEASE

The replicative cycle of phage-infected bacterial cells ends in a dramatic explosion, but the mechanisms by which animal cells release the virus they contain is quite different. Cell death is the end result of infection in the animal cell-virus systems discussed here, but virus release begins hours before the cell dies and is a continuous process. After the cell dies, much of the virus remains in the cell or attached to cell debris, so only a small portion may be available to infect more cells.

The discussion of the DNA-containing animal viruses in this chapter has amply demonstrated that the replicative cycle of these viruses resembles that of the T-even phages. The eclipse phase is marked by synthesis of virus-directed enzymes, and viral components are synthesized prior to assembly. The viral DNA seems to replicate semiconservatively.

In the next chapter, phages that contain single-stranded DNA will be discussed. The mechanism by which their DNA replicates is quite different from that of double-stranded DNA in that additional stages seem to be necessary. These complications preserve the Watson-Crick proposal for replication of DNA so that it applies, with modification, to the single-stranded DNA of these unusual phages.

Further Reading

Green, M.: Biosynthetic Modifications Induced by DNA Animal Viruses. Annual
    Review of Microbiology, 20:189-222, 1966.
Joklik, W. K.: The Molecular Basis of the Viral Eclipse Phase. Progress in Medical
    Virology, 7:44-96, 1965.
Joklik, W. K.: The Poxviruses. Bacteriological Reviews, 30:33-66, 1966.
Summers, D. F.: Biochemistry of Animal Virus Replication. New England Journal of
    Medicine, 276:1016-1023, 1076-1081, 1967.
Wittmann, H. G., and C. Scholtissek: Biochemistry of Viruses. Annual Review of Bio-
    chemistry, 35:299-334, 1966.

10

REPLICATION OF PHAGES CONTAINING SINGLE-STRANDED DNA

How the viruses that contain double-stranded DNA replicate has been discussed in the preceding chapters. Once in the cell, viral DNA functions and replicates in the same fashion as does cellular DNA, but since the information contained in viral DNA differs from that in cellular DNA, the cell undertakes new activities. Replication of the viral DNA does not seem to differ from that of the cell.

It might be expected that the replication of the viruses that contain single-stranded DNA might present some features that differ from the replication of the cell's own DNA and the other DNA-containing viruses. Replication of single-stranded DNA, for instance, cannot be semiconservative in the same sense that replication of double-stranded DNA is semiconservative.

We will now trace the function and replication of the single-stranded DNA phages S13 and ϕX174 replicative cycle in their host cell, *Escherichia coli*. Brief mention will also be made of several filamentous phages.

THE VIRAL DNA

It has already been stated that the DNA of these viruses is single stranded. At the time this unusual condition was first suspected, there was no precedent. Watson and Crick had described conventional DNA, but it was difficult for anyone to imagine that there might be

187

other forms. Therefore, a vast amount of evidence was gathered on the DNA of ϕX174, all of which pointed to its being single stranded.

Sinsheimer (1959a, 1959b) made an extensive study of the DNA from ϕX. By measuring light scattering of dilute solutions, he found that the DNA of ϕX has a molecular weight of 1.7×10^6 daltons and that there is one molecule per virion. He also found that the molecules were single stranded. The molecular weight therefore corresponded to about 5500 nucleotide residues.

The basis for concluding that ϕX DNA is single stranded came from the following evidence. Base analysis of the DNA showed it to contain molar ratios of 1.0 for adenine, 1.33 for thymine, 0.98 for guanine, and 0.75 for cytosine. If the DNA were double stranded, with complementary base pairing, the molar ratio of adenine should equal that of thymine, and the molar ratio of guanine should equal that of cytosine. Formaldehyde reacted with viral DNA, even when the DNA was encapsidated; this was shown by the fact that there was an increase in the absorption of ultraviolet light as the reaction progressed. This could happen only if the formaldehyde could react with the amino groups on the bases; and as these amino groups are involved in the hydrogen bonding that holds the two strands together, they would not be available for reaction if the DNA were double stranded.

The hyperchromic effect for ϕX DNA was different from that which would be expected for double-stranded DNA. Ordinarily, as the temperature of a DNA solution is increased about 75° C., its ultraviolet absorption increases rapidly as the hydrogen bonds break and the two strands separate and assume a random configuration. It is even possible to determine the molar fraction of guanine plus cytosine in a double-stranded DNA, as there is a linear dependence of the T_m or "melting temperature" (the temperature at which one half of the increase of ultraviolet absorbance has occurred) on the base composition (Marmur and Doty, 1962). With single-stranded DNA, the hyperchromic effect is gradual, without a sharp melting temperature. Finally, measurements of the light scattering indicated that the molecule was more flexible than would be expected if it were a conventional double-stranded DNA.

It was a further surprise to find that the single-stranded DNA molecule was a ring. Not only has the ring been seen by electron microscopy (Freifelder *et al.*, 1964), but Fiers and Sinsheimer (1962a, 1962b, 1962c) found that deoxyribonucleases that attack free ends of DNA (the exopolynucleotidases) cannot degrade ϕX DNA. That is, there is no free 3'-hydroxyl terminus that is susceptible to phosphodiesterase (deoxyribonuclease) prepared from *E. coli*, and there is no free 5'-hydroxyl end that is susceptible to spleen phosphodiesterase. The enzymes convert some molecules to mononucleotides, but without altering infectivity of the preparation.

This last finding is as would be expected if the preparation consisted of two components: one, an infective form, resistant to the enzymes and a second, a noninfective form, susceptible to the enzymes and therefore possessing free ends. Fiers and Sinsheimer separated the ϕX DNA into these two components by ultracentrifugation. The faster component was infective. It could be converted to the slower component by the action of pancreatic phosphodiesterase. (This enzyme attacks DNA at any point in the strand and is therefore an endonuclease.) A single hit or break in the strand was sufficient to convert the fast component to the slow form.

The ring structure of the ϕX DNA molecule differs from that of the polyoma virus DNA molecule in being single stranded. This property does not allow for supercoiling as occurs with polyoma, because the molecule is quite free to twist or untwist without constraint.

The demonstration that the molecule of ϕX DNA was single stranded and that the ring has to be intact for the molecule to be infective clarified an earlier, puzzling finding. Tessman (1959a) and Tessman et al. (1957) had observed that the decay of incorporated P^{32} inactivated S13 and ϕX174 phages much more efficiently than it did the T phages. In fact, nearly every P^{32} decay was sufficient to inactivate the S13 or ϕX particle in which it had been incorporated, whereas only one decay in 10 did so for the T phages. A single decay of a P^{32} atom in a single-stranded DNA breaks the ring, inactivating the particle, whereas both strands of a double-stranded DNA have to be broken for destruction of infectivity.

The DNA molecule of ϕX174 has been completely synthesized in a cell-free system in an infective form (Goulian et al., 1967). This achievement marks the first time that a biologically active DNA molecule was synthesized, although a similar synthesis had already been accomplished for the RNA of a phage (Chapter 11).

VIRAL PROTEIN

The protein component of ϕX174, studied by physical and biochemical means, was found to have subunits of about 25,000 daltons (Carusi and Sinsheimer, 1963). We can therefore calculate that a particle weight of 6.2×10^6 daltons, and a DNA molecule of 1.6 to 1.7×10^6 daltons, means that the capsid must be 4.5×10^6 daltons and must contain 180 such protein molecules. Each of the 12 morphological subunits or capsomers must be composed of 15 molecules.

Serologically, however, ϕX has two accessible antigenic sites and a third site that becomes accessible to antibody in the empty (70S) particles (Rolfe and Sinsheimer, 1965). Whether these sites represent different polypeptide chains or only different configurations of the same chain is not known. But biochemical analysis also indicates the presence of two distinct protein subunits (Dann-Markert *et al.*, 1966).

The DNA of φX (or S13) contains enough nucleotides to code for about eight proteins. At most, three proteins are accounted for by the capsid components. Others presumably are enzymes necessary for replicative functions. Good progress has been made in identifying the genes of S13, using genetic tests, with seven accounted for (Tessman and Tessman, 1966; Tessman *et al.*, 1967a).

REPLICATIVE CYCLE

The replicative cycle of these phages does not differ appreciably from that of other phages. As shown in Figure 10-1, there is the typical division of the curve into the latent period, with an eclipse, and the rise time, during which mature phage forms and is released. The time

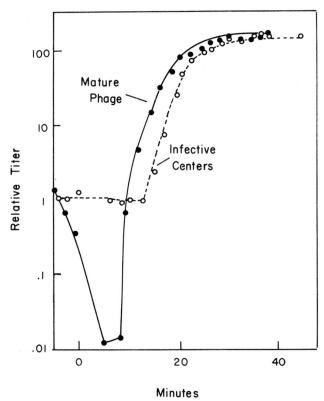

Figure 10-1.   One-step growth curve of φX174. (Redrawn from Denhardt and Sinsheimer, 1965a.)

scale is perhaps somewhat shorter than that for other phages, and the burst size is comparable.

How ϕX attaches and penetrates is not understood, since the virion has no visible tail structure or organelle for infection. Phenol-extracted DNA is infectious (Guthrie and Sinsheimer, 1963) when applied to protoplasts prepared from *E. coli* by removing the cell wall, for example, with enzymes. Free DNA can therefore enter the cell only when the cell wall has been removed, but the intact virion infects in the presence of the cell wall.

Phage protein is formed during the latent period and its presence is detectable by precipitation with antiphage serum. About 6 minutes after the appearance of phage protein, mature phage can be detected (Rueckert and Zillig, 1962). Rueckert and Zillig found that infection by ϕX caused only minimal changes in the host cells prior to lysis and that cell division and synthesis of nucleic acids and protein continue essentially unchanged after infection.

Little is known of how phage components are assembled into mature phage. Assembly probably occurs spontaneously. At least it is possible to incubate a mixture of isolated phage components, with the result that particles having some properties of complete phage are produced (Takai, 1966).

Hutchison and Sinsheimer (1963) performed an ingenious experiment to measure the time course of lysis of single infected cells. They used a filter membrane that would retain *E. coli* but would allow ϕX to pass through. A single infected cell was suspended in a small amount of culture medium and any phage present was filtered out. More medium was added for a period of time and then the medium was again filtered. Repetition, with assay of each filtrate, led to the conclusion that the complement of progeny ϕX is released within a half-minute period from the infected cell, terminating the infective cycle. There is considerable variability in the time at which an individual cell releases its phage, explaining the extended rise time when a large population of cells is studied, as in Figure 10-1.

Turbidity measurements of cultures during the latent period indicated that there may be cell lysis at the time of phage release (Denhardt and Sinsheimer, 1965a; Markert and Zillig, 1965). Electron microscopic study, however, showed that the cell walls were still intact after phage release, indicating that the decreased turbidity must be due only to leakage of cell contents. Nor does the cell expand rapidly, as was described with T-even phage lysis. Lysis-from-without does not occur even with high multiplicities of adsorption (Markert and Zillig, 1965).

Apparently, therefore, lysis is not due to a phage-induced enzyme comparable to the lysozyme induced by T phages. A protein is involved in lysis, however, since blockage of protein synthesis by chloramphenicol prevents lysis (Markert and Zillig, 1965), and mutants of ϕX have been found that replicate normally but cannot cause lysis (Hutchison and Sinsheimer, 1966). The nature of the protein is not known.

DNA REPLICATION

The fact that ϕX DNA is single stranded raises an interesting problem: Since it is not of typical Watson-Crick structure, how does it replicate? A great deal of effort has been expended on this problem, and the results of the experiments will now be summarized.

One of the first questions asked was this: Does the parental DNA reappear in the progeny virus? To investigate this problem, Kozinski (1961b) infected *E. coli*, heavily labeled with P^{32}, with nonradioactive ϕX174. He then determined the fraction of survivors as the incorporated radioactivity decayed. Progeny synthesized utilizing the P^{32} were subject to suicide at a high efficiency while progeny containing an intact parental DNA molecule, unlabeled, were not subject to suicide. A resistant fraction of virus would therefore measure the amount of transfer that had taken place. Results of the experiment indicated that transfer from parental to progeny virus does not occur.

What becomes of the parental DNA strand if it does not reappear in the progeny? Either it is degraded, in which case the genetic information it contains is transferred to some other molecule, or it is changed into some form that distinguishes it from newly formed DNA molecules that become incorporated into the progeny virions.

The first clue was discovered when Sinsheimer and his collaborators (1962) found that a parental DNA strand forms a second strand with conventional complementary hydrogen bonding. This double-stranded form of DNA, a necessary intermediate in replication, was called the "Replicative Form," sometimes abbreviated to RF. Because of its unusual nature, the replicative form has been extensively studied. It has interesting properties.

First, how is RF detected and what are its physical properties? Sinsheimer *et al.* (1962) found the replicative form by infecting cells with ϕX containing two kinds of label. P^{32} was a tracer tag for the DNA, and the density of the DNA had been increased by the incorporation of the heavy nitrogen isotope N^{15}. After the infective cycle had progressed for a short while, the DNA was extracted from the cells and analyzed in a CsCl equilibrium density gradient in the ultracentrifuge. The radioactivity did not occur at the density expected for single-stranded DNA, but at a lesser density. This can be explained if it is postulated that the parental (heavy) strand acquired a second strand of normal isotopic composition and therefore normal density, forming a complex of intermediate density.

The replicative form, like the viral form, is circular (Burton and Sinsheimer, 1963; Kleinschmidt et al., 1963; Chandler et al., 1964; Jaenisch et al., 1966; and Pouwels et al., 1966). The circles are super-coiled; a single hit or nick of one strand by an endonuclease (pancreatic deoxyribonuclease) allows the supercoil to open into a more slowly sedimenting ring (Burton and Sinsheimer, 1965; Roth and Hayashi, 1966). This process is exactly comparable to that already described (Chapter 9) for polyoma virus and its relatives. Furthermore, the change in absorption of ultraviolet light as the temperature is increased, breaking the hydrogen bonds between the strands, is exactly as would be expected if the double-stranded form were a conventional DNA molecule of the base composition of ϕX DNA (Hayashi et al., 1963a; Benzinger and Hofschneider, 1963).

Of greater interest, perhaps, is the biology of the single- and double-stranded molecules. It has already been pointed out that inhibition of protein synthesis does not inhibit the formation of the replicative form, but it does prevent the synthesis of single-stranded progeny molecules (Sinsheimer et al., 1962; Stone, 1967). The implication is that preëxisting cellular enzymes convert the single-stranded form into the replicative form without new enzyme synthesis (Tessman, 1966). The new, second strand is synthesized from components of the medium, rather than from preëxisting intracellular materials (Denhardt and Sinsheimer, 1965b).

Denhardt and his collaborators (1967) reasoned that if a cellular function is involved in the conversion, mutants of E. coli should exist that are unable to carry out the conversion. They further reasoned that ϕX would not be able to replicate in such mutant cells. Such is the case with a mutant of E. coli. ϕX adsorbs to and penetrates the mutant; its DNA is converted into typical replicative-form molecules, but no progeny molecules are formed. Either the replicative form is "defective" or the enzyme required for forming progeny single-strand DNA molecules is not functional.

What enzyme is responsible for synthesizing the new strand to make the replicative form? It was first thought that it might be the same enzyme that repairs DNA after ultraviolet-induced thymine dimers have been excised, an enzyme that may also play a role in recombination. However, recombination-deficient mutants of E. coli that were unable to repair irradiated DNA were still found to be able to replicate ϕX (Denhardt et al., 1967).

The first step (Fig. 10-2) in the infective cycle is the conversion of the parental single-stranded DNA molecule into a double-stranded molecule. Next, the newly formed, double-stranded RF replicates

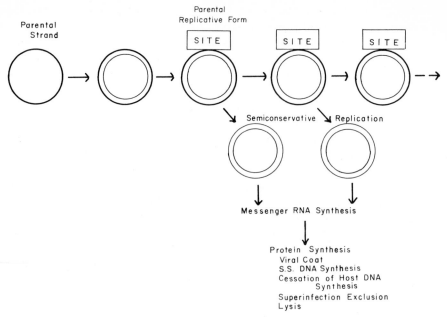

Figure 10-2. Diagram showing stages in φX174 replication leading to formation of the replicative form and phage-specific proteins. (Redrawn from Sinsheimer *et al.*, 1967.)

semiconservatively. The new molecules that result from these replications are also double stranded. It is interesting, however, that they are somehow different from the original replicative form containing the parental DNA molecule.

For instance, only the molecule containing the parental DNA strand forms new double-stranded molecules (Denhardt and Sinsheimer, 1965b). This also means that the double-stranded forms lacking the parental strand do not replicate to yield more double-stranded molecules.

Further evidence indicating a difference between the parental replicative-form molecule and its progeny comes from experiments in which the infecting strand was heavily labeled with P^{32} (Denhardt and Sinsheimer, 1965c). The inactivation efficiency is unity for the single-stranded viral form, and, as would be expected, the inactivation efficiency rapidly drops to about 0.2 about 6 or 7 minutes after infection, as the DNA is converted to a double-stranded form. However, the φX-*E. coli* complex remains relatively sensitive to P^{32} decay late in the cycle, even after many new double-stranded replicas have been formed. The one containing the parental strand, therefore, must perform some function that the replicas cannot perform.

Whatever the difference, however, it is lost if the DNA is extracted from the infected cell and tested for infectivity in the spheroplast assay for infective DNA (Guthrie and Sinsheimer, 1963). Consequently, the difference between the initiating double-stranded form and its replicas lies in the unique position of the initiating double strand within the infected cell, or with some cellular component with which it is complexed (Sinsheimer *et al.*, 1967). This could be the growing-point region of bacterial DNA (Smith and Hanawalt, 1967). In cells that have been irradiated with ultraviolet light, the double-stranded form is produced but progeny molecules are not made (Matsubara *et al.*, 1967), perhaps because the parental double-stranded form cannot become properly associated with the bacterial DNA.

Single-stranded DNA molecules that become incorporated into progeny virions are synthesized starting about 10 minutes after infection. Because single strands are not synthesized in cells in which the parental strand is labeled with P^{32} and subject to radiation damage, the replicative form containing the parental DNA must be responsible for their synthesis (Denhardt and Sinsheimer, 1965b). If this original molecule replicated semiconservatively to yield single-stranded molecules, radioactive label should be transferred to the progeny. That is, at each replication there would be a 50 per cent probability that the single-stranded molecule would be labelled. Experiments have shown, however, that such transfer does not occur (Matsubara *et al.*, 1963). Therefore, it has been concluded that the double-strand-

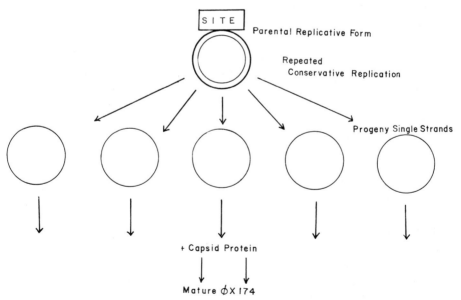

Figure 10-3. Diagram showing synthesis of progeny single strands by repeated conservative replications of the parental replicative form and assembly of the progeny strands into mature ϕX174 virions. (Redrawn from Sinsheimer *et al.*, 1967.)

ed form containing the parental strand replicates conservatively (Fig. 10-3) to yield the single-stranded progeny molecules (Denhardt and Sinsheimer, 1965d).

No pool of single-stranded molecules accumulates. The single strands are detected only in the progeny virions (Sinsheimer *et al.*, 1962), meaning that they are incorporated into mature particles without delay, and there is no precursor pool.

Apparently the function of the progeny double-stranded forms is simply to synthesize messenger RNA molecules (see Fig. 10-2) for synthesis of virus-specific proteins (Denhardt and Sinsheimer, 1965d; Denhardt and Silver, 1966). The double-stranded, circular replicative form acts as template for in vitro RNA synthesis using *E. coli* RNA polymerase. RNA synthesis on this template proceeds in the 5' to 3' direction (Tonegawa and Hayashi, 1966). Presumably, this corresponds to the in vivo condition (Tessman *et al.*, 1967b), but single-stranded DNA will also serve as template for RNA synthesis (Sinsheimer and Lawrence, 1964). Some replicative-form molecules that are multiples of the lengths of normal molecules occur in infected cells (Rush *et al.*, 1967; Rush and Warner, 1967). These molecules probably play no part in normal infection, although they may be intermediates in genetic recombination.

One strand of a duplex DNA molecule is the "sense" strand, meaning that it codes for protein synthesis, while the other is the "nonsense" strand, because its code is complementary to that which codes protein synthesis and its sequence presumably cannot code protein synthesis. The question can be asked, then, whether the viral strand is the "sense" strand or whether the new strand synthesized in forming the replicative form is the "sense" strand. Ordinarily it is the complementary or "minus" strand that is transcribed into messenger RNA molecules (Hayashi *et al.*, 1963b, 1964). However, either single-stranded virus strands or their complement isolated from denatured replicative forms are infective in protoplasts (Rüst and Sinsheimer, 1967; Siegel and Hayashi, 1967). This can be explained because either strand would synthesize the opposite strand as the initial stage of infection.

A phage-directed protein causes the cessation of host-cell DNA synthesis (Lindqvist and Sinsheimer, 1967), because DNA synthesis does not stop when chloramphenicol is added to the cells before infection to block protein synthesis.

THE FILAMENTOUS DNA-CONTAINING PHAGES

Several coliphages are known to have a filamentous structure (see Fig. 3-4) and to contain a single-stranded DNA molecule. These phages include f1 (Zinder *et al.*, 1963), M13 (Hofschneider, 1963), and fd (Marvin and Hoffmann-Berling, 1963) and infect male strains of *E. coli*. The DNA molecule is a ring (Marvin and Schaller, 1966).

The reason for the male specificity lies in the mode of attachment of the phage to the cell. It will be recalled that male *E. coli* cells possess minute tubular structures called F pili, thought to play a role in bacterial conjugation (Brinton, 1965). Caro and Schnös (1966) showed by electron microscopy that the end of the f1 phage filament attaches to the tip of the F pilus. Specific attachment organs were not seen. There seems to be a receptor site at the end of the F pilus, however, because the phages attached only to one end of a broken piece of F pilus. Removal of a piece of F pilus from the cell makes the newly exposed tip of the remaining portion available for attachment. A given cell has as many attachment sites as it has F pili.

Further evidence that the male specificity resides only in attachment comes from experiments in which the DNA was extracted from the phage by phenol. Such DNA is infective for spheroplasts of *E. coli*, whether the cells are male or female (Hoffmann-Berling *et al.*, 1963).

It is thought that after attachment, the phage's DNA enters the cell through the axial hole of the F pilus. Penetration is rapid; detectable numbers of cells are infected if penetration is stopped by antiserum as early as 20 seconds after phage is mixed with cells. Experiments with S^{35}-labeled phage and a Waring blender after the method of Hershey and Chase (1952; Chapter 7) showed that only the nucleic acid enters the cell.

In Chapter 3 the structure of the filamentous phages was described as a rubber band or a circle of string pulled from opposite sides so that the two strands lie side by side. The protein of each filament seems to be a tubular structure (Marvin, 1966), presumably surrounding the DNA. Thus, a better descriptive analogy would be a loop of insulated wire, the wire representing the DNA and the insulation representing the protein. It would seem that the phage protein would have to be degraded for the nucleic acid to penetrate the cell.

Details of DNA replication of these phages have not been worked out as yet, but, in general, replication seems to resemble that of ϕX174. For instance, a double-stranded replicative form can be isolated from cells infected by M13 phage (Ray *et al.*, 1966a). The DNA molecule of the replicative form, like that in mature phage, is circular with supercoiling (Ray *et al.*, 1966b), as already described for ϕX replicative DNA and for polyoma viral DNA (Chapter 9). Assembly is probably spontaneous, as isolated protein will combine with isolated DNA in vitro to form structures resembling normal phage (Knippers and Hoffmann-Berling, 1966a, 1966b, 1966c).

Another unusual feature of this group of viruses is their mode of release from the infected cells. There is no evidence that a lytic enzyme is formed; bacterial cell walls are intact following release of virus. Instead, the viral filaments "leak" from the cells as the cells continue to grow (Hoffmann-Berling *et al.*, 1963; Hofschneider and Preuss, 1963; Hoffmann-Berling and Mazé, 1964; Bradley and Dewar, 1967).

Replication of the nucleic acid of phages containing single-stranded DNA is complicated by the apparent necessity for prior conversion to a double-stranded state. As will be seen in the next chapter, a similar situation exists for the viruses that contain single-stranded RNA.

Further Reading

Hoffmann-Berling, H., H. C. Kaerner, and R. Knippers: Small Bacteriophages. Advances in Virus Research, 12:329-370, 1966.
Sinsheimer, R. L.: Single-Stranded DNA. Scientific American, 207(July):109, 1962.

11

REPLICATION OF VIRUSES THAT CONTAIN RNA

Normal, uninfected cells (plant, animal, or bacterial) possess no self-replicating RNA systems. All known RNA molecules synthesized by a cell are complementary to the cell's DNA. Their synthesis is catalyzed by DNA-dependent RNA polymerase, an enzyme whose activity can be blocked by the antibiotic actinomycin D.

When a virus that contains RNA infects a cell, drastic changes result. The virus brings a completely new type of genetic system into the cell and must be able to do more than merely modify existing cellular functions since appropriate ones do not already exist. New functions must be introduced so that the viral RNA can be self-replicating.

VIRUSES TO BE CONSIDERED

All known higher plant viruses, such as tobacco mosaic virus, contain RNA, as do some of the phages, including MS2, f1, and R17, and some small animal viruses, such as poliovirus and the EMC-Mengo group. In these plant, bacterial, and animal viruses, the molecular weight of the single-stranded RNA molecule is about 2×10^6 daltons or less. Adequate tests for circularity of the molecules have not been done. In addition to the RNA similarities, capsid similarities exist: All the capsids are simple, being composed of only one or a few species of proteins and possessing no lipid. Infectious RNA is easily obtained from many of these viruses.

Myxoviruses and paramyxoviruses also contain single-stranded

199

RNA, but their RNA differs in some respects from that of the others. It may be present as several pieces in the virion (Nayak and Baluda, 1967), sometimes along with some cellular RNA. Unlike the other viruses to be discussed, the myxoviruses and paramyxoviruses mature at the cell membrane, incorporating cell membrane material in the process.

Still other viruses form a third group, based on biological properties and on the double-stranded structure of their RNA. These viruses form the reovirus-wound tumor virus group. Their capsids contain some single-stranded RNA as well as the double-stranded RNA (Shatkin and Sipe, 1968; Bellamy and Joklik, 1967).

GROWTH CYCLES

The time course of replication of the RNA-containing viruses (Fig. 11-1) resembles that of the DNA viruses. The latent period varies from a few minutes for the phages to several hours for the animal viruses. It is evident that the one-step growth of the RNA viruses can be divided into the same phases as the growth cycles of DNA-containing viruses. It might be expected, therefore, that many details of replication of the two kinds of viruses will also be similar.

Attachment

One similarity between DNA and RNA viruses is that these RNA viruses come into contact with their host cell by the forces of simple diffusion, as do other viruses. They possess no mechanism for intrinsic motility, nor do they possess elaborate attachment organs as do the T-even phages.

For some of these viruses, receptor sites on cells have been well demonstrated. This is especially true for the myxoviruses, particularly influenza virus, whose mechanism of attachment is often incorrectly thought to be a model for the attachment of all animal viruses to cells.

The attachment of the myxoviruses is most simply illustrated by hemagglutination. Red blood cells are not infected by myxoviruses, but myxoviruses attach to them in the same way that they attach to other cells: Surface structures of the virion attach to receptor material on the cell surface.

Soon after Hirst (1941) discovered hemagglutination, work in many laboratories revealed a number of related phenomena (reviewed by Gottschalk, 1959). For instance, cells agglutinated at 4° C. separate soon after being warmed to 37° C. The virus eluted from the

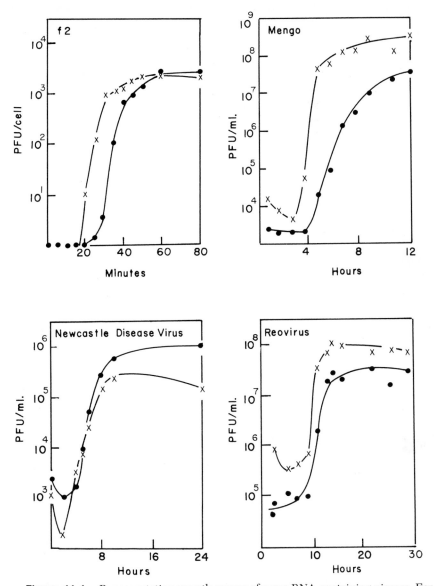

Figure 11-1. Representative growth curves of some RNA-containing viruses. For f2, the upper curve (filled circles) is total virus and the lower curve (crosses) is cell-associated virus. For mengo, the upper curve (crosses) is the total virus content (cell-associated + released) and the lower curve (filled circles) is released virus. For Newcastle disease virus and reovirus, the filled circles represent released virus and the crosses represent cell-associated virus. (f2: Loeb and Zinder, 1961; mengo: Franklin and Baltimore, 1962; Newcastle disease virus: Rubin *et al.*, 1957; reovirus: Gomatos *et al.*, 1962.)

cells under these conditions can again cause agglutination when supplied with fresh red blood cells, but the cells from which it elutes cannot reagglutinate by the same virus. An enzyme was postulated to explain this behavior.

Further evidence for the existence of such an enzyme came from the discovery that an extracellular enzyme occurs in cultures of *Vibrio cholera* that renders erythrocytes incapable of being agglutinated by myxoviruses. The enzyme was therefore called receptor destroying enzyme, universally abbreviated to RDE.

It was soon shown that influenza virus adsorbs to and elutes from the cells lining the respiratory tract of animals in the same way that it does from red cells. RDE treatment of the respiratory tract of an animal makes the animal insusceptible to infection by influenza virus. It was then found that certain mucoproteins and mucopolysaccharides block hemagglutination, an effect that can be destroyed by treating the mucoid material with RDE. This was interpreted as meaning that the mucoid material contains substances similar or identical to the receptor material, and that it competes for the RDE.

The nature of the receptor was finally worked out by Gottschalk (1959) by analyzing the products released by the action of RDE. The product split off is N-acetylneuraminic acid, one of a group of related compounds collectively called sialic acid. It is part of an oligosaccharide, which in turn, is a prosthetic group of a protein. The enzyme RDE, called variously sialidase or neuraminidase, removes the terminal acetylated neuraminic acid, rendering the receptor unable to attach virus.

Because one influenza virion is sufficient to remove the receptors from the entire surface of a red cell, it has been supposed that the virion rolls over the cell's surface, enzymatically removing receptors as it goes. This activity is called browsing.

Red cells whose receptors have been removed by one kind of myxovirus can no longer adsorb more of that virus, but they may adsorb certain other myxoviruses which can then remove their receptors. The myxoviruses can be arranged in such an order that each can destroy the receptors for itself and for viruses below it in the series, whereas those above can still adsorb. This ordering is called the receptor gradient. The receptor gradient seems to be a result of the arrangement of enzyme molecules on the viral surface, although slight differences can be found in the enzymes purified from various myxoviruses (Drzeniek *et al.*, 1966).

Although both the sialidase activity and the hemagglutinin occur at the surface of the myxovirion, they are not the same substance. It is thought that the hemagglutinin resides in the radial spikes (Noll *et al.*, 1962) (see Fig. 3-8). These are not removed by trypsin treatment of influenza virus, but sialidase activity is removed.

Poliovirus, on the other hand, has never been shown to hemagglutinate, although some of its close relatives do. Perhaps the right conditions (buffer, pH, ionic strength, etc.) have not been found as yet. More likely, perhaps the receptors for poliovirus that occur on somatic cells simply do not exist on red blood cells. In any event, receptors for enteroviruses have been convincingly demonstrated on the surface of somatic cells (see Holland, 1964a, for review of extensive work on enterovirus receptors).

The receptors for poliovirus are protein, or contain protein, because any treatment of the cell that destroys protein, such as exposure to proteolytic enzymes, also destroys receptor activity (Holland and McLaren, 1961). It is possible to solubilize the receptors and to detect them by their ability to attach to poliovirus and neutralize its infectivity. Holland and McLaren (1961) found that more receptor material is released from the cells by disruption than could be detected in the intact cell, suggesting that most of the receptors were not at the cell surface.

More recent experiments (Zajac and Crowell, 1965) have led to another conclusion, one that requires a reinterpretation of the previous work. Live cells were first treated with trypsin to remove surface receptors. After chilling, the cells were disrupted. No receptor material was detectable. It is therefore concluded that receptors are rapidly regenerated at the cell's surface. Cellular metabolic activity would be required, a prediction that has been demonstrated to be true (Levitt and Crowell, 1967). In the work of Holland and McLaren (1961) previously cited, it is probable that regeneration of receptors occurred during the isolation procedure instead of a release of internal receptors.

It has long been known that only certain of the cells of an infected animal or person support the growth of a virus such as poliovirus. The spectrum of cells infected and killed or injured by a given virus results in the different clinical picture of various viral diseases. Holland (1961) found that susceptible human tissues (brain, spinal cord, intestine) have receptors for poliovirus, whereas nonsusceptible tissues do not. A nonvirulent variant of poliovirus that does not cause paralysis is bound not by receptors of nervous tissue but by receptors of intestinal tissue. When cells of nonsusceptible tissues are grown in culture, however, they acquire receptor activity, accounting for the ability of nearly any cultured primate cell to support growth of poliovirus. How receptors are acquired is unknown, but receptor development might be a result of the disturbance of normal cell contacts when the cells are dispersed to be placed in culture.

Could it be possible that tissue and species tropism is not a result of the presence or absence of specific receptors but rather the result of intracellular mechanisms? That this is not so, at least within certain limits, is shown by experiments with RNA isolated from poliovirus. Such RNA is infective for cells that support replication of intact virus, and it is infective for cells of other species, such as chicken cells, that do not have receptors for poliovirus and do not normally allow growth of poliovirus. It was shown not only that the necessity for receptors can be bypassed by infecting the cells with isolated RNA, but also that the cells produce complete infectious progeny virus (Holland *et al.*, 1959; Mountain and Alexander, 1959; de Somer *et al.*, 1959). The progeny virus is serologically like the parent virus from which the RNA is extracted; it is not able to undergo a second infective cycle in chick cells because the progeny coat protein prevents it from attaching to the cells. Similar results have been shown for many other of the RNA-containing viruses.

It is possible to bypass the receptor system of hamster and chicken cells that are otherwise insusceptible to poliovirus by treating the cells with Sendai virus at the time of adding poliovirus. Even when it is inactivated by ultraviolet light, Sendai virus causes changes in the cell surface that result in the engulfment of poliovirus, and the poliovirus undergoes one cycle of replication (Enders *et al.*, 1967), showing that in this case the normal inability of poliovirus to replicate in chicken cells is only because poliovirus cannot attach to the cells.

Reversibility of attachment of poliovirus to receptors is temperature dependent. Under usual conditions, with highly susceptible cells at 37° C., more than 57 per cent of the adsorbed virus subsequently elutes. At 0° C., however, no elution occurs. Eluted virus is altered in such a way that it cannot subsequently readsorb to cells (Joklik and Darnell, 1961); it may carry cellular components; and other changes of the eluted virions, such as acquiring trypsin sensitivity, suggest that the eluted virus may have undergone the early stages of eclipse (Fenwick and Cooper, 1962).

Virions that do not elute become eclipsed; that is, they become inaccessible to neutralization by antiserum, and they cannot be removed from the cells in an infective form (except as an infectious RNA). Eclipse begins with uncoating: It is the process that releases the viral RNA into the cell where it begins to function.

RNA phages are specific for male *E. coli*. Like the filamentous DNA phages, they attach to the F pili, but they do so along the sides, not at the ends (Caro and Schnös, 1966). For a brief time, the viral RNA is vulnerable to ribonuclease in the medium. Then the viral RNA enters the cell through the central opening that runs the length of the F pilus (Valentine and Wedel, 1965). Conjugating bacteria can adsorb RNA phage on the F pili, but the phage RNA cannot enter the cell, presumably because the central opening of the F pili is occupied by the bacterial DNA (Knolle, 1967). The manner of release of phage RNA from the virion is unknown.

The Latent Period

Major investigative interest centers on the function and replication of viral RNA because of its unique relationship to the cell. Not only are there no self-replicating RNA systems in normal cells, but the viral RNA resembles cell RNA in many respects. Its different functions must therefore arise from subtle differences between it and cellular RNA.

Viral RNA Function. Polioviral RNA, for instance, is single stranded, as is cellular messenger RNA. Probably most, if not all, cellular messenger RNA molecules are monocistronic, possessing genetic information to be translated into a single species of polypeptide. But a viral RNA molecule codes for several proteins and is therefore polycistronic. Possibly each cistron of the viral RNA gives rise to a monocistronic messenger molecule, one for each protein, or perhaps the entire molecule acts as a polycistronic message.

The latter possibility seems to be the case. Following infection of HeLa cells by poliovirus, for instance, there is a progressive decrease in the number of polysomes. About 3 hours after infection, the polysomes again begin to increase (Penman et al., 1963). These polysomes are larger than the ones usually found in uninfected cells. When examined with the electron microscope, they are found to consist of strings of ribosomes that are much longer than usual, indicating that the messenger RNA forming the polysome is longer than cellular messages. The number of ribosomes is what would be expected, based on the length of the polioviral RNA (Rich et al., 1963). Viral protein synthesis occurs in the polysomes, even when extracellular (Attardi and Smith, 1962; Summers et al., 1964; Stubbs and Kaesberg, 1967).

The findings so far do not indicate whether it is the incoming viral RNA molecule or the progeny molecules that associate with the ribosomes. The fact that the polysomes become detectable late in infection, however, suggests that at least the majority utilize progeny molecules. If only the incoming viral RNA formed polysomes, it would be difficult to detect. To increase the experimental sensitivity in the hope of detecting the incoming strand in polysomes, Tobey (1964b) infected cells with Mengo virus labeled in its RNA with tritium. When he isolated the polysomes from cells, even shortly after infection, radioactivity was found in the polysomes. Godson and Sinsheimer (1967) found a similar early association between labeled MS2 RNA and polysomes in infected bacteria. It therefore seems that the incoming strand can itself act as a messenger RNA to direct the synthesis of proteins, probably enzymes, needed for further events.

Regulation of Protein Synthesis. At least 12 new proteins, including the four viral capsid proteins shown in Figure 11-2, can be

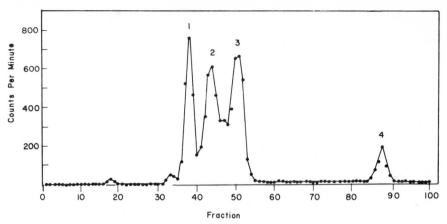

Figure 11-2. Polyacrylamide gel electrophoretic analysis of labeled polioviral capsid protein. The four peaks indicate that the capsid is composed of four distinct molecular species of polypeptide chains (Redrawn from Summers *et al.*, 1965.)

found in cells infected with poliovirus (Summers *et al.*, 1965). Some of these undoubtedly are enzymes required for viral synthesis, while others may be regulatory, interfering with or blocking certain cellular functions that are not to the advantage of viral replication. Since different quantities of the different proteins would be required at different stages of replication, it would be interesting to know whether all cistrons are translated throughout the cycle or whether there is some mechanism that turns some on and others off to meet changing needs.

The operon (Jacob and Monod, 1961; Beckwith, 1967) is a precedent for regulation of transcription, but all operons described to date occur in DNA. Conflicting reports have appeared concerning the regulation of translation of viral RNA cistrons. For instance, Ohtaka and Spiegelman (1963) detected differences in the rates of synthesis of different proteins after infection of *E. coli* by MS2, suggesting that a regulatory mechanism was operative. Their findings with MS2 have been well confirmed for this phage by Eggen *et al.* (1967), who found distinct differences in the rates of synthesis of different proteins during the growth cycle and by Sugiyama and Nakada (1967), who demonstrated that the presence of viral capsid protein shuts off "early" protein synthesis. Similar in vitro results were obtained with f2 (Ward *et al.*, 1967).

On the other hand, Summers *et al.* (1967) could find no differences in relative amounts of the 14 proteins detectable in poliovirus-infected cells. There was an increase in the rate of overall synthesis as the infective cycle progressed, but the amounts of all proteins increased proportionately, perhaps reflecting an increasing number of viral RNA molecules engaged in protein synthesis. Also, the total amount of each of the different proteins varied; whether this resulted from differences in size or differences in relative numbers of molecules is not clear.

Generality of the messenger function of viral RNA is evident from many experiments in other systems. RNA extracted from purified turnip yellow mosaic virus (Ofengand and Haselkorn, 1961; Haselkorn *et al.*, 1963) or tobacco mosaic virus (Nirenberg and Matthaei, 1961) attaches to ribosomes purified from *E. coli* and directs the synthesis of proteins. Similar experiments have shown that the RNA of phage f2 also attaches to *E. coli* ribosomes in a cell-free system, directing the synthesis of viral coat protein (Nathans *et al.*, 1962).

Virus-Directed Enzymes. Not all proteins coded by viral RNA are capsid proteins. As was discussed for the DNA viruses, enzymes concerned with viral replication are synthesized early in the cycle. The nature of these enzymes differs from that of the DNA viruses, however.

As stated before, no self-replicating RNA system has been identified in normal cells. RNA ordinarily is transcribed from DNA with the aid of DNA-dependent RNA polymerase. Since enzymes for synthesis of RNA from RNA templates do not occur in normal cells, it can be predicted that either a new enzyme with this function is coded by the viral RNA or the preëxisting DNA-dependent enzyme is also able to use RNA as template.

That a new enzyme is induced in cells infected with the single-stranded RNA viruses has been convincingly demonstrated in several systems. For instance, RNA-dependent RNA polymerase has been described in L cells (a continuously propagated line of cells derived from mouse fibroblasts) infected by Mengo virus (Baltimore and Franklin, 1962a, 1962b; Horton *et al.*, 1964), in HeLa cells infected with poliovirus (Baltimore and Franklin, 1963; Eggers *et al.*, 1963), in mouse cells infected with EMC virus (Eason *et al.*, 1963), in *E. coli* infected with MS2 (Haruna *et al.*, 1963) and with another RNA phage, Qβ (Haruna and Spiegelman, 1965a), and in many others.

RNA-dependent RNA polymerase, sometimes called replicase, does not form in HeLa cells infected with poliovirus when protein synthesis is blocked (Eggers *et al.*, 1963). This is further evidence that the appearance of replicase activity is coded by viral information. Synthesis of new RNA catalyzed by the enzyme is not blocked by actinomycin D. This distinguishes it from the enzyme, present in normal cells, that uses DNA as template (Plagemann and Swim, 1966).

Haruna and Spiegelman (1965b) made a study of the template specificities of replicases induced by MS2 and Qβ. They found that each replicase was quite specific for its own RNA. When tested with other RNA, each replicase showed little activity and no synthesis in the absence of template. This is quite convincing evidence that the synthesis of the enzyme is directed by viral information. Further, for long periods the enzyme actively synthesized RNA, a property that is useful for experiments to be described in a later section.

Therefore, it may be concluded that single-stranded viral RNA can function as messenger. Presumably the incoming RNA molecule does so directly to code for the new replicase. Whether it or progeny molecules are translated to form other necessary proteins is not known. Although other new proteins are present in infected cells, extensive identification of viral-related enzymes and proteins has not been made.

Reovirus apparently uses the preëxisting DNA-dependent RNA polymerase for synthesis of RNA. The fact that reovirus RNA is double stranded may account for its ability to be a template in place of DNA for the cellular enzyme. The synthesis of new RNA using reovirus RNA as template is blocked by actinomycin D, and no virus is released from cells infected by reovirus in the presence of the antibiotic (Gomatos *et al.*, 1964). The single-stranded RNA synthesized from viral double strands has the characteristics of messenger RNA molecules (Gomatos, 1967).

Replication of Single-Stranded Viral RNA.   The DNA of the cell is not involved in the synthesis of viral RNA. Poliovirus and Newcastle disease virus (Simon, 1961) and the RNA phage f2 (Cooper and Zinder, 1962) can replicate when synthesis of new DNA is blocked by metabolic inhibitors. Further, there are no DNA sequences complementary to viral RNA either before or after infection (Doi and Spiegelman, 1962). These results mean that the information contained in the RNA is not somehow transferred to some DNA intermediate: The RNA itself acts as template. Although actinomycin D has no effect on replication of Newcastle disease virus, it does inhibit influenza virus (Fig. 11-3), perhaps indicating DNA participation (Barry *et al.*, 1962). The experiments by Pons (1967) seem to offer a possibly better explanation that actinomycin D inhibits influenza virus replication by direct action on the replicative form of the virus (to be discussed later).

RNA does not transfer from parental to progeny virus. To test for transfer, MS2 was labeled with heavy isotopes to increase its density and was labeled with P^{32}. The virus preparation was used to infect cells; the progeny, of normal density, contained no radioactivity (Davis and Sinsheimer, 1963). Other experiments showed that the radioactivity of the infecting virus remains in the cells after lysis (Doi and Spiegelman, 1963).

An experiment with animal viruses to test for transfer is much more difficult technically because of the large amount of unadsorbed virus in the cultures (Homma and Graham, 1965). Since it is very difficult to remove all the extraneous virus by repeated rinsing, parent

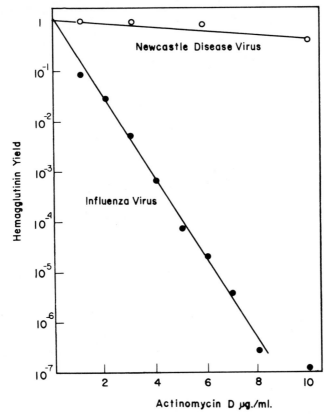

Figure 11-3. Effect of actinomycin D on hemagglutinin yield in chick chorioallantoic cells infected with Newcastle disease virus or influenza virus. (Redrawn from Barry *et al.*, 1962.)

must be separated from progeny harvested after infection. An experiment to test for transfer became possible with the finding of a peculiar mutant of EMC virus (Goodheart, 1965). It has a higher density than normal or wild-type virus, and its density decreases after a cycle of replication. In the transfer experiment, cells were infected with P³²-labeled mutant. Progeny virions of lighter density (therefore separable from parental virions) did not contain significant P³² (Goodheart, 1967). Thus, once in the cell, the RNA must become altered in such a way that the cell distinguishes parental RNA and progeny RNA. The situation resembles that for the single-stranded DNA viruses, which also do not show transfer from parent to progeny (see Chapter 10).

In tracing the replication of viral RNA, we will discuss the methods used in detecting the various forms of RNA, the properties of the different forms, and finally the replicative scheme.

One common analytic procedure is shown in Figure 11-4. A sucrose gradient analysis is performed by forming the gradient in the centrifuge tube with a machine or mixer that delivers a decreasing concentration of sucrose (commonly, the sucrose is 20 or 30 per cent at the bottom of the tube and 5 to 10 per cent at the top). Then the RNA to be analyzed is layered on top of the gradient and centrifuged at a high speed for several hours or overnight. RNA molecules sediment through the sucrose at different rates, depending on their size, shape, and molecular weight. After centrifugation, the contents of the tube are split into successive fractions. This is done by making a hole in the bottom of the celluloid centrifuge tube and catching the sucrose drops in test tubes as they fall out. It is common practice, as in Figure 11-4, to use ribosomal RNA as a marker; the locations of its 28S and 16S peaks are found by measuring the ultraviolet absorbancy of the fractions (RNA has an absorption peak at 260 mμ). Viral RNA is in such low concentration that it does not absorb significantly, and it is detected by radioactivity or by infectivity. As shown, viral RNA sediments more rapidly than 28S ribosomal RNA.

RNA gives much the same pattern whether it is extracted from virus, as in Figure 11-4, from cells within the first few hours following infection with the animal viruses, or from cells within the first few

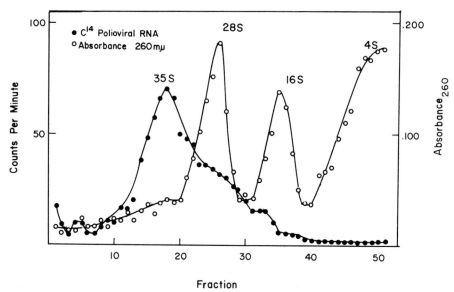

Figure 11-4. Sucrose gradient analysis of a mixture of polioviral RNA labeled with C^{14} and normal HeLa cell RNA, unlabeled (concentration determined by measuring the absorbance at 260 mμ wavelength). Shown are two peaks (28S, 16S) due to ribosomal RNA and a single peak (35S) due to viral RNA. (Redrawn from Zimmerman *et al.*, 1963.)

minutes with the RNA phages. This means that any viral RNA present is single stranded.

However, Montagnier and Sanders (1963) found that if they extracted the RNA from cells after infection with EMC, a small new peak of RNA occurred toward the end of the replicative cycle (Fig. 11-5). As shown, the RNA in the new peak, which sedimented just ahead of the 16S peak at about 18 to 20S, was relatively resistant to the action of ribonuclease. The treatment, however, degraded the cellular RNA into small molecular weight pieces, which sediment slowly and therefore remain at the top of the gradient. Other tests indicated that the

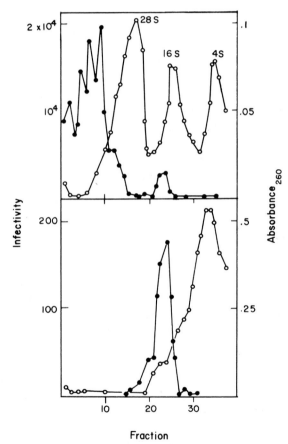

Figure 11-5. Sucrose gradient analyses of RNA extracted from cells 6 hours after infection with EMC virus. Viral RNA was assayed by infectivity (filled circles) and cellular RNA by absorbance (open circles). The RNA in the upper analysis was not treated further after extraction, whereas that in the lower analysis was treated with ribonuclease, which selectively digests single-stranded RNA molecules. (Redrawn from Montagnier and Sanders, 1963.)

18 to 20S, ribonuclease-resistant RNA must be double stranded, like ordinary DNA. By analogy with ϕX174, the new RNA was named replicative form, or RF, and was immediately assumed to be involved in RNA replication.

Double-stranded forms of RNA with properties similar to those of EMC virus have since been reported for many virus-host cell systems. The double-stranded form has been reported in cells infected with poliovirus (Baltimore et al., 1964; Pons, 1964; Watanabe, 1965; Bishop et al., 1965; Watanabe et al., 1965); Semliki Forest virus (Sonnabend et al., 1967a); dengue virus (Stollar et al., 1967); influenza virus (Nayak and Baluda, 1968a, 1968b); the RNA phages R17 (Fenwick et al., 1964), MS2 (Kelly and Sinsheimer, 1964; Weissmann et al., 1964a), and ZIK/1 (Bishop, 1966a); and the plant viruses tobacco mosaic virus (Shipp and Haselkorn, 1964; Burdon et al., 1964) and turnip yellow mosaic virus (Mandel et al., 1964).

The initial duplex is formed shortly after infection by the parental (plus) strand, which acts as template for the synthesis of the complementary (minus) strand (Kelly and Sinsheimer, 1964, 1967a; Weissmann et al., 1964b; Erikson et al., 1964). Formation of the duplex by synthesis of the minus strand is a prerequisite for viral plus-strand synthesis (Billeter et al., 1966; Bishop, 1966b). Double-stranded RNA has the base composition (Weissmann et al., 1965), denaturation, and sedimentation characteristics (Katz and Penman, 1966; Francke and Hofschneider, 1966a, 1966b) to be expected for a duplex molecule.

The double-stranded form also results when RNA is synthesized in vitro from cell-free extracts of leaves infected with turnip yellow mosaic virus (Ralph and Wojcik, 1966). Partially purified RNA-dependent RNA polymerase from E. coli infected with MS2 yields double-stranded RNA as its product (Weissmann and Borst, 1963).

The evidence in favor of such a double-stranded form seems overwhelming. There have been dissenting reports, however. For instance, Tobey (1964a) and Homma and Graham (1965) could find no evidence for a double-stranded RNA in Mengo virus-infected cells, and Doi and Spiegelman (1963) did not find double-stranded RNA in cells infected with MS2. Spiegelman and Haruna (1966a) summarized the experiments that led them to the conclusion that when a double-stranded form of RNA is found in an infected cell, it is an artifact of preparative procedures and is not related to viral replication.

When RNA is extracted from infected cells and analyzed in a sucrose gradient, a third kind of RNA molecule is found in addition to the single- and double-stranded RNA molecules. This third kind occurs with the small RNA viruses (Fenwick et al., 1964; Franklin, 1967; Erikson and Franklin, 1966; Baltimore and Girard, 1966) and with at least two arboviruses (Sreevalsan and Lockart, 1966a;

Friedman *et al.*, 1966; Sonnabend *et al.*, 1967a; Friedman and Berezesky, 1967). It is found to sediment slightly faster than the double-stranded form but not as fast as the single-stranded. Mild treatment with ribonuclease causes this kind of RNA to sediment as double-stranded. It was therefore proposed that this third kind of RNA consists of a double-stranded core with "tails" of single-stranded RNA attached. Ribonuclease digestion is thought to remove the tails, leaving the double-stranded core. The results of extensive studies of sedimentation characteristics of these forms of RNA are consistent with this hypothesis (Francke and Hofschneider, 1966a, 1966b; Franklin, 1967; Bishop and Koch, 1967).

Very brief labeling (15 seconds) of cells infected with R17 phage has resulted in labeling of the third peak with no labeling of the single-strand viral peak. Longer labeling periods, or a "chase" period in nonradioactive medium (Lodish and Zinder, 1966b), permits the new strand to be completed, and isotope appears in the single-strand region of the gradient. It was concluded that the third RNA peak contained a precursor to single-stranded viral RNA, and it was named the "replicative intermediate" (Fenwick *et al.*, 1964; Franklin, 1966). The replicative intermediate can be separated from other types of RNA by column chromatography (Kelly and Sinsheimer, 1967b).

To recapitulate: Cells infected with single-stranded RNA viruses contain several new kinds of RNA related to the infection. The one that sediments fastest is the single-stranded viral RNA. It is sensitive to ribonuclease and it is infective. The component that sediments next is the so-called replicative intermediate, thought to have a double-stranded core with single-stranded "tails" that may be precursors to viral RNA. The slowest component is double stranded, without the "tails." These forms have been examined and photographed by electron microscopy (Granboulan and Franklin, 1966, 1968).

In considering the relationship of these forms of RNA, it should be remembered that the single molecule of incoming viral RNA, or its derivatives, must fulfill all the functions ordinarily performed by DNA. These include directing the synthesis of proteins, perhaps programming the replicative cycle, and undergoing replication giving rise to progeny molecules to be incorporated into mature virions.

It can be deduced that the incoming viral RNA molecule must act as a messenger since an initial event in the infected cell is the synthesis of new enzymes. Lodish and Zinder (1966a) considered that one of these enzymes must be concerned with converting the single-stranded viral RNA into the double-stranded form, since this function does not preëxist in normal cells. With the prospect that mutant viruses deficient in the capacity to cause the synthesis of the postulated enzyme would reveal information about viral replication, these workers set out to find and study such mutants.

One type of mutant they studied was unable to cause the synthesis of the complementary strand. In other words, once inside a cell, the viral RNA did not become double stranded. No progeny particles resulted. Various experiments showed that the reason for the lack of conversion to double strand was the absence of a necessary enzyme function. The mutant was one of a type in which the gene product functions at normal temperature but not at a higher temperature. Thus, at the higher temperature, enzyme was not functional in the infected cells, and label in parental RNA did not appear in double-stranded form. However, when the temperature of the infected cell culture was lowered, the conversion took place.

Study of other temperature-sensitive mutants revealed that a second enzymatic step is involved in synthesis of single strands for incorporation into virions and for function as messenger. It would seem, then, that the double-stranded form acts as template for synthesis of single strands. Further evidence for this conclusion comes from experiments using labeling times of only a few seconds. Under these conditions, the incorporated label is entirely associated with the double-stranded material. When infected cells are in contact with radioactive isotope for a few seconds and then incubated in nonradioactive materal for a further period, label is found mostly in the single strands.

Another question concerning the replication of RNA is whether the double-stranded form replicates to give new double-stranded molecules. This type of replication would be entirely analogous to the replication of double-stranded DNA and would be expected to be semiconservative. Alternatively, the single strands that are synthesized could act as template for synthesis of a new complementary strand, giving rise to the observed increase in double-stranded forms (Weissmann et al., 1964a). Evidence is entirely consistent with the second possibility.

The production of single strands from the double-stranded intermediate could occur by either of two mechanisms (Fig. 11-6). Lodish and Zinder (1966b) reasoned that once parental RNA (plus strand) is incorporated into the replicative form, it will remain there if replication is by the conservative method. On the other hand, it will be displaced if replication is by the asymmetric semiconservative method. Lodish and Zinder infected cells with labeled virus, then assayed the radioactivity in double-stranded RNA. Their experiments showed that the parental RNA passed through a double-stranded form, then changed back to single strands; these results are consistent with asymmetric semiconservative replication. Similar results were obtained by Kelly and Sinsheimer (1967a) and Erikson and Erikson (1967) from experiments testing the same idea by a different method, but further experiments showed that the new strand could arise either

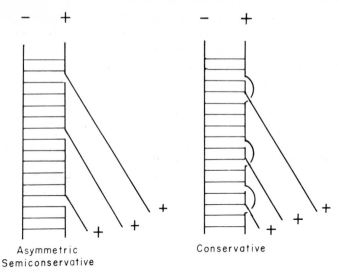

Figure 11-6. Two possible modes of synthesis of single-stranded viral RNA from a double-stranded template. (Redrawn from Lodish and Zinder, 1966b.)

by conservative or by semiconservative replication, each occurring equally often (Kelly and Sinsheimer, 1967c).

As stated before, transfer from parent to progeny apparently does not occur with these RNA viruses. However, the replication scheme outlined indicates that transfer should occur. This seeming paradox needs to be explained, but data are not available. Careful examination of published data on transfer reveals that a small residue of parental radioactivity appears in the progeny. Perhaps what happens is that the incoming, labeled strand undergoes incorporation into the replicative form. When displaced by the newly formed plus strand, it again becomes a duplex molecule. In this manner the labeled strand becomes diluted with many other plus strands. Later in the replicative cycle, when plus strands are liberated from the intermediate, each can be incorporated into a virion. The plus strand can then become associated with ribosomes and synthesize protein, or it can form a new duplex. The overall probability that the parental strand is incorporated into progeny might be quite low, below present limits for detection.

In Vitro RNA Synthesis. Experiments performed chiefly by Spiegelman and his group have yielded the fascinating fact that cell-free synthesis of viral RNA can occur. The crucial biological characteristic, infectivity, is retained (Spiegelman *et al.*, 1965; Haruna and Spiegelman, 1965b). This result raises an important philosophical question as well as several biological questions.

If we accept viruses as living, biological entities (organisms?)

because they can reproduce and maintain genetic continuity, it then seems necessary also to accept free viral RNA molecules as living, because they, too, reproduce and maintain genetic continuity. For example, when the RNA from the last transfer (Fig. 11-7) was used to infect *E. coli* protoplasts, it caused a typical replicative cycle. The Qβ virions that resulted were entirely normal; their protein coats were serologically identical to ordinary Qβ.

Some of the properties of the RNA-synthesizing system have been reviewed (Spiegelman and Haruna, 1966b; Spiegelman, 1967). Briefly, the enzyme these workers isolated can be highly purified (Pace and Spiegelman, 1966a). The molecular weight of the enzyme is about 110,000 daltons and it has a specific template requirement for

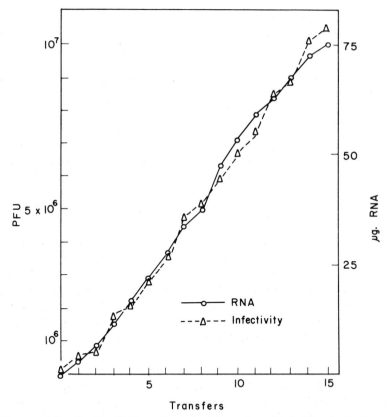

Transfers

Figure 11-7. In vitro RNA synthesis and formation of infectious units in a serial transfer experiment. Tubes containing RNA-replicating enzymes and cofactors were set up, and viral RNA was added to the first tube. After 40 minutes, an aliquot was transferred to the second tube. The transfers were repeated as indicated. All tubes were assayed for RNA content and for infectivity. The accumulated amounts are plotted here against the number of transfers. (Redrawn from Spiegelman *et al.*, 1965.)

the RNA of the virus that induced the enzyme. The template RNA has to be intact for the enzyme to copy it (Haruna and Spiegelman, 1965a). When supplied with template RNA from a mutant virus, the product of the synthesis carries the mutant genes (Pace and Spiegelman, 1966b).

Spiegelman and his collaborators at first found only virus (plus) strands produced in vitro by the RNA-synthesizing enzyme. They did not detect a double-stranded form or complementary (minus) strands (Haruna and Spiegelman, 1966). Using an enzyme preparation furnished by Dr. Spiegelman, however, other workers (Weissmann and Feix, 1966) did obtain the production of minus strands early in the synthesis, followed by the production of plus strands. Minus strands can serve as template for in vitro synthesis of plus strands (Feix et al., 1968).

More recent experiments may have resolved the conflict by examining the very early products of in vitro synthesis (Bishop et al., 1967; Feix et al., 1967b) and by using gel electrophoresis to obtain better resolution of the products of the reaction than is possible with sucrose gradients (Pace et al., 1967, 1968). The time course of appearance of the various forms (Fig. 11-8) indicates in a convincing way that the

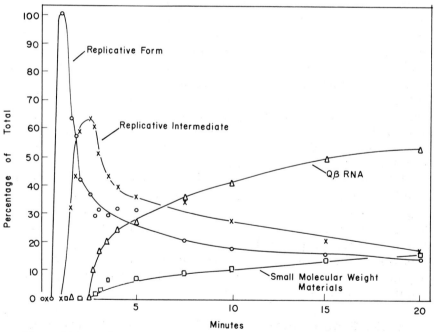

Figure 11-8. Relative amounts, at various times, of the replicative form, replicative intermediate, $Q\beta$ RNA, and small molecular weight materials in the in vitro synthesis of viral RNA. The reaction mixture was analyzed into its components by acrylamide gel electrophoresis at each of the indicated times. (Redrawn from Pace et al., 1967.)

first step in synthesis is the formation of the double-stranded replicative form. Next, the replicative intermediate is detected, and then single-stranded viral RNA molecules.

It will be necessary to determine whether these in vitro results are pertinent to the in vivo replication of RNA phages. There is no necessity, for instance, for phage RNA to have messenger RNA activity in vitro, as all the enzymes and cofactors are supplied. Further, if there are in fact two enzymes involved in the cell — one for synthesis of duplexes from viral strand and another for synthesis of viral strands from the duplexes (Lodish and Zinder, 1966a) — then both may not be necessary for in vitro synthesis. It will be necessary to isolate and purify the two enzymes and to study them separately. Already there seems to be a difference in the product depending on the enzyme preparation used (Feix *et al.*, 1967a). The in vitro synthesis, free of possible competing cellular processes, may be much simpler and may require less enzymatic help. The in vitro occurrence of the duplex may be entirely dependent on such experimental conditions as pH, temperature, and ionic strength, which ordinarily are controlled by the cell rather than by the experimenter's reaction mixture.

In any event, the in vitro synthesis of a biologically active genetic structure opens vast new areas of exploration. Spiegelman and his colleagues have begun to explore some of these areas. They have, for instance, studied the "evolution" of the replicating RNA entirely in vitro (Mills *et al.*, 1967). They performed a serial transfer experiment, similar to that shown in Figure 11-7, but sampled each reaction tube to make the transfer after a short reaction time. Thus, they "selected" for the most rapidly replicating molecules. It is not necessary in this system for many of the viral genes to be propagated. For instance, those that code for enzymes and for coat proteins are not necessary, and deletions of one or more are not lethal mutations, although they would be for phage growth in cells.

Mills and his coworkers found that the RNA originally derived from Qβ was still replicating after 75 transfers, but the product was no longer infective for *E. coli* protoplasts and its molecular weight had decreased until only 17 per cent of the original genome remained. What did remain replicated at a high rate in vitro and had become stabilized in the sense that further transfers resulted in no further loss of genetic material. It will be interesting to learn the nature of the bit of self-replicating RNA genome that remained.

Replication of Double-Stranded Viral RNA. Many questions can be asked about the replication of double-stranded RNA of the reovirus-wound tumor virus group. Some pertinent questions are whether transfer of RNA from parent to progeny occurs, whether the RNA replicates semiconservatively or by some other mechanism, whether it uses a preëxisting cellular enzyme for its replication, and how it directs the synthesis of messenger RNA. Answers to most of these questions are not available. Definitive experiments pertaining to replication and to the possibility of transfer have not been done.

Some information is available, however. It is possible to distinguish single-stranded forms of reovirus RNA from double-stranded, because the latter is relatively resistant to ribonuclease. By this criterion, both forms of RNA have been detected in infected cells. Kudo and Graham (1965) centrifuged RNA of infected cells through gradients and found peaks corresponding to the single-stranded and double-stranded forms, as had been found in cells infected with single-stranded RNA viruses. In this case, however, the peak of double-stranded RNA corresponded to viral RNA, of both parental and progeny origin.

The origin of the peak of single-stranded RNA was not as clear. Presumably it contained messenger RNA synthesized using viral RNA as template, but this supposition has not been tested. Also unknown is whether messenger RNA is transcribed from double-stranded viral RNA in any way analogous to its transcription from DNA.

Cells have been exposed to actinomycin D to test whether viral RNA uses cellular DNA-dependent RNA polymerase. Actinomycin D blocks transcription of DNA into RNA by combining with DNA and inhibiting the enzyme. At doses of the drug that effectively block cellular RNA synthesis, viral RNA synthesis continues (Kudo and Graham, 1965) and may even be augmented (Loh and Soergel, 1965, 1966). Viral replication is inhibited by higher doses of the drug (Gomatos *et al.*, 1962), but this presumably is due to secondary effects on the cell rather than being the direct effect of blocking the enzyme. In tests with isolated enzymes it was found that reovirus RNA does not direct polynucleotide synthesis by either RNA polymerase or DNA polymerase of *E. coli* (Shatkin, 1965). It is supposed, therefore, that reovirus directs the synthesis of new enzymes for its replication.

Further evidence that a new enzyme is required comes from studies with puromycin, an inhibitor of protein synthesis. Synthesis of both single- and double-stranded viral-related RNA begins about 7 hours after infection. Puromycin added at 9 hours does not inhibit the formation of single-stranded RNA, which continues to be synthesized. Puromycin added at 5 hours completely blocks viral RNA synthesis. Apparently a new enzyme for synthesis of single-stranded RNA arises between 5 and 9 hours after infection. If puromycin is added to cells at 9 hours, even after synthesis of double-stranded viral RNA has begun, it inhibits further synthesis of the double strands. This suggests that perhaps another new enzyme is involved in replication of the double-stranded form and that this enzyme has a high turnover (Kudo and Graham, 1966).

The fragmentary evidence available on reoviruses is sufficient to indicate that further studies on their mode of replication should prove interesting.

Effects on Host Cells

Infection of animal cells with RNA-containing viruses, as with DNA-containing viruses, produces visible changes in the cells. The changes, called cytopathic effects, are characteristic for the virus causing the infection. Poliovirus, for instance, causes cells to become rounded, to have increased refractility, and to become detached from the culture vessel. A few RNA viruses, for instance measles virus, cause the formation of giant cells. All these changes are transient, leading finally to cell death with release of virus.

The mechanisms by which the virus causes the changes are poorly understood, although some viral-induced changes in the host cell have been worked out. Infection of mouse cells with EMC virus (Fig. 11-9) causes a rapid initial drop in RNA synthesis (Martin *et al.*, 1961; Martin, 1967); others have shown similar results for other small RNA viruses (Holland, 1962; Holland and Peterson, 1964; Holland, 1964b; Hausen and Verwoerd, 1963; Fenwick, 1963). The shutting-off of cellular RNA synthesis occurs rapidly, not by breakdown of cellular DNA, but by interference with the host cell's DNA-dependent RNA polymerase (Baltimore and Franklin, 1962a; Holland, 1962; Balandin and Franklin, 1964). This interference, very similar to interference by actinomycin D, is brought about by the viral genome that directs the synthesis of a new, inhibitory protein as one of its first activities in the newly infected cell (Baltimore *et al.*, 1963). The later increase in RNA synthesis shown in Figure 11-9 is due to synthesis of viral RNA for incorporation into virions.

Host cell protein synthesis also diminishes following infection by these viruses (Fig. 11-9). The effect cannot be a result of only the cessation of RNA synthesis, since the inhibition of protein synthesis occurs before the similar inhibition caused by actinomycin D (Holland and Peterson, 1964). The rapid cessation of protein synthesis is reflected in a similarly rapid decrease in the polysomes of infected cells; the decrease in polysomes also occurs more rapidly because of virus infection than because of actinomycin D (Penman *et al.*, 1963, 1964). Later in the infective cycle, when viral-specific protein synthesis increases (Fig. 11-9), there is an increase in polysomes. At this time, the polysomes contain viral proteins (Penman *et al.*, 1963, 1964; Dalgarno *et al.*, 1967). It is not known whether the drastic changes in the cellular macromolecular syntheses account for the development of cytopathic effect in infected cells. Although cytopathic effects are not apparent in bacteria infected with RNA phages, there is

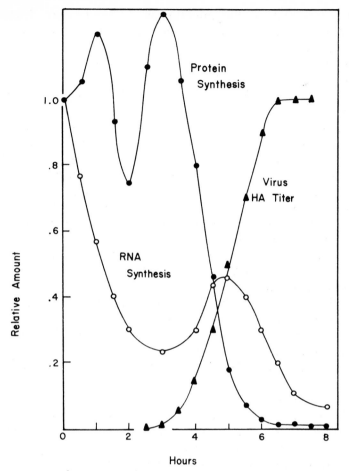

Figure 11-9.   Relative rates of synthesis of RNA and protein during the growth cycle of EMC virus in Krebs ascites tumor cells. (Redrawn from Martin, 1967.)

a similar pattern of suppression of host cell RNA (Hudson and Paranchych, 1967).

Maturation

The shift in emphasis from synthesis of cellular RNA and polysomes to synthesis of viral RNA is accompanied by a shift in the intracellular site of RNA synthesis. In the normal cell, RNA is synthesized almost exclusively on DNA templates in the nucleus; however, viral infection changes this. For example, autoradiographic studies have demonstrated that the uptake of tritium-labeled uridine in the nucleus is greatly diminished after infection with Mengo virus. Instead, the label (showing RNA synthesis) occurs around the nucleus in the cytoplasm (Franklin and Rosner, 1962). This is the same site where electron microscope studies have indicated some evidence of viral replication: an increase of ribosomal or viral particles and cytoplasmic vesicles (Horne and Nagington, 1959; Franklin and Baltimore, 1962; Becker *et al.*, 1963).

A different kind of experiment suggests that poliovirus also multiplies in the cytoplasm. Using microsurgery, Crocker *et al.* (1964) and Dunnebacke (1962) cut off bits of cytoplasm from poliovirus-infected cells. Such cytoplasmic remnants produced poliovirus. Fractionation of poliovirus-infected cells by centrifugation accomplishes somewhat the same separation of cells into nuclear and cytoplasmic portions, and Holland and Bassett (1964) found that infectious RNA can be extracted from the cytoplasm but not from the nucleus. None of the studies rules out a rapid, early stage of replication in the nucleus with later stages in the cytoplasm.

Final stages of reovirus assembly take place in the cytoplasm around the mitotic spindle fibers (Dales, 1963b; Spendlove *et al.*, 1963). It is not clear why maturation occurs at this site, since treatment of cells with colchicine, which causes mitotic spindle fibers to disappear, does not abolish formation of reovirus; in fact, it seems to have no substantial effect on reovirus production (Dales, 1963b; Dales *et al.*, 1965).

Little is known about how the RNA viruses are assembled. Presumably, assembly occurs by a process similar to crystallization, as it does with the DNA-containing viruses. Supporting this conclusion is the observation that tobacco mosaic virus can be disrupted in such a way that when the isolated protein and RNA components are mixed they reassemble into infectious particles (Fraenkel-Conrat and Williams, 1955). Infective R17 virions have been assembled in vitro from purified components; assembly is greatly enhanced by adding a minor protein component that may initiate assembly (Roberts and Steitz, 1967). Extensive studies with cowpea chlorotic mottle virus, a small icosahedral plant virus, indicate that it, too, may be induced to reassemble in vitro (Bancroft *et al.*, 1967).

Of the RNA viruses, the mechanism of final assembly is best known for the myxoviruses. What is known, however, is not applicable to the other RNA viruses.

Influenza virus and other myxoviruses undergo two stages of assembly that can be identified with the electron microscope (Morgan *et al.*, 1962). The first stage is the assembly of the nucleoprotein core occurring in the nucleus of the infected cell (Fig. 11-10). This nucleoprotein material has been identified as the noninfectious soluble antigen that is released from dying infected cells, apparently as cores left

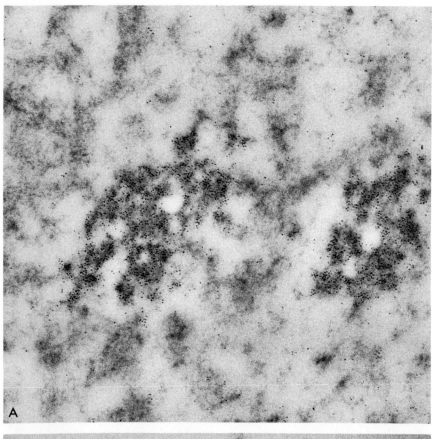

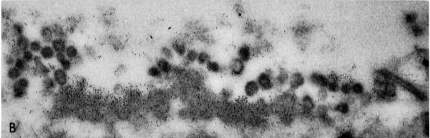

Figure 11-10. Stages in the formation of the nucleoprotein "core" of influenza virus. Specific antigenic components of the virus can be identified in these electron micrographs of thin sections of infected cells by means of ferritin-labeled antibody. Antibody in this case was prepared using the soluble antigen of the virus. A sectioned nucleus is shown in *A*; the clumps of material in the center are viral soluble antigen (that is, the internal nucleoprotein) because it has reacted with the antibody. The field shown in *B* contains the cytoplasmic membrane (the outside of the cell is toward the top). Just below the membrane, inside the cell, is an accumulation of soluble antigen, and some seems to have been released from the cell. The viral particles just outside the cell have not reacted with the antibody. (Morgan *et al.*, 1962. By permission of the authors and the editors of the Cold Spring Harbor Symposia on Quantitative Biology.)

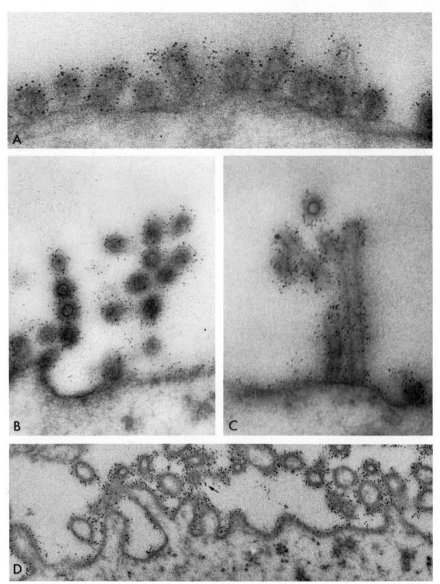

Figure 11-11. Stages in the formation of influenza virions. As in Figure 11-10, antibody tagged with ferritin was used to label specific virus components. In this case, the antibody is against the mature virion, not the internal component. In these pictures, the cytoplasmic membrane runs horizontally, with the outside of the cell toward the top. Virions are shown in *A* and *B* as they bud from the cell membrane. Filamentous forms are shown in *C*. One virion is shown in *D* (marked by the arrow); the other "particles," labeled with the antibody, are incomplete forms lacking the internal component but with viral antigenic specificity. (Morgan *et al.*, 1962. By permission of the authors and the editors of the Cold Spring Symposia on Quantitative Biology.)

over and not assembled into virions. The antigenic components of the soluble antigen are different from those of infectious virus. After assembly in the nucleus, the soluble antigen, or viral core, migrates somehow to the cytoplasm just beneath the cytoplasmic membrane where the second stage of assembly occurs. The viral core is extruded through the membrane in a process called "budding." After being pushed into a small pocket of the cytoplasmic membrane, it is pinched off as a completed virion (Fig. 11-11). Variable-sized packages are formed, accounting for the variability in size and morphology of influenza virions (see Fig. 3-8).

A similar mechanism adds the envelope to Sindbis virus, and it has been shown that the phospholipid of the viral envelope comes from preëxisting cellular material, whereas the protein of the viral envelope is newly synthesized (Pfefferkorn and Hunter, 1963; Pfefferkorn and Clifford, 1964). Synthesis of some of the components of viral membrane may be directed by the viral genome, while other components are cellular in origin. This could account for the occurrence of partial, incomplete, antigenic specificity. Some of the RNA-containing tumor viruses are quite similar to the myxoviruses in that they bud from the cell surface and have mixed antigenic specificities.

The RNA-containing phages are released from their host cells by lysis. The lysis of f2 is mediated by the coat protein, as evidenced by the fact that mutants that make defective coat protein do not cause lysis (Zinder and Lyons, 1968). The remarkable economy possessed by f2, and presumably other RNA phages, is quite evident. Instead of possessing three genes to specify proteins for each of three purposes, one protein serves three functions: It forms the capsid, regulates translation, and lyses the cell.

Previous chapters have shown that viral genetic material insinuates into the genetic mechanisms of host cells in diverse patterns. The net result, the production of more virus particles, occurs by patterns of growth curves that are similar for different viruses, but by a mode of replication not possessed by any other biological entity. Viruses parasitize host cells at a fundamental level of organization — at the level of macromolecules involved in genetic expression. An even more subtle level of parasitism is exhibited by some viruses that are "parasitic" on other viruses.

Further Reading

Darnell, J. E., M. Girard, D. Baltimore, D. F. Summers, and J. V. Maizel: The synthesis and Translation of Poliovirus RNA. *In* Colter, J. S., and W. Paranchych (eds.): The Molecular Biology of Viruses. New York, Academic Press Inc., 1967, pp. 375-401.

Erikson, R. L., and R. M. Franklin: Formation and Properties of a Replicative Interme-
    diate in the Biosynthesis of Viral Ribonucleic Acid. Bacteriological Reviews,
    30:267-278, 1966.
Martin, E. M.: Replication of Small RNA Viruses. British Medical Bulletin, 23:192-197,
    1967.
Shatkin, A. J., and B. Rada: Studies on the Replication of Reovirus. *In* Colter, J. S., and
    W. Paranchych, (eds.): The Molecular Biology of Viruses. New York, Academic
    Press Inc., 1967, pp. 427-447.
Spiegelman, S.: An In Vitro Analysis of a Replicating Molecule. American Scientist,
    55:221-264, 1967.

12

VIRUSES "PARASITIC" ON OTHER VIRUSES

Many viruses are defective in the sense that they do not contain sufficient information to code for all the proteins necessary for their replication. They can attach to cells, penetrate, and release their nucleic acid within the cell; but the cell does not produce infectious virus except under certain circumstances, such as being infected at the same time with a "helper" virus.

Many defective viruses arise as mutants which can replicate only in the highly artificial circumstances of a laboratory experiment, but some defective viruses occur naturally. Four naturally occurring defective virus-helper virus systems will be discussed in this chapter. They have been selected from the many possibilities because they present problems that are of special interest.

In all four systems, one virus is unable to replicate except in the presence of a second virus, but the basis for the defectiveness and for the helper activity is different in each system. These examples illustrate that the dependence of viruses on a cell's metabolic machinery can extend to dependence on machinery newly introduced into the cell by another virus.

TOBACCO NECROSIS VIRUS AND ITS SATELLITE VIRUS

One strain of tobacco necrosis virus, the Rothamsted strain, is distinguishable from other strains in that two sizes of virions are present. Early work with this strain showed that the two kinds of particles are serologically unrelated and that only the larger of the two particles is infective. Both always seemed to occur together, even in cultures prepared from repeated single-lesion isolations. Partial separation of the two classes of particles has been achieved by centrifugation through sucrose gradients (Kassanis and Nixon, 1961).

More recent electron microscopy (Kassanis, 1962) with the phosphotungstic acid negative contrast technique confirmed the two size classes, and measurements showed their diameters to be about 28 mμ and about 20 mμ respectively (Fig. 12-1). The smaller virion probably has 42 structural units or capsomers. Further details of its structure will be presented later.

The larger particles, sometimes designated TNV, cause characteristic necrotic lesions when inoculated on tobacco leaves. Isolated satellite particles, however, do not; nor do leaves inoculated with satellite virus yield particles. Inoculation of mixtures of tobacco necrosis virus and its satellite yield both kinds of particles. RNA prepared from tobacco necrosis virus by phenol extraction is infectious, but RNA prepared from satellite virus is not unless it is mixed with intact tobacco necrosis virus or RNA isolated from tobacco necrosis virus (Kassanis and Nixon, 1961). Other strains of tobacco necrosis virus, but no other plant viruses, can serve as "helper" viruses.

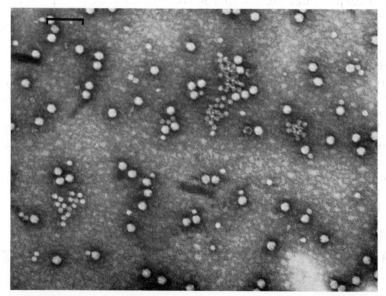

Figure 12-1. Electron micrograph, by negative staining, of tobacco necrosis virus, about 28 mμ diameter, and its satellite virus, about 20 mμ diameter. (Bar is 100 mμ.) (Kassanis and Nixon, 1961. By permission of the authors and the editors of the Journal of General Microbiology.)

Multiplication of satellite tobacco necrosis virus reduces the size and number of lesions caused by tobacco necrosis virus, a phenomenon on which an assay for the satellite virus is based (Kassanis, 1962). Consequently, there is evidence that satellite tobacco necrosis virus is unable to replicate by itself, that it is specifically dependent on tobacco necrosis virus for help in replication, and that as a result of the interaction of the two viruses during replication, the helper virus is inhibited.

A clue to how satellite tobacco necrosis virus depends on tobacco necrosis virus is derived from consideration of the small particle's structure. Reichmann (1964) pointed out that the virion's molecular weight is only 1.97×10^6 daltons. Of this, 20 per cent, or 3.94×10^5 daltons, is RNA; and the remainder, 1.58×10^6 daltons, is protein.

Electron microscopy indicates that there are probably 42 structural units, which means that each has a molecular weight of about 38,000 daltons. This value agrees well with the 39,000 daltons found by direct analysis. Each morphological subunit, therefore, corresponds to a single protein molecule. By direct analysis, each protein subunit contains 372 amino acid residues, plus an undetermined number of tryptophan residues.

The molecular weight and base composition of the RNA molecule indicate that it must contain about 1200 nucleotides. With a coding ratio of three nucleotides for each amino acid, satellite tobacco necrosis virus contains only enough nucleotides to code for its coat protein. The RNA molecule of satellite tobacco necrosis virus therefore contains only one gene or cistron. Its dependency on tobacco necrosis virus probably means that it has a need for enzymes that are coded by the tobacco necrosis virus genes and not otherwise possessed by plant cells. The nature of these enzymes is unknown, but an RNA-dependent RNA polymerase is one possibility. Competition for this or some other enzyme by the two viral RNA molecules could result in the inhibition of the tobacco necrosis virus.

However, circumstantial evidence that satellite tobacco necrosis viral RNA contains only one gene is not sufficient. Direct evidence that the satellite's RNA codes only for its coat protein was obtained by using the RNA in a cell-free protein synthesizing system. The protein produced under these conditions consists only of viral coat protein (Clark *et al.*, 1965).

ADENOVIRUS AND ITS ASSOCIATED VIRUS

A somewhat similar system occurs with adenoviruses. Almost simultaneously, three groups of investigators in different laboratories (Archetti and Steve-Bocciarelli, 1965; Mayor *et al.*, 1965; Melnick *et al.*, 1965; Atchison *et al.*, 1965) reported that stock preparations of adenoviruses examined by electron microscopy contain two kinds of particles: small particles measuring about 20 mμ and adenovirus that measures about 70 to 85 mμ in diameter (Fig. 12-2). The small particles are called adeno-associated virus (AAV) or adeno-satellite virus (ASV).

Smith *et al.* (1966) found that electron micrographs of the small particles are indistinct and that it is difficult to deduce the structure of the particles. They seem, however, to be icosahedral and to be composed of subunits. There may be 12 capsomers in the capsid (Mayor *et al.*, 1965) but this is not certain. "Full" as well as "empty" particles are easily found and no envelope has been observed.

Because the particles are more dense (about 1.40 g./ml.) than adenovirus particles (about 1.34 g./ml.), separation of the two can be achieved by density gradient ultracentrifugation. However, there is cross-contamination of each type of particle by the other (Smith *et al.*, 1966). A better way to remove adenovirus from mixtures is based on their difference in size. Filtration of the virus preparation through a membrane with 50 mμ pore diameter allows the small particle to pass through but retains the larger adenovirus (Atchison *et al.*, 1965).

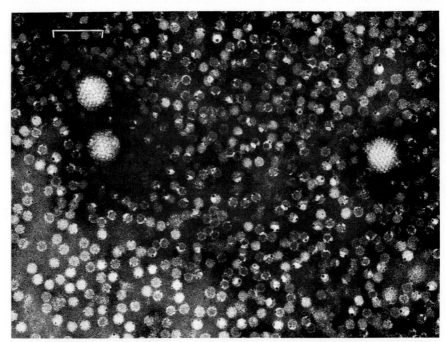

Figure 12-2.   Electron micrograph, by negative staining, of simian virus 15, about 85 mμ in diameter, and adeno-associated virus, type 1, about 24 mμ in diameter. (Bar is 100 mμ.) (Unpublished electron micrograph courtesy of Dr. R. W. Atchison.)

The DNA of the adeno-associated virus (AAV) has been studied in some detail (Rose *et al.*, 1966; Parks *et al.*, 1967a). It is double stranded, is linear, has a molecular weight of about 3.5×10^6 daltons, and contains about 55 per cent guanine plus cytosine residues.

The DNA molecule is almost 10 times the molecular weight of the RNA molecule of satellite tobacco necrosis virus and could contain five to eight genes. Being about the same molecular weight as polyoma virus, adeno-associated virus could perhaps be independent. So far, it has been found to replicate only in cells coinfected with an adenovirus. Thus, adeno-associated virus may replicate independently in some type of cell that has not been tried as yet, or it may lack some essential function that always must be coded by an adenovirus.

There are four known serotypes of adeno-associated viruses (Hoggan *et al.*, 1966; Parks *et al.*, 1967b), all of which originally were found in preparations of adenoviruses grown in either simian or human cell cultures. Types 2 and 3 have been isolated from children experiencing an adenovirus infection. Although the children had an increase in antibody to the adeno-associated virus, showing that the virus multiplied, there was no disease attributable to the adeno-associated virus (Blacklow *et al.*, 1967, 1968). Rapoza and Atchison (1967) screened 92 human sera and found 19 with antibodies to type 1 adeno-associated virus; seven of 14 rhesus monkeys tested had antibodies. Adeno-associated virus type 4 seems to be a simian virus (Mayor and Ito, 1967).

Adenoviruses from other species can serve as helper to the adeno-associated virus in any kind of cell in which the adenovirus can grow. For instance, the adenovirus from dogs, infectious canine hepatitis virus, will act as helper for adeno-associated viruses of monkey origin (Smith and Gehle, 1967; Casto *et al.*, 1967b; Hoggan *et al.*, 1966). Whatever missing function is supplied by the adenovirus helper, it is apparently a function common to all adenoviruses.

Electron microscope pictures of infected cells show that both the adenovirus and its associated virus are present in the same nucleus. When the adeno-associated virus is present, however, there is a decreased number of adenovirus particles (Archetti *et al.*, 1966; Atchison *et al.*, 1966). Similar results were obtained by use of fluorescent-labeled antibodies, which indicated that when a cell nucleus contains antigen of one virus, it has less antigen of the other (Mayor *et al.*, 1967). Measurement of adenovirus yields from cells with and without adeno-associated virus shows that the associated virus inhibits the adenovirus (Casto *et al.*, 1967a, 1967b; Parks *et al.*, 1967b, 1968). The relationship between virus concentration and number of cells yielding adenovirus suggests that the presence of a single infectious adeno-associated particle in a cell infected with one or a few adenovirus particles is sufficient to inhibit completely that cell's output of adenovirus (Casto *et al.*, 1967a). Figure 12-3 demonstrates that adeno-associated virus inhibits plaque formation by the adenovirus.

Studies on the nature of the interaction between adenovirus and its associated virus are underway to determine the mechanism for the helping and inhibiting reactions. Electron microscopic counts of virus released from cells (Parks *et al.*, 1967b) and similar studies using an immunofluorescent assay (Ito *et al.*, 1967) revealed that the titer of adeno-associated virus increases in a typical growth curve when adeno-virus helper is present. The adeno-associated virus enters a latent period for 6 to 8 hours before rising to a step about 18 to 24 hours later.

Preinfection of the cells with adenovirus shortens the latent period for growth of its associated virus. If the helper adenovirus has a 12 to 16 hour head start, the latent period of the associated virus is

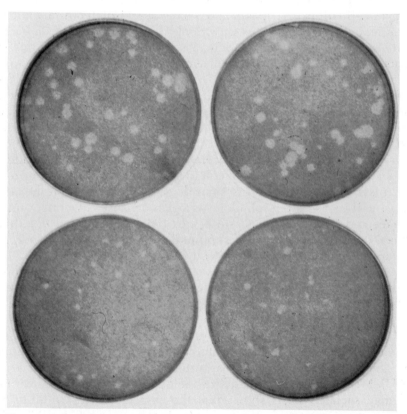

Figure 12-3.   Inhibition of adenovirus by adeno-associated virus. The upper two dishes were seeded with adenovirus alone, in a concentration sufficient to produce about 45 plaques. The lower two dishes received the same amount of adenovirus as the upper two and, in addition, were infected with adeno-associated virus at a multiplicity of one infectious unit per cell. The plaques in the latter case were smaller and the dishes contained about 25 adenovirus plaques each. (Courtesy of Dr. B. Casto.)

shortened to as little as 4 hours. It seems, therefore, that whatever gene function of the adenovirus the dependent virus needs, either it is transcribed late in the adenovirus cycle or it is an early function whose product must build up to some threshold level for the associated virus (Parks *et al.*, 1967b; Ito *et al.*, 1967).

The nature of the inhibition of adenovirus by AAV is not known. Apparently it is not due to interferon (a protein to be discussed in more detail in the next chapter), because interferon is not detectable in cultures containing adenovirus and its associated virus, nor does adeno-associated virus inhibit other viruses that are known to be sensitive to interferon (Casto *et al.*, 1967a).

It is also possible that adeno-associated virus is not as dependent as presently thought. Perhaps it requires adenovirus helper in cell cultures but infects independently in some cells. For instance, with human adenovirus as helper, the H-1 virus will grow in human cells, but not if the helper is not present (Ledinko and Toolan, 1968). As will be discussed in the next section, defectiveness in one cell type but not in another occurs with certain other viruses; this could also occur with adeno-associated virus.

SV40-ADENOVIRUS INTERACTION

Under certain conditions, adenoviruses assume the role of dependent virus rather than helper (see review by Rapp and Melnick, 1966). The many different combinations of helper and dependent viruses and cell type in which they are grown present a picture too complex to be discussed in its entirety. Therefore, the major part of the SV40-human adenovirus interactions to be discussed here will be of adenovirus types 7 and 12, as they have been more extensively studied. Both grow only to a limited extent (if at all) in cultures of monkey kidney cells. Like other human adenoviruses, both grow very well in human cells. SV40, in contrast, grows well in African green monkey kidney cells.

One of the first indications of an interaction between SV40 and adenovirus was reported by O'Conor *et al.* (1963) in an electron micrographic study of the infection of monkey kidney cells by SV40 and human adenovirus type 12. The difference in size of the two kinds of particles allowed them to be identified in the nuclei of infected cells.

When the two viruses were added simultaneously to the cells, about 1 per cent of nuclei had both types of particle. When addition of adenovirus type 12 was delayed by 18.5 or 24 hours, however, the percentage of nuclei with both kinds of particles increased to 15 and 40 per cent respectively. Thus, simultaneous infection of a cell by two unrelated viruses can occur, and preinfection by SV40 increases the likelihood of infection by adenovirus type 12. Further studies (Rabson *et al.*, 1964) showed that when SV40 is present, the number of doubly infected nuclei is somewhat increased, and the yield of adenovirus type 12 is increased by about a hundredfold.

Part of the infective cycle of adenovirus takes place in African green monkey kidney cells even in the absence of SV40 helper activity (Rapp *et al.*, 1967). For instance, O'Conor *et al.* (1965) found that material related to virus infection and visible by electron microscopy developed in nuclei of cells infected with adenovirus alone or with adenovirus and SV40 together. Mature adenovirus particles developed only in the latter cells.

Similar conclusions were reached by Rowe and Baum (1965) who studied the development of two antigens in infected cells. The first antigen is called the T (tumor) antigen; it is present in tumor cells induced by the adenoviruses, and it is also present in infected cells early in the replicative cycle. The second antigen tested for was the virus capsid antigen that appears late in the infective cycle, after mature virus begins to form. Human adenovirus infection of African green monkey kidney cells results in the production of capsid antigen unless SV40 is also present. Similar results, shown in Table 12-1, were reported by Rapp (1966) for adenovirus types 2 and 7. Furthermore, the production of human adenoviral hemagglutinin in African green monkey kidney cells requires SV40 helper (Wertz *et al.*, 1965). It therefore seems reasonably certain that "early" functions of human adenoviral DNA occur without helper activity in simian cells, but for both "early" and "late" functions to occur, resulting in a complete infective cycle, the SV40 helper activity must be present.

In Chapter 9 several examples were presented to demonstrate

TABLE 12-1. EFFECT OF SV40 ON FORMATION OF ANTIGENS AND INFECTIOUS VIRIONS IN AFRICAN GREEN MONKEY KIDNEY CELLS INFECTED WITH ADENOVIRUS°

	ADENOVIRAL ANTIGEN		TITER (PFU/ml.) (hours postinfection)	
	TUMOR	VIRION	1	72
Adenovirus Type 7	+	−	5×10^4	6×10^3
+ SV40	+	+	3×10^4	6×10^6
Adenovirus Type 2	+	−	8×10^4	1×10^4
+ SV40	+	+	10×10^4	2×10^7

°Modified from Rapp, 1966.

that mature virus need not be produced for the cultures to develop viral cytopathology and typical cytopathic effects. Typical adenoviral cytopathic effect develops in monkey kidney cells even if the replicative cycle aborts (Rabson *et al.*, 1964). Thus, we have another example illustrating that the cause of cytopathic effect must be the production of viral-related materials rather than the production of mature virus particles.

Reich *et al.* (1966a) used molecular hybridization to measure amounts of various specific DNA molecules synthesized in infected cells. To do this, they first prepared radioactively labeled RNA complementary to DNA extracted from purified virus. This tagged RNA specifically binds to its DNA even when the DNA is part of a mixture of various kinds of DNA. By this method, they found that synthesis of adenoviral DNA occurs in monkey kidney cells even in the absence of SV40 helper activity. About two or three times as much adenoviral DNA is synthesized if SV40 is present, but under the same conditions, 1000 times as much infectious adenovirus is synthesized.

The net effect of adenovirus infection of monkey kidney cells without SV40 resembles infection of human kidney cells in the presence of an agent that blocks DNA synthesis, such as 5-fluorodeoxyuridine. In both cases, cytopathology occurs and the early T antigen forms. With the drug, however, DNA synthesis does not occur. SV40 must therefore enhance adenoviral replication by some mechanism other than stimulation of adenoviral DNA synthesis. This mechanism, which has yet to be worked out, could involve other macromolecular functions. For instance, it could enhance transcription of adenoviral DNA information into messenger RNA, or translation of the information into protein.

Whatever the mechanism, adenovirus can perform the function in human cells but not in monkey cells. However, the function for which human adenovirus cannot code in monkey cells can be supplied by a monkey adenovirus; at least, coinfection of monkey cells by both human and monkey adenovirus results in an enhancement of replication of the human adenovirus (Naegele and Rapp, 1967).

Furthermore, Schell *et al.* (1966) reported that SV40 enhances the tumor-producing ability of the adenoviruses. An SV40-adenovirus type 12 mixture grown in monkey kidney cells produced more tumors, and produced them more quickly, than did either virus alone. Viral carcinogenesis will be discussed more fully in a later chapter; however, it can be mentioned here that the enhancing effect of SV40 on adenovirus replication also extends to the oncogenic effect. This suggests that some common mechanism may be operative in both the oncogenic and the lytic interactions, but it does not, of course, establish it.

ROUS SARCOMA VIRUS AND ITS ASSOCIATED VIRUSES

Rous sarcoma virus is one of the oldest, best-studied tumor viruses. As such, it will be discussed in greater detail in a later chapter. Recently, it was reported that Rous sarcoma virus is defective, unable to replicate without helper activity. This aspect of growth of Rous sarcoma virus, reviewed by Hanafusa and Hanafusa (1967), will be discussed here.

Unlike most viruses, Rous sarcoma virus and its relatives do not produce a lytic cycle of infection. Instead, they cause the cells to become malignant and to continue to grow and divide. These cells continually produce virus. Exceptional cells, however, do not produce virus at all. The proportion of nonproducers can be increased greatly by growing the cells in the presence of antiserum to the Rous associated virus (Hanafusa *et al.*, 1963), which has been found in many stocks of Rous sarcoma virus. Various other experiments have confirmed that the Rous associated virus plays a helper role for production of Rous sarcoma virus. For instance, nonproducers continue to grow indefinitely, without producing any infectious virions (but may produce noninfectious virions [Robinson, 1967]). When Rous associated virus is added, the cells change immediately into producers of both Rous sarcoma virus and Rous associated virus. The genome of the defective Rous sarcoma virus must therefore be present in the nonproducing cells and propagated to progeny cells, but must be unable to mature into complete virus.

The Rous associated virus is one of several viruses closely related to Rous sarcoma virus (Rubin and Vogt, 1962; Hanafusa, 1965). This group makes up the avian leukosis complex, the members of which induce various kinds of malignancies in chickens. Any other member of the avian leukosis complex can also serve as helper for the Rous sarcoma virus (Hanafusa *et al.*, 1964).

Detailed antigenic analysis of the Rous sarcoma virus produced with the help of various associated viruses or leukosis viruses reveals the antigenic stamp of the helper on the newly synthesized virus. Since the antigenic properties of these viruses reside in the envelope, the function that Rous sarcoma virus lacks and that is supplied by the helper must code for envelope synthesis (Hanafusa, 1965; Hanafusa *et al.*, 1964).

Much remains to be learned about the enhancing effects of one virus on another. Present knowledge indicates that varying degrees of dependence exist and that dependence can occur as a result of a multitude of molecular mechanisms.

In the next chapter, virus interactions of the opposite kind—resulting in inhibition—will be discussed.

Further Reading

Rapp, F., and J. L. Melnick: Papovavirus SV40, Adenovirus and Their Hybrids; Transformation, Complementation, and Transcapsidation. Progress in Medical Virology, 8:349-399, 1966.
Rubin, H.: A Defective Cancer Virus. Scientific American, 210(June):46-52, 1964.

13

INTERFERENCE WITH VIRAL REPLICATION

In the preceding chapter, several examples of interacting viruses were presented, illustrating the fact that sometimes one virus can enhance the growth of a second virus. Interaction between viruses can also result in inhibition of one virus by another.

Such interference can occur at the level of a host population. For instance, epidemics of virulent poliovirus have apparently been shortened by rapid mass administration of active attenuated poliovirus. In such instances, a decrease in new poliovirus cases occurred within a few days, even when the vaccine virus was of a different serotype from the virulent virus. Thus, interference was not due to the development of antibodies.

The behavior of poliovirus in the population is a reflection of its behavior in the individuals who make up the population. In other words, if an individual has an intestinal infection with one virus, such as an attenuated variant of poliovirus, that individual is relatively insensitive to infection by a second enteric virus, such as the poliovirus causing the epidemic.

Can the behavior of poliovirus in a human enteric infection be a manifestation of its behavior in the cells of that person's intestinal trace? The answer is yes, and the mechanisms by which this may occur will be discussed in this chapter.

A point brought out by the poliovirus example should be emphasized. It is obvious that previous infection by a virus can cause the development of antibodies, making the individual relatively resistant to a second infection by the same or a closely related virus. Such immunity does not fall within the scope of this chapter. The kind of interference to be discussed occurs between viruses that may be sero-logically unrelated; it can be demonstrated in cell cultures, where there are no antibody immune systems.

INTERFERENCE AT THE CELLULAR LEVEL

As previously discussed, infection of a bacterial cell by certain phages excludes other phages from that cell (see Chapter 8). The ex-clusion seems to be due to a deoxyribonuclease synthesized by the cell under the direction of the first phage. The enzyme degrades the DNA of any virus that subsequently infects the cell, thereby pre-venting its replication. Another example of interference, occurring in lysogenic cells, will be discussed in a later chapter.

As Schlesinger (1959) pointed out, there are many pairs of more-or-less related animal viruses that interfere with one another. In many of these cases, it has been shown that the interference occurs at the level of the individual infected cells.

For example, Baluda (1957) studied viral interference in tissue cultures. The Newcastle disease virus that induced the interference had been inactivated by ultraviolet irradiation so that only the super-infecting virus would be capable of replication. In his experi-ments, Baluda asked whether interference was all or none — that is, whether a given cell infected by an irradiated virion would be com-pletely incapable of yielding virus when superinfected by active virus — or whether the yield per cell was diminished. He found that a given cell produced either a full yield of superinfecting virus or none at all.

He also asked how many irradiated particles were required to induce interference in susceptible cells. With the assumption that the Poisson distribution would apply, he found that infection of a cell by a single irradiated virion was sufficient to confer immunity on that cell.

Immunity developed promptly, within less than a minute, but it was not permanent; after a period of 24 to 48 hours, the cell became susceptible again to infection.

At the time Baluda was performing his experiments, the nature of interference was a mystery. He added much new information con-cerning interference, but the mechanism remained unknown. Now it is known that at least several mechanisms can account for interference between animal viruses. One of these is mediated by a substance called *interferon*.

INTERFERON AND VIRAL INTERFERENCE

Isaacs and Lindenmann (1957) had been performing experiments with influenza virus as follows: Pieces of the chorioallantoic membrane from embryonated chicken eggs were placed in a suspension of heat-inactivated influenza virus. After 3 hours of incubation at 37° C., during which time virus adsorbed, the pieces of membranes were rinsed and transferred to tubes containing buffered salt solution. These tubes were incubated at 37° C. for 24 hours, then the membranes were discarded. The salt solution in which the membranes had been incubated was tested for viral-inhibitory activity. This was done by placing a fresh piece of membrane in the solution for a 24 hour incubation period, then challenging the membrane with active influenza virus. It was found that membranes so treated did not support the growth of active virus but that untreated membranes would, under the same condition of infection. It was concluded that an extracellular product had been produced in response to inactive influenza virus and that this substance could confer immunity on the other cells.

The extracellular substance, named interferon, has since been shown to be a family of substances (Merigan, 1967) whose properties will now be discussed.

Biological Properties of Interferons

One of the most interesting properties of interferons is their specificity in some respects and lack of specificity in other respects. Many biological phenomena display such clear specificities as antigen-antibody reaction, attachment of virions to receptor sites, and distinction between templates by nucleic acid polymerases.

But, as noted by Isaacs et al. (1957), influenza virus is not specific for the kind of virus it inhibits. The interferon produced inhibited the replication of Newcastle disease virus, Sendai virus, and vaccinia virus—all of which are unrelated to the inducing influenza virus. It might be thought, therefore, that the primary action of interferon is not on the virus but on the cell. Evidence demonstrating that this is the case and other evidence concerning the mode of action of interferon on cells will be discussed later.

Interferon seems to be specific for cells of the same species. For example, Baron et al. (1964) and Buckler and Baron (1966) examined the problem of cell specificity in detail. An interferon induced in mice and found circulating in the peripheral blood was tested on cultured cells from several species. Mouse embryo cells were given the highest resistance by the interferon to challenge infection with vesicular stomatitis virus. The effect on hamster or rat cells was about 5 per cent as great, and on chicken or monkey cells it was only about 0.1 per cent as great. Reports describing lack of specificity were based on interferon preparations that may have been impure, and, as pointed out by Buckler and Baron (1966), the preparations could have contained nonspecific inhibitors of virus replication other than interferon. When highly purified preparations of interferon were tested, it was found that they had a high degree of species specificity (Merigan, 1964; Merigan *et al.*, 1965). Exceptions have been found, however (Bucknall, 1967; Desmyter *et al.*, 1968).

A great variety of viruses can induce interferons (reviewed by Ho, 1966). Representatives of nearly every known group of animal viruses are known to induce interferons under suitable conditions. In general, the myxoviruses and other enveloped RNA-containing viruses seem to be the best inducers of interferons (and also perhaps the most susceptible to interferon), but DNA-containing viruses also induce interferons. Ability to induce interferons may vary greatly among strains of the same virus.

The inducing virus need not be active. Virus that has been inactivated by ultraviolet light or by heat can still induce interferon production. Furthermore, many nonviral materials induce interferon production (reviewed by Ho *et al.*, 1966; Borecký, 1968). These materials include bacteria, bacterial endotoxins, and various nucleic acids (Jensen *et al.*, 1963). Statolon, originally thought to be a polysaccharide, probably is a virus of the mold *Penicillium stoloniferum* (Kleinschmidt and Ellis, 1967). When statolon is administered to an experimental animal at the appropriate time, just before a challenge virus infection, the animal is resistant to the virus (see review by Kleinschmidt and Murphy, 1967).

Chemical and Physical Properties of Interferons

The protein nature of interferon was first inferred by Lindenmann *et al.* (1957). They came to this conclusion because interferon was not sedimented when centrifuged at forces of 10^5 times gravity, which indicated that its molecular weight was much less than that of a virus particle. But it was retained by a dialysis membrane, indicating that its molecular weight was at least 10,000 to 15,000 daltons. Moreover, trypsin destroyed the activity of interferon, but nucleases did not.

Subsequent work by many investigators has added much information about interferons. It seems best to consider interferons as a class of proteins with molecular weights of 2 to 4×10^4 daltons (Burke and Ross, 1965; Kreuz and Levy, 1963). They are stable in a pH range of 2 to 10 and to heating at 56° C. for at least 30 minutes. Interferons contain a small amount of carbohydrate in addition to the protein. Amino acid analysis reveals a typical composition with no unusual amino acids. Other properties of interferons and methods for their purification have been reviewed by Fantes (1966).

Although interferons are proteins, they are poor antigens. Only after many attempts was an antibody that could neutralize interferon finally produced (Pauker and Cantell, 1962).

Mechanism of Interferon Synthesis

Studies of the kinetics of interferon production indicate that different inducing agents may set different mechanisms in operation. For example, Youngner and Stinebring (1964), Stinebring and Youngner (1964), and Ho (1964a), using mice or rabbits, demonstrated that interferon reaches maximum levels about 2 hours after the injection of certain bacteria or bacterial endotoxins. After induction by Newcastle disease virus, however, serum interferon levels in mice reach a peak only after 6 to 12 hours. A similar response obtained in tissue culture is shown in Figure 13-1.

Other differences have also been noted between interferons induced by different agents. For example, Hallum *et al.* (1965) found a difference in the molecular weight of interferons in mouse serum induced by Newcastle disease virus or by endotoxin. The molecular weight of interferon induced by endotoxin or by bacteria was two to three times as large as that induced by virus. Because of its ability to be released even when protein synthesis is inhibited (Youngner and Stinebring, 1966) and because of its short induction time, statolon- or endotoxin-induced interferon may be merely the result of release of preformed interferon already contained in the cells. Or, interferon production by virus may require double-stranded RNA, as suggested by Lampson *et al.* (1967), Tytell *et al.* (1967), and Field *et al.* (1967a, 1967b). The delay may result from the requirement that the incoming, single-stranded viral RNA has to become double stranded before inducing interferon. Our discussion will be restricted to virus-induced interferons.

Actinomycin D blocks virus induction of interferon (Heller, 1963); other inhibitors of RNA synthesis also block production (Walters *et al.*, 1967). Because of this it is thought that the cell's DNA is involved in interferon production. To be more precise, since actinomycin D blocks transcription of genetic information from DNA into messenger RNA, it must be that the information for interferon production is contained in the cell's DNA.

It becomes clear, then, how apparently identical interferons arise when a given cell is infected with different viruses, even when one virus contains RNA and the other DNA (Lampson *et al.*, 1965); for if the information is stored in the cell, only to be induced by the virus, then the nature of the inducing virus is not important. It also becomes clear why the same virus induces different interferons in different

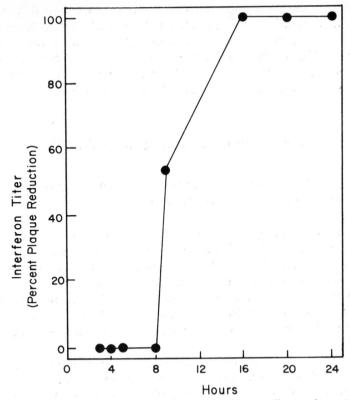

Figure 13-1. Interferon production by chick embryo cells in culture. Newcastle disease virus that had been inactivated by ultraviolet irradiation was added to the cells. At the indicated intervals, the medium was assayed for the titer of interferon. This was done by determining the number of plaques that developed in cells treated with the sample and then challenged with an aliquot of virus. Untreated controls were also challenged with a similar aliquot. The results are expressed as the percentage of plaque reduction caused by the sample, comparing the treated cells with the controls. (Redrawn from Ho, 1964b.)

host cells. The previously mentioned delay in virus-induced interferon production can thus be explained, because the cell's protein-synthesizing machinery would need time to reach full production.

Inhibitors of protein synthesis also block interferon production, as would be expected if interferon is newly synthesized (Youngner *et al.*, 1965; Wagner and Huang, 1965). On the other hand, if it is true that endotoxin-induced interferon activity is due merely to the release of preformed interferon or other inhibitory material contained within cells, it would be expected that inhibitors of RNA and protein synthesis would not prevent the increase of circulating interferon after administration of these inducers. Such has been shown to be the case (Ho and Kono, 1965; Youngner *et al.*, 1965).

It is unknown how the virus induces the cell's DNA to begin

synthesizing the messenger RNA for interferon. Conceivably the viral nucleic acid could interact directly with the cell's DNA. It could also code for a product, such as a messenger RNA, that in turn interacts with the DNA; or the viral nucleic acid might combine with some factor in the cell that controls the transcription of the interferon cistron, such as a repressor substance that might ordinarily be present.

Mechanism of Interferon's Action

Before discussing the mechanism by which interferon blocks viral replication, it might be well to discuss some mechanisms that can be ruled out.

In the first place, unlike an antibody, interferon acts on the cell, not on the virus. Full yields of virus result when interferon is mixed with virus, incubated, diluted, and used to infect cells. The interferon must be added to the cells for inhibition to occur. It can be added many hours prior to adding the virus (Fig. 13-2) so that it does not come directly into contact with the virus. However, only a small amount of the interferon is actually taken up by the cells (Buckler et al., 1966).

When a purified interferon is used, no toxic effects can be demonstrated (Buckler et al., 1966) on cellular replication (Baron et al., 1966c) or on synthesis of RNA or protein (Levy and Merigan, 1966); nor does interferon block adsorption and uncoating of the virus (Ho and Enders, 1959a; Vilcek, 1960; Wagner, 1961). It is necessary to look within the cell to see how interferon interferes with virus replication.

One approach to the problem is to ask at what stage interferon acts in the viral replicative cycle. As discussed by Ho (1962) these stages can be divided into adsorption, penetration, uncoupling of viral RNA from viral protein, synthesis of viral components, assembly into virions, and release of the virions from the cell.

Several of these stages can quickly be ruled out. For instance, if interferon blocked release of mature virions, it should be possible to recover virions from interferon-treated, infected cells by artificially disrupting the cells. However, no such accumulation of virions occurs in cells blocked by interferon (Ho and Enders, 1959b). Consequently, interferon must affect some earlier event in viral replication. The effect occurs after the cell removes the protein coat from the viral RNA. This is known because interferon inhibits the replication of poliovirus infectious RNA (Ho, 1961; de Somer et al., 1962). If it acted on the adsorption, penetration, or uncoating steps, interferon would have no effect on infection by isolated RNA because these stages are bypassed. Therefore, interferon must act either on the stage of

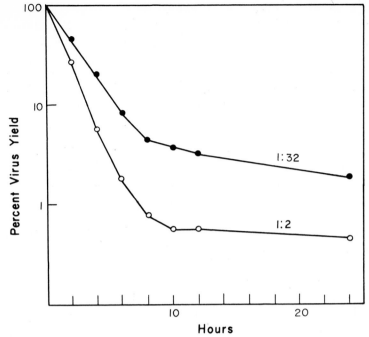

Figure 13-2. Inhibition of Western equine encephalitis virus production by interferon. Chick embryonic fibroblasts were incubated from the indicated time with interferon diluted 1:8 or 1:32 and challenged with virus at a multiplicity of 50 PFU per cell. The yield of virus was measured after 12 hours and compared with the controls that received no interferon. (Redrawn from Lockart and Sreevalsan, 1963.)

synthesis of viral components or on their assembly into virions.

Another experiment rules out the possibility that interferon inhibits assembly of virus components into virions. de Somer *et al.* (1962) and Lockart *et al.* (1962) extracted RNA from cells infected with Western equine encephalitis virus so as to obtain viral precursor RNA. Cells treated with interferon contained no detectable viral RNA, whereas untreated cells contained more than 10^4 infectious units. By analysis of extracted RNA in sucrose gradients, it has been determined that all forms of viral RNA are inhibited by interferon (Gordon *et al.*, 1966), although not all to the same extent (Mécs *et al.*, 1967). By exclusion, interferon must act somehow to prevent synthesis of viral RNA.

Which macromolecules are involved in viral RNA synthesis can be determined by the use of metabolic inhibitors. Actinomycin D inhibits synthesis of cellular messenger RNA but does not inhibit synthesis of viral RNA molecules that use viral RNA as a template. Puromycin, also an antibiotic, inhibits protein synthesis; *p*-fluorophenylalanine is an amino acid analog that is incorporated into proteins and causes them to be nonfunctional.

Use of these inhibitors (Taylor, 1964, 1965; Lockhart, 1964; Levine, 1964; Friedman and Sonnabend, 1964) reveals that blockage of RNA or protein synthesis in infected cells treated with interferon results in a reversal of the interferon inhibition of viral synthesis. The action of actinomycin D shows further that interferon causes the synthesis of a new cellular messenger RNA and that interferon acts at the level of cellular genetic transcription or translation rather than on the virus. The fact that protein synthesis is required for interferon to inhibit viral replication (Baron *et al.*, 1967) means that interferon itself is not the primary inhibitor. Instead, presumably by derepressing a gene, it causes the cell to synthesize a new protein that effects the inhibition.

Marcus and Salb (1966) performed experiments to elucidate the mechanism by which the new protein acts to inhibit synthesis of viral RNA. They used Sindbis virus, an arbovirus, because it grows easily and quickly in chick embryo cell cultures and also because it induces interferon production and is easily inhibited by interferon.

Before we discuss the results of experiments by Marcus and Salb, it is first necessary to list several pertinent facts about cells not treated with interferon. At 0° C., RNA extracted from purified Sindbis virus attaches to ribosomes extracted from chick embryo cells. Attachment of viral RNA to the ribosomes forms polysomes whose length depends on the length of the RNA; in this case, a fairly uniform population of polysomes results, since the viral RNA is homogeneous. The polysomes remain stable at 0° C. but break down when the temperature is raised to 37° C. and proper protein precursors and an energy source are supplied. Active protein synthesis accompanies the breakdown of the polysomes.

The behavior of ribosomes extracted from infected cells treated with actinomycin D is identical to the behavior of ribosomes extracted from untreated infected cells. This is not surprising when it is remembered that actinomycin D does not inhibit the replication of Sindbis virus.

In contrast, Marcus and Salb found that ribosomes extracted from cells treated 11 to 15 hours with interferon attached only about two-thirds as much viral RNA (Table 13-1). The polysomes that formed seemed to be of normal length, judging from their sedimentation rate. However, their behavior was distinctly different from normal when the temperature was raised to 37° C. Instead of synthesizing protein and decreasing in quantity, as did the normal, they synthesized only a small amount of protein, if any at all, and remained quite stable without being degraded. Pretreatment with actinomycin D, in addition to the interferon, restored the ribosomes to normal behavior toward the viral RNA. Other experiments showed that interferon's effect on decreasing formation of polysomes by viral RNA and pre-

TABLE 13-1. SINDBIS VIRAL RNA ATTACHED TO RIBOSOMES
AND DIRECTING PROTEIN SYNTHESIS[*]

TREATMENT OF INFECTED CELLS	RNA BOUND AT 0°	AFTER TRANSLATION AT 37°
Untreated	1395[+]	2[+]
Interferon	879	1009
Actinomycin D	1653	15
Actinomycin D + Interferon	1488	97

[*]Modified from Marcus and Salb, 1966.
[+]Counts per minute in viral RNA in polysome region of sucrose gradient.

venting translation of any that do form is specific for viral RNA: Ribosomes from interferon-treated cells still formed functional polysomes with nonviral RNA. Similar results were obtained by Carter and Levy (1967) using different experimental conditions.

The mechanism by which interferon acts can be schematized, as shown in Figure 13-3. The protein synthesized by a cellular cistron derepressed by interferon acts to inhibit translation of viral RNA and therefore has been named the "translation inhibitory protein" by Marcus and Salb. By preventing viral RNA from being translated into protein, early enzymes, such as RNA-dependent RNA polymerase, are not synthesized (Sonnabend et al., 1967b; Miner et al., 1966), double-stranded RNA does not form (Friedman et al., 1967), and viral RNA replication cannot proceed (Lockart et al., 1962).

The discussion so far has emphasized work with RNA-containing viruses, yet interferon is produced in cells infected by DNA-containing viruses and it inhibits their replication. Might the mechanism of action of the two kinds of viruses be the same? Very much the same kinds of experiments as described for Sindbis virus were performed by another group of investigators using vaccinia virus (Joklik and Merigan, 1966; Joklik et al., 1967). Although the experiments were

Interferon + cellular DNA $\longrightarrow$ messenger RNA for translation - inhibitory protein

mRNA (TIP) + ribosomes $\longrightarrow$ translation - inhibitory protein molecules

Cellular mRNA + TIP-ribosomes $\longrightarrow$ polysome $\longrightarrow$ protein

Viral $-\begin{cases} \text{RNA} \\ \text{mRNA} \end{cases}$ + TIP-ribosomes $\xrightarrow{\text{decreased}}$ polysomes $\xrightarrow{}$ protein

Figure 13-3. Mechanism of interferon's action.

performed independently and simultaneously, the results obtained with the DNA-containing virus essentially agreed with those for the RNA-containing virus.

To summarize the results of these investigators, interferon seems not to inhibit transcription of messenger RNA from vaccinia virus DNA—if anything, there may be an increase. In interferon-treated cells, however, the viral messenger RNA forms fewer polysomes. In addition, viral DNA polymerase and other proteins essential for viral replication are made in smaller amounts, less DNA is synthesized, and the replicative cycle aborts (Levine *et al.*, 1967).

Much work remains to be done to clarify the nature of the translation-inhibitory protein and the characteristics of its interaction with ribosomes. Such work is especially interesting and important because of the specificity displayed by the protein for inhibiting translation of viral messenger RNA molecules without affecting cellular function.

Interferon and Disease

It is beyond the scope of the present discussion to consider in great detail the possible medical uses of interferon. Finter (1966, 1968) has recently reviewed this subject with references to the extensive literature.

Some of the possible uses of interferon as an antiviral agent should be obvious from some of the preceding discussion. For instance, because interferon is effective against a wide variety of viruses, accurate viral diagnosis should not be necessary before beginning therapy; and although interferon is a protein, it is a poor antigen and antibodies would probably not be developed against it.

It is probable that the disadvantages of an exogenous interferon preparation that could be administered to treat virus infections outweigh the advantages. Sufficient work has been done to indicate that human interferon would probably be needed to treat human viral infections. Such an interferon could be prepared in human cell cultures. A large volume of culture fluids would be required, and extensive purification would be necessary to remove extraneous proteins (which could provoke serious immune responses) and to concentrate the interferon. With present knowledge, such an undertaking would be enormously difficult and expensive.

An alternative approach would be to administer some agent capable of eliciting the production of interferon. For instance, statolon or synthetic compounds could be injected (Merigan and Regelson, 1967), and the endogenous interferon might be effective in alleviating the infection. Many such experiments have been done, chiefly in animals, and the results indicate that when the timing of administration of statolon is precisely controlled with respect to the virus challenge, virus infection decreases. Everyday human exposure to viruses is not precisely controlled, so this approach seems impractical at present.

More detailed study of the translation-inhibitory protein synthesized in response to interferon may offer some new approaches to an effective antiviral chemotherapy. It would be useful to inhibit viral messenger RNA translation without inhibiting cellular messenger RNA. Further work toward understanding this protein might be very rewarding.

It is also pertinent to ask whether interferon plays a role in natural defense against viral infection (reviewed by Baron, 1966). Symptomatic infection from many viruses occurs a few days after exposure, and sometimes the infection has run its course within a few more days. The infection is over before appreciable development of antibodies occurs. Furthermore, many individuals have defective immune mechanisms and are unable to develop significant antibodies against foreign proteins. Acute viral infections in these people are usually not detectably different from infections in normal people. Interferon could be responsible for ending many viral infections before antibodies are synthesized. In addition, interferon is normally present in the circulating blood at the same time that virus may be circulating, that is, during the viremic stage of the infection (Baron and Buckler, 1963; Baron *et al.*, 1966a, 1966b), and may be especially useful when virus concentrations are low (Finter, 1967). It is thus in the most useful form and location to be maximally beneficial. Other evidence as well points to the possible importance of interferon in recovery from virus infection.

However, as outlined in Chapter 6, as more sensitive methods have become available for detecting neutralizing antibody, it has been found that antibodies are produced even within a few hours after an infection, much more rapidly than previously thought. The antibody immune mechanism may play a role in early response to infection, along with interferon, as well as giving lifelong protection against reinfection by a virus.

INTERFERENCE WITHOUT INTERFERON

In Chapter 12, the examples of satellite tobacco necrosis virus and adeno-associated virus were presented to illustrate the interference of dependent viruses with the replication of their helper viruses. The mechanism for the interference is unknown, but evidence indicates that the production of interferon is probably not responsible. Two more examples of interference of one virus with another will now be presented, neither of which apparently is mediated by interferon.

Pereira (1960) observed that HeLa cells infected with any of several adenoviruses produced an extracellular material that inhibited viral replication in other cells. The material was smaller than the virus particles, as it did not sediment by ultracentrifugation. Experiments showed that the inhibitory material was not interferon and that it was neutralized by antibody prepared against adenoviruses. Not only did the material inhibit adenovirus replication, but it also inhibited the replication of other viruses, such as vaccinia and poliovirus. Careful chromatographic purification of various cell products showed that the inhibitory protein was the fiber antigen of the virus (see Chapter 2).

More detailed studies have shown that the adenovirus fiber antigen acts on the cell rather than on the virus (Levine and Ginsberg, 1967). The lack of specificity for the type of virus excluded can then be easily explained. Ruled out are effects of fiber antigen on virus adsorption and uncoating. The fiber antigen completely stopped synthesis of RNA, DNA, and protein whether the cells were infected or not. The cessation of macromolecular synthesis occurred about 20 to 30 hours after addition of the fiber antigen. Because the effect of fiber antigen was not blocked by actinomycin D, these workers concluded that the fiber antigen did not require synthesis of messenger RNA for its effect.

Several other examples of interference between viruses have been reported, and interferon does not seem to play a role in any of them (Huang and Wagner, 1966; Marcus and Carver, 1965, 1967; Cords and Holland, 1964; Roizman, 1965; Galasso and Sharp, 1964; Sreevalsan and Lockart, 1966b; Khoobyarian and Fischinger, 1965). These systems possess differing degrees of interference and display widely different specificities; some interfere only with closely related mutants, whereas others interfere with quite unrelated viruses. In most cases, the possibility that interference is due to a blockage of adsorption or uncoating has been ruled out, leaving inhibition of intracellular events as the remaining likely possibility. Further details have to be worked out.

Interference Between Plant Viruses

As described in the preceding chapter, satellite tobacco necrosis virus inhibits replication of its helper virus. The mechanism for the inhibition is unknown, but it must occur intracellularly. Many other instances of interference between plant viruses have been described.

Freitag (1964) described an interference system between strains of aster yellows virus: The first virus inoculated and the challenge virus were suppressed, and neither virus caused symptoms. Many of the "cured" asters still contained one or both of the viruses.

The mechanism by which the interference occurs in this system is not known, nor is it known for any of the other plant virus systems. The possibility exists that an interferon-like mechanism may be operative, since proteins having some of the characteristics of interferon have been isolated from infected plants (reviewed by Baron, 1966).

Chemical Interference

Interferon, a chemical inhibitor of viral replication, is a natural product, but many other inhibitors, some of which are synthetic, are also known to inhibit viral replication. The natural products are often derived from fermentation products of various fungi and fall into the class of substances called antibiotics.

The list of substances that are able to inhibit viral replication is much too long to reproduce here. Many of the compounds have been characterized and their properties were summarized in a conference on antiviral substances held in 1965 (Whipple, 1965). Examples will be chosen for discussion here to show that inhibition of viral replication can occur at many of the stages of the replicative cycle, depending on the virus and the inhibitory drug.

Such studies are of obvious value for the future treatment of viral disease. Specificity of drug action against a given virus could be achieved by pinpointing a reaction necessary for viral replication, and inhibiting that reaction. Such would be the case for inhibiting RNA viruses, for instance, if there were a specific inhibitor of viral RNA-dependent RNA polymerase.

Adsorption and Penetration.   Amantadine (1-adamantanamine hydrochloride), a symmetrical compound containing three rings and an amino group (Fig. 13-4), is an effective agent for preventing infection with influenza virus (Stanley *et al.*, 1965). It is one of the few antiviral drugs presently available on prescription. It prevents attachment of virus to cell (Davies *et al.*, 1964), but how it does this is unknown. In cell cultures, it also inhibits other myxoviruses or their close relatives (Wood, 1965; Hoffman *et al.*, 1965; Wallbank *et al.*, 1966).

Transcription.   Actinomycin D (Fig. 13-5) is a polypeptide antibiotic that inhibits RNA synthesis (Reich *et al.*, 1961) by combining with DNA and blocking transcription by RNA polymerase (Hurwitz *et al.*, 1962). The inhibition occurs rapidly in plant, animal, and bacterial cells; and it has only slight effect on DNA replication. Actinomycin D blocks the replication of DNA-containing viruses but not RNA-con-

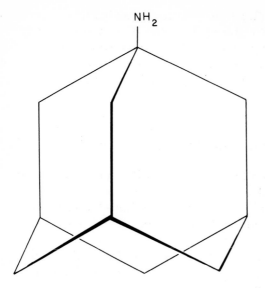

Figure 13-4. Amantadine (1-adamantanamine).

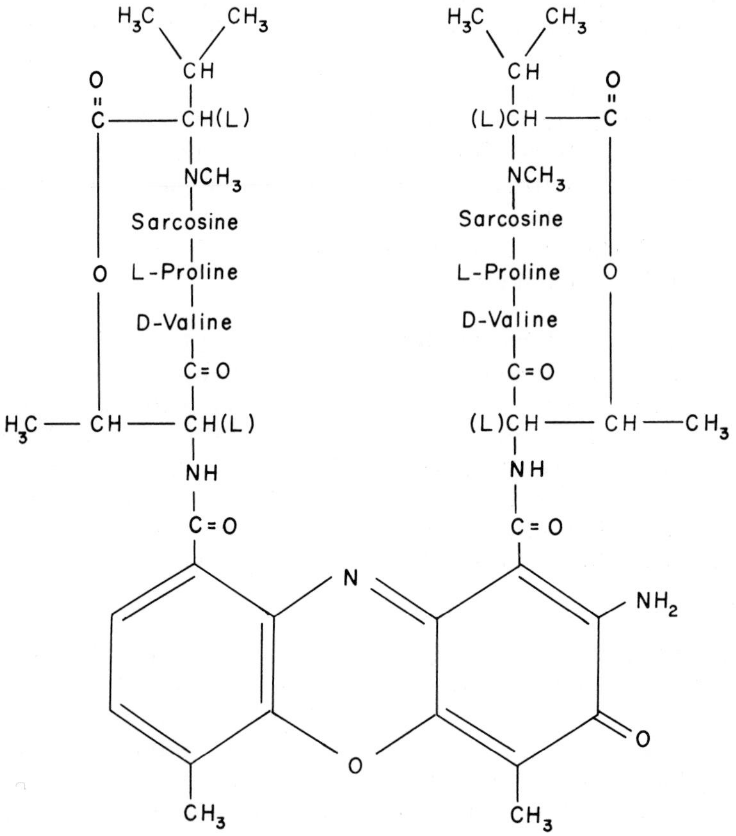

Figure 13-5. Actinomycin D.

taining viruses. The reason for this is that the DNA-containing viruses are unable to transcribe their information into messenger RNA for the synthesis of necessary proteins, whereas RNA-containing viruses are unaffected (Reich *et al.*, 1962). The RNA-dependent RNA polymerase of the latter viruses is not blocked by actinomycin D. The compound is quite useful in the study of macromolecular metabolism in normal and infected cells, and many experiments based on its action have been described.

Some anomalous results have occurred with actinomycin D, as when the compound was used with the myxovirus group (see Fig. 11-3) and with the related Rous sarcoma virus. Another anomaly exists with reovirus, which is inhibited by actinomycin D (Gomatos *et al.*, 1962). Perhaps reovirus RNA, being double stranded, uses DNA-dependent RNA polymerase of the cell for its transcription and is inhibited by this mechanism.

Mitomycin C, another antibiotic, inhibits DNA transcription. It acts, however, by degrading DNA, stimulating the action of deoxyribonuclease (Reich *et al.*, 1961). Any cellular or viral DNA present in a cell is thus rendered nonfunctional. At low concentrations, mitomycin C has little or no effect on RNA and protein synthesis, and it does not impede the replication of RNA viruses.

DNA Replication.   Most of the many compounds that can block DNA synthesis are analogs of nucleosides with a slight modification of the molecule. For instance, uridine is formed if a hydrogen atom is substituted for the methyl group on the pyrimidine ring of thymidine. Halogens can also be substituted at the same position (Fig. 13-6), resulting in a series of analogs with differing properties and different modes of action. Some of these analogs have been useful in virologic

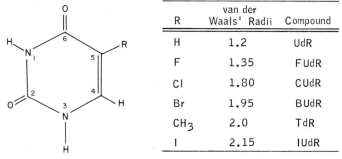

R	van der Waals' Radii	Compound
H	1.2	UdR
F	1.35	FUdR
Cl	1.80	CUdR
Br	1.95	BUdR
CH$_3$	2.0	TdR
I	2.15	IUdR

Figure 13-6.   The uracil nucleus and possible substitutions at the 5-position. With hydrogen, the compound is uracil; with a methyl group, the compound is thymine. The halogenated deoxyribosides, with their van der Waals' radii, are also indicated. (Redrawn from Prusoff *et al.*, 1965.)

studies. Depending on the size of the halogen, the analog may interfere with some intracellular pathway.

One of the more widely used compounds, 5-fluorodeoxyuridine (FUdR), acts by completely blocking thymidylate synthetase (Cohen *et al.*, 1958). Without this enzyme, the cell is unable to synthesize thymidine and DNA synthesis rapidly ceases. When thymidine is added to the medium, the blocked enzyme is bypassed and DNA synthesis resumes. Another compound, 5-iododeoxyuridine, blocks DNA synthesis by much the same mechanism, but by blocking any of several enzymes in the thymidine pathway; which enzyme is blocked depends on the cell type (Delamore and Prusoff, 1962; Prusoff *et al.*, 1965). Its effect may sometimes be bypassed by exogenous thymidine, again depending on which enzyme is blocked.

The brominated analog, 5-bromodeoxyuridine, does not block enzymes and does not inhibit DNA synthesis appreciably, presumably because the bromine is approximately the size of the methyl group it has replaced. This analog is then incorporated into newly synthesized DNA in place of thymine. The substituted DNA has several altered properties. Its density is increased, enabling it to be separated from nonsubstituted DNA in density gradients. Substitution of the bromine for the methyl group also changes the distribution of electrons in the molecule, resulting in increased mutability. The chlorinated analog has not been widely used.

The list of analogs of nucleic acid precursors is very long. Most of the analogs have a modification of the base residue, but some are modified in the sugar residue (such as 1-β-D-arabinofuranosylcytosine or cytosine arabinoside). Many have been tried as treatment for various viral infections, but generally they are too toxic to be practical. Perhaps less toxic analogs will be found. Iododeoxuridine is available on prescription and is used to treat herpetic and vaccinial infections of the eye.

Translation. Several compounds have been useful in blocking the translation of information stored in messenger RNA into protein. One of these is an amino acid analog, *p*-fluorophenylalanine. Proteins are synthesized to some extent in its presence, but they are "defective"; enzymes, for instance, lose their activity, and the net effect is a blockage of protein synthesis. It is best to think of the action of *p*-fluorophenylalanine as impairment of synthesis of functional proteins rather than impairment of protein synthesis. Puromycin (Fig. 13-7) is an antibiotic that inhibits protein synthesis by interfering with normal chain growth of the amino acids into peptide chains at the polysome (Allen and Schweet, 1962; Morris *et al.*, 1962), because it is, in effect, an analog of a transfer RNA molecule coupled to an amino acid (Darken, 1964).

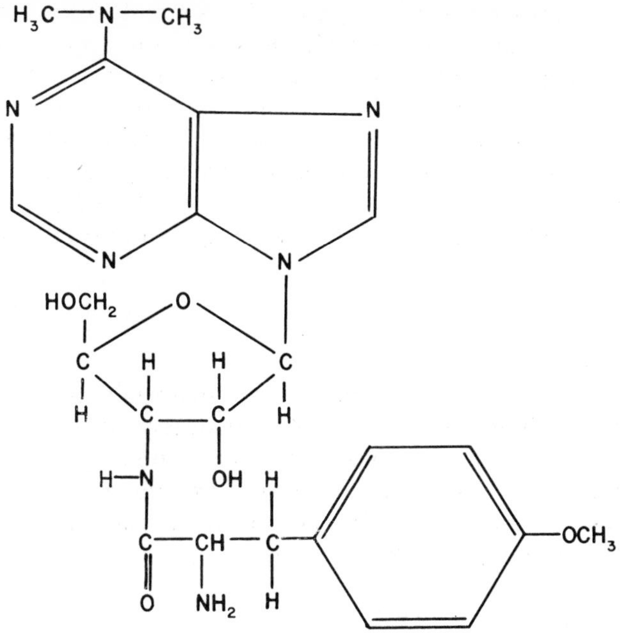

Figure 13-7. Puromycin.

The last compound to be discussed here is called isatin-β-thio-semicarbazone (Fig. 13-8), a compound effective only against poxviruses. The mechanism by which this compound acts and the nature of its specificity are beginning to be understood (Woodson and Joklik, 1965; Joklik *et al.*, 1967). Thiosemicarbazone does not become incorporated into viral materials, nor does it block enzymes as do some of the analogs. Viral DNA and "early" proteins are synthesized, apparently because of inhibition of translation of polysomes formed with viral messenger RNA synthesized late in the cycle. More specifically, the compound seems to be selective in inhibiting translation of messenger RNA formed from progeny DNA molecules, while leaving

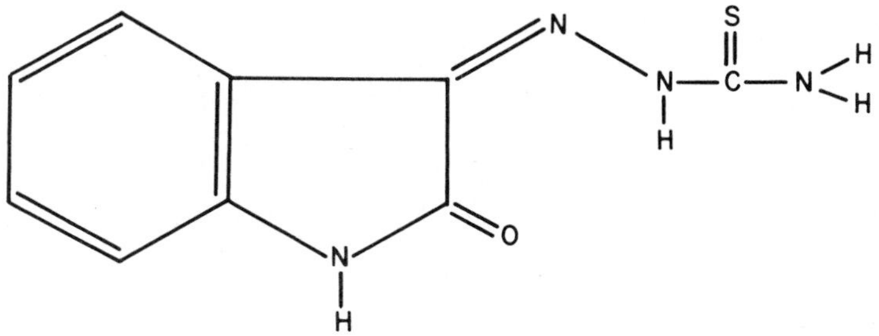

Figure 13-8. Isatin-β-thiosemicarbazone.

polysomes of messengers from parental DNA molecules untouched. It is thought that progeny DNA molecules code for a protein that breaks down all polysomes when thiosemicarbazone is present. It is speculated that this protein may be one that is synthesized under normal conditions of infection and that normally "switches off" the function of "early" messenger RNA transcribed by the parental DNA. When isatin-β-thiosemicarbazone is present, however, the protein may be modified in such a way that it stops activity of all polyribosomes.

The various ways that viral genetic materials interact with each other — to inhibit or help — are genetically determined, as are the replicative cycles and the synthesis of viral-induced proteins. Because these functions are controlled by genetic information contained in the viral genome, they are also subject to mutational change, as will be described in the next chapter.

Further Reading

Baron, S., and H. B. Levy: Interferon. Annual Reviews of Microbiology, 20:291-318, 1966.
Lockart, R. Z., Jr.: Recent Progress in Research on Interferons. Progress in Medical Virology, 9:451-475, 1967.
Wagner, R. R.: Viral Interference; Some Considerations of Basic Mechanisms and Their Potential Relationship to Host Resistance. Bacteriological Reviews, 24:151-166, 1960.

14

VIRAL GENETICS: MUTATION

Genetics is the study of how offspring come to resemble their parents. Externally visible characteristics are, of course, passed from one generation to the next; more subtle characteristics, such as biochemical content and life cycles, may also be inherited.

Offspring sometimes differ from their parents in one or more characteristics. Study of these differences and how they arise is a major means for determining the mechanism of normal inheritance. The two major mechanisms for genetic change, mutation and recombination, result in the adaptation of organisms to changing conditions and the evolution of new organisms.

Viruses resemble their progenitors in morphology, biochemical composition, replicative cycle, effects on host cells, and many other parameters. Furthermore, viruses can mutate and recombine, giving rise to new lineages that may not have existed formerly. New forms that are generated test new environmental conditions; evolution results when the new forms are better able to survive than those of preceding generations. With viruses, mutation is probably the more important natural adaptive process, but study of virus recombination is of great interest to the geneticist because of its usefulness in studying many aspects of viral replication.

ADVANTAGES OF VIRUSES FOR GENETIC STUDY

Mendel's work with sweet peas laid the foundation for systematic study of inheritance. The long period required for sweet peas to mature is a disadvantage for genetic studies, and many organisms now used for genetic study have shorter generation times. The fruit fly, for instance, matures rapidly, and each pair of parents gives rise to many offspring, making possible a better statistical analysis of the results. Also, the rare mutant can be found more readily because a large number of individual flies can be examined easily. Work with fruit flies has yielded many facts and concepts we now take for granted, including the fact that the chromosome is the repository of the genetic material in higher organisms, with the genetic information stored in it as a linear array of genes.

Genetic study with fruit flies and other higher organisms finally reached the point where the questions being asked demanded more detailed results than the systems could yield. Greater detail in genetics usually results from study of more individual organisms. It was at this point that phages were introduced to geneticists, chiefly by the pioneering work of Dr. Max Delbrück. He saw the potentiality of phage for genetic study; and because of his work and that of his many highly creative students, we can now understand many genetic mechanisms at the molecular level.

VIRAL MUTATIONS

The tools of viral genetic research are the normal or wild-type virus and the mutants it sports during the course of its normal replication. These mutants must be easily detectable to be useful to the geneticist. Many such mutants have been described, and they generally fall into certain categories. These include plaque-type mutants, host-range mutants, temperature-sensitive mutants, conditional-lethal mutants, mutants of biochemical function, and many others.

Some mutants have already been discussed, such as those that lack the code for a given functional enzyme. Certain other kinds of mutants are of more value to the geneticist, and these will be described briefly here. It should be remembered that a mutation is an alteration in the genetic makeup of a virus, that is, in its genotype. To be detectable, the mutation must somehow be expressed, usually as a change in its phenotype. The phenotype can be modified, however, by events or conditions other than mutations.

Mutants with Altered Plaque Morphology

Plaque-type mutants are easily seen under the usual conditions of plating. Assume for instance that a petri dish contains several hundred plaques of essentially the same morphology. If one plaque among this

Plaque-Type Mutants

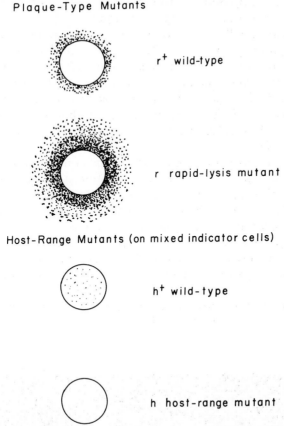

r+ wild-type

r rapid-lysis mutant

Host-Range Mutants (on mixed indicator cells)

h+ wild-type

h host-range mutant

Figure 14-1. Diagrammatic representation of certain T2 or T4 phage plaques. The rapid-lysis mutant has a large halo surrounding a clear center when plated on *E. coli* B cells, in contrast to wild-type which has a faint halo. The host-range mutants are detected by plating on mixtures of cells; the mixture contains *E. coli* B cells, infectible by either wild-type or the host-range mutant, and *E. coli* B/2 or B/4, infectible only by the mutant. Plaques caused by the mutant are clear because all cells are lysed; plaques caused by wild-type are diffused or turbid because some cells remain alive.

group has some visible difference in its morphology, it can be spotted easily. If the unusual plaque is actually due to a mutation, virus picked from the plaque should cause new plaques with the same changed morphology.

Many such plaque mutants have been described. Some that have been widely studied are the rapid-lysis mutants of T2 and T4 phage. Normal or wild-type T2, designated T2r+ with respect to this character, produces small plaques with a clear center and a surrounding, narrow, hazy halo (Fig. 14-1). About one in 10^3 or 10^4 plaques also has the clear center but with a large diffuse halo with a sharp edge. Even more rarely, the mutant, called T2r, will mutate back to r+

during the development of the plaque. The joint growth of both kinds of phage results in a mottled plaque.

Doermann (1948) described how this mutant caused altered plaque morphology. Wild-type $T2r^+$ is lysis inhibiting, meaning that if a bacterium that has been infected with T2 is superinfected with another phage of the same kind before the end of the latent period, the latent period is delayed. In the formation of a plaque, the first event that occurs is the infection of a single cell with a single virus particle. The cell then dies, releasing its complement of progeny phages, and the cycle repeats.

Early in the formation of a plaque, the concentration of phage in the center of the plaque is relatively low, but as the plaque progresses the number of virus particles per cell tends to increase, resulting in superinfection. In the center of the plaque all the cells are killed, but toward the periphery of the plaque the cells are inhibited from lysis by being superinfected. The mutant phage, on the other hand, is not lysis inhibited, and all bacterial cells that are infected lyse, regardless of whether they are superinfected. The plaque that results is therefore clear.

In addition to the rapid-lysis mutants, there are many other kinds of phage plaque-type mutants. For example, there is a mutant that

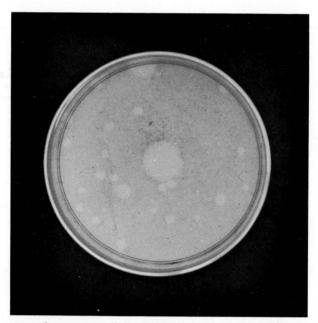

Figure 14-2. Plaques caused by EMC virus on mouse embryo cell cultures. Most of the plaques are small but there are two large plaques. The small-plaque virus (wild-type) is inhibited by components of the agar overlay; the large-plaque mutant is insensitive to the inhibitor.

produces only a minute, pinpoint size plaque (Hershey and Rotman, 1949).

Plaque-type animal virus mutants are also known (Takemoto, 1966). A picture of the plaques caused by one such mutant of EMC virus is shown in Figure 14-2. Wild-type EMC virus causes the small plaques; frequently occurring spontaneous mutants cause the large plaques (Breeze and Subak-Sharpe, 1967). The mutation is expressed because the mutant is resistant to certain polysaccharides in the agar, whereas wild-type virus is sensitive (Takemoto and Liebhaber, 1961, 1962; Liebhaber and Takemoto, 1961, 1963). The differences in surface properties between wild-type virus and the mutant also permit them to be separated by column chromatography (Burness, 1967).

Mutants with Altered Host Range

Another major category of mutants useful in phage research consists of the host-range mutants, so named because their mutation either allows them to grow on a new host cell that they were not able to grow on before or prevents them from growing on their usual host.

Host-range mutants are selected in a somewhat complicated series of experiments. Let us follow a hypothetical example. The experimenter starts with a stock of T2, which grows quite well on *E. coli* strain B. Next he makes a mixture of bacterial cells and excess virus in the usual plating method for obtaining plaques. The plaques that result overlap, giving confluent lysis of the cells. When these agar plates are incubated further, rare colonies of cells develop from these few cells that survived the initial infection. The cells of the colony, grown into a pure culture, are found to be resistant to T2. The newly isolated cell is designated *E. coli* B/2, indicating its resistance to phage T2.

But the investigator still has not obtained the desired host-range mutant of the phage. His next step is to mix an excess of phage with the resistant cells. A rare plaque, caused by phage able to grow on the otherwise resistant cells, contains the desired mutant. The mutant is designated T2h, while wild-type is called T2h^+ with respect to host range.

The experimenter uses mixtures of cells for rapid identification of the mutant phages. On a bacterial lawn formed by a mixture of B and B/2 cells, wild-type phage lyses only the B cells, leaving the B/2 alive, and the plaque is diffuse or turbid. A host-range mutant phage, on the other hand, lyses both types of cells, producing a clear plaque. Since these phages also have the rapid-lysis character, four combinations are possible. Each of the four produces its own characteristic plaque type (see Fig. 14-1).

Conditional-Lethal Mutants

A mutation usually results in the alteration of synthesis or the absence of a protein. Host-range mutants have proteins that are altered, but not so severely altered that the virus is unable to multiply. Instead, the altered protein merely changes the host specificity.

Other types of mutants, the conditional-lethal mutants, have been especially useful in genetic analysis of phage replication. Beginnings have also been made in identifying similar mutants of animal viruses. Conditional-lethal mutants are unable to replicate under certain restrictive conditions but can replicate under certain other permissive conditions. Temperature-sensitive and suppressor-sensitive mutants are two examples of this type of mutant.

A temperature-sensitive mutant is not one that is inactivated by temperature at a different rate than the wild-type, although such mutants are also known. Instead, the temperature sensitivity has its effect during the intracellular stage of viral replication. The usual temperature-sensitive mutant can replicate at one temperature but not at another. The reason for this is that some essential protein, perhaps one of the viral-induced enzymes, is formed and functions at the lower, permissive temperature, such as 28° C., but is either not formed or cannot function at a higher temperature, such as 37° C. These mutants are found by growing virus from plaques at the lower temperature; when plated at a higher temperature, a few are found that do not form plaques, and these are the temperature-sensitive mutants. One mutant of ϕX174 functions at the higher temperature but not at a lower temperature (Dowell, 1967). Temperature-sensitive mutants are widely known for various phages; some have been found in animal viruses (Burge and Pfefferkorn, 1965, 1967; Fenner, 1965b; Fried, 1965a; Pfefferkorn and Burge, 1967).

Temperature-sensitive mutations also occur in higher organisms. It is well known that the color pattern of a Siamese cat, for instance, results from such a mutation. An enzyme in the pathway of biosynthesis of hair pigment is not functional at the cat's normal body temperature. Consequently, most of the cat's fur lacks pigment and is white, or nearly white. The cat's feet, his ears, the tip of his nose, and other cooler parts are covered with pigmented hair because the enzyme is functional at the lower temperatures. Raising the cat in a warm environment results in loss of pigment even from the extremities, illustrating that the function of the gene is subject to experimental, outside conditions. Of course, the Siamese cat's mutation is not lethal, even though a gene product does not function at one temperature. With viruses, evolution has eliminated almost all genes not absolutely essential to viral replication, so that nearly any temperature-sensitive mutation is lethal at the nonpermissive temperature.

Another type of conditional-lethal mutation of viruses is one that is detectable in cells that have a suppressor gene. The suppressor gene in the permissive host can suppress certain kinds of mutations that may occur in any gene of the virus, restoring their function. Without the compensating effect of the host's suppressor genes, the mutation of the viral gene results in a "nonsense" codon in the messenger RNA, which in turn prevents proper translation of the information in the messenger RNA into protein. The suppressor gene changes the translation of the nonsense codon so that it either is translated properly or has other substitutions. Certain of these conditional-lethal mutants, the *amber* mutants, contain the codon UAG. In a host cell without a suppressor gene, UAG behaves as a nonsense codon, with termination of the peptide chain during translation (Brenner and Stretton, 1964; Sambrook *et al.*, 1967). In a host cell with a suppressor gene, it may code for serine (UCG), for glutamine (CAG), or for tyrosine (UAU or UAC) (Kaplan *et al.*, 1965; Weigert *et al.*, 1965; Garen, 1968). Which substitution occurs depends on the suppressor mutation of the host cell. Several such suppressor mutations have been studied, and it has been shown that the suppressor effect occurs in a cell-free system (Gesteland *et al.*, 1967).

The *amber* mutant was the first such mutant described. The name does not refer in any way to color but is merely a fanciful term applied to this type of mutant (Epstein *et al.*, 1963; Edgar and Epstein, 1965). Other nonsense mutants have also been found, such as the *ochre* mutant (Brenner and Beckwith, 1965). UGA is another nonsense codon (Brenner *et al.*, 1967). These are made functional by host-cell suppressors but by a different set of suppressors than those that suppress *amber* mutants. The *azure* mutant (Horiuchi and Zinder, 1967) is still another type of host-dependent mutant; this type is restricted by suppressor genes, in contrast to *amber* and *ochre* mutants that require the help of suppressor genes.

Amber mutants have also been reported for RNA-containing phages (Horiuchi and Zinder, 1967; Notani *et al.*, 1965). These seem to have the same substitutions as those in the DNA phages (Tooze and Weber, 1967).

Origin of Mutant Viruses

In discussing titration of viruses (Chapter 4), it was pointed out that a single virus particle is sufficient to initiate a plaque. If a highly diluted virus suspension is plated so that only one or a very few plaques are on a given assay plate, there is great likelihood that each plaque was initiated by a single virion. A virus stock prepared by growing virus from the plaque will therefore be genetically homogeneous: All the virions will have been derived from a single progenitor virion. But when the population is examined with respect to the possible mutant types just discussed, or with respect to others appropriate for other viruses, a small fraction of virions can be found that possess the mutant character. How do mutant virions arise?

It is possible that extracellular virions change and become mutants. If so, it would be expected that the fraction of mutants in a given stock would increase with storage. Such is not the case. However, the fraction of mutant virions in a population does increase during replication (Luria, 1951), or even during the intracellular stage if DNA is prevented from replicating (Drake, 1966b).

In fact, it is possible to calculate the mutation rate by comparing the proportion of mutants in a stock before and after a series of replications (Luria and Delbrück, 1943). The resulting rate may be interpreted as the probability that a given type of mutation will occur during a single replication of the viral genetic material. A few representative mutation rates are shown in Table 14-1. These range from one mutation in 10^4 to one in 10^8 replications, a 10,000-fold variation.

Watson and Crick (1953b) proposed a mechanism for mutation derived directly from their proposed structure of DNA (Watson and Crick, 1953a). They pointed out that the hydrogen bonding between the bases on complementary strands depends on the tautomeric form of the base. The bases change from one to another tautomeric form by a shift in the distribution of electrons in the molecule. The equilibrium between the tautomeric forms favors an electronic distribution such that adenine pairs with thymine (or uracil in RNA) and cytosine pairs with guanine. If replication of a given base pair occurs at the rare moment that the base is in its less likely tautomeric form, adenine could pair with cytosine and guanine with thymine. In this case, a mutation would occur with insertion of a wrong base into the sequence. Such a mechanism would, of course, be operative only during replication.

Mutations can be induced in viral nucleic acids by various

TABLE 14-1. REPRESENTATIVE MUTATION RATES

VIRUS	MUTATION	RATE[*]	REFERENCE
T2	$r^+ \to r$	5×10^{-5}	Luria, 1951
	$h^+ \to h$	10^{-8}	Hershey, 1946
	$h \to h^+$	10^{-4}	Streisinger and Franklin, 1956
Influenza virus	Resistance to β-inhibitor	10^{-8}	Medill-Brown and Broidy, 1955
Poliovirus	$d \to d^+$	2×10^{-5}	Dulbecco and Vogt, 1958
	$m \to m^+$	3×10^{-7}	Takemori and Nomura, 1960
EMC	$r^+ \to r$	10^{-4}	Breeze and Subak-Sharpe, 1967

[*]Mutation per particle per duplication.

chemical and physical agents. In contrast to spontaneous mutations, however, mutations can be induced either intracellularly during replication or extracellularly by direct action on the nucleic acid.

The base analog, 5-bromouracil, resembles thymine sufficiently that during replication it can be inserted into DNA in place of thymine. Its base-pairing properties resemble those of thymine so that the substitution is not, in itself, mutagenic. However, the substitution of the bromine for the methyl group at the 5-position of thymine shifts the tautomeric equilibrium. Therefore, 5-bromouracil is much more likely than thymine to be in the rare *enol* form at the time of replication, and mutation by insertion of the wrong base is more likely to occur than if thymine had been present. The number of T2 mutants is greatly increased when the infected cells are grown in the presence of 5-bromouracil (Litman and Pardee, 1956).

Mutation with this analog, however, is not merely due to the increase in the probability that a spontaneous mutation will occur. This was shown by Benzer and Freese (1958), who determined the position in the viral DNA molecule of many spontaneous and many 5-bromouracil-induced mutants of T4. Examination of the locations of mutations revealed "hot spots" with a higher probability of mutation than surrounding regions. Although there were hot spots for spontaneous mutations and for induced mutations, the hot spots did not coincide. Thus, the mutability of a given nucleotide pair depends on its position in the DNA molecule and therefore on what other bases are in its immediate neighborhood.

Nitrous acid is an example of another chemical mutagen. It was first shown to cause mutations in tobacco mosaic virus or in the RNA isolated from the virus (Gierer and Mundry, 1958), but since then it has been used to induce mutations in many viruses or in isolated nucleic acids (phages: T2, Vielmetter and Wieder, 1959, and ϕX174, Tessman, 1959b; Newcastle disease virus: Granoff, 1961; poliovirus: Boeyé, 1959). Nitrous acid thus acts on single- or double-stranded DNA or RNA. In all cases, it has been shown that inactivation of infectivity or the induction of mutations is a single-hit process.

Nitrous acid acts on the nucleic acid by deaminating bases: Adenine is deaminated to hypoxanthine, which pairs with cytosine in place of thymine; cytosine is deaminated to uracil, which pairs with adenine in place of guanine; and guanine is deaminated to xanthine, which still pairs with cytosine but with two hydrogen bonds instead of the usual three (Freese, 1963). Because the induction of a mutation is single hit, it is concluded that deamination of a single base can result in a mutant particle. Nitrous acid acts on the nucleic acid of the virus in its extracellular state, but at the next replication, the alteration becomes permanently embedded in the nucleic acid molecule.

Analysis of many mutants of tobacco mosaic virus induced by ni-

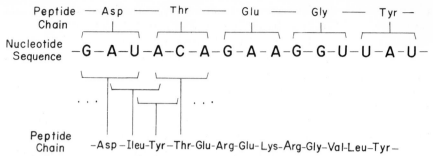

Figure 14-3. Two possible ways to "read" the genetic code. The nucleotide sequence shown in the center directs the synthesis of different polypeptide chains depending on how it is "read." The upper chain results if the sequence is transcribed in nonoverlapping triplets, and the lower chain results from overlapping triplets. Change of a single base to another base by mutation causes one amino acid substitution by the upper scheme and three by the lower scheme.

trous acid have led to the conclusion that the triplet code in nucleic acids is not overlapping (Tsugita, 1962; Wittmann, 1963; Tsugita and Fraenkel-Conrat, 1960). It had been postulated that triplets of bases, each corresponding to a specific amino acid, might be "read" either of two ways. The reading mechanism could start with a group of three bases as one triplet, then move to the next independent group of three—just as a person reading a book may read a word as an independent entity. Alternatively, the genetic code could be "read" by moving along the sequence by one base and taking the next group of three. These schemes are shown in Figure 14-3. Change of a single base would change one amino acid if triplets did not overlap, but would change three amino acids if triplets did overlap. The data clearly showed that the genetic code is nonoverlapping.

The last type of chemical mutagen to be discussed here consists of a class of compounds called the acridines. These are dyes, such as acridine orange and proflavin. They react with nucleic acids by intercalation; that is, a molecule of the dye inserts between two adjacent base pairs, forcing them apart. The distance between base pairs becomes 6.8Å instead of 3.4Å (Lerman, 1961). The dye molecule thus in effect becomes a new "base" in the chain without an opposite member in the complementary chain; during replication, a purine or pyrimidine can be added or subtracted at that position in the complementary chain (Brenner *et al.*, 1961a). Frame-shift mutants of the lysozyme gene of phage T4 in which two base pairs have been added have been reported (Okada *et al.*, 1966; Inouye *et al.*, 1967).

The addition or deletion of a base shifts the whole frame of reading of the triplets (Fig. 14-4), resulting in the frame-shift mutants. Such a mutation can be reversed by a second insertion or deletion farther down the sequence, restoring the reading frame to the correct groups of bases. Between the two altered spots, the read-out results in

A

— G A U A G C A U G A G C C A C G A A C G A —
  — Asp — Ser — Met — Ser — His — Glu — Arg —

B

— G A U A G A U G A G C C A C G C A A C G A —
  — Asp — Arg — Try — Ala — Thr — Glu — Arg —

Figure 14-4. Frame-shift mutation. A wild-type nucleotide sequence and its corresponding polypeptide chain are shown in **A**. If one base (the underlined −C−) is deleted from **A**, the reading frame is shifted, resulting in an altered sequence of amino acids in the peptide chain. The reading frame can be restored to proper register by the addition of another base (the underlined −C− in diagram **B**) farther "down" the sequence. (Although a −C− was used here, any other base would do.) Between the points of deletion and addition, the peptide chain is incorrect, but it is correct outside the region. Frame-shift mutation can also result from addition of bases.

changed amino acids (Crick *et al.*, 1961) and a nonfunctional or partially functional protein.

MODE OF REPLICATION OF VIRAL NUCLEIC ACID

Because spontaneous mutations occur when viral nucleic acid replicates, Luria (1951) could test his earlier prediction (1945) about the mode of replication of phages. He proposed four possible ways by which vegetative phages (that is, the viral nucleic acids) could replicate; the theory has since been developed in more detail (Steinberg and Stahl, 1961).

One possibility is that viral nucleic acid replicates exponentially, each molecule of DNA giving rise to two new molecules (Fig. 14-5A). In this way, seven replicative cycles would yield 128 progeny molecules. The number of mutant phages would depend on when during the replicative cycle a random mutation occurred. If it occurred early, there would be a large number of mutant virions in that cell, and the distribution of mutants among infected cells would not be random. There would be a random distribution of cells yielding one or more mutants, however. (In the exponential case, the likelihood of a mutation arising increases toward the end of the vegetative stage because more phage DNA molecules are replicating. More, but smaller, mutant clones are likely to arise.)

As a second possible mode of replication, Luria proposed that the single parental DNA molecule could replicate repeatedly, giving rise to the progeny molecules (Fig. 14-5B). This would require 128 replications by the parental molecule and none by the progeny molecules. If a mutation occurred by chance during one of the replications, the

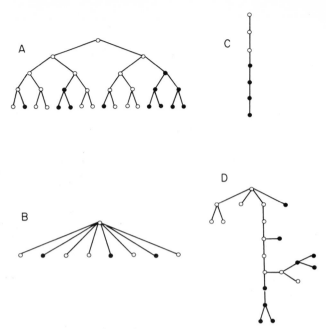

Figure 14-5. Four possible replicative schemes for viral DNA, showing the distribution of wild-type (open circles) and of mutants (closed circles) to be expected in each scheme. (Redrawn from Luria, 1945.)

progeny virion would be a mutant, but it would not give rise to further mutant progeny until it began a new replicative cycle in another cell. The distribution of mutants among infected cells under this hypothesis would be strictly random. That is, the number of mutants per cell would be determined by the Poisson distribution.

A third proposed mechanism was that from each replication only one of the progeny molecules would replicate (Fig. 14-5C). If a mutation occurred during one of the replications, all the progeny molecules from that point on would have the mutation. Cells containing one or more mutants would be randomly distributed, and the number of mutant virions in each cell would also be randomly distributed. If a mutation occurred at the first replication, the entire complement of virus in that cell would be mutant. Such an event is as likely as the chance that the mutation would occur at the last replication and therefore that only one virion would carry the mutation. The distribution of clone sizes would be strictly random; the likelihood that a cell would contain one mutant is the same as the likelihood that its entire complement would be mutant. The fourth possible case is a combination of the others (Fig. 14-5D).

Experimental distinction between these possibilities can be made if it is possible to determine the proportion of mutants among the progeny liberated from each infected cell when it lyses. The single-burst experiment is the tool for obtaining the necessary data.

Ellis and Delbrück (1939) developed the single-burst experiment for studying the growth of phage. The experiment consists simply of infecting cells at a low multiplicity to minimize double infections and then distributing highly diluted samples among many culture vials or tubes. The dilution is made so that each tube will most likely receive only one infected bacterium. If the dilution factor is known, the average number of infected cells per tube can be calculated; the Poisson distribution function then allows calculation of the expected number of tubes receiving no infected cells and one, two, or more infected cells. After sufficient incubation to allow infected cells to lyse, the entire contents of each tube is plated to determine the number of plaques. A tube containing no cells or only uninfected cells will of course yield no plaques. Other tubes will contain the progeny released from one infected cell, or from more than one, depending on the number of infected cells per tube.

Luria (1951) used a modified single-burst experiment to determine the distribution of mutant T2 phages among the progeny. The experiment was therefore a test to determine which scheme accounts for phage replication. Since the number of mutant phages was expected to be small, it was not necessary to look at true single bursts. Instead, his platings had 22,620 bursts on 2874 plates, or about eight bursts per plate. Separate experiments showed that each burst yielded about 80 plaques. Luria, therefore, examined about $80 \times 22,620 = 1,809,000$ plaques. Among these he found a total of 90 plates with r mutant plaques and 103 with w mutants. More meaningful, however, was the distribution of mutant clone size. Luria observed a total of 766 mutant plaques on the 2874 plates. If these plaques had been randomly distributed according to the Poisson distribution, he would have expected 586 plates with one mutant, 85 with two or three mutants, and one or two with four or more mutants. The results, shown in Table 14-2, clearly show the nonrandom distribution of mutants. This result indicates that T2 viral DNA replicates exponentially, with each molecule of viral DNA, whether parental or progeny, replicating successively.

Also shown in Table 14-2 are results obtained in a similar way for another virus. The single-stranded DNA-containing virus ϕX174 replicates by a mechanism that differs from that of the double-stranded T-even phages. The difference in replicative mechanism is reflected in the different distribution of mutants. The random distribution of mutants for ϕX174 indicates that it replicates by successive duplications of the parental nucleic acid (or its derivative) and that progeny strands do not replicate. At least, it can be said that replicative products of the progeny strands, if there are any, are not used for formation of mature virions. This replicative mechanism is consistent with that shown in Figure 14-5B. If either virus replicated by the scheme shown in Figure 14-5C, there should be as many clones con-

TABLE 14-2.   MUTANT CLONE SIZE DISTRIBUTIONS
FOR T2 AND ϕX174

NUMBER OF MUTANTS PER CLONE	T2[*]		ϕX[†]	
	OBSERVED	EXPECTED	OBSERVED	EXPECTED
0	2691	2199	1835	1810
1	93	586	228	266
2	27	78	30	20
3	22	7	4	1
4	6	1	1	0
5	3	0	1	
6	7			
7	4			
8	2			
9	0			
10	3			
10+	16			

[*]766 mutants/2874 clones, average = 0.267 mutants/clone; $e^{-0.267} = 0.765$ (Luria, 1951).

[†]309 mutants/2099 clones, average = 0.147 mutants/clone; $e^{-0.147} = 0.863$ (Denhardt and Silver, 1966).

taining a large number of mutants as there are containing a small number.

HOST-CONTROLLED VARIATION

Not all phenotypic changes that occur with viruses are due to mutation. Many instances are known in which the virus takes on certain phenotypic characteristics determined by the type of cell in which it is grown. Examples of host-controlled variation have been found in many groups of viruses, but it is especially common among the myxoviruses, paramyxoviruses, and their relatives. This is easily understood because these viruses acquire a portion of the cell during their replication. The cell contribution, of course, varies according to the cell types.

Newcastle disease virus, for instance, can differ in several of its properties, depending on whether it is grown in cells of the chorioallantoic membrane of chick embryos or in the fibroblastic cells of the embryo itself. Virus from the chorioallantoic membrane cells is more stable to heat inactivation than is virus from fibroblasts, and it inactivates as a multiple-hit curve rather than as a single-hit. There are also different pH dependencies and different sensitivities to ultraviolet inactivation. These altered properties are conferred on the virus by a single passage, under conditions in which mutants are not selected (Drake and Lay, 1962).

Other experiments with Newcastle disease virus (Stenback and Durand, 1963) showed that the density of the particles grown in avian cells differs from the density of the particles grown in mammalian cells. Again, this is not the result of selection of mutants with different densities, but probably results from having different amounts, or different kinds, of lipids added to the virion during its maturation at the cell surface.

Because there are so many examples of host-controlled modification with the bacteriophages, this phenomenon might be universal (see review by Arber, 1965). However, unlike the examples described for animal viruses, host modification of phages usually results in restricting their host range. After being injected into a nonpermissive bacterium, the DNA of the restricted phage is degraded and cannot replicate. The modification that results in restricting the host range is conferred on the phage by a single growth cycle; the modification is nongenetic in that it does not involve a change in the sequence of bases.

However, the DNA of the phage is involved (Arber and Dussoix, 1962). If, for instance, λ, grown on *E. coli* strain K, is used to infect *E. coli* strain C, the yield of about 100 phages per cell contains two types of particles. Most are changed so that they no longer grow on strain K. The other type, about 1 per cent, still contain the original DNA. The exact chemical change conferred on the newly synthesized DNA by its single growth cycle is unknown but may consist of an altered pattern of methylation of certain bases of the DNA. These patterns are probably controlled by cell enzymes rather than by viral-induced enzymes.

Many of the phages that are controlled by host modification are temperate; as such, they carry host genetic material between bacteria by a process called transduction. This mode of genetic interchange between bacteria will be described in greater detail in Chapter 16, but it can be seen that host-controlled modification of phages may have adaptive value for bacteria, since it may control which phages can infect given cells. This, in turn, controls the bacterial strains between which genetic exchange can take place.

The study of mutants has been most rewarding in leading to an understanding of the molecular mechanisms behind many genetic phenomena. No less rewarding have been studies using the mutations to mark positions on the viral DNA molecule so that their location relative to one another can be determined. Recombination between two molecules, giving progeny with predictable characteristics, readily occurs in cells infected by certain viruses. Virologists have performed many elegant and incisive experiments based on recombination. Some of these experiments will be the subject of the next chapter.

Further Reading

Edgar, R. S., and R. H. Epstein: The Genetics of a Bacterial Virus. Scientific American, 212(February):71-78, 1965.

Fenner, F., and J. F. Sambrook: The Genetics of Animal Viruses. Annual Reviews of Microbiology, 18:47-94, 1964.

Kilbourne, E. D.: Influenza Virus Genetics. Progress in Medical Virology, 5:79-126, 1963.

Luria, S. E.: Genetics of Bacteriophage. Annual Review of Microbiology, 16:205-240, 1962.

Pontecorvo, G.: Microbial Genetics: Retrospect and Prospect. Proceedings of the Royal Society, Series B, 158:1-23, 1963.

15

VIRAL GENETICS: RECOMBINATION

Production of mutations yields new forms that, in effect, test the environment. If the new form has increased survival value, it will eventually replace the old form. In an environment that continually changes, organisms must produce mutants better adapted to the new conditions or the species succumbs. Consequently, production of mutations is an important evolutionary mechanism for all organisms.

Higher organisms, however, have an additional mechanism, one that speeds the spread of a successful mutation through the population so that it more rapidly replaces the old. This mechanism is one of mixing genetic material from two organisms, resulting in offspring that possess some of the genetic information of each parent. In higher organisms, the mixing process occurs by mating, which brings one half of the genetic information of each parent together into a single new cell. The information possessed by each parent is arranged in packets, the chromosomes, and one of each pair of chromosomes, chosen randomly, is contributed to the offspring.

Under certain conditions viruses, too, can be replicated so that their genetic material mixes. When two genetically different viruses simultaneously infect a cell, the progeny may have some properties derived from each parent. Proper conditions may seldom occur naturally and may be important only under laboratory conditions. But studies of mixed infections, the subject of this chapter, have been of tremendous value to the virologist in his attempts to understand the means by which viruses replicate.

Because differences between organisms disappear or fade into minor differences in detail at the genetic level, many conclusions reached by the study of viral genetics have been generalized to explain intracellular mechanisms of all organisms. Viral geneticists have made major contributions to understanding how genetic information is stored, transcribed into protein, and passed on to succeeding generations in all organisms.

MIXED INFECTION: PHENOTYPIC MIXING

A cell that is infected by two related viruses sometimes produces progeny with capsid components of each parental virus. This phenomenon, called phenotypic mixing, has already been described (see Chapter 7) to illustrate the method of virus maturation: the accumulation of viral components in pools and the later random withdrawal of the components for assembly into mature virions.

Demonstration that a new kind of progeny is due to phenotypic mixing is done by infecting cells at high dilution of the progeny virus to be tested. This is to prevent mixed infection. The progeny of the test infection will have new capsids determined by the genotype of the parent, whether or not the virus in the test infection has phenotypically mixed capsid materials (see Fig. 7-11). This test is commonly used in studies of viral genetics to determine whether the virions resulting from a mixed infection are new genetic types, or whether observed changes, such as host-range variation, are due to nongenetic changes in the capsid.

MIXED INFECTION: COMPLEMENTATION

Infection of a bacterial cell with two defective phages sometimes results in replication. The defectiveness of one or both phages is due to a mutation that prevents their replication in single infection. In such a case, replication in mixed infection is not due to reverse mutation or to recombination that produces one complete phage genome from the two defective genomes, because the progeny phage retains the defective mutation. Instead, the gene function of one virus is compensated by the other.

As an example, consider a phage that contains a mutation in the gene coding for an enzyme essential for its replication. Because it lacks the function of that gene, it cannot replicate. If a second phage, with normal function of that gene, also infects the same cell, it is able to code for the essential enzyme and both phages can replicate. The mutated gene is not corrected, so progeny still carry the mutation and will be unable to replicate.

MIXED INFECTION: PHAGE RECOMBINATION

How is a phage recombination or cross experiment performed? First, it is necessary to have genetically pure stocks of phage with two or more mutations that can easily be assayed. For instance, these could be plaque-type or host-range mutations. Aliquots of the two phage stocks to be crossed are added to a suspension of appropriate cells at a high enough concentration to ensure that many of the cells will be infected with a phage of each type. The number of phages of each type that take part in the infection of each cell is determined by the concentration of each phage type. Infection must be carried out in such a way that one phage does not exclude the other. After sufficient time to allow phages to adsorb to the cells, unadsorbed particles are removed by dilution, by treatment with antiserum, or by centrifuging the cells and rinsing. The cells are then incubated to allow phage to develop. If the progeny of individual cells are to be examined, the cells are diluted into single culture tubes so that the single bursts can be plated. After the cells have lysed, the progeny are plated on appropriate cells and examined for the various characteristics.

Let us take some specific examples. Assume that cells are doubly infected with phage that are wild-type with respect to plaque-type and host-range mutation (see Fig. 14-1) and with phage that are mutants in these characters. The cross is indicated $T2r^+h^+ \times T2rh$.

The progeny are plated on mixed cells to score for the occurrence of different plaque types. Some plaques will be of parental phenotype and will have diffuse centers with narrow, hazy halos (r^+h^+) or clear centers with broader halos (rh). New plaque types also appear, however, that were not present in platings of the parental stock. These have narrow halos and clear centers (r^+h) or broad, diffuse halos with turbid centers (rh^+). These four types can be distinguished from one another and counted.

The new plaque types could have arisen by mutation, were it not for the fact that they occur too frequently. They are, instead, recombinants, and they possess genetic characters of both parental phages. If $T2h$ is crossed with $T2r$, the progeny contain both parental types, some wild-type with respect to both characters, and some with both mutant characters, $T2rh$. In this case, the wild-type arises as a recombinant.

If none of the progeny types has a selective advantage, then the number of progeny virions of one recombinant type equals the number of progeny of the other recombinant type. The frequency of recombination can be calculated by counting the number of plaques of each type in the progeny. Take, for example, the following cross:

$$T2r^+h^+ \times T2rh \to T2r^+h^+ + T2rh + T2r^+h + T2rh^+$$

Here the frequency of recombination would be

$$R = \frac{r^+h + rh^+}{r^+h^+ + rh + r^+h + rh^+}$$

It is thus possible to cross pairs of phages containing various mutations and obtain recombination frequencies for the various crosses.

Before seeing how these recombination frequencies are used in drawing certain conclusions about the arrangement of genetic information in the phage DNA, let us examine the mating event in more detail. In a cross between higher organisms, one mating can result in the production of one set of progeny that can be analyzed genetically. With phages, however, an intracellular pool of phage DNA develops, some molecules of which are parental and some of which are progeny. In the T series of phages, apparently all the DNA molecules replicate and are subject to recombination or mating events with other molecules. Thus, during one growth cycle, multiple interchanges of genetic information can take place between phages.

Visconti and Delbrück (1953) were led to this conclusion by considering certain apparent anomalies that had been found in phage crosses. For instance, there was the observation that inhibition of cell lysis resulted not only in a larger burst size, but also in a higher frequency of recombination. If only one mating event took place in any one bacterial cell during a phage growth cycle, the recombination frequency would not increase with delayed lysis.

Another observation was that infection of a cell with three parental phages, each carrying a different mutation, resulted in the appearance of all three mutations in some of the progeny. This result could occur if two of the parental types exchanged genetic information and the progeny of that mating then exchanged with the third parental type. This, of course, would require multiple matings during the growth cycle. The extensive theory developed by Visconti and Delbrück (1953) made it clear that events in a single infected cell are really a problem in population genetics. The multiple pairwise matings that occur during the vegetative phase explain the anomalies.

Two major means by which two replicating DNA molecules could exchange genetic information can be postulated. One is called the copy-choice mechanism (Fig. 15-1). Under this mechanism, it is proposed that during the "copying" of the genetic information in one phage DNA molecule to the daughter molecule, a switch occurs: Genetic information from one molecule is copied part way, then the information from a second molecule is copied.

The second possible mechanism, breakage and reunion, is shown

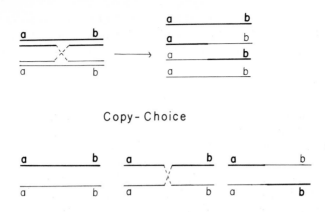

Copy-Choice

Breakage and Reunion

Figure 15-1. Two possible mechanisms for recombination of DNA: copy-choice and breakage and reunion.

in the bottom of Figure 15-1. Here it is supposed that the two DNA molecules undergoing the exchange actually break at the same point in each, and the fragments are rejoined so that the new molecule contains part of each.

Since both possible mechanisms result in reciprocal recombinants, it was difficult to decide between them simply on the basis of genetic crosses. The answer was found when physical methods were combined with genetic crosses: Even though there is no difference between the two proposed mechanisms that can be detected genetically, there is a physical difference. In the copy-choice mechanism, the integrity of the parental strands would be preserved: The progeny recombinant strands would contain only newly synthesized DNA. Recombinants resulting from breaking the molecule and rejoining the fragments would of course contain the original DNA.

The test of whether recombination occurs by breakage and reunion or by copy-choice requires that phages containing original DNA be distinguishable from those containing some original and some newly synthesized DNA. Meselson and Weigle (1961) and Kellenberger *et al.* (1961a) used density gradients and density-labeled phages to demonstrate that recombination involves the breakage and reunion of DNA molecules. Two methods were used to produce density differences in the parental λ phages used in the cross.

One method consisted of growing one parent in medium containing heavy carbon and nitrogen. This parental phage was therefore more dense than the other parent, grown in normal medium. The cross was performed in normal medium. If recombination occurred by copy-choice, recombinant phages would be of normal density. But if recombination occurred by breakage and reunion, recombinant phages would have an increased density because of having received some high-density DNA from the labeled parent. Fractions from the density gradient were assayed for the various genotypes and it was found that the recombinant types did have an increased density.

In the second type of experiment, λ mutants of decreased density (missing a small portion of the DNA) served the same purpose as the artificially density-labeled phages. Because of the altered host-range characteristics of these mutants, they could be assayed selectively. A cross between wild-type phage, $\lambda b2^+b5^+$, and phage that are mutant in the $b2$ and $b5$ characters, $\lambda b2b5$, and much lighter in density, yielded four genotypes: $b2^+b5^+$, $b2b5$, $b2^+b5$, and $b2b5^+$. Under copy-choice mechanism of recombination, if one parent is labeled with P^{32}, the progeny would be labeled only in that parental type. Under the break-

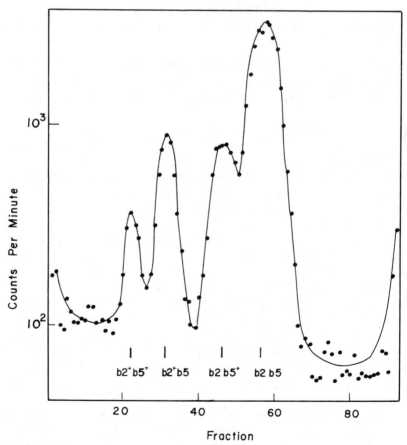

Figure 15-2. Demonstration that recombination in λ occurs by breakage and reunion. The cross, $\lambda b2b5(P^{32}) \times \lambda b2^+b5^+$, was made and the progeny were analyzed by CsCl density gradient analysis. The two parental types are in the most widely separated peaks, and the progeny, labeled with P^{32}, have intermediate density. Peaks in the gradient were identified by assay for infectivity on selective cells. (Redrawn from Kellenberger *et al.*, 1961a.)

age-reunion mechanism, however, the label would be found in all four genotypes. (It would find its way into the cold parental genotype band by recombinations of markers other than the two scored.) As shown in Figure 15-2, the results indicate that most, if not all, recombination in phage involves physical exchange of DNA between parents.

Experiments reported by Anraku and Tomizawa (1965) showed two steps that take place when the fragments are rejoined during recombination. The first step involves hydrogen bonding of the broken ends of the two parental DNA molecules. Synthesis of DNA is not required for this step (Tomizawa and Anraku, 1964; Simon, 1965), but it is required for the second step, in which phosphodiester bonds are formed. The DNA synthesis step requires the synthesis of phage-coded DNA polymerase, as the second step of recombination does not occur when the parental phages are *amber* mutants unable to code for this enzyme. Protein synthesis is required for the first step in recombination; the newly synthesized protein may enzymatically break the parental strands and bring about initial hydrogen-bonding of the fragments. Mutants unable to induce synthesis of the "breaking" enzyme do not recombine (Kozinski and Felgenhauer, 1967). Completion of the new molecules by permanent phosphodiester bonds is thought to be performed by the same enzyme that repairs DNA after excision of thymine photodimers (see Chapter 5). The fact that the final step can be performed in mutant *E. coli* lacking the ability to recombine suggests that phages carry the information for directing the synthesis of enzymes to reform complete molecules (Clark and Margulies, 1965).

GENETIC MAPS

Mixed infection of a bacterial cell with two identifiable parental types yields a certain proportion of recombinants. Analysis of the frequencies of recombinants reveals information about the structure of the genetic material. For instance, the fact that genetic markers of T-even phages are linked in a single group was deduced this way (Streisinger and Bruce, 1960). Genetic experiments therefore confirm physical data, presented in preceding chapters, that the genetic information of a virus is contained in a single molecule of nucleic acid per virion. (In most cases, however, the information was actually obtained genetically and confirmed physically.)

Genetic analysis can also give much more detailed information, such as the order of the markers in the linkage group and their distance from each other.

To understand how this information is derived from the recombination frequency, consider the cross $ab \times a^+b^+$. As was discussed before, a recombination frequency can be calculated from an examination of the progeny yield. A frequency of recombination can also be determined for a similar cross performed with another marker in place of b, $az \times a^+z^+$. If the frequency of recombinants from the first cross is less than the frequency of recombinants from the second cross, the marker, b, is said to be closer to a than a is to z.

This conclusion is derived from a consideration of the probabilities: There is more chance for a crossing-over to occur between two distantly linked markers than between two closely linked markers. In fact, the frequency of recombinants is a measure of the relative likelihood of crossing-over between the two sets of markers, and therefore it is a measure of the distance between the markers.

The type of cross just described is a two-factor cross. A three-factor cross can also be performed using phages that have three markers. Analysis of the recombinants in the progeny in this case gives an unambiguous ordering of the markers. For instance, the cross might be $abc \times a^+b^+c^+$. If the order is as written, the progeny will include the recombinants ab^+c^+, abc^+, a^+bc, and a^+b^+c. There can also be, in very low frequency, the double recombinants ab^+c and a^+bc^+. To produce the double recombinants, a double crossing-over is required, accounting for the low frequency; the chance that two crossings will occur is the product of the probabilities of the single crossings.

If the investigator has a large collection of phages carrying different mutations, he can perform crosses between them, calculate the frequency of recombination obtained in each cross, and obtain a map showing the relative position of each mutation on the phage's genome. This type of genetic analysis has been performed for several phages (as well as for many higher organisms), and it has been concluded that the various genetic markers fall along a single, linear map; often, the map is circular, as will be discussed in a later section. Distances between markers can be obtained by crossing in various combinations; when this is done, the map distances are found to be additive.

One interesting conclusion to be drawn from such a map of T4 is that genes for various functions do not occur randomly on the genome, but are somewhat grouped according to function. There is a cluster of genes for DNA synthesis, for instance, and other clusters of genes for tail fiber synthesis (Edgar and Wood, 1966).

The closer two markers are, the fewer recombinations occur between them. Consequently, many progeny from a cross must be analyzed if the few recombinants are to be detected. Such an extensive analysis has been carried out by Benzer on a small region of the T4 genome. The class of mutants he studied is the rII group, consisting of mutants that plaque with the r phenotype on $E.$ $coli$ B. In $E.$ $coli$ that are lysogenic for phage λ (see Chapter 16), the rII mutants cannot multiply, but wild-type can. There are two adjacent regions on the phage genetic map where all the *r*II mutants map; some are in the A region and some in the B region. Mixed infection of lysogenic cells [*E. coli* K-12 (λ)] with two phages, one mutant anywhere in A and one mutant anywhere in B, allows multiplication. The A and B regions are called cistrons (Benzer, 1957) because each is a unit of function that can be complemented by the other. The function of the *r*II region is unknown, but knowing the function is not necessary for genetic mapping.

Because of the selectivity of host conferred on the phages by mutation, a single wild-type phage can be detected easily out of 10^8 mutant phages. The *r*II system makes it possible to calculate very low recombination frequencies and therefore very short map distances. Benzer (1959, 1962) produced a map of the fine structure of the *r*II point mutants, which mapped at 308 different sites; 202 of these were in cistron A and 106 in cistron B. The mutations were not scattered randomly among the 308 sites, but a few sites, the "hot spots," contained the vast majority.

Benzer's detailed investigation confirmed that the map was linear with no branching. He found this to be true even at such high resolution that the distances between mutant loci were of the order of the distance between nucleotides.

THE NUCLEOTIDE SEQUENCE AND THE GENETIC MAP

The genetic map, as it has been described, is based on calculations of recombination frequencies. No physical data are involved. It is conceivable that the genetic map, although self-consistent, does not correspond to the physical map.

To test this, the physical distance between markers was measured by infecting spheroplasts with T4 and with fragments of T4 DNA (Mosig, 1966; Goldberg, 1966). Under these conditions, markers in the DNA fragments are incorporated into mature phage. Knowing the size of the fragments, the investigators could calculate the maximum physical distance between the markers. In this way, it was shown that the physical map of markers on the phage DNA molecule correspond well with their positions on a map derived from recombination frequencies.

Genetic analysis of the order of markers and the distance between markers on the phage DNA has physical meaning; analysis at higher resolution also has physical meaning. This was shown by Sarabhai *et al.* (1964) as follows: These investigators isolated a number of *amber* mutants of T4 that were defective in producing phage head protein. In such mutants, the normal protein is synthesized until the mutated codon is reached, at which point the peptide chain is terminated. The length of the peptide produced is a measure of the distance between the mutant codon and the point on the DNA where "reading" of the cistron begins. It was thus possible to construct a physical map of the position of the mutant sites. The positions of the same mutations were also determined by genetic crosses and analysis of the frequency of recombinants. The physical and genetic maps coincided.

HETEROZYGOTES

Analysis of the progeny from a cross reveals, in addition to parental type and recombinant type plaques, a few plaques (1 or 2 per cent) of another kind. These plaques may show characteristics of both parents with regard to one marker. A plaque of this type can be produced if a virus of each parental type infects neighboring cells in the assay plate. Such an origin is easily ruled out, however, when a high dilution of the phage is used to infect the cells. If dilution does not eliminate plaques with the two forms of marker, both markers must be

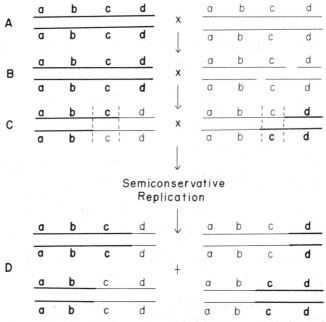

Figure 15-3. Formation of recombinational heterozygotes. The two molecules that are about to recombine are shown intact in **A**. The first step in recombination involves breakage of both strands of the DNA duplex molecule; as shown in **B**, this may occur at different loci in the two strands. After reciprocal exchange and rejoining, as shown in **C**, a heterozygous region is present. This is eliminated at the first semi-conservative replication to give the molecules diagramed in **D**.

in the same phage. Phages that carry both parental markers are called heterozygotes.

One way that heterozygotes can arise is shown in Figure 15-3. These are called internal heterozygotes, heteroduplex heterozygotes, or recombinational heterozygotes. The heterozygote probably is an intermediate in the formation of a recombinant. A DNA molecule has to be broken before it can rejoin in forming a recombinant, and sometimes the break of one strand of the helix occurs near the break in the complementary chain, but not exactly opposite to it. In a small region of the rejoined chain, therefore, one strand originates from each parent, forming the heterozygote. At the first semiconservative replication of the molecule, the heterozygous region is eliminated, yielding two pure recombinant molecules. If the heterozygous molecule is "packaged" before it replicates, a heterozygous phage results (Drake, 1966a, 1967).

A second kind of heterozygote arises when the duplicated markers are at the ends of the molecules, a situation that can occur only if there is terminal redundancy (Séchaud et al., 1965), that is, if the information at one end of the molecule is identical to that at the other end. If the ends are identical, the phage is scored as homozygous; if the ends are different, and each end carries the information contributed by a different parent, the phage produces a heterozygous plaque.

THE CIRCULAR GENETIC MAP

Terminal redundancy is one of several factors that led Streisinger and his colleagues (Streisinger et al., 1964; Séchaud et al., 1965; Streisinger et al., 1967) to propose that the genetic map of phage T4 is circular. Circularity was proposed also to account for the finding that certain markers on the T4 genome are distant from each other by some crosses but are close by others. Extensive mapping studies of many conditional-lethal mutants show that the genetic map is circular (Fig. 15-4) (Edgar and Wood, 1966).

But isolation and study of the DNA by various physical methods indicates that the molecule is linear. Therefore, it was proposed that the phage DNA molecule consists of a single, linear, double-stranded helix that is circularly permuted. A collection of DNA molecules from a population of phages contains a random assortment with markers at any location within the molecule.

The existence of the postulated terminal redundancy was demonstrated (Thomas, 1966) by treating isolated T2 DNA with exonuclease III. This is an enzyme prepared from E. coli, which removes nucleotides stepwise from the 3'ends of double-stranded DNA (Fig. 15-5).

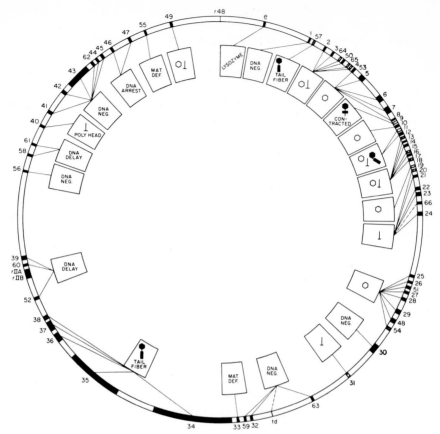

Figure 15-4. The circular genetic map of phage T4. (From Edgar and Wood, 1966. By permission of the authors and the editors of the Proceedings of the National Academy of Sciences.)

After treatment the molecules possess a 5′-ended single-stranded portion at each end. Gentle heating allows the ends to double back and homologous regions to join together, resulting in physically circular molecules. Sometimes, long chains of individual molecules, called concatenates, are formed. These are joined end-to-end rather than circularly.

Thomas (1966) also described physical tests to demonstrate that T2 (or T4) DNA consists of a circularly permuted collection. Thomas first broke P³²-labeled T2 DNA by sonication; such treatment breaks the molecules approximately at, but rarely exactly at, the center, so that the population of broken molecules is composed of "short halves" and "long halves." By column chromatography, Thomas separated out the molecules that were slightly shorter than half the original lengths, discarding the "long halves" (Fig. 15-6). If the original collection were permuted, then all sequences would be represented in the

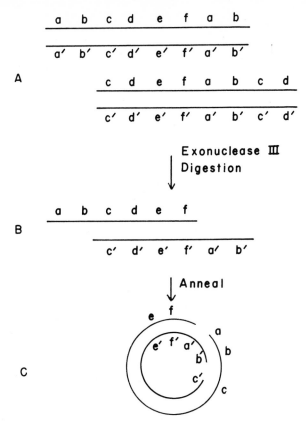

Figure 15-5. A test for terminal redundancy in double-stranded DNA molecules. Two circularly permuted molecules with redundant ends are shown in **A**. Treatment with exonuclease III removes a short portion of each strand; the upper of the two molecules in **A** thus has free, single-stranded ends, as shown in **B**, after the enzyme treatment. Gentle heating allows the free ends to form hydrogen bonds, making a circular molecule as shown in **C**.

"short halves." But if the original molecules were not permuted, the "short halves" would contain only unique portions of the original molecules and a portion of the center would be missing.

The test devised to decide between these possibilities is based on the difference in information content between populations of "short halves," depending on whether they were derived from an original population that was unique or one that was circularly permuted (Thomas and Rubenstein, 1964; Thomas, 1966). The "short halves," labeled with P^{32}, were annealed to whole molecules labeled with C^{14}. The whole molecules, of course, contain a complete set of information. The complexes, consisting of intact strands with "short halves" hybridized to part of their length, were then sonicated to produce short segments and heated to separate the strands. At this

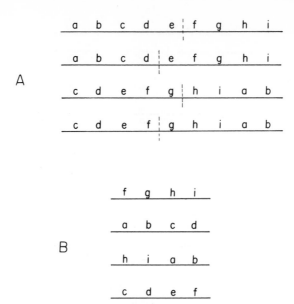

Figure 15-6. Production of "short halves" of T2 DNA. Sonication of the circularly permuted DNA molecules shown in **A** breaks the molecules into "long halves" and "short halves." The "short halves," separated out by column chromatography, contain all possible sequences. If the original collection of molecules in **A** had been a unique collection, without circular permutation, the "short halves" would be an equal mixture of molecules of two kinds, neither of which would contain the central portion of the original molecules.

point, the mixture consists of short, single strands, some labeled with C^{14} and some with P^{32}. The mixture is now annealed to denatured, whole, unlabeled viral DNA embedded in agar. If there is a difference in sequences represented in the molecules labeled with C^{14} as compared to P^{32}, one isotope will be fractionated with respect to the other. The test showed that T2 DNA is circularly permuted and that T5 DNA is not.

Consideration of how a phage DNA molecule could possess terminally redundant ends and how phage DNA comes to be circularly permuted led to an interesting proposal about the synthesis of phage DNA (Streisinger *et al.*, 1967). The scheme, diagramed in Figure 15-7, has as its first step a recombination between redundant ends of two or more molecules, resulting in a longer molecule than normal. Then, the long molecule is enzymatically cut, starting at a randomly selected spot, with subsequent cuts the proper distance away to yield one phage "headful" of DNA. The "headful" of DNA is a little more than a complete genome, so that each cut occurs farther down the chain than the previous cut.

The proposed scheme also predicted that if a deletion had occurred, shortening the genetic length, a "headful" length would have longer regions of terminal redundancy and there would be an in-

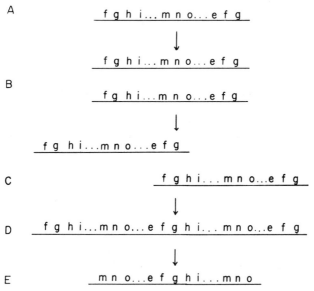

Figure 15-7. Diagram illustrating how circular permutation and terminal redundancy arise in T4. The original molecule (**A**), with terminally redundant ends, replicates (**B**). In **C** the molecules pair, with recombination occurring (**D**) between the homologous sequences of each molecule. The single long molecule is then "cut" enzymatically into "headful" lengths (**E**), the size of the original molecule, but with a different starting point. (Redrawn from Streisinger *et al.*, 1967.)

creased frequency of heterozygotes. A test of this prediction showed it to be the case (Streisinger *et al.*, 1967).

Another kind of abnormality of phage replication results from the cutting process. In addition to the normal phage particles, a phage lysate contains defective particles that are separable from normal phage by CsCl density gradient analysis. These defective phages have apparently normal protein coats but contain a DNA molecule that is two-thirds normal length. These phages cannot replicate unless two or more coinfect a cell, in which case progeny result. The part of the genome that is present must be a random part of the whole genome — otherwise, coinfection with two particles, if they contained identical genetic material, would not produce complete progeny (Mosig, 1963, 1966).

Not all viruses are like T2 and T4 in having terminal redundancy and circular permutation; there are many variations. DNA of the human adenoviruses, for instance, exists as linear molecules, a small percentage of which can be converted to circles by treating with exonuclease III and annealing (Green *et al.*, 1967b). Genetic data are not available, nor is information available on circular permutation. The single-stranded DNA virus S13 has both a circular molecule and a circular genetic map (Baker and Tessman, 1967). Phage λ (see Chapter 16), on the other hand, has a circular molecule at some stages of its replicative cycle and, at other times, a linear molecule with "sticky ends" that easily forms circles when the DNA is isolated from extra-cellular virions. Its genetic map is linear without circular permutation.

RECOMBINATION IN ANIMAL VIRUSES

Genetic work with animal viruses has been severely limited by several factors. Many mutants have been described, but in general these are more difficult to work with than those of bacterial viruses. A factor that may contribute to a low likelihood of recombination is the greater volume of animal cells compared to bacterial cells. The greater separation between replicating viral nucleic acid molecules may give less chance for genetic interaction.

Nevertheless, recombination has been demonstrated for a few animal viruses. These include vaccinia (Gemmell and Fenner, 1960), influenza virus (Simpson and Hirst, 1961; Hirst, 1962), foot-and-mouth disease virus (Pringle, 1968), and poliovirus (Hirst, 1962; Ledinko, 1963). Recombination has been demonstrated to occur between influenza viruses that would seem to be distantly related, that is, a human strain and an equine strain (Kilbourne, 1968). Little work has been done in any of these systems pertaining to mapping markers or to the mechanism of recombination. It is worth emphasis that influenza virus, poliovirus, and foot-and-mouth disease virus contain single-stranded RNA; and their mechanism of recombination would be of considerable interest.

MIXED INFECTIONS: "HYBRIDS"

A recombinant that arises from two parental virus strains that are not of the same "species," such as the influenza viruses of human or equine origin, should perhaps be called a "hybrid" rather than a re-combinant. An unusual case of hybrid formation among temperate phages has been described by Anderson (1963).

Hybrids of various kinds seem to occur easily between SV40 and adenoviruses. In Chapter 12 evidence was presented indicating that SV40 helps human adenovirus to replicate in simian cells. When the two viral genomes are present in the same cell, they interact during the replicative cycle. The interaction is not fully understood but seems to be genetic, and it apparently results in hybrid viruses.

The interaction occurs as follows: Human adenovirus does not grow well, if at all, in simian cells. If SV40 is added to the cultures, however, both the human adenovirus and the SV40 replicate. If the mixture of viruses is used in the presence of antiserum against SV40 to infect more monkey cells, the human adenovirus continues to replicate. Now, the virus that is produced in the replicating mixture is neutralized only by antiserum against the original adenovirus, not by antiserum to SV40. After several such passages in SV40 antiserum, all the SV40 virions are removed, and the adenovirus can continue to replicate without antiserum and without the production of SV40 virions.

The apparent loss of the need for the presence of SV40 helper virus was puzzling until it was discovered that at least some SV40 genetic material was present in the adenovirus stock. The SV40 component was not neutralized by SV40 antiserum, but it was neutralized by adenoviral antiserum. The presence of the SV40 was detected by its ability to form tumors in hamsters (Huebner *et al.*, 1964) and by its ability to induce SV40-specific "T" antigens in infected cells (Rowe and Baum, 1964; Rapp *et al.*, 1964).

The new stocks, prepared as described, contain two kinds of particle. One is the original adenovirus, unable to replicate by itself in simian cells. The other kind of particle contains both SVro and adenovirus genetic material in an adenovirus capsid; these particles are "defective" and do not replicate, but they do serve as helper for the adenovirus present (Rowe and Baum, 1965).

Because it has not been possible to remove the SV40 genetic determinants from the adenoviral stock by density gradient analysis (Rapp, 1966; Rowe *et al.*, 1965) or by other methods, the particles are believed to contain the SV40 genetic material in the capsid. There is further biophysical evidence that the genetic information of both viruses may be in the same DNA molecule (Baum *et al.*, 1966).

When a stock of adenovirus type 4 was grown first with SV40 and later in the presence of SV40 antiserum, complete infectious SV40 was again produced when the antiserum was removed (Easton and Hiatt, 1965, 1966). This is suggestive, but by no means conclusive, that in this system, the adenoviral capsid contains a complete SV40 genome. Whether such a capsid contains adenoviral DNA as well is unknown.

It has also been possible to transfer the SV40 genetic material between adenovirus types (Lewis *et al.*, 1966; Rowe, 1965) by growing, for instance, the SV40-adenovirus type 7 hybrid with adenovirus type 2. In this case, the adenovirus type 2 acquired the SV40 genetic material.

There seems to be some variability in the amount of SV40 genetic material present in the hybrid. The fact that in some experiments infection with hybrid yields complete, infectious SV40 probably means that the entire SV40 genome was present. In other cases, the SV40 is not produced, nor is SV40 capsid antigen produced, but certain "early" antigens are produced. This probably means that only part of the SV40 genome is present in these hybrid particles.

Another kind of hybrid has been reported. It is called the

"monkey cell adapting component" because it furnishes the necessary information for human adenovirus replication in monkey cells (Butel *et al.*, 1966b; Butel, 1967). This type of virion arises in the same way as the SV40-adenovirus hybrids but does not induce formation of the "early" SV40 antigens. This type of hybrid could be more limited, possessing only that part of the SV40 genome that aids adenovirus replication in monkey cells. It was not possible, however, to demonstrate homology between DNA extracted from cells infected with the hybrid and RNA synthesized using SV40 DNA as template. If only one or two SV40 genes had been present in the hybrid, however, this test might not have detected it.

The exact nature of these hybrid particles is not clear. Some could be adenoviral capsids containing a complete SV40 genome and no adenoviral DNA; these perhaps could occur by a kind of phenotypic mixing. Other adenoviral capsids could contain a complete adenoviral DNA molecule and a portion of SV40 DNA, or vice versa, with no actual continuity between the two kinds of DNA. These perhaps could be called "nongenetic hybrids," and the process could be "genotypic mixing." Other adenoviral capsids might contain a single molecule of DNA consisting of all or part of the genetic material of both viruses. These could arise if molecular recombination occurred between the two kinds of DNA; because SV40 and adenoviruses are in different groups, they would be hybrids rather than recombinants.

In this chapter, we have seen that intimate interaction of one viral nucleic acid with another during intracellular replication seems to be a general phenomenon of viruses. In the next chapter another kind of interaction will be discussed—the interaction of the DNA of certain viruses with the DNA of their host cell. This can lead to molecular recombination between DNA molecules that are quite distantly related.

Further Reading

Crick, F. H. C.: The Genetic Code. Scientific American, 207(October):66-74, 1962.
Luria, S. E.: Genetics of Bacteriophage. Annual Review of Microbiology, 16:205-240, 1962.
Nirenberg, M. W.: The Genetic Code; II. Scientific American, 208(March):80-94, 1963.

16

LYSOGENY

Evolution has given viruses a rich variety of mechanisms for survival. Their nucleic acid molecule contains information that usually suffices to direct an infected cell in the manufacture of more virus particles. In the process, the viral nucleic acid undergoes many forms of interaction with the cell's nucleic acids and with the nucleic acid of other related or unrelated viruses. Having made more virus particles, the cell dies.

However, there is another major kind of phage-cell interaction — one in which the viral genetic material becomes an intimate part of the bacterial cell and can persist in this close relationship for prolonged periods, even while the cell undergoes many division cycles. The information encoded in some phage genes is expressed, just as is cellular information. Phages that undergo this type of interaction are called temperate, and a bacterial cell that contains a phage in such close relationship is said to be lysogenic. There are no known counterparts in plant or animal virus systems, but certain of the tumor viruses possess some of the characteristics of the temperate phages. In this chapter we will discuss temperate phages, and in the next two chapters we will discuss tumor viruses.

SOME GENERAL ASPECTS OF LYSOGENY

Under ordinary conditions, it is not possible to know whether a given strain of bacteria is lysogenic. Cultures of lysogenic bacteria grow in a seemingly normal manner, with no widespread clearing of the culture that would indicate mass lysis. A few free extracellular virions might be present, but they would not be detectable.

291

The usual way of identifying a lysogenic strain of bacteria is to plate samples of the culture to be tested on various related "indicator" cells. Plaques may form on one or more of the other cell types, indicating that phage is present and that it has undergone a lytic cycle with the indicator cell. A virus may form plaques on one cell type and interact with other cell types without causing lysis. If a given strain is tested against several indicator cells and no plaques appear, it cannot be concluded that the tested strain is not lysogenic. Perhaps the correct indicator cells were not used.

Lysogenic strains of bacteria may be quite common. In a classic study, Burnet (1932) tested 34 strains of *Salmonella enteritidis* for lysogeny. The 27 strains that proved to be lysogenic contained three antigenic types of phage. Several of the bacterial strains contained more than one serotype of phage. Similar studies with staphylococci have revealed some bacterial strains with as many as five serotypes of phage (Williams Smith, 1948; Rountree, 1949).

A classic example of unsuspected lysogeny occurred with the K12 strain of *E. coli* that had been used for years and was used by Lederberg and Tatum (1946) when they discovered bacterial conjugation. Unknown to them at the time, but reported later (Lederberg, 1951), was the fact that *E. coli* K12 is lysogenic. The phage it released was named λ and it is the temperate phage that has been most widely studied. It will form the main subject of this chapter.

PROPERTIES OF LYSOGENIC CELLS

Lysogenic cells appear perfectly normal in all respects unless special indicator cells are used to detect the presence of free extracellular phage in the medium. If free phage is assayed during growth of a lysogenic culture, it is found that the phage are in a constant proportion to the number of bacterial cells (Fig. 16-1). At one time this finding was interpreted to mean that the lysogenic cells secrete phage, that is, that every cell in the culture continually releases a small number of phage particles.

This reasonable, although incorrect, conclusion was reached when experiments showed that the lysogenic property existed in every cell of the culture. Even single-colony isolates of lysogenic bacteria were lysogenic. Several other kinds of experiments disproved the notion and showed instead that all cells possessed the lysogenic property, but only a small proportion of cells in the culture lysed at any one time, releasing their phage to the culture medium.

For instance, Burnet and McKie (1929) lysed lysogenic bacteria with unrelated phages. Examination of the contents of the lysed bacteria revealed that only about one in a thousand or more bacteria contained phage at the time of lysis. If all had been excreting virus, it would be expected that all would contain at least some phage particles.

   More direct experiments, performed by Lwoff and Gutmann (1950), demonstrated certain features of lysogeny in a conclusive, convincing manner. Lwoff and Gutmann studied single isolated cells in microdrop cultures. Lysogenic bacteria were placed in the microscope chamber, one bacterium per microdrop. The medium surrounding the dividing cells was repeatedly sampled, but at no time were any infective phage detected.

   In another experiment, a small amount of medium and one of the daughter cells were removed each time the single bacterium divided. Tests showed no free phage in the medium, and the bacterium was still lysogenic. Thus, the lysogenic character was perpetuated in the absence of external phage and therefore in the absence of reinfection.

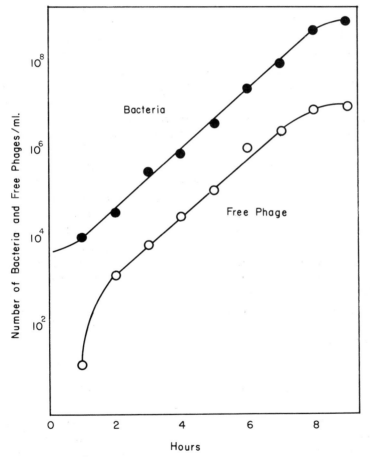

Figure 16-1. Production of extracellular phages during the growth of lysogenic *Pseudomonas aeruginosa* 13(8). (Redrawn from Jacob and Wollman, 1959.)

It is possible, of course, that reinfection did not occur, but that the phage was merely "carried along" extracellularly. Because these experiments were continued for 19 bacterial generations, there would have had to have been 2^{19} free phages present at the outset to have persistent phage after so much dilution. This quantity of phage surely would have been detected at the beginning.

Lwoff and Gutmann had thus established beyond doubt that lysogeny is perpetuated by some mechanism in the cell. Lysogeny then came to be considered a genetic property of the cell, one that confers on the cell bearing the character the ability to produce virus at some future time. The character is passed on to descendent cells, conferring the same ability on them. Thus, a lysogenic bacterium is one that perpetuates the ability to form bacteriophages without intervention of exogenous bacteriophages.

How, then, are phages released from lysogenic bacteria? Microdrop experiments of Lwoff and Gutmann also answered this question. They observed, on occasion, a cell in the process of lysis. After such a cell had undergone spontaneous lysis, free phage particles were present in the medium in the microdrop. Release of phages from lysogenic cells is known to be similar to release of phages from cells infected with virulent (T-even, for instance) phages. The genetic property of lysogeny is therefore a lethal property: When it is expressed, the cell makes phage particles and dies.

Although it is an exceedingly rare event, occasionally a cell loses the lysogenic property. Because of this, it is possible to "cure" a bacterial strain of its lysogenic property by growing it for repeated generations under conditions that prevent reinfection of the cells, such as in a calcium-free medium. The cured cells then can be grown into pure cultures that are unable to form phage. However, addition of free phage to such cultures results in either of two types of response. The cells may undergo a lytic or productive response, in which the phage eclipses, phage components are synthesized and assembled, and the cell lyses. The cycle is entirely analogous to the replicative cycle with the T-even phages. Alternatively, the cell may undergo the reductive response, in which it becomes a lysogenic bacterium. In this case, no phages are synthesized or released until an occasional descendent cell undergoes a lytic cycle.

NATURE OF THE PROPHAGE

As was pointed out by Lwoff (1953), the phage itself confers the specific hereditary property on the susceptible cell. The phage, or some part of the phage, is carried within the bacterial cell in a dormant condition. In this condition it is called the prophage.

The prophage does not consist of intact phage. It has already been mentioned that Burnet and McKie (1929) disrupted lysogenic bacteria by "lysis-from-without" with an unrelated phage and found there was less than one temperate phage per thousand lysogenic bacteria. Nor do lysogenic bacteria contain even phage antigen (Miller and Goebel, 1954), which of course means that phage proteins are not present. Lysogenic cells do contain phage DNA, as would be expected since the genetic material would have to be present for phage production.

Evidence that the entire phage genome is present as the prophage was obtained from measurement of target size (Stent *et al.*, 1957). Phages labeled with P^{32} were used to lysogenize susceptible cells. The cells were frozen to give time for the P^{32} to decay, in turn inactivating the prophage. Survival of the ability to produce free phage by the lysogenized bacteria was compared to the survival of infectivity for indicator strains by the free phage. Because both survival rates are similar, the same number of phosphorus atoms must be involved in both types of measurements; therefore, the amount of DNA must be the same in both.

Next, we might ask how many prophages there are in a lysogenic cell. Estimation of this number was achieved by superinfecting lysogenic bacteria with homologous phage that could be distinguished from the temperate phage by genetic markers. Both phages develop under these conditions if the prophage is induced to enter the vegetative state by a process to be described in a later section. The relative multiplicities of the two phages in a mixed infection determine the relative proportions of the two phages in the yield. In experiments in which lysogenic bacteria are superinfected with exogenous phage at a known multiplicity, the proportion of the two phages in the yield measures the "multiplicity" of the prophage. This type of experiment reveals that each lysogenic bacterium contains about three prophages—a number that corresponds to the number of bacterial chromosomes (Bertani, 1953; Jacob and Wollman, 1953). There is, therefore, one prophage per bacterial chromosome.

Further evidence that the prophage is associated with the bacterial chromosome came from mapping experiments. This was first done soon after the discovery that conjugation in *E. coli* results in recombination between the DNA in the chromosomes of the two bacteria (Lederberg and Tatum, 1946). Studies of recombination between two strains of *E. coli*, one of which was lysogenic, revealed that the lysogenic character could be mapped, just as can any other genetic marker (Lederberg and Lederberg, 1953). Furthermore, the λ lysogeny marker is localized on the bacterial chromosome at a site closely linked to the *gal* locus (a marker responsible for the fermentation of galactose).

A second method of mapping the bacterial chromosome gave a

similar result. During bacterial conjugation a bridge forms between the two conjugants. It is through this bridge that the DNA passes from the F⁺ to the F⁻ cell. The circular bacterial DNA is opened at a definite point in the ring, and the DNA then passes through the bridge at a fixed rate. Breaking the cells apart by periodic agitation in a Waring blender after the beginning of conjugation permits only part of the DNA to be transferred from the donor to the recipient cell. Loci can be mapped on the basis of the time at which they enter the recipient. In this way, it was found that the λ prophage is situated between the *gal* and the *try* (tryptophan) loci.

Because the prophage is located at a definite site on the bacterial chromosome, it is easy to understand how the number of λ prophages per bacterial chromosome is limited. However, bacterial cells can be simultaneously lysogenized by more than one kind of temperate phage, suggesting that they might occupy different sites. Examination of *E. coli* lysogenized with various unrelated temperate phages revealed that each occupies its own characteristic locus (Jacob and Wollman, 1957). Each behaves independently of any others that may be present. It is even possible for one λ prophage to occupy a site already occupied by a λ prophage by insertion into the first (Calef *et al.*, 1965). In bacterial cells containing a heterozygous region in the prophage site, a prophage can attach to each of the two sites, resulting in another form of double lysogen (Campbell, 1965a).

Because it is attached to the bacterial chromosome and forms an integral part of it, the prophage DNA replicates with the bacterial DNA and is passed on to the daughter cells at each division.

LYSOGENIZATION

When bacteria of a nonlysogenic strain are infected with a temperate phage, individual cells undergo either the productive or the reductive response. In the productive response, the viral genes direct the cellular synthesis of viral components, the components are assembled into virions, and the cell lyses, releasing the virions to the medium. In the reductive response, the viral genes are made nonfunctional and viral components are not synthesized. As will be discussed later, sometimes a few viral genes function, but not those necessary for virus replication.

Jacob and Monod (1961) recognized that lysogenization is a problem of gene regulation. This observation, along with a consideration of other systems, led them to propose a theory of gene regulation that accounts for the steps leading to the choice of which type of response will occur.

It is first necessary to consider briefly the genetic map of a representative temperate phage, such as λ (Skalka *et al.*, 1967) (see Fig. 16-2). As in other phages, some genes are concerned with "early" functions, and others are concerned with "late" functions. Temperate phages, however, have additional genes concerned with lysogenization (Gingery and Echols, 1967). In λ, genes c_I, c_{II}, c_{III}, *int* (for integration), and the b_2 region are concerned with lysogeny. Genes N, O, and P are concerned with DNA synthesis, and Q controls late gene expression (Joyner *et al.*, 1966; Dove, 1966). The late genes, A through J, to the left of b_2, are concerned with the production of phage structural proteins: Mutations in A through E result in lysates containing tails but no heads, whereas mutations in G through M result in production of heads without tails (Weigle, 1966). Other genes are concerned with DNA maturation, and gene R is responsible for lysozyme synthesis (Dove, 1966). R is therefore also a late gene, but it is not displaced from the other late genes; the λ DNA molecules form circles under certain conditions, as will be discussed, and R then comes around to lie next to A.

The *c* genes control lysogeny; temperate phages λ or P22 (a phage of *Salmonella typhimurium*) that carry mutations in the *c* genes cannot lysogenize but cause only the lytic reaction with susceptible cells. Infection of a single cell with phages mutated in different *c* genes, however, results in a high frequency of lysogenization (Levine, 1957). The *c* genes not only are necessary for lysogenization and for maintaining the lysogenic state once established, but also are responsible for superinfection immunity (Kaiser and Jacob, 1957).

Jacob and Monod (1961) proposed the following model to explain whether lysis or lysogeny took place: After infection of a nonlysogenic cell with a temperate phage, various phage genes begin to function. The "early" genes, concerned with synthesis of enzymes, start to transcribe messenger RNA to direct the synthesis of a repressor substance. A postulated "race" ensues between the synthesis of repressor substance and early proteins. If the enzymes become sufficiently concentrated, new viral DNA is synthesized, and the cell produces more phage particles and lyses. If, however, the repressor substance reaches a sufficient concentration in the cytoplasm, it represses the expression of other phage genes, and lysogenization results.

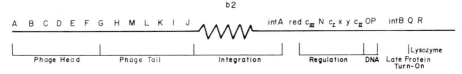

Figure 16-2. The λ genetic map. (Modified from Echols *et al.*, 1968.)

The Repressor

It is well known that a lysogenic cell is immune to superinfection by a closely related phage. Under ordinary conditions, the lysogenic cell is immune to further lysogenization, and a superinfecting phage cannot even undergo a lytic, productive cycle. The repressor substance, sometimes called the immunity substance, accounts for this phenomenon because it immediately combines with the DNA of the superinfecting phage. The repressor renders the phage DNA unable to replicate (Green *et al.*, 1967). As discussed in Chapter 8, the T-even phages prevent superinfection by causing the synthesis of a deoxyribonuclease that breaks down the DNA of a superinfecting phage. Temperate phages, like λ, use this more subtle but equally effective means of preventing superinfection by simply "turning off" the genes of the superinfecting phage.

Wiesmeyer (1966) reasoned that if this is the mechanism for this kind of interference and if, as seemed probable, only one repressor molecule is required to inactivate each phage DNA molecule, then he should be able to measure the average number of such molecules in a lysogenic cell. As he increased the multiplicity of superinfection, the number of phage DNA molecules would exceed the number of repres-

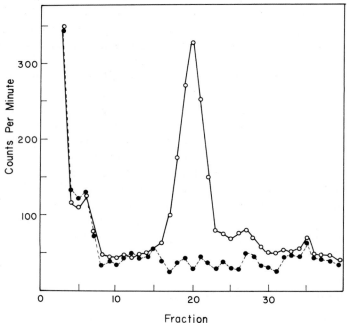

Figure 16-3. Isolation of the λ repressor. An extract of a mixture of λ wild-type infected cells labeled with H^3-leucine and λ M c_1 *sus* 10 infected cells (containing no repressor) labeled with C^{14} was chromatographed on a DEAE column. The H^3-peak is the labeled repressor. (Redrawn from Ptashne, 1967a.)

sor molecules, and replication would ensue with the release of active phage. The experimental results indicated that, on the average, a lysogenic cell contains about 20 molecules of the repressor substance.

The repressor substance has been isolated (Fig. 16-3) and characterized (Ptashne, 1967a). It is a protein, with a molecular weight of about 30,000 daltons, although the possibility exists that the protein of that size is merely a subunit of the repressor, which would then be some higher multiple. The fact that the protein is directed by the c_I gene is substantiated by the finding that it is not made by *amber* mutants in c_I, and it is made in modified form in temperature-sensitive mutants of that gene.

Isolation of the repressor permitted experiments that could test

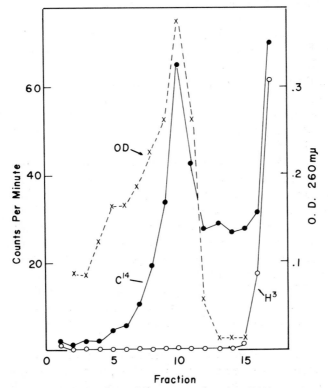

Figure 16-4. Specific binding of the λ c_I product to λ DNA. λ repressor, labeled with C^{14}, from a strain of lysogenic cell that synthesizes normal repressor was mixed with repressor, labeled with H^3, from a lysogenic cell with an *amber* mutation in the c_I gene of the prophage. The repressor mixture was incubated with purified λ DNA and then layered on a sucrose gradient. During centrifugation, the molecules migrated through the sucrose, from right to left in the diagram. After centrifugation, drops were collected serially from the bottom of the plastic centrifuge tube, and each fraction was analyzed for absorption at 260 mμ (to measure λ DNA) and for radioactivity (to measure repressor). (Redrawn from Ptashne, 1967b.)

directly for binding of the repressor protein to DNA (Ptashne, 1967b). Some of the isolated, labeled repressor was mixed with DNA from wild-type λ and centrifuged through a sucrose gradient. The radioactivity migrated through the gradient with the DNA. To indicate that it was bound to the DNA, some was also mixed with DNA from a λ mutant that is not sensitive to the repressor, λ imm^{434}. It did not bind to the mutant DNA (Fig. 16-4). Centrifugations performed at differing salt concentrations indicated that the binding is probably electrostatic.

The repressor can exert its control by acting on only a small segment of the λ genome. This group of genes x, y, c_{II} and O are apparently an operon under control of the repressor (Pereira da Silva and Jacob, 1967). In this way, the single small repressor molecule exerts an effect on the entire phage DNA molecule. The repressor also inhibits transcription of λ DNA in a cell-free system (Echols et al., 1968).

Experiments with phage P22 in its host, Salmonella typhimurium, have shown several stages in the repression process. P22, like λ, has given many mutants of the c region; these mutants are affected in their ability to become prophage. Double infection of a cell by pairs of these mutants reveals three classes of mutants, c_1, c_2, and c_3, that can complement each other. That is, double infection by phages that are mutated in c_1, and c_2, for instance, leads to lysogeny (Smith and Levine, 1964, 1965).

Figure 16-5, for example, shows the results of experiments in which the rates of DNA synthesis were measured at 1 minute intervals after infection. Infection by wild-type, c^+, causes the rate of DNA synthesis to undergo a characteristic series of changes: First, immediately following infection there is a brief decrease in overall synthesis. This is followed by an increase that reaches a maximum at about 6 minutes. At 6 minutes, synthesis is chiefly viral DNA, but some bacterial DNA is synthesized. Between 6 and 18 minutes the rate of synthesis of DNA in the cell-virus complex rapidly falls. The subsequent increase in the rate of synthesis returns the complex to an apparently normal state; in the later times, bacterial DNA is the chief product.

Cells doubly infected by phages that are mutant in the c_1 and c_2 genes behave as if infected by wild-type phage. Cells infected with phage carrying a mutation in c_1 behave quite differently. Repression of synthesis of all DNA after the sixth minute does not occur; instead, phage DNA is synthesized at a high rate, leading to cell lysis and, of course, cessation of DNA synthesis. Cells infected with the c_2 mutant also undergo a productive response, but in these complexes, DNA synthesis undergoes the transient repression characteristic of wild-type. After the eighteenth minute, however, phage DNA is synthesized.

These results can be explained as follows: The product of both the c_1 and c_2 genes must be present for lysogeny to occur. The c_2 mutant makes the c_1 product but not the c_2 product; in cells infected

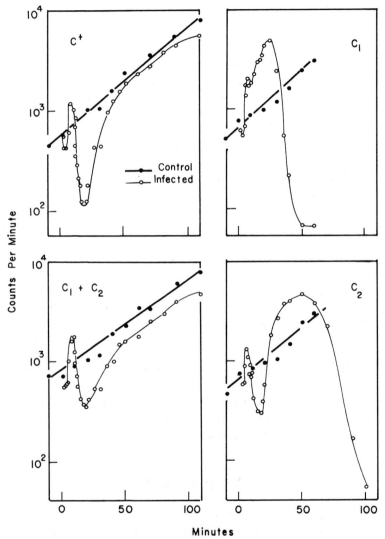

Figure 16-5. Rate of incorporation of H³-thymidine into DNA of P22 phage-infected cells. Shown is the amount of H³-thymidine incorporated into DNA in a 1 minute exposure to the compound in cells infected with wild-type (c^+), infected with either of two mutants (c_1 or c_2), or doubly infected with both mutants. (Redrawn from Smith and Levine, 1964.)

with the c_2 mutant, the transient inhibition that occurs indicates that the c_1 product must be a temporary repressor. The c_2 product, made in c_1 mutant complexes, begins to function about the sixteenth minute and maintains the repression of viral DNA. Bacterial DNA resumes synthesis, however.

This explanation was clarified and more detailed studies of the time sequence were made by the selection of temperature-sensitive mutants (Levine and Smith, 1964). The mutants were selected to include some in the c_1 region and some in the c_2 region. At 31°C., both genes gave a functional product and the virus could undergo lysogeny; that is, the virus had wild-type phenotype at that temperature. At 42°C., however, one or the other gene gave a nonfunctional product, and, as a result, the virus could undergo only the virulent, productive interaction.

Cells were then infected with the c_1 mutant at the lower temperature and treated for 2 minute intervals at the higher temperature. At the interval around 6 to 8 minutes after infection, heat treatment prevented lysogenization. Before or after that interval, heat treatment had no effect. The c_1 product is therefore only transiently necessary.

Cells were infected with the c_2 mutant at 42°C and were then shifted to 31°C. In this case, the high temperature had no influence during the first 11 minutes, and the cells were lysogenized. After 12 minutes, exposure to 42°C. caused a decrease in the frequency of lysogenization. Application of high temperature anytime after 25 minutes caused the cells to lyse; that is, the lysogenic state was broken and production of phage began. Again, these results indicate that the c_1 product is needed only transiently early in the reaction while the c_2 product is needed continuously after a time that begins considerably later.

In λ, the c_1 product is the repressor substance and is responsible for the permanent repression. A similar sequential expression of cistrons occurs in λ (Kaiser, 1957) as it does in P22, but the nomenclature and other details are different (the c_I and c_{II} cistrons of λ are equivalent to the c_2 and c_1 cistrons, respectively, of P22).

INTEGRATION

It is possible to determine the order of genes in λ by phage crosses and by crosses between lysogenic bacteria. In each case measurement of recombination frequencies leads to a genetic map. Crosses between phages give information resulting in a map of the order of genes in free phages, whereas crosses between lysogenic bacteria lead to a map of the genes in the prophage.

When the location of genes in λ prophage was determined in detail (Calef and Licciardello, 1960), it was found that they are not in the same order as in free phage. Nevertheless, the order in segments of the prophage is similar to that of the free phage.

These puzzling results were clarified by a model proposed by Campbell (1962) to explain how the phage genome inserts in the bacterial genome. His proposed model, diagramed in Figure 16-6, postulated that the phage genome becomes circular (even though it is not circularly permuted as in T2 or T4) and that it attaches to the bacterial chromosome at a region of homology. The phage circle is broken at that position and recombination, or crossing-over, between phage and bacterial DNA completes the insertion. The resulting order of genes in the integrated prophage, as shown in Figure 16-6, fits with the order that had been determined by mapping.

But what of the other requirements of the model? For instance, what about circularity? The genetic map of λ is linear, and DNA extracted from free phage is linear. But several groups of investigators (Hershey *et al.*, 1963; Hershey and Burgi, 1965; Strack and Kaiser,

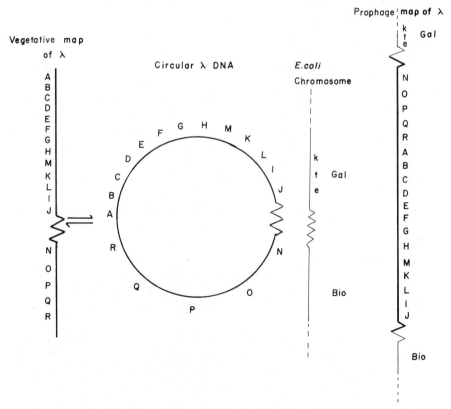

Figure 16-6. The Campbell model for the insertion of λ DNA into the bacterial chromosome. (Redrawn from Hogness, 1966.)

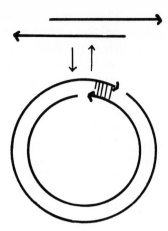

Figure 16-7. Circularization of λ DNA.

1965) demonstrated that DNA isolated from free phage particles has "cohesive" ends. That is, the ends of the molecules are "sticky"; the molecule tends to fold back upon itself; and when the ends come into contact, they stick together, forming a circular molecule (Fig. 16-7).

The single-stranded segments at the ends of the molecule therefore have complementary base sequences; the molecule is held together by the hydrogen bonding between the two strands (Wu and Kaiser, 1967). The cohesive single-stranded ends are 10 to 20 nucleotide residues long (Kallenbach and Crothers, 1966; Wang and Davidson, 1966a, 1966b). The contour length of the linear molecules is the same as that of the circular molecules, 16.3 μ, as determined by electron microscopy (Ris and Chandler, 1963; MacHattie and Thomas, 1964; Kaiser and Inman, 1965) because the short single-stranded segments are only a small percentage of the total molecular length, and the difference in length of 10 to 20 residues is too small to be detectable.

Similarly, cohesive ends have been found in the DNA molecules extracted from other temperate phages: ϕ80 (Yamagishi *et al.*, 1965) and coliphages 21, 186, 424, and 434 (Baldwin *et al.*, 1966). This characteristic may therefore be a general one for temperate phage DNA molecules.

As examination of Figure 16-7 reveals, each strand of the circularized molecule has a break. The two strands are held together by hydrogen bonds, but a covalent phosphodiester bond is necessary to complete the joining of the individual strands to close each as a covalently bonded circle. An enzyme called ligase or sealase that performs this function has been isolated from *E. coli* (Olivera and Lehman, 1967; Gellert, 1967; A. Becker *et al.*, 1967; Little *et al.*, 1967; Gefter *et al.*, 1967). It may also be involved in repairing single-strand "nicks" in circular λ DNA (Boyce and Tepper, 1968).

One of the first steps following infection of *E. coli* with λ is the conversion of the DNA from a linear to a circular form. The circular form contains the label of the incoming DNA and is detectable within 5 minutes after infection (Salzman and Weissbach, 1967a). Three forms of molecules of DNA have been isolated from λ-infected cells: some with the characteristics of linear DNA, circles with hydrogen-bonding joining the ends, and circles with one or two covalently completed strands in addition to the hydrogen bonds. The completely closed circular form is supercoiled; the various forms are therefore analogous to the various configurations taken by polyoma virus DNA (see Chapter 9) (Young and Sinsheimer, 1964; Ogawa and Tomizawa, 1967; Bode and Kaiser, 1965). The supercoiling results from the action of the joining enzyme (J. C. Wang *et al.*, 1967).

It has been shown that shortly after infection λ DNA undergoes changes that result in loss of infectivity if the DNA is extracted. The changes are presumably due to circularization because it has been shown that free ends must exist for the λ DNA to be infective. The loss of infectivity, and therefore probably the circularization step, can occur without the synthesis of new enzymes (Dove and Weigle, 1965). The enzyme mentioned (ligase or sealase) has been extracted from uninfected *E. coli*, giving further evidence that the reaction does not require new enzyme synthesis.

Therefore, one prediction of Campbell's model seems to have been fulfilled: There is ample evidence that λ DNA can become circular and that this step is involved in its replication as well as in lysogenization.

Another prediction of the Campbell model is that a region of homology must exist between the DNA of the phage and of the bacterium. By hybridizing denatured *E. coli* DNA with purified λ DNA, Cowie and McCarthy (1963) showed that regions of homology exist. About one third of the λ DNA could bind specifically to about 0.2 per cent of the *E. coli* DNA, a result that is consistent with their relative molecular weights. Binding of λ DNA with DNA isolated from lysogenic *E. coli* was increased over that of the nonlysogenic cells by an amount to be expected if the lysogenic cells contained one complete λ DNA molecule as prophage.

The region of the λ DNA molecule that is homologous to the bacterial DNA was identified by study of certain mutants of λ. These mutants differ from wild-type by being less dense; the density difference indicates that about 18 per cent of the λ DNA has been lost. The lost DNA seems to have no effect on the replicative function, as these mutants grow as well as wild-type. They do not lysogenize, however. Instead, under conditions that would result in lysogeny if wild-type phage had been used, the density mutant undergoes abortive lysogeny. The repressor is synthesized so that the cells are immune to lysogenization by wild-type.

Because in abortive lysogenization the phage DNA does not insert into the bacterial chromosome, it does not replicate. It is therefore transmitted to only one of the two daughter cells at each division of the bacterium. The missing region of the λ genome, which would be responsible for attachment, is the b_2 region, the region of base sequence common to phage and cell DNA. Mapping experiments located the position of the b_2 region as shown in Figure 16-2 (Kellenberger *et al.*, 1961b). The region serves a structural purpose only; abortive lysogenization due to deletion of this region does not result in physiologic changes (Campbell, 1965b).

Campbell's model predicts that λ DNA inserts into the bacterial DNA at the region of homology by a crossing-over or recombination between the two molecules. Support for the recombination step in insertion comes from experiments with coliphage $\phi80$, in which it was shown that a new enzyme system induced by this phage carries out the recombination steps. Mutants of this phage that are unable to direct the synthesis of the necessary enzymes can lysogenize wild-type *E. coli*, in which a cellular recombination enzyme can carry out this step, but the mutants cannot lysogenize rec^- cells, that is, *E. coli* lacking the recombination system. The phage-induced recombination enzyme system has a specificity for carrying out the recombination at the attachment site, whereas the bacterial recombination system lacks that specificity (Signer and Beckwith, 1966).

PROPHAGE FUNCTION

Once integrated into the bacterial chromosome, the phage DNA, now called the prophage, carries out certain functions as any other DNA. It replicates in unison with the bacterial chromosome and under control of the host mechanisms. The time of its replication depends on its position in the host chromosome, since host DNA replication begins at one end of the chromosome (Nagata, 1963). Each daughter cell receives a copy of the prophage just as each daughter cell receives a copy of the bacterial DNA. As was discussed in previous sections, the prophage behaves like any other bacterial DNA marker in bacterial recombination.

The prophage also introduces new functions to the cell. One of these new functions is the synthesis of the repressor or immunity substance as already discussed. In λ, the repressor prevents messenger RNA synthesis by any other prophage cistrons (Attardi *et al.*, 1963), so no other gene expression occurs. Continued synthesis of the repressor is necessary to maintain the lysogenic state; failure to synthesize a sufficient quantity results in induction, a process to be discussed in the next section, whereby the phage DNA enters the vegetative state. The immunity substance also confers on the lysogenic bacterium an immunity to superinfection by the same or a related phage, because if superinfection occurs, the immunity substance immediately represses the function of the DNA of the superinfecting phage. Therefore, the lysogenized bacterium may be considered to benefit from the presence of the prophage, even though the prophage itself is a potentially lethal factor for the bacterium.

The prophage is best considered an addition of new genetic material to the lysogenized cell. Since the phenotype of a cell is the resultant of all the genes that are functioning, the prophage may change the phenotype of the cell. In a given case, if it were not known that a bacterium had acquired a prophage, it might instead be thought that the cell had mutated. This phenomenon is called conversion.

One example of conversion occurs in strains of *E. coli* K12 lysogenic for λ. These strains do not support the growth of rII mutants of T-even phages, but the nonlysogenized strains do. The lysogenized strains, however, support growth of wild-type T-even phage (Benzer, 1955). The immunity substance that is present in the lysogenic cells apparently inhibits the rII mutants of T-even phages but not wild-type (Tomizawa and Ogawa, 1967); the mechanism for repression of T-even mutants is probably different from that which represses λ.

Prophage products also change the surface properties of *Salmonella*. The phage in this case is ϵ^{15}. Following lysogenization, the bacterial surface acquires new antigens. It also acquires the ability to adsorb the phage ϵ^{34} (Uetake *et al.*, 1955, 1958). Lysogenized cells retain the new antigen and adsorptive capacity; segregants of the lysogenized cells lose the surface changes, reverting to the original constitution. Because mutants of the ϵ^{15} phage with different conversion properties have been isolated, it can be concluded that the phage itself, as prophage, is responsible for the conversion (Uetake and Uchida, 1959). The phage converts the surface antigens by changing the enzymatic activities involved in synthesis of cell wall polysaccharides (Robbins *et al.*, 1965). The change is in the saccharides and their linkage (Losick and Robbins, 1967; Bray and Robbins, 1967).

Yarmolinsky and Wiesmeyer (1960) and Yarmolinsky (1963) have investigated another kind of prophage effect. In this case, λ prophage influences the rate of synthesis of enzymes of the galactose operon. These genes are normally repressed; enzyme induction occurs with the addition of galactose to the medium. Lysogenization or productive infection does not alter the state of the galactose operon. Induction of the prophage, however, causes a derepression of the galactose operon.

Still another prophage effect occurs in *Corynebacterium diphtheriae*. Freeman (1951) discovered that nontoxigenic strains of *C. diphtheriae* are converted into toxigenic strains by infection with temperate diphtheria phages and that the newly formed toxigenic strains are lysogenic. Prophage genes are responsible for the production of the toxin (Groman, 1953, 1955; Groman *et al.*, 1958; Barksdale and Pappenheimer, 1954). Some mutants of the temperate phages are unable to lysogenize but are still able to cause toxin production (Matsuda and Barksdale, 1966, 1967), so it is not necessary that the prophage be integrated for toxin production. In fact, the toxin is synthesized during induction of the prophage to the vegetative state or during lytic interaction. It is not synthesized by the integrated prophage (Barksdale, 1959).

INDUCTION

As indicated in Figure 16-1, a growing culture of lysogenic bacteria continually produces a small amount of virus. This is due to the lysis of a small but constant proportion of the cells. In other words, each cell in the culture has a small probability of undergoing some change that allows the prophage to enter the vegetative state leading to virus production and cell lysis.

By proper treatment, however, this low probability can be increased to near certainty. It was first discovered that irradiating the cells with ultraviolet light would cause all cells in the culture to lyse and produce phage (Lwoff *et al.*, 1950). As shown in Figure 16-8, there is a latent period of about 60 or 70 minutes following exposure to ultraviolet light, during which time the cells continue to grow but at a decreasing rate. The lysis begins, resulting in a decrease in turbidity and release of virus (Jacob and Fuerst, 1958). Experiments such as this, of course, confirmed what had been learned from single-cell microdroplet experiments: that each cell of a lysogenic population can produce virus.

After it had been learned that ultraviolet irradiation induces cells to produce virus, it was soon discovered that other agents can also cause induction. These other agents include x-rays, γ rays, nitrogen mustard, organic peroxides, epoxides (Jacob and Wollman, 1959), thymine starvation (Melechen and Skaar, 1962), mitomycin C, 5-fluorouracil (Marcovich and Kaplan, 1963), and many others.

Many of these physical and chemical agents are either mutagenic or carcinogenic, a characteristic that initially was thought to have a bearing on the problem of carcinogenesis. More likely, however, the correlation exists only because carcinogens, like inducing agents, act on the intracellular macromolecules responsible for genetic transmission and expression. Inducing agents inhibit DNA synthesis; but in the case of induction, the action is one of inhibiting the production of the repressor substance. Once its concentration falls below a certain critical value, the prophage enters the vegetative state.

Zygotic induction is an illustration of the importance of the intracellular concentration of repressor. It was noted that conjugation between lysogenic bacteria sometimes results in induction (Wollman and Jacob, 1954; Jacob and Wollman, 1957). This occurs when a male (Hfr) lysogenic bacterium conjugates with a female cell not lysogenic for the same prophage. The chromosome from the male cell penetrates the female cell, carrying the prophage with it. Cytoplasmic exchange does not take place, and therefore the prophage from the male cell suddenly is in an environment where there is no repressor. It is immediately induced, and after a latent period the cell lyses and releases its crop of phage.

Dilution is not the only means of removing the repressor. Some λ phages that have temperature-sensitive mutations in the c_I region

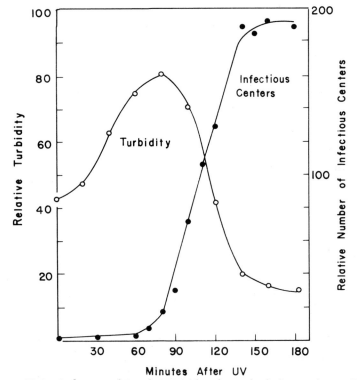

Figure 16-8.   Induction of *E. coli* K12 (λ) by ultraviolet light. A culture of bacteria in the logarithmic phase of growth was exposed to the ultraviolet light at 37°C. Turbidity and infectious centers are plotted as a function of time. (Redrawn from Jacob and Fuerst, 1958.)

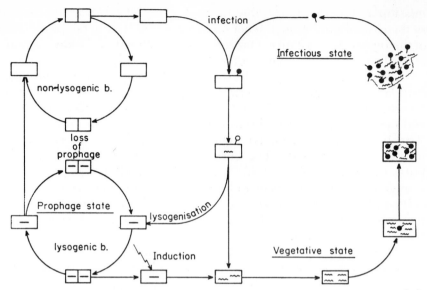

Figure 16-9. The lysogenic cycle. (From Braun, 1965. By permission of the author and the editors of the W. B. Saunders Company.)

have been isolated. Their repressor substance is inactivated by shifting to a higher temperature, causing lysogenic cells to be induced. The function of the repressor is restored by lowering the temperature. For induction to occur at the higher temperature, however, there must be protein synthesis as well as repressor inactivation (Lieb, 1964; Green, 1966, 1967).

Use of these mutants, along with results from other kinds of experiments by many investigators (Green, 1966, 1967; Lieb, 1966; Naono and Gros, 1967; Campbell and Killen, 1967; Weisberg and Gallant, 1967; Konrad, 1968) has permitted the induction process to be separated into stages, leading to the following picture of induction: Once derepressed, the "early" function cistrons of λ begin to synthesize messenger RNA, which is translated into a protein (possibly the deoxyribonuclease isolated by Korn and Weissbach, 1963) that detaches the prophage from the host chromosome. The detachment probably occurs by a reversal of the insertion procedure; that is, the prophage portion of the chromosome is twisted into a loop and recombination between the sides of the loop releases the prophage from the chromosome as a circle of DNA. When the next step begins (replication of the λ DNA), the "late" cistrons begin to function and the cycle proceeds to lysis.

The circular form of λ DNA can be isolated from lysogenic cells shortly after induction (Lipton and Weissbach, 1966a, 1966b). Experiments reported by Ptashne (1965) indicated that the λ prophage DNA can be found intact in progeny phage following induction. The DNA

goes through several maturation steps, however. The first intermediate is a linear molecule the same length as the DNA isolated from
mature λ virions but lacking the single-stranded ends (Weissbach and
Salzman, 1967). Intermediates formed later are long, concatenated
forms of the λ genome, ready to be cut into lengths that are a
"headful" of DNA for the virion (Salzman and Weissbach, 1967b).
Mutants of λ are known which produce only one or another form of the
DNA intermediates (Salzman and Weissbach, 1968).

Later stages in the assembly of λ components into mature virions,
synthesis of the phage-induced lysozyme, and lysis of the infected
cells resemble the cycle already discussed in detail for the T-phages
and will not be discussed further here. The overall cycle of lysogeny
is summarized in the diagram shown in Figure 16-9.

TRANSDUCTION

According to Campbell's model, prophage detachment from the
bacterial chromosome involves the formation of a loop with a crossing-
over between adjacent sides of the loop. Sometimes, as shown in
Figure 16-10, the loop forms in such a way that the adjacent sides are
not in the b_2 region, as they should be, but in the *gal* region of the
bacterial chromosome. The resulting phage thus acquires bacterial
genes (the process is called transduction) of the *gal* operon and loses
some of its own genes. Because it lacks phage genes, such a phage
cannot undergo a subsequent replicative cycle unless a normal phage
is also present in the same cell to serve as helper. The defective λ
phage that has acquired bacterial *gal* genes is called λ*dg*, signifying
that it is λ, defective, with galactose markers. Hogness (1966) and
Hogness *et al.* (1967) have begun to determine the order of genes in λ
and λ*dg*. They have found that the order is entirely consistent with
that predicted by the Campbell model.

Transduction ordinarily occurs at a very low frequency. Let us
say, for instance, that from a single cell an investigator has prepared a
pure culture of bacteria lysogenic for λ. No transducing phage is
present in the culture. Mass lysis of the culture, induced by ultraviolet, yields a lysate containing λ and a very small fraction of
transducing particles (λ*dg*). The lysate is said to be LFT or low frequency transducing. The fact that the frequency is low implies that
some rare event is responsible, such as the abnormal crossing-over
just discussed.

Experiments have shown that the transducing particles in LFT
lysates are genetically different, containing different genetic markers
(Campbell, 1959). If the LFT lysate is used to infect susceptible cells
in the presence of normal λ helper, it is found that the lysate contains

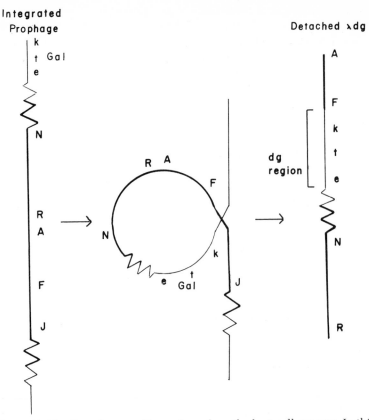

Figure 16-10. Detachment of λ prophage from the host-cell genome. In this case, the loop of DNA was formed in such a way that not all the viral genome was included, but instead was replaced by cellular genome. The viral genome, therefore, is defective and carries the cellular genes of the galactose region. (Redrawn from Hogness, 1966.)

roughly one-half normal λ and one-half λ*dg*. The high frequency transduction in this case results in the name HFT lysate. If such an experiment is performed using clonally derived λ*dg*, the progeny transducing particles in the HFT lysate are genetically the same.

Differences between defective transducing particles in the LFT lysates must occur at the time of their formation. Weigle (1961) found that different λ*dg* particles have different densities. In most cases the defective particles in his series of experiments were less dense than λ. Since the protein capsids seemed normal, and since each transducing particle seemed to carry the same amount of bacterial DNA, it was calculated that up to one third or one fourth of the λ DNA has been deleted. The density alteration correlates well with the amount of λ genome that is missing (Kayajanian and Campbell, 1966). Subsequent work showed that about 10 per cent of the transducing particles are also missing one or more genes of the galactose operon (Adler and Templeton, 1963).

Although defective, λdg particles can perform certain functions. Bacteria lysogenic for λdg are immune to infection by λ, indicating that the repressor genes are present and functioning. Ultraviolet irradiation of these cells results in lysis but not synthesis of mature phage. Since the missing genes lie between G and the b_2 region and perform "late" functions, it is easily understood that phage maturation does not occur. The lysozyme gene R is present, so lysis occurs. Infection with λ as helper results in production of both λ and λdg because λ supplies the missing gene functions.

Infection of mutant bacterial cells lacking the galactose genes with λdg brings that function to the cells. Such a gal^- cell lysogenized by a λdg (gal^+) phage is therefore a heterogenote (the gal-chromosomal component is the endogenote and the gal^+ component of the prophage is the exogenote).

Reference to the Campbell model indicates why the gal region is so frequently involved; occasionally the biotin gene lying on the opposite side of the b_2 region is transduced. Because of the specificity, and because of the precise mechanism, the type of transduction just described is called specialized transduction.

Another type of transduction also occurs, called general transduction. This was the first type of transduction described (Zinder and Lederberg, 1952), and it has been observed primarily with phage PLT22 of *Salmonella typhimurium* or P1 of *E. coli*. In general transduction, the transducing particles can contain any part of the bacterial genome. In effect, a portion of the bacterial DNA, rather than phage DNA, is packed into a phage head.

Because a "headful" of bacterial DNA is only a small portion of the bacterial genome, and because it consists of a short segment of DNA that may contain only a few genes, it is possible to map the bacterial genome by deducing linkages from transduction data (Lennox, 1955). The farther two linked markers are from one another, the less frequently they are cotransduced. To the extent that phage genes are missing from a transducing particle, the transducing particle is defective. Not only can transducing particles carry any of the bacterial genes, they can even carry one or more unrelated prophages (Jacob, 1955).

Transducing phages of this type do not require that lysogenization occur, and it has been common practice to use virulent mutants to produce transducing particles. Ikeda and Tomizawa (1965) infected *E. coli* cells with a virulent mutant of P1; the cells had previously been grown in 5-bromouracil so that the bacterial DNA had an increased density. Analysis in CsCl density gradients showed that the phages in the lysate were of two types: One type was of normal density and was infective, and the other type was of increased density and was not infective. These authors concluded that the majority of transducing particles do not carry any phage genetic material.

The amount of DNA carried in the phage head seems to be constant, about 6×10^7 daltons (Ikeda and Tomizawa, 1965). This is regardless of whether the DNA is of bacterial origin or of phage origin.

General transducing phages could arise by either of two mechanisms. During replication, the phage DNA could recombine randomly with bacterial DNA, producing particles containing a single molecule with DNA from both sources. It is also possible that the enzyme that cuts "headful" lengths of phage DNA could "mistakenly" cut bacterial DNA to the right length, and this DNA could then be incorrectly packed into the phage head. Information is not available to decide between these possibilities.

Lysogeny may have evolutionary significance. Bacteria able to incorporate a phage into their genome, rather than being lysed by the phage, would seem to have a better chance of surviving than bacteria unable to do this. The bacteria benefit also by gaining a mechanism for distributing bacterial genetic material among other bacteria.

Whether a similar type of virus-cell interaction exists with animal viruses is under active investigation and is the subject of the next two chapters. Tumor viruses seem to possess at least some of the characteristic properties of temperate phages.

Further Reading

Barksdale, L.: Symposium on the Biology of Cells Modified by Viruses or Antigens; I, Lysogenic Conversions in Bacteria. Bacteriological Reviews, 23:202-212, 1959.
Bretscher, M. S.: How Repressor Molecules Function. Nature, 217:509-511, 1968.
Jacob, F.: Genetics of the Bacterial Cell. Science, 152:1470-1478, 1966.
Lwoff, A.: Lysogeny. Bacteriological Reviews, 17:269-337, 1953.
Lwoff, A.: Interaction among Virus, Cell, and Organism. Science, 152:1216-1220, 1966.

17

TUMOR VIRUSES THAT CONTAIN RNA

The last kind of virus-host cell interaction to be discussed occurs when certain viruses cause cells to become malignant. The viruses that do this are the tumor viruses.

The study of tumor viruses has several objectives. One is a directly practical one: The study of how tumor viruses cause malignancy could lead to better methods of preventing or treating cancer. Additional objectives include the possibility that such studies could lead to better understanding of cellular regulation of growth, for tumors are formed as a result of loss of regulation.

TUMOR CELLS AND TUMORS

In general, cells may change in any of several ways in response to a virus and acquire new properties. Under appropriate conditions, tumor viruses cause cells (1) to grow in an uncontrolled, unregulated fashion. The regulation of growth has to do with another interesting property of cells of higher organisms: (2) response to contact. In their relationship to one another, normal cells are orderly and respond to contact with their neighbors (normal cells are said to be "contact inhibited"), while malignant cells do not respond. Normal cells in culture form a single layer on the bottom surface, finding a spot where they have a minimum amount of contact with their neighbors. When the surface of the culture vessel is covered, normal cells stop dividing. Malignant cells tend to cause multilayered piles. Because they do not

315

seem to "mind" forming such piles, they frequently continue to grow after the available space is covered.

Malignant cells may also (3) acquire an ability to divide without limitation on the number of generations, in contrast to normal cells, which seem to have a "built-in," predetermined limit to the number of divisions they can undergo (Hayflick, 1968). Virus-induced tumor cells (4) acquire one or more new antigens with specificities determined by the virus. The new antigens may be related to the changed morphology of the tumor cells and perhaps may be related to new enzymes. (5) Metabolic patterns of the cells may also be changed, as evidenced by an increased production of lactic acid, although the easily observed increased acid production in many instances may only be a reflection of a greater metabolic rate. In addition (6) some tumor viruses cause cells in culture to differentiate or to dedifferentiate.

In the usual context, a tumor is any abnormal growth. A benign tumor, such as a common wart, is localized and the cells are relatively regulated in their behavior. In contrast, a malignant tumor, frequently called a cancer, usually grows rapidly, and its cells tend to invade adjacent tissues. The tumor may erode through blood vessel walls, allowing malignant cells to be carried by the blood to distant sites in the body. A malignant tumor usually leads to death of the host.

Malignant tumors are called sarcomas if they arise from mesodermal derivatives and carcinomas if they arise from ectodermal or entodermal derivatives. Leukemia is usually considered to be a form of malignancy in which the malignant cells are elements of the white blood cell series.

Our emphasis here will be on tumor cells rather than on tumors. To be more specific, the emphasis will be on the viruses that can cause cells to acquire malignant properties. Much of the discussion will be based on experiments performed in cell culture, since many of the tumor viruses have been shown to induce cultured cells to become malignant. Tumor cells that arise in a host animal as a response to a tumor virus do not seem to differ from tumor cells induced in tissue culture by the same virus. Because there is no basic difference, it is valid to do experiments with tumor viruses in tissue cultures, where results are obtained more rapidly and where extraneous effects caused by host variability and host defense mechanisms are avoided. Tumor cells induced in culture are frequently referred to as "transformed" cells, and that convention will be followed here.

The changes that cause a cell to be malignant seem to be genetic; they seem to be due to the continued presence and function of the viral genetic material, as are the changes that occur in lysogenization of bacteria. For this reason, lysogeny is frequently taken as a model for the study of how tumor viruses interact with their host cells. The analogy has limits, of course. Some of these limits are based on experimental data, but others exist only because present knowledge is incomplete. The present discussion will consider the various aspects of these changes in greater detail to show how at least some are directly under control of the viral genome.

TUMOR VIRUSES

Normal cells can be changed to tumor cells by many agents, including various chemicals, cigarette combustion products, ionizing radiation, ultraviolet light, hormones, and viruses. Some of these agents must act together to produce tumors; others can act alone, but have an increased efficiency when combined with some other agent. How any of them act on a cell to produce the malignant change is unknown, although a clear-cut cause-and-effect relationship has been adequately demonstrated for all.

Tumor viruses present a good opportunity to perform experiments directed at the cause of the changes. The reason for this is that the virus introduces into the cell a limited bit of genetic material and it must be this material that in some way causes malignancy. As has been shown in previous chapters, techniques for studying viruses have been developed to a high degree of sophistication; and, because of the general nature of viral oncogenesis and the belief that what is learned will be of general biological interest, considerable effort has been expended in discovering tumor viruses and in studying their properties.

Tumor viruses are like all other viruses in being divisible into those that contain RNA and those that contain DNA. The RNA-containing tumor viruses (Table 17-1) seem to fall into a natural group resembling the myxovirus-paramyxovirus group (see Chapter 3), whereas the DNA-containing tumor viruses, to be discussed in the following chapter, are in the pox, adeno, and polyoma virus groups.

RNA-Containing Tumor Viruses

Evidence for classifying the RNA tumor viruses is far from complete. In general, this group of tumor viruses has been difficult to purify and to work with, and definitive biochemical analysis has not been done on most of them. Nevertheless, it is probably safe to group them together as RNA viruses because of their great morphological resemblance to one another and because of the fact that several representatives have been shown to contain RNA. It is common to refer to them, according to their morphology by electron microscopy, as type A, B, or C particles (Fig. 17-1).

TABLE 17-1.   REPRESENTATIVE RNA-CONTAINING TUMOR VIRUSES

TYPE OF VIRUS	KINDS OF TUMORS	ANIMALS FOR IN VIVO TUMORS	ANIMALS FOR IN VITRO TRANSFORMATION
Chicken Viruses			
Avian Leukosis Complex	Leukemia; erythroblastosis; osteopetrosis; lymphomatosis; kidney, ovarian, and other carcinomas and sarcomas	Chicken	Chicken
Rous Sarcoma Virus			
Bryan Strain	Fibrosarcoma	Chicken, hamster, turkey	Chicken
Schmidt-Ruppin Strain	Fibrosarcoma	Chicken, rat, hamster, mouse, guinea pig, rabbit, marmoset, Chinese hamster	Chicken, rat, guinea pig, mouse, human, monkey
Carr Strain	Fibrosarcoma	Chicken, cotton rat, monkey	
Mouse Viruses			
Murine Leukemia			
Gross (Graffi, Moloney, etc.)	Lymphoid leukemia	Mouse, rat	Rat
Friend (Rauscher, etc.)	Erythroblastosis, reticulum cell sarcoma	Mouse	
	Lymphoid leukemia	Rat	
Murine Sarcoma Virus	Sarcomas, rhabdomyosarcomas	Mouse, other rodents	Mouse, hamster, rat
Mammary Tumor Virus (Bittner)	Adenocarcinoma	Mouse	Mouse
Cat Virus			
Feline Leukemia Virus	Leukemia	Cat	
Guinea Pig Virus			
Guinea Pig Leukemia	Leukemia	Guinea pig	

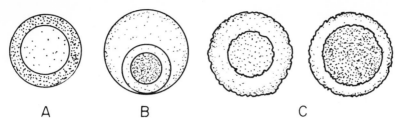

A   B   C

Figure 17-1. Morphological types of RNA tumor viruses as they appear in sectioned material examined by electron microscopy. The significance of type A (doughnuts) is not clear. Type B is found in purified preparations of the mammary tumor virus, and type C is found in the various leukemias. The type B particle in the diagram has an outer diameter of 100 mμ. (Redrawn from Bernhard, 1960.)

All RNA tumor viruses seem to mature at the cell membrane by budding, as do the myxoviruses, and all have many structural features common to the myxoviruses. However, unlike the myxoviruses, no RNA tumor virus causes visible cytopathic effect; the production of virions becomes a new "excretory" function of a transformed cell, which it performs without dying in the process.

Because of the mild form of virus-cell interaction, the RNA tumor viruses have been called "moderate." Perhaps also because of this characteristic, they are transmitted "vertically." That is, the lymphomatosis virus (Rubin, 1962b; Rubin *et al.*, 1961, 1962), the Gross leukemia virus (Gross, 1951b, 1952, 1961, 1962a), the Moloney leukemia virus (Ida *et al.*, 1965), and the mammary tumor virus (Bittner, 1936) are transmitted from parent to offspring through the egg, sperm, or milk. They can also be transmitted "horizontally" in some cases, as are most viruses, by the more usual method of contact with excreta containing viable virus.

Studies with these viruses are complicated by their "vertical" transmission. For instance, the virus may be passed to an offspring where it may grow, sometimes even to high titer, without producing disease. It can then be passed on to a subsequent generation, still perhaps without disease, although disease may develop in a later generation. Whether or not disease is present, the virions can often be seen by electron microscopy.

Virus-like particles have been seen by electron microscopy in tissue from apparently normal animals. They have also been seen in cells in tissue culture, including some cells that have been maintained in culture over extended periods and that had been thought to be virus free (Hall *et al.*, 1967; Kindig and Kirsten, 1967; Cromack, 1968). Biological activity has not been demonstrated for these virions, and when they are found in the cells of a leukemia patient, for instance, great care must be taken to avoid the temptation to attribute the leukemia to the unknown virions. Morphological analogy with some of the avian or murine leukemias is not sufficient evidence to establish a causative role of these virions in the disease.

The Avian Leukosis Complex.   The first tumor virus to be discovered (Ellermann and Bang, 1908) causes leukemia in chickens. It is now known that chicken leukemias and related tumors are caused by a group of viruses, the avian leukosis complex. Serologically, these viruses are difficult to distinguish from one another, as they share common antigens.

Many of the properties of this group of viruses have been reviewed by Beard *et al.* (1963), who recognize at least three strains of viruses that differ chiefly in their biological behavior. The BAI strain A causes myeloblastic leukemia in chickens, but it occasionally also causes visceral lymphomatosis, osteopetrosis, and kidney tumors. Which type of tumor develops depends on the virus dose inoculated. At high doses, leukemia results. At low doses, only a transient disturbance of blood cells develops, sometimes followed later in life by kidney tumors and tumors of other organs (Baluda and Jamieson, 1961). The RPL 12 strain (Beard *et al.*, 1963) causes chiefly erythroblastosis in chickens (erythroblastosis is a proliferation of young and immature forms of red blood cells in the circulating blood). The virus also transforms bone marrow cells to myeloblasts in tissue culture (Beaudreau *et al.*, 1960).

Much work has been done on disease in chickens caused by the various strains of viruses, and several points should be emphasized here. For one thing, one virus particle is sufficient to induce a tumor (Baluda and Jamieson, 1961). In addition, one virus can cause any of several different kinds of tumors, depending on the cell it infects. More will be said on this point when we consider mechanisms of viral carcinogenesis.

The Rous Sarcoma Virus.   In 1911, Rous described the cell-free transmission of a tumor-producing agent. This discovery, which followed the earlier discovery of the leukosis viruses, showed that solid tumors, in addition to tumors of blood cells, can be caused by viruses.

The Rous sarcoma virus has been studied extensively. Prior to about 1956, all assays had to be performed in chickens. Manaker and Groupé (1956) noticed that Rous sarcoma virus caused cells in tissue cultures to grow into localized foci. This observation served as a starting point for the development of a tissue culture assay for the virus (Temin and Rubin, 1958), which made it possible to do more detailed experiments at the level of individual cells.

Most of the work with Rous sarcoma virus has been with either of two strains (Rubin, 1964a). The Bryan strain grows to high titers but may be defective (see Chapter 13), requiring another of the avian viruses as a helper in order to replicate (Rubin and Vogt, 1962). The Schmidt-Ruppin strain does not seem to be defective and can rep-

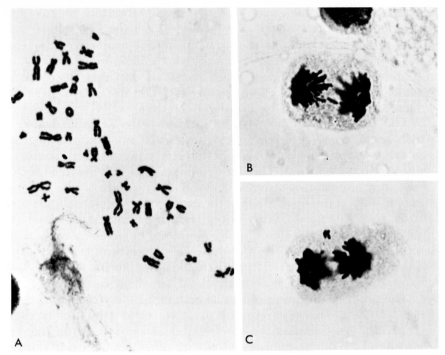

Figure 17-2. Abnormalities of human chromosomes caused by the Schmidt-Ruppin strain of Rous sarcoma virus in human lymphocyte cultures. The cell in metaphase shown in *A* contains at least one chromosome with a broken chromatid. The cell shown in *B*, in anaphase, contains an acentric fragment. *C* shows a cell, also in anaphase, containing a lagging fragment. (Courtesy of Dr. W. Nichols.)

licate without helper virus. But the addition of helper virus does enhance the yield of this strain as well.

The Bryan strain produces tumors almost exclusively in fowl (chickens and turkeys: Spencer and Groupé, 1962; Japanese quail: Pienta and Groupé, 1967), although exceptions include production of tumors in hamsters (Rabotti *et al.*, 1965; Eidinoff *et al.*, 1965). In contrast, the Schmidt-Ruppin strain produces sarcomas in fowl and in many mammalian species (Deinhardt, 1966; Ahlström and Forsby, 1962; Ahlström *et al.*, 1964). It also causes malignant change and chromosomal abnormalities in human cells in culture (Fig. 17-2; Jensen *et al.*, 1964; Nichols *et al.*, 1964). The Carr strain produces sarcomas in cotton rats (Svet-Moldavsky and Svet-Moldavskaya, 1964) and monkeys (Munroe and Windle, 1963).

Murine Leukemia Viruses. Until 1951, all work with leukemia viruses was done using chickens, and it was generally believed that the avian model had little or no relevance for mammalian or human leukemia. In that year, however, Gross (1951b, 1952) reported his success in passing leukemia from one mouse to another with cell-free extracts, thus providing a mammalian analogy to the chicken leukemia virus. The virus he isolated, now called either the Gross leukemia virus or the "passage A" virus, has been studied extensively in mice. The Gross leukemia virus has been shown, by electron microscopy, to resemble the Rous sarcoma virus (Parsons, 1963). Gross has recently reviewed much of the work on his virus (1962b, 1963, 1965b, 1965c). Another recent review is by Boiron *et al.* (1967).

The murine leukemia viruses include many separate isolates, which seem to fall into two groups on the basis of their biological properties. Gross' passage A virus induces many different forms of leukemia in mice or rats. The most common form of leukemia is lymphatic, but other forms also occur, depending largely on the genetic susceptibility of the host. Many of the other strains of mouse leukemia viruses resemble Gross' virus in the form of pathology produced. At least one causes proliferation of immature red blood cells rather than white blood cells and is therefore called erythroblastosis virus (Kirsten *et al.*, 1967). Its relationship to the other murine viruses is not clear.

The other major group of strains resembles the virus isolated by Friend (1959) and causes erythroblastosis as well as solid tumors, such as reticulum cell sarcoma. An electron microscopic study (de Harven and Friend, 1960) demonstrated the progression of forms during budding of the virus at the cell membrane (Fig. 17-3).

Some workers (Gross, 1965a) believe that only two different murine leukemia viruses have been isolated and that all other isolates represent reisolations of one of these. There is no agreement on this point, however; like the avian leukosis complex, the murine viruses are difficult to sort serologically.

A further problem is that tissue culture studies with the murine viruses have been severely limited. Many of the viruses have been grown in cultured cells (Boiron *et al.*, 1967) but quantitative assays have not been developed. Cytopathic effect has not been observed with the murine viruses, nor has it with the avian leukosis viruses and Rous sarcoma virus. The Gross agent has been shown to transform rat cells in vitro (Ioachim, 1967). The avian viruses, however, more easily cause transformation of cells in culture; with suitable agar overlays on the cells to prevent diffusion of virus, these serve as quantitative assays (Moscovici, 1967; Temin and Rubin, 1958).

Other Leukemia Viruses. Leukemia is a common disease of mammals. In addition to the virus-induced leukemias already discussed, it has also been shown that guinea pig leukemia is virus induced (Opler, 1967a, 1967b). Particles that resemble the virions of known viral leukemias have been isolated, partially purified, and concentrated from plasma of cats with leukemia; but biological activity for these virions has not been demonstrated as yet (Kawakami *et al.*, 1967).

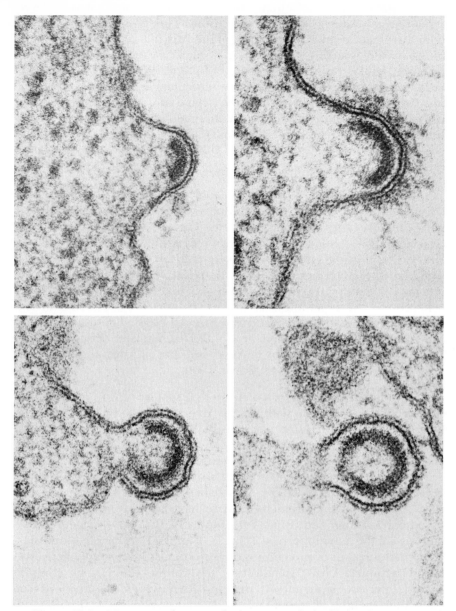

Figure 17-3. Maturation of a murine leukemia virus by budding. The sequence of electron micrographs of thin sections of cells cultured from leukemic mice shows the progression of the formation of a virus particle. In the upper left picture, there is a small accumulation of material, presumably the viral nucleoid (core, or nucleocapsid), just beneath the cytoplasmic membrane. The nucleoid continues to mature as the cytoplasmic membrane bulges and is finally pinched off as a mature virion. (Magnification approximately 240,000×.) (Courtesy of Dr. E. de Harven. Reprinted with permission of Appleton-Century-Crofts.)

As more animal leukemias are studied, it is found that many have virus-like particles associated with them. This type of study is often done by electron microscopy. Although virus-like particles have been found by this type of search, even in human cases of leukemia (see, for instance, Viola *et al.*, 1967), it cannot be determined by electron microscopy whether the particles have biological activity, and therefore it is impossible to say whether they have any association with the disease. Furthermore, mycoplasma and even cell debris can be indistinguishable from leukemia virions; the investigator pursuing this type of search must be alert to the many artifacts that can be misleading.

Murine Sarcoma Virus.   The analogy between the RNA-containing tumor viruses of mice and chickens became more complete with the discovery of a mouse virus that causes sarcomas in mice (Harvey, 1964; Moloney, 1966; Perk and Moloney, 1966; Huebner, 1967). The murine sarcoma virus seems to be defective in the same sense as the Rous sarcoma virus. It is helped to replicate by the murine leukemia viruses in the same way that the Rous sarcoma virus is helped by the avian leukosis viruses (Huebner *et al.*, 1966; Hartley and Rowe, 1966; O'Connor and Fischinger, 1968). The murine virus can transform mouse (Simons *et al.*, 1967b), hamster (Simons *et al.*, 1967a), and rat (Ting, 1966) embryo cells in culture; and it can be assayed this way (Hartley and Rowe, 1966).

Mammary Tumor Virus.   A model system for human breast cancer became available with the discovery that at least some kinds of mammary tumors in mice are caused by an agent secreted in the mother's milk (Bittner, 1936). Much work was done and many years elapsed before the agent was accepted as a virus.

Recently the virus was isolated and purified (Lyons and Moore, 1962, 1965; Moore *et al.*, 1959; Nowinski *et al.*, 1967). Electron microscopy of the isolated virus shows it to have an envelope and an internal core or nucleoid (Fig. 17-4); typically, the core is eccentrically located in the envelope (see type B, Fig. 17-1). The envelope has many radial spikes or projections on the outer surface, somewhat similar to influenza virus. In addition to protein, the virions contain about 27 per cent lipid and 0.8 per cent RNA, which is equivalent to a molecular weight of about 3.7×10^6 daltons of RNA (Lyons and Moore, 1965).

The mammary tumor virus is present in the mammary glands and other tissues of certain high-incidence strains of mice. During the time that a baby mouse is nursing, it acquires the virus from the mother's milk. This has been shown, for instance, by removing newborn, high-incidence mice from their mothers before they nurse and foster-nursing them on low-incidence mothers. In this way, mammary tumors do not develop in the babies.

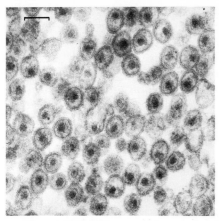 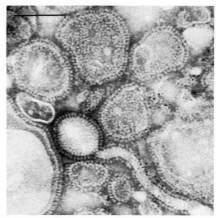

Figure 17-4. Electron micrographs of the mammary tumor virus. On the left is a section of an ultracentrifuged pellet of virus purified from mouse milk, showing the eccentrically situated "nucleoids" typical of type B particles. On the right, the virions have been negatively stained with phosphotungstic acid. Most of the particles in this field have been injured by the purification process. One intact particle with a long "tail" can be seen near the center of the picture. The "tail" probably occurs as an artifact during drying of the preparation. The outer membrane of the virions is covered with knobbed spicules about 8.5 mμ long, spaced about 6.5 mμ apart. (Bars are 100 mμ.) (Courtesy of Dr. D. H. Moore.)

The presence of the virus is necessary for tumors to develop, and it is not certain whether mammary tumors can develop at all in mice without the virus (Moore, 1967). But it is also necessary that estrogenic hormones be present. Female mice deprived of estrogens by removal of the ovaries have a decreased incidence of mammary tumors. Male mice ordinarily have a low incidence of tumors despite the presence of virus, but if estrogens are administered to them, the males have a greatly increased incidence of tumors (Hall and Moore, 1966).

Although the pathogenesis of mammary tumors has been studied in detail in mice (DeOme, 1963), there is as yet no satisfactory in vitro system for growing or assaying the virus. Progress is slow when the investigator has to wait 6 to 12 months for the results of an assay. Under certain conditions, tumor tissue will release virus when grown in culture (Lasfargues *et al.*, 1959; Cardiff *et al.*, 1968) and it may now be possible to cause mouse mammary tissue to undergo malignant transformation in culture (Lasfargues and Moore, 1966). These developments may aid in exploiting the potentialities of studies with this system.

MECHANISM OF CARCINOGENESIS BY RNA-CONTAINING VIRUSES

Although certain crucial information is missing, much detail is known about the mechanism of carcinogenesis by RNA-containing viruses. Most work on this subject has been done with either Rous sarcoma virus or myeloblastosis virus in cell cultures. Our emphasis will be on these systems.

The first question we might ask is whether the viral genome is present and functioning in the virus-transformed cells. This question is easily answered experimentally, since transformed cells continue to release virus, even after many generations of growth. "Nonproducing" cells are those that contain only the Rous sarcoma virus genome and do not produce infectious virus. Addition of helper virus to these (see Chapter 12) causes prompt production of both Rous sarcoma virus and helper virus (Hanafusa *et al.*, 1963). It is also possible to induce the transmission of the viral genome to another cell (Sarma *et al.*, 1966). This can happen only if at least one Rous sarcoma viral genome is present within each cell.

The evidence also indicates that, with the exception of one portion, the entire viral genome is present. The portion that is lacking accounts for the defectiveness. It is possible that the missing portion is the part that codes for coat components, as the Rous sarcoma virus produced by the transformed cells carries the antigenic markers of the helper. But the defectiveness is not complete. Careful work has revealed that small amounts of Rous sarcoma virus are synthesized and released even in the absence of helper (Vogt, 1967a, 1967b; Courington and Vogt, 1967; Haguenau and Hanafusa, 1968; Valentine and Bader, 1968). The helper effect is therefore one of increasing yield rather than one of releasing virus. The defectiveness may be due to lack of expression of a certain portion of the genome rather than to a physical lack of that part of the genome. In contrast, the viruses of the avian leukosis complex do not seem to be even partially defective; the fact that the Rous sarcoma virus is defective, therefore, cannot account for its ability to induce transformation.

What is the nature of the viral genome in the transformed cells and where is it located? Neither question can be answered, although evidence exists to support either of two major possibilities.

It is believed by some workers (Temin, 1966a, 1966b, 1966c, 1967a, 1967b) that after infection the information contained in the RNA of the viral genome is transferred to a newly synthesized DNA molecule. It is further proposed that this DNA replicates in synchrony with the cell DNA and serves as a template for synthesis of progeny RNA molecules.

This idea arose as an attempt to explain the effect of DNA inhibitors on replication of Rous sarcoma virus. In 1963, Temin reported that actinomycin D inhibits production of Rous sarcoma virus. The drug also inhibits the growth of Rauscher leukemia virus (Bases and King, 1967). Similar results were obtained by Bader (1964), who further concluded that DNA synthesis is required for replication of

Rous sarcoma virus. Blocking DNA synthesis prevents initiation of infection by avian myeloblastosis virus (Knudson *et al.*, 1967).

Additional work (Bader, 1965a, 1965b; Temin, 1964a) has confirmed these findings and has indicated that inhibitors of DNA synthesis interfere with replication of Rous sarcoma virus, in contrast to their lack of effect on replication of influenza virus. A DNA that is homologous to the viral DNA has been detected in cells infected with Rous sarcoma virus (Temin, 1964b). Furthermore, a polymerase that uses Rous sarcoma viral RNA is not detectable in cells infected with other DNA-containing viruses (Wilson and Bader, 1965). Infection of synchronized cultures of cells when they are synthesizing DNA results in a greater number of transformed foci (Bader, 1967) than occur in cells not synthesizing DNA. It appears, then, that the necessity for DNA participation in its replication may cause the sensitivity of Rous sarcoma virus to the action of actinomycin D. These results are consistent with the "provirus" model. They could also mean that DNA synthesis is required, but perhaps for some other reason than for synthesis of a "provirus."

Alternatively, the viral genetic information could remain in RNA. For example, Dulbecco (1965) has proposed that the viral RNA replicates at such a rate that the newly formed molecules replace those lost by being incorporated into progeny virions and those diluted out by cell division. The number of viral genomes per cell would therefore remain constant. The steady-state level of viral genomes would not have to be high, because only a few infectious virions are released during each cell generation (Temin and Rubin, 1959), and a minimum of two would be needed if one were to be distributed to each of the two daughter cells.

It might be expected that if this model is an accurate representation of the Rous sarcoma cell, occasionally cells would arise that by chance had received no virus genome. Under ordinary cultural conditions, these "cured" cells would grow in contact with cells releasing virus, and reinfection would occur promptly. But MacPherson (1965) used a technique for growing a continuous line of hamster cells in such a way that reinfection was prevented. In one such cell line infected with the Schmidt-Ruppin strain of Rous sarcoma virus, he found no revertants. One to 10 per cent of the cells from three other clones gave rise to cells that no longer had the changed morphology of the transformed cells. He called these subclones revertants because they had lost not only the morphological characteristics of the transformed cells but also the ability to induce tumors in chickens. In addition, they no longer had the Rous sarcoma viral genome.

These important results, unfortunately not confirmed as yet, indicate that the continued presence of the viral genome is necessary if the transformed state is to be maintained. Transformation is not simply due to a change in the cell that occurs at the time of infection and continues without the further influence of the viral genetic information. The steady-state hypothesis predicts that more than one viral genome must be present in the transformed cell. In fact, it is possible to calculate about how many viral genomes would be necessary in a cell so that the revertant frequency would be what MacPherson (1965) had observed. If a cell has $2x$ genomes prior to dividing, and if these are distributed randomly to the two daughter cells, the probability, P, that a cell would receive none, and therefore would be a revertant, is

$$P = e^{-x}$$

from the zero term of the Poisson distribution. MacPherson found about 5 per cent revertants, indicating that each cell had an average of about six viral genomes prior to division. This estimate is slightly low because it does not include genomes in the process of being incorporated into infectious virions.

Although the occurrence of revertants is consistent with the steady-state model, it is not decisive evidence in favor of either model. Such segregation could also arise from the DNA-provirus model. Another finding, however, is against the provirus. It has already been mentioned that the avian leukosis viruses are transmitted "vertically" from parent to offspring. If the viral genome is incorporated into the cell's DNA, it would be expected that virus could be transmitted through either the egg or the sperm, because both contain DNA. If, however, the viral genome is not incorporated in the DNA but is mixed in the cell's RNA, it would probably be transmitted only through the egg, which contains RNA, and not the sperm, which contains little or no RNA.

Studies of transmission of virus (Rubin *et al.*, 1962) indicate that only hens transmit an avian leukosis virus to chicks, a finding consistent with lack of incorporation of a DNA-provirus into the cellular DNA. The viral nucleic acid is not likely to reside in the nucleus of the transformed cell; instead, it is probably cytoplasmic.

Therefore, either of two major possible models could account for the condition of the viral genome in transformed cells: the steady-state or the provirus model. The steady-state hypothesis postulates that the viral genetic information remains in RNA that replicates at a rate sufficient to maintain the steady state. The replicating RNA could remain cytoplasmic, and its products could cause the many cellular changes that have been observed. Statistical considerations of the number of genomes required per cell to maintain the steady state are consistent with the observation that probably only a few are present. Statistical fluctuations might be minimized by mechanisms that regulate the rate of replication of the viral genome, keeping the number per cell closer to the necessary level.

But the steady-state model does not explain several findings, including the apparent requirement for DNA synthesis and the presence in the transformed cell of DNA that apparently hybridizes with viral RNA. Furthermore, chromosomal changes have been noted in cells transformed by the Schmidt-Ruppin strain of Rous sarcoma virus (see Fig. 17-2) (Hlozanek *et al.*, 1966; Nichols, 1966a, 1966b). Although the provirus model would explain these findings, there is insufficient independent evidence to support this concept. Crucial experiments have not yet been done to determine which of these two (or possibly some other) models accurately portrays the viral presence in transformed cells.

An analogy with lysogeny has sometimes been made to account for the condition of the viral genome in the transformed cells; such an analogy is implied by the word "provirus." But, as pointed out by Rubin (1965), little or no evidence supports the analogy to lysogeny. Such an analogy would require that the viral information be in DNA, a finding that is far from established. Further, the DNA "provirus" would have to be inserted into the cellular DNA, and there is no evidence to support this possibility. The steady-state hypothesis makes no such demands.

Perhaps the most striking difference between lysogenization by temperate viruses and transformation by the avian viruses is the mode of virus release from the cells. As was discussed in the previous chapter, when the prophage detaches from the DNA of a lysogenic cell, the prophage enters the vegetative state; when the phage particles have matured in a cell, the cell lyses, releasing a burst of phage particles. In a culture that has not been artificially induced, only a few cells synthesize phages. In contrast, cells transformed by avian leukosis or Rous sarcoma viruses continually synthesize and release infectious virus, without dying in the process.

Yet viral information is expressed in the transformed cells, as it is in lysogeny. Of course, such expression could also occur if, as suggested by the steady-state hypothesis, the cell contained several copies of the RNA-viral genome. The fact that expression of viral genes causes the observed transformation changes has been demonstrated by several interesting experiments.

In one such experiment, Temin (1960) isolated several mutants of the Rous sarcoma virus. In replicate cultures of a clone of chick embryonic fibroblast cells, one mutant caused the transformed cells to be round and refractile, whereas another mutant caused the transformed cells to be long and spindle shaped. The two mutants consistently caused the two kinds of response when they were tried on various fibroblastic cell lines. The control of cell morphology extended to tumors induced in chickens; these tumors had a cellular morphology typical of the virus mutant inoculated.

The kind of cell transformed by the virus is also important. Temin found that fibroblast clones gave one morphological response to one of the mutants, and other clones gave a different response. But a given clone responded differently to the different mutants, and its response was consistently the same with a given mutant.

Further experiments (Temin, 1961) showed that cells transformed by one mutant can be superinfected with a second mutant. Clones of the transformed cells continue to release the first infecting virus, the second virus, or both viruses. Whichever mode of virus release that occurs is passed on to progeny cells in a stable way, indicating that perhaps some mechanism regulates the distribution of viral genomes to the daughter cells at division. This same mechanism could be responsible for maintaining the steady-state number of viral genomes per cell.

The fact that different target cells give rise to different kinds of transformed cells when exposed to the same virus was clearly shown by Baluda et al. (1963) in experiments with the avian myeloblastosis virus. Cultures were made from two different kinds of chick embryo cells: One from cells of the yolk sac, which is responsible for blood cell production in the embryo, and the other from the bursa of Fabricius, which gives rise to cells that synthesize humoral antibody in the chicken. When these cells were infected with avian myeloblastosis virus, the yolk sac cells gave rise to cells that resembled the myeloid cells that circulate in leukemic chickens. Some transformed cells resembled erythroblasts and other cells of the red blood cell series. In contrast, cultures of transformed cells of the bursa of Fabricius contained plasma cells in various degrees of differentiation; some of these cells can synthesize proteins that resemble antibodies (Marinkovich and Baluda, 1966). Therefore, one virus could give rise to various types of leukemia, depending on the cell type initially infected.

These experiments also demonstrate that virus induction of malignant cells does not necessarily lead to dedifferentiation, because the transformed cells are more differentiated than the original cells in culture. Nevertheless, certain facts remain: The viruses induce changes in the cell, the changes are characteristic of the virus as well as the cell, and the changes are transmitted to the offspring cells as long as the viral genome persists.

The induced changes include altered enzyme systems (Gelbard et al., 1966; Temin, 1966b) and increased synthesis of such materials as acid mucopolysaccharide. The latter material is the product of hyaluronic acid synthetase, an enzyme normally present in cells and increased after transformation (Ishimoto et al., 1966). Although serologic tests of the enzyme have not been done, the enzyme appears to have the same kinetic characteristics before and after malignant transformation, so probably the virus merely causes an increased synthesis or activity of cell-coded enzyme.

This enzyme and its product are of special interest because of their association with the cell's surface. The cell surface seems to be implicated in the malignant change caused by Rous sarcoma virus and perhaps other avian leukosis viruses (Vogt, 1963).

One of the most striking of the new properties acquired by viral-transformed cells is their loss of contact inhibition (Rubin, 1961). They do not stop moving in a given direction when they come into contact with another cell, but instead tend to pile on top of each other. Normal cells stop moving and stop dividing under these conditions. The transformed cells are no longer regulated with regard to contact inhibition of movement or of division (Stoker and Rubin, 1967), and this deregulation is probably the essence of the oncogenic process. The "signals" received by the cell that "tell" it of the close proximity of other cells and cause it to stop moving and dividing probably arise at the cell surface. How this regulation is effected is unknown, but it is a central problem in studies of viral oncogenesis.

The RNA-containing cancer viruses, as a group, have some common features. All apparently mature at the cell membrane, perhaps altering it in the process. None have been shown to cause cytopathic effect, but they multiply at a slow rate without causing cell death. Their alteration of the cell into a malignant cell may have arisen through evolution as a mechanism for keeping alive the "factory" that produces virus particles. Any viral mutants that may have arisen that cause only a cytocidal effect could not, of course, cause tumor formation.

But, as will be seen in the next chapter, the DNA-containing viruses are able to undergo either the oncogenic or the cytocidal interaction with their host cells. Perhaps the analogy to temperate phages and lysogeny is more valid with these viruses.

Further Reading

Andrewes, C.: Tumour-viruses and Virus-tumours. British Medical Journal, 1:653-658, 1964.

Bryan, W. R.: The Search for Causative Viruses in Human Cancer; a Discussion of the Problem. Journal of the National Cancer Institute, 29:1027-1034, 1962.

Luria, S. E.: Viruses, Cancer Cells, and the Genetic Concept of Virus Infection. Cancer Research, 20:677-688, 1960.

Rous, P.: Viruses and Tumor Causation; an Appraisal of Present Knowledge. Nature, 207:457-463, 1965.

Rous, P.: The Challenge to Man of the Neoplastic Cell. Science, 157:24-28, 1967.

18

TUMOR VIRUSES THAT CONTAIN DNA

The fundamental differences between the viruses that contain DNA and those that contain RNA have been mentioned repeatedly in previous chapters. The differences also extend to the cancer viruses. As discussed in the preceding chapter, the most likely way that the genome of the RNA-containing viruses is perpetuated in malignant transformed cells is by achieving a steady state, with production of new genomes balancing the losses of genomes. Losses are due to dilution between daughter cells at division and to synthesis and release of mature virions.

Apparently all the transformed tumor cells contain the RNA viral genome in a complete, or nearly complete, functional form, because all transformed cells can synthesize virus. Virus production is undertaken by the cell as one of its activities, but one that is only a small part of its total activity; virus production thus is not so overwhelming that the cell dies. Virus production itself apparently is not responsible for the malignant change. Instead, it seems that some product of the viral genome somehow releases the usual restrictions on the cell's division, allowing it to divide without limitation.

The situation with the tumor viruses containing DNA is quite different. With some of these viruses it has been shown that once the virus has changed the cell to the malignant state, the virus is no longer present as such in the cell, nor does the cell synthesize more virions. As will be discussed, a major problem has been to determine whether any viral genetic information is present in the transformed cell. Present evidence indicates that it is present and that at least some viral genes are functioning.

332

In a few DNA virus-host cell systems, transformed cells that do not release virus can be made to do so under certain conditions. These conditions apparently are not the same as those under which the prophage in lysogenic cells enters the vegetative state and the cells begin to produce virus. Nevertheless, there may be some value in examining the extent to which an analogy holds between lysogeny and tumor induction by the DNA-containing viruses.

DNA TUMOR VIRUSES

The DNA-containing viruses that are known to induce tumors are in the pox, polyoma-papilloma, and adenovirus groups; and several "candidate" viruses are in the herpesvirus group. All the known DNA tumor viruses cause solid tumors, usually sarcomas; none has been found that induces leukemia or other blood malignancies.

Pox Viruses

Borrell's astute observations of the proliferative effects of various animal and human pox viruses led him to postulate that cancer was viral induced (Borrell, 1903). He noted that cancer is unregulated cell growth, that viruses propagate in cells and usually kill them, but that certain pox viruses induce a temporary stage of cellular proliferation before the cells die. Therefore, a virus that propagated slowly might not kill the cells as rapidly as cell division might produce new ones.

Viruses of the pox group other than those observed by Borrell produce a cellular proliferation that more clearly qualifies as a tumor. One of these is the Yaba virus (Andrewes *et al.*, 1959; Niven *et al.*, 1961), isolated from tumors that appeared in a colony of rhesus monkeys in Yaba, Nigeria (Bearcroft and Jamieson, 1958). The tumors are usually about 2 to 5 cm. in diameter (Sproul *et al.*, 1963); they occur on the head, face, or limbs of monkeys; and they regress spontaneously in 1 to 3 months. The monkey develops permanent immunity to reinfection.

The virus that causes molluscum contagiosum is also considered to be a tumor virus. The tumors, occurring only in human skin, are small nodules (about 2 mm. in diameter) that may persist for several months before regressing spontaneously. Virions are present in the tissue and can be seen by electron microscopy in thin sections (Hasegawa, 1964; Middelkamp and Munger, 1964). Isolation of the virus is difficult because a suitable cell system for virus growth has not yet been found. The virus appears to induce interferon synthesis in chick embryo cell cultures (Friedman-Kien and Vilcek, 1967).

Shope (1932a, 1932b) described a virus that causes fibromas in rabbits. The virus is closely related to a rabbit virus that causes myxomatosis. Serologic methods used to distinguish between the two viruses have at times given equivocal results. Although information is limited, the viruses do seem to be different in certain biological characteristics: In tissue cultures, the myxoma virus produces plaques and the fibroma virus produces foci of proliferating cells (Padgett *et al.*, 1962).

The disease that a specific virus produces depends on the species of rabbit. The myxoma virus produces localized gelatinous swellings in some rabbit species and a rapidly fatal disease in others. The fibroma virus usually produces localized, subcutaneous, soft, rubbery swellings that persist for 2 or 3 weeks before regressing. The behavior of this virus also varies somewhat depending on the host species, and in some rabbits it produces fatal disease.

The myxoma virus was used in an attempt to control the rabbit population in Australia (reviewed by Fenner, 1959). At first, after the virus was introduced and had spread through the country, the rabbit population was quickly reduced in number. Genetically resistant rabbits survived and replaced those that died, so the rabbit population now consists of individuals that are relatively resistant to the virus. A new balance has developed between reproduction of virus, death of the host, and development of genetically resistant rabbits.

The last tumor-producing pox virus to be discussed here is the milker's nodule virus. As the name implies, this virus causes small nodules on people who come in contact with infected cows. The incubation period in man is about 5 days and the disease is self-limited. Some success has been achieved in growing the virus in cultures of bovine kidney cells (Friedman-Kien *et al.*, 1963).

Other pox viruses cause varying degrees of cellular proliferation before the cells lyse and release more virus. The pox viruses do not produce malignant tumors, but do cause self-limited cellular proliferation. Although technically tumors, the neoplasms are not cancerous. The virus-cell interaction that results in the temporary cellular proliferation has not been extensively studied, but it does not seem to involve a direct mixing of the viral genome with the cell, as seems to be true for other tumor viruses to be discussed.

Herpesviruses

No viruses in the herpes group are known to induce tumors, but two might fit into this category.

One is a virus that might be responsible for causing a renal carcinoma of certain leopard frogs. Because Lucké (1934, 1938, 1939) thoroughly investigated the tumor and virus, it is often called the Lucké virus. The intranuclear inclusions that form in kidney cells and in cultured cells (Maes *et al.*, 1967), the base composition of the viral DNA (Maes and Granoff, 1967; Morris *et al.*, 1966), and electron microscopic morphology (Darlington *et al.*, 1966) all suggest that the virus is of the herpes group. It has been difficult to perform definitive studies with the virus in tissue culture, but work has been done with the in vivo tumors (Rafferty, 1963). Reviews of the work with this virus are available (Rafferty, 1964; Mizell and Zambernard, 1965; Duryee *et al.*, 1960).

A second candidate virus is often found in cultures derived from tumors that usually affect the jaws but can occur elsewhere in the body, chiefly in African children. Burkitt, a surgeon, postulated a viral cause when he noticed several peculiar features about these tumors: The age of the tumor victims is unusual when compared to the age of those with other childhood tumors; the histology of the tumors is somewhat different; and the tumors respond to treatment more readily than do other kinds of tumors. When he investigated more closely, Burkitt found that the afflicted children nearly always came from areas where mosquitos were prevalent—the geographical distribution of the tumors nearly matches the yellow fever belt of Africa. He therefore proposed that the causative agent of the tumor might be mosquito borne and, if so, was probably viral (Burkitt, 1963; Burkitt and Wright, 1966). The evidence for an association with mosquitos is not universally accepted, however (Dalldorf *et al.*, 1964).

Cells from many of these tumors have been cultured (Epstein *et al.*, 1965). When the cultures are examined by electron microscopy, a high percentage of them are found to contain particles that are morphologically identical to viruses of the herpes group (Toplin and Schidlovsky, 1966; Yamaguchi *et al.*, 1967; Hinuma *et al.*, 1967; Hummeler *et al.*, 1966). It has also been possible to demonstrate the presence of virus by its interference with the replication of other viruses (Henle and Henle, 1965) and by the presence of an antigen in the cells that reacts with antibody in the serum of patients with the tumor (Old *et al.*, 1966).

By using the serologic reaction, it has been found that people in all parts of the world have a high incidence of antibody to the virus in the cultured cells (Gerber and Birch, 1967). Furthermore, there is strong serologic evidence that having infectious mononucleosis causes the development of antibodies against the virus in the cultured cells (Henle *et al.*, 1968).

Attempts to infect animals with this virus may finally have been successful (Stewart *et al.*, 1968). Virus from freshly established cell lines from Burkitt tumors was inoculated intracerebrally in hamsters and could be passed serially from hamster to hamster. Inoculated hamsters develop central nervous system disease resembling that of other herpesviruses. This development may well open new approaches to the study of this most interesting virus.

Polyoma-Papilloma Viruses

All known viruses in this group except the K virus produce tumors (Kilham and Murphy, 1953). The papilloma viruses cause warts of the skin or mucous membranes in a number of species (human, rabbit, cow, pig, dog, and others) (see Olson, 1963, and Rowson and Mahy, 1967, for extensive references). Morphologically, these viruses are closely similar (see Chapter 2), and they all seem to have a circular DNA molecule (see Chapter 9). They are not closely related serologically (Le Bouvier *et al.*, 1966).

The virus may be present in high concentration in the wart (Barrera-Oro *et al.*, 1962). The rabbit papilloma, caused by the Shope papilloma virus, seems to be the only wart that regularly becomes malignant. After a rabbit papilloma becomes malignant, the virus can no longer be isolated from the tumor. However, DNA extracted from malignant warts will cause tumors in rabbits (Ito, 1960, 1961; Ito and Evans, 1961, 1965).

Tissue culture studies with the papilloma viruses have been limited because of inability to establish the virus in cultured cells. The rabbit papilloma virus (De Maeyer, 1962) and the human wart virus (Oroszlan and Rich, 1964) may have been grown in tissue culture. Although the bovine papilloma virus has not been induced to grow in cultures, it has produced transformation of cultured embryonic bovine skin cells to a malignant state (Boiron *et al.*, 1964).

Polyoma virus was discovered during experiments in which Gross' leukemia agent was being passed in mice. In addition to the leukemia that occurred in some mice, parotid tumors also developed. After further cell-free passage of the unknown virus, other tumors also occurred (Stewart *et al.*, 1957; Stewart, 1960), accounting for the name, polyoma, that was given to this virus that can cause many kinds of malignancies — sometimes several in a single animal.

Polyoma virus is widespread among the wild mouse population (Rowe, 1961), in which it causes little or no apparent disease. Because it is so widespread and causes tumors only rarely under natural conditions, and because the tumors are of many kinds, polyoma virus has brought about renewed interest in the possibility that human malignancy is viral. Polyoma virus and its close relative, SV40, have been studied intensely; what has been learned about how these viruses induce the malignant change will be discussed in a later section.

The vacuolating agent, SV40, was isolated from cultures of rhesus monkey kidneys (Sweet and Hilleman, 1960). The rhesus monkey is the natural host, but the virus seems to cause only mild disease, if any, in that species (Ashkenazi and Melnick, 1962). When grown in cells cultured from rhesus monkey kidneys, SV40 does not produce extensive cytopathic effect. However, in kidney cultures from African green monkeys, SV40 grows actively and produces an extensive cytopathic effect consisting of vacuolations of the cells.

SV40 causes malignant tumors in hamsters (Eddy *et al.*, 1961, 1962; Girardi *et al.*, 1962, 1963; Hsiung and Gaylord, 1961), but unlike polyoma-induced tumors, SV40-induced tumors are slow to appear. In tissue culture, SV40 causes transformation of cells from many species, including man. Yet SV40 has not been shown to induce tumors in its natural host species, the rhesus monkey.

Adenoviruses

The discovery that adenoviruses can induce tumors came about in an interesting way. Studies with polyoma virus and SV40 had already indicated that both easily produce tumors in hamsters. Reasoning that the hamster is somehow particularly sensitive to viral tumor induction, Trentin and his co-workers (Trentin *et al.*, 1962; Yabe *et al.*, 1962, 1963, 1964) injected baby hamsters with viruses of as many types, groups, and strains as they could obtain. They found that human adenovirus type 12 (Fig. 18-1) could produce tumors. Other workers, using the same approach, soon showed that human adenovirus type 18 (Huebner *et al.*, 1962; McLeod and Ham, 1963), type 7 (Girardi *et al.*, 1964), and type 31 (Pereira *et al.*, 1965) also were oncogenic. Once a tumor has been induced, the virus can no longer be isolated from it.

The list of human adenoviruses that can induce tumors is now quite long. The 31 serotypes of human adenoviruses have been arranged informally into four groups: the highly oncogenic adenoviruses, the moderately oncogenic, the weakly oncogenic, and the nononcogenic. The grouping is based on the ability of the viruses to induce hamster tumors. Such tests necessarily involve more than simply the effect of the viruses; the immune system of the animal, to be discussed later, is also involved. The classification breaks down in tissue cultures, where the immune response cannot come into effect, since many of the "nononcogenic" viruses are as oncogenic as the "highly oncogenic" adenoviruses.

Adenoviruses of other species also induce tumors, either in animals or in cultured cells, and the list lengthens constantly. Of the monkey adenoviruses, six of 18 have demonstrated oncogenicity, and one of the three serotypes of bovine adenoviruses is oncogenic (Darby-

Figure 18-1. A hamster with a tumor produced by human adenovirus type 12. On the day of birth, the hamster was injected under the skin between the shoulders with about 5×10^6 PFU of virus. The picture, showing the tumor at the site of injection, was taken 34 days later. (Courtesy of Dr. B. Casto.)

shire, 1966). One of the two chicken adenoviruses is oncogenic (Sarma *et al.*, 1965), and the virus of infectious canine hepatitis is oncogenic (Sarma *et al.*, 1967). The two types of mouse adenovirus have not been adequately tested.

TRANSFORMATION OF CELLS IN CULTURE

Work with the DNA-containing tumor viruses took on a new dimension when it was shown that polyoma virus could cause transformation of hamster or mouse cells in tissue culture (Vogt and Dulbecco, 1960; Sachs and Medina, 1961). Later, it was found that SV40 could transform hamster cells (Rabson and Kirschstein, 1962) and even human cells (Shein and Enders, 1962; Koprowski *et al.*, 1962) in culture.

To produce transformation, the investigator may simply add polyoma virus to cultures of hamster or mouse cells. In the mouse cultures, many cells undergo a lytic response, with widespread death of cells and virus release. A few cells in the culture grow into colonies after a delay of many weeks (Weisberg, 1963). Hamster cultures undergo only the oncogenic response (Sachs *et al.*, 1962); polyoma virus replicates poorly, if at all, in hamster cells (Dulbecco and Vogt, 1960).

That is, polyoma may be thought of as defective for replication in hamster cells.

Development of a quantitative assay for transformation permitted Stoker and MacPherson (1961) to measure the efficiency of polyoma virus transformation. They found that transformation is inefficient: With a multiplicity of 96 PFU/cell, only one transformed colony occurred in every 10,000 cells exposed. Linearity with virus dilution indicates that a single infectious unit is capable of causing the transformation.

Somewhat similar results were reported by Todaro and Green (1964) who used a continuous line of mouse embryo cells called 3T3. SV40 does not cause any detectable lytic response in these cells, but it does cause transformation. In this system, the efficiency of transformation is low: The ratio of plaque-forming units to focus-forming units is about 10^4:1 to 10^5:1.

Because of considerable interest in the oncogenic properties of human adenoviruses, many attempts were made to obtain transformation of cells in culture. McBride and Wiener (1964) and Pope and Rowe (1964) reported successful transformation of hamster embryo cells by human adenovirus type 12. Other investigators were unable to confirm these reports and to obtain transformed cells, until Freeman *et al.* (1965) discovered that the calcium level in the medium has an effect. Specifically, cells from tumors induced in hamsters could be grown in culture if the calcium ion concentration was greatly reduced (from the normal 1.8 mM to 0.1 mM). This finding suggested to many investigators that in vitro transformation should also be tried in the low-calcium medium. Many laboratories almost simultaneously reported success at inducing transformation (Fig. 18-2) of many kinds

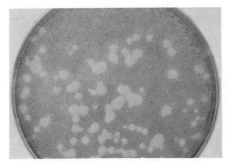

Figure 18-2. Two modes of interaction of adenovirus with cells. The picture on the left shows a petri dish containing human embryonic kidney cells that had been infected with human adenovirus type 12. The white, clear areas are the plaques caused by lytic action of the virus. The background cells are stained by a vital stain (neutral red). The picture on the right is a petri dish of hamster embryo cells, also infected with human adenovirus type 12. The dark spots are colonies of transformed cells (an enlarged view of a colony is shown in Figure 18-3). The background cells in the rest of the dish are so lightly stained by this technique that they do not show. Both dishes were photographed about 2 or 3 weeks after infection. (Courtesy of Dr. B. Casto.)

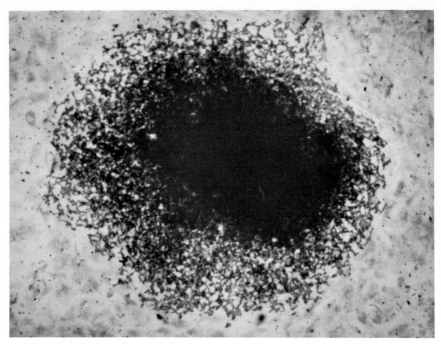

Figure 18-3.   A colony of hamster embryo cells transformed by human adenovirus type 12. The transformed cells are much more darkly stained with the Giemsa stain than are the surrounding normal cells, and the transformed cells have formed a dense pile. (Magnification about 75×.) (Courtesy of Dr. B. Casto.)

of cells by many of the human and simian adenoviruses (Freeman *et al.*, 1967b; Kusano and Yamane, 1967a, 1967b; McAllister and Mac-Pherson, 1968; Rafajko, 1967; Riggs and Lennette, 1967; Strohl *et al.*, 1967; Rapoza *et al.*, 1967; Casto, 1968a; Reed, 1967; Altstein *et al.*, 1967b).

Adenoviruses previously thought to be nononcogenic or weakly oncogenic (Freeman *et al.*, 1967a, 1967c) can cause transformation in tissue culture. Casto (1968a) and MacAllister and MacPherson (1968) have shown that the ratio of focus-forming units to plaque-forming units is about $1:2 \times 10^6$ for human adenovirus type 12 and about $1:2 \times 10^5$ for a monkey adenovirus, SA7. On this basis, SA7 is about 10 times as oncogenic as human adenovirus type 12.

Transformed cells differ from normal cells in several ways. The most easily visible change is one of morphology: The transformed cells appear as dense colonies in a field of normal cells (Fig. 18-3). The transformed cells take on a random arrangement; cells transformed by polyoma virus and by SV40 tend to grow in a random crisscross, three-dimensional array with considerable piling up. In contrast, the spindle-shaped normal cells grow in orderly, parallel bundles in a two-dimensional array, with no piling. Normal cells in tissue culture are contact inhibited and neither cross over one another nor continue to divide after the available space is filled. The rate of division of the transformed cell is higher than that of the normal cell; more distinctive, however, is the fact that the transformed cell acquires the ability to grow indefinitely—it becomes "immortal," instead of having a limited number of possible divisions like the normal cell. A final difference between normal cells and those transformed by the adenoviruses (Fig. 18-4) is the difference, already mentioned, in the reaction to the concentration of calcium in the medium. Cells transformed by SV40 or by polyoma virus do not change in their sensitivity to calcium ion concentration.

Although many changes occur when a cell is transformed by one of these viruses, is the cell actually malignant? Is a cell transformed in tissue culture comparable to one that arises in a tumor in an animal? The evidence pertinent to these points seems to indicate that a cell undergoes the same changes whether it is transformed in tissue culture or in an animal. For instance, cells transformed in tissue culture form tumors when injected into animals. Conversely, cells derived from tumors and grown in tissue cultures seem to be identical to cells derived from normal tissues and transformed in culture. Further evidence on these points will be presented in a later section.

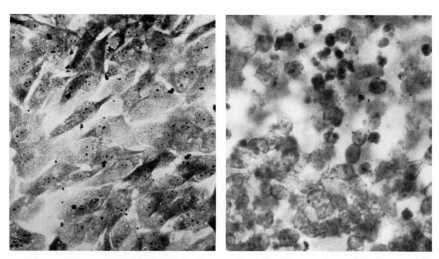

Figure 18-4.   Normal hamster embryo cells and cells transformed by human adenovirus type 12. The normal cells on the left, in an orderly single layer on the surface of the culture vessel, show a fairly regular size of the nucleus and fairly even staining. The transformed cells on the right were difficult to photograph because of the many layers. The nuclei are quite variable in size and the cytoplasm is scant. (Magnification about 200×.) (Courtesy of Dr. B. Casto.)

MECHANISM OF TRANSFORMATION BY
DNA-CONTAINING VIRUSES

As indicated in the preceding chapter, there is little solid evidence to support an analogy between transformation by the RNA-containing viruses and lysogeny in bacteria. It is also worthwhile to compare transformation by the DNA-containing viruses to lysogeny to determine the extent to which the lysogeny model may aid in understanding malignant transformation. Emphasis will be on viruses of the polyoma-papilloma group and the adenovirus group.

Several aspects of lysogeny are pertinent in a discussion of polyoma, SV40, and adenoviral oncogenesis. For a complete analogy with lysogeny, there should be (1) integration of the viral genome in the cell's genome so that the viral genome disappears as such; (2) a repressor substance; (3) at least partial expression of the viral genome; (4) ways of inducing the viral genome to detach from the cell's genome and begin independent replication; and (5) transduction of cellular genetic material by virions produced following induction.

The superficial resemblance between viral oncogenesis and lysogeny has been noted many times. It became a more important possibility when hamster cells transformed to malignancy in culture were shown not to release detectable virus; sensitive methods were used to detect even trace amounts of virus. Thus, it was thought possible that the viral genome was integrated during transformation and did not ordinarily detach.

An alternate possibility was that the virus transformed cells by indirect means. In some cells in a culture, for instance, the virus could induce the production of an extracellular substance that acts on neighboring cells, causing them to become malignant. The malignant cells would not contain the viral genome and of course would not be able to give rise to infective virus. This became a highly unlikely possibility when it was shown for polyoma virus, and later for adenoviruses, that the number of transformed foci is directly dependent on the number of virions placed in contact with the cells. In addition to forming the basis for a quantitative assay of transforming particles, this finding indicates that the virus is directly responsible for transformation and that a single virion is sufficient to transform a single cell. In addition, it has been shown that it is the viral DNA, not viral protein, that causes the transformation (Crawford et al., 1964).

Nevertheless, as already discussed, the efficiency of transformation is quite low. The low efficiency could arise several ways. The virus population could, for instance, consist of more than one genetic type of virus, so that some virions could induce transformation and some could not. Studies using plaque-purified virus indicate that this possibility is unlikely.

Another possibility is that some unlikely event must occur for transformation to result from the virus-cell interaction. For instance, there might be a "race" between synthesis of viral progeny DNA strands and synthesis of repressor, such as in reduction of temperate phages to the lysogenic state; because of the low efficiency of transformation, it would have to be further postulated that synthesis of viral progeny usually "wins" the "race." Against such a possibility is the fact that adenoviruses transform hamster cells with low efficiency, but most human and simian adenoviruses do not undergo a lytic interaction with hamster cells. But simply because adenoviruses are defective for replication in hamster cells does not negate such a "race"; perhaps the "race" is between being integrated into the cell's genome or being degraded by cellular deoxyribonucleases.

Because transformation by polyoma virus seems to resemble lysogenization, Vogt and Dulbecco (1962) reasoned that perhaps the viral genome could be induced to function in transformed cells. They had already demonstrated (Dulbecco and Vogt, 1960) that most clones of polyoma-transformed hamster cells do not release infectious virus, and that those clones that do release virus are "carrier cultures." In a carrier culture, an equilibrium exists between the release of virus by productively infected cells and the production of new, susceptible cells by cell division. When single transformed cells are isolated carefully so that uninfected, susceptible cells are avoided, all clones are found not to release virus.

Attempts were undertaken to induce virus production in virus-free clones of transformed cells. Agents effective in inducing virus production by lysogenic cells were found not to be effective in inducing virus production in transformed cells. Vogt and Dulbecco checked carefully for release of infectious virus and for induction of antigen in the cells that would react with antibody prepared against virus antigen. No such reaction was detectable, indicating that the viral genome, if present in the transformed cell, did not cause synthesis of viral capsid antigen. Furthermore, infectious DNA could not be extracted from transformed cells, either before or after exposure to inducing agents. Because no evidence could be obtained for the presence of the viral genome, the DNA tumor viruses became known as the "hit-and-run" viruses.

The name did not last long because several lines of evidence soon showed beyond doubt that at least part of the viral genome is present in the transformed cells.

One of the first indications that the viral genome might be present in transformed cells came from Sabin's discovery that he could recover trace amounts of SV40 from hamster cells transformed by that virus (Sabin, 1963; Sabin and Koch, 1963). Even with great care to be certain that he had avoided establishing a carrier culture and that he had not merely carried along virus with the cells, Sabin could still detect small amounts of virus. He therefore concluded that each transformed cell contained a complete SV40 genome.

Furthermore, SV40-induced tumor cells yield large amounts of virus if they are allowed to grow in mixed cultures with cells such as African green monkey kidney cells, in which the virus can replicate (Gerber, 1963, 1964). When inactivated Sendai virus is added to the cultures, it causes the monkey kidney and hamster tumor cells to fuse, mixing the cellular contents; and the virus is more easily produced (Gerber, 1966; Watkins and Dulbecco, 1967; Koprowski *et al.*, 1967). The mechanism by which the SV40 is induced to replicate is unknown, but it may be similar to zygotic induction of lysogenic cells. If this is the mechanism, it implies that a repressor substance might be synthesized by the viral genome, as in lysogenic cells. Such a repressor has not, as yet, been demonstrated.

Cells that can be induced to synthesize virus are said to be virogenic (the term lysogeny is reserved for bacteria). Although most cells transformed by SV40 are virogenic, some clones grown from single transformed cells are not virogenic. The most reasonable explanation is that virogenic clones contain the entire viral genome and that nonvirogenic clones may contain only a portion of the viral genome (Black, 1966a; Dubbs *et al.*, 1967).

Whether cells transformed by adenoviruses are virogenic is not yet clear. Kusano and Yamane (1967a), Larson *et al.* (1966), and Landau *et al.* (1966) have been unable to induce adenovirus production in transformed or tumor cells. But Marti *et al.* (1968) did recover adenovirus type 12 from tumor cells; the cells, however, were taken from tumors soon after induction, and the virus may have been residual from the original inoculum. Smith and Melnick (1964) examined by electron microscopy tumor cells induced by adenovirus type 12 and were able to find a few virus-like particles that resembled adenoviruses. These particles were misshapen, "ghostlike," and seemed to contain no DNA. They may have been synthesized by the cell, indicating continued presence of the viral genome; or they may have been left over from the original inoculum.

Further evidence for the presence of the viral genome came from the discovery that polyoma virus and SV40 induce a specific new transplantation antigen in the transformed cell (Sjögren *et al.*, 1961; Sjögren, 1964a, 1964b, 1964c, 1964d; Habel, 1961, 1962a, 1962b; Klein and Klein, 1962; Koch and Sabin, 1963; Habel and Eddy, 1963). Animals can be protected against tumor formation by immunization with antigen (Fig. 18-5), and animals injected with either virus will reject tumor cells induced by that virus but not the other. Transplantation antigens also occur in adenovirus-transformed cells (Black *et al.*, 1967; Sjögren *et al.*, 1967). The mechanism of the rejection will be dis-

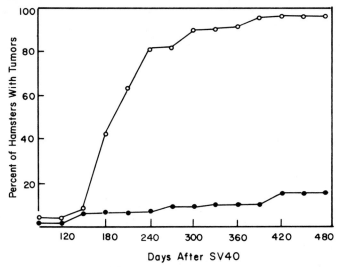

Figure 18-5. Protection of hamsters against formation of tumors by SV40. Hamsters were injected with SV40 within a few days of birth. When the animals were 34 days old, they were injected with an antigen consisting of SV40 tumor cells that had been irradiated with x-rays to prevent them from dividing. The upper curve (open circles) shows the cumulative percentage of tumors that developed in the control animals that had been inoculated with SV40 but received no antigen. The lower curve (filled circles) shows a similar plot for animals that received the antigen. This group clearly was protected against tumor formation. (Redrawn from Hilleman, 1966.)

cussed further in a later section, but it is mentioned now to demonstrate the presence of the viral genome.

The transplantation antigen is a surface antigen of the cell (Tevethia *et al.*, 1965; Malmgren *et al.*, 1968; Tevethia and Rapp, 1965). It might correspond to the mucopolysaccharide studied by Defendi and Gasic (1963). Although the transplantation antigen is specific for the inducing virus, it has not been demonstrated whether the transplantation antigen is coded by the viral or cellular genome. If it is coded by the viral genome, then the phenomenon resembles antigenic conversion of bacterial cells by temperate phages.

Another new antigen, called the tumor or T antigen, is induced by polyoma virus, SV40, and the oncogenic adenoviruses. This antigen, which is also specific for the inducing virus, is detected by the complement-fixation reaction or by fluorescent-labeled antibody. The latter method and ferritin-tagged antibody have localized this antigen to the nucleus (Kalnins *et al.*, 1967).

Although they are virus specific, the new antigens could be cellular: The viral genome could derepress a cellular gene that synthesizes the new antigen (Bendich, 1967). It seems more likely, however, that the antigen is coded by the virus. It is difficult to see how each virus would derepress a specific, but different, cell gene, rather than

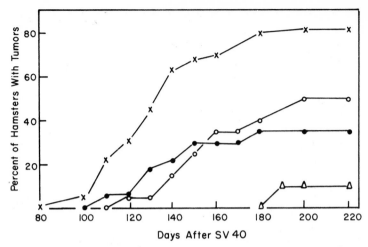

Figure 18-6. Protection of hamsters by various antigens against formation of tumors by SV40. The experimental design used here differed from that described in Figure 18-5 in that the cells used for antigen were not transformed cells but were productively infected with SV40 in the presence of inhibitors of DNA synthesis. The upper curve (crosses) shows the cumulative percentage of development of tumors in unprotected control hamsters. The middle two curves show tumor development in animals given antigen from 24 hour infected cells (open circles) and antigen from 24 hour infected cells in which DNA synthesis was blocked by FUdR. The lowest curve (triangles) shows tumor formation in animals receiving antigen from 24 hour infected cells treated with cytosine arabinoside to block DNA synthesis. The protection in the last group is like that in animals receiving antigen from transformed cells, as in Figure 18-5. (Redrawn from Defendi, 1967.)

all acting on the same cellular gene. In the latter case, the new antigen would not be viral specific, even though induced by the virus.

Yet, as shown by various serologic tests, the new antigens are not part of the virion. In cells being transformed, infected, or abortively infected, the antigens occur soon after exposure to virus (Hayashi and Russell, 1968). It is therefore thought that they may be "early" enzymes coded by the viral genome. Further evidence for this comes from the finding that inhibitors of DNA synthesis prevent a cell from synthesizing viral capsid antigen, a "late" function, but the T antigen is synthesized (Rapp *et al.*, 1965a, 1965b), as is the transplantation antigen (Fig. 18-6) (Defendi, 1967). The T antigen is thought to be one of the enzymes or other proteins synthesized under the direction of the viral genome. Which enzyme or other viral-induced protein it might be is unknown, but the possibility that it is thymidine kinase or several other known enzymes has been ruled out (Kit *et al.*, 1967b).

If the new antigens are actually coded by the viral genome, all or part of the viral genome must be present in the tumor cells. More direct evidence for this conclusion will be presented in a later section.

Whether either the T antigen or the transplantation antigen plays any part in malignant transformation is unknown. The transplantation antigen might be important, because it occurs at the cell's surface and could account for the changed response of the cell to contact with other cells. Polyoma strains of differing oncogenicity, however, do not seem to differ in their ability to induce transplantation antigen (Friedman and Rabson, 1964). Conversely, polyoma tumor cell lines that differed in their transplant antigen content did not differ in their ability to form tumors (Hare, 1964; Hare and Godal, 1965; Hare, 1967). A similar situation may exist for SV40 (Black and Rowe, 1965). Purification and characterization of the antigens may lead to some understanding of their possible role in oncogenesis (Hollinshead et al., 1967, 1968; Gilead and Ginsberg, 1968a, 1968b; Hakomori and Murakami, 1968).

Other indirect evidence also indicates the presence of the viral genome in the transformed cells. Different adenoviruses, for instance, give rise to tumors that differ in their morphology (Strohl et al., 1967; Berman, 1967; Hull, 1965). Some tumors induced by adenovirus-SV40 hybrids morphologically resemble tumors induced by SV40; others resemble tumors induced by adenovirus (Igel and Black, 1967; Schell et al., 1966). Cells transformed by SV40 continue to synthesize a high level of thymidine kinase; the enzyme synthesized serologically is like the enzyme synthesized during a lytic infective cycle with SV40 (see Chapter 9) and unlike the enzyme normally present in an uninfected cell (Carp, 1967).

There have also been many attempts to obtain more direct evidence for the presence of part or all of the viral genome in the transformed cells. Axelrod et al. (1964) attempted to demonstrate the viral genome by hybridizing DNA from purified polyoma virus with DNA from transformed cells. The results are difficult to interpret because the virions contained some cellular DNA. A similar type of study with SV40-transformed hamster cells (Reich et al., 1966b) is subject to the same objection. Extensive purification to remove all cellular DNA from the polyoma DNA preparation eliminated the ability of viral DNA to hybridize with cellular DNA (Winocour, 1967). Winocour (1965) also looked for the viral genome by hybridization experiments, but he used synthetic labeled RNA made from a polyoma viral DNA template to hybridize with DNA extracted from cells. He was unable to detect any hybridization, but perhaps the sensitivity of his experiments was not high enough.

Firm evidence for the presence of the polyoma and SV40 genomes in transformed cells was obtained by Benjamin (1966) from hybridization experiments. He extracted isotopically labeled RNA from transformed cells and tested its ability to hybridize with viral DNA that had been denatured and firmly attached to cellulose filters. Some of his results are shown in Table 18-1. A small amount of RNA binds to the filters regardless of which DNA is on the filter, and even

TABLE 18-1. TESTS FOR VIRUS-SPECIFIC RNA IN NORMAL AND TRANSFORMED CELLS*

| CELL (FOR RNA) | VIRUS (FOR DNA) | RELATIVE AMOUNT OF RNA BOUND TO FILTERS | | PERCENTAGE INCREASE DUE TO DNA |
		With DNA	Without DNA	
3T3 cell line (untransformed)	Polyoma	2.8	4.0	−30
	SV40	5.1	3.7	+38
Polyoma-transformed 3T3	Polyoma	6.8	1.1	+568
	SV40	1.5	1.4	+7
SV40-transformed 3T3	Polyoma	0.9	1.4	−36
	SV40	5.2	1.2	+333
SV40, polyoma doubly transformed 3T3	Polyoma	19.2	2.1	+813
	SV40	9.2	2.8	+221

*Modified from Benjamin, 1966.

when no DNA is on the filter. Binding data obtained by using labeled RNA from cells transformed by polyoma virus or SV40, or extracted from a line of cells successively transformed by both viruses (Todaro *et al.*, 1965) clearly show that viral genetic material must be present in the transformed cells. (Results were described in Chapter 9, Figure 9-9, showing that viral-specific RNA was detectable by hybridization experiments in cells undergoing a productive infection.)

Similar experiments were performed by Fujinaga and Green (1966, 1967a, 1967b) with RNA extracted from adenovirus-induced hamster tumors. The tumor cells contained no detectable virus but did contain viral-specific RNA. The RNA in the case of adenovirus transformation was shown to be messenger, because it was extracted from polysomes of infected cells.

However, these experiments leave an important question unanswered: Is all of the viral genetic material present? With SV40, all the viral genome must be present since virus production occurs spontaneously; although the rate is ordinarily low, it can be increased by cell fusion. Probably only part of the SV40 genome functions in the transformed cell. Presumably, if the entire genome were functioning, the virus would replicate and form mature virions. Polyoma virus and the adenoviruses have not been induced to begin replication, possibly because not all the viral genome is present.

Evidence has accumulated that less of the viral genome is required for transformation or for induction of early antigens than for viral replication. (Polyoma virus—Benjamin, 1965; Basilico and DiMayorca, 1965; Latarjet *et al.*, 1967. SV40—Altstein *et al.*, 1966, 1967a, 1967c; Defendi and Jensen, 1967; Defendi *et al.*, 1967. Adenovirus—Gilead and Ginsberg, 1966; Inoue and Nishibe, 1967; Casto, 1968b.) These experiments (Fig. 18-7) are based on a comparison of the irradiation target size for plaque formation and that for transformation; the target for transformation is smaller than the target for plaque formation. Presumably the viral genome must be functional in its entirety to undergo the lytic interaction that results in plaque formation, but only a portion of it is necessary for it to induce transformation. Comparison of inactivation rates indicates that the ratio of target sizes for the two functions is about two to one.

The fact that roughly one-half the viral genome is all that is required to induce transformation suggests that transformation results from either the "early" or the "late" function genes (Benjamin, 1967). It would seem that the "early" genes are involved, since transformed cells usually contain both the T antigen and transplantation antigen, and both of these are "early" functions (Defendi, 1967; Rapp *et al.*, 1965a, 1965b).

Experiments with SV40, polyoma, and SV40-adenovirus hybrid to measure the relative target sizes for plaque formation and for ability to

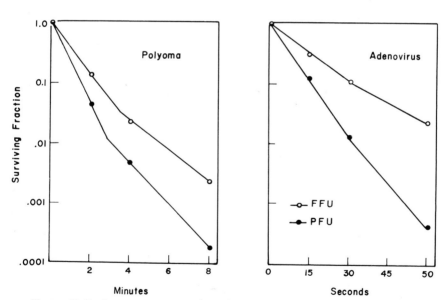

Figure 18-7. Inactivation rates of two functions of polyoma virus and adenovirus (the simian adenovirus, SA7). In each case a preparation of virus was exposed to ultraviolet irradiation and samples were taken at the indicated intervals. Each sample was assayed for residual plaque-forming ability (PFU) and for residual transformed focus-forming ability (FFU). The ability of the viruses to form plaques is more easily inactivated than their ability to cause malignant transformation. (Polyoma virus: Redrawn from Benjamin, 1965. Adenovirus: Redrawn from Casto, 1968b.)

induce tumors in hamsters led to a different result. It was found that partial inactivation of the virus by irradiation enhanced its ability to induce tumors (Defendi and Jensen, 1967; Defendi *et al.*, 1967). Further experiments (Jensen and Defendi, 1968) revealed that not all colonies of cells transformed by irradiated virus produce T antigen. The ability of irradiation to enhance tumor production in animals is probably due to inactivation of the gene (or genes) responsible for the transplantation antigen so that the tumor cells are not rejected. The new antigens are therefore probably not primarily the cause of the transformation.

These findings offer a clue to a possible reason for the low efficiency of transformation. Defective virions can be detected in preparations of adenovirus (Butel *et al.*, 1966a) and of SV40 (Altstein *et al.*, 1967b; Sauer *et al.*, 1967; Yoshiike, 1968; Uchida *et al.*, 1968). These are not defective mutants but seem to be particles that are assembled without a complete complement of functional DNA. They are detectable by their ability to induce antigen formation in appropriate cells, but without causing the cell to produce new virions. Therefore they contain "early" genes, and they may be the virions that induce transformation. It is possible, of course, that SV40 transformation usually occurs by complete particles and that the "late" functions are merely repressed; the rare nonvirogenic clones could arise from transformation by incomplete virions.

Nevertheless, continued expression of at least some viral genes may be necessary to maintain the malignant state. Apparent "revertant" cells have been isolated from populations of polyoma-transformed hamster cells. The "revertants" have a phenotypically normal structure, but it has not been demonstrated whether they still retain the viral genome. Because chromosome loss accompanies reversion, it was tentatively assumed that the viral genome, possibly associated with the chromosome, was also lost (Marin and Littlefield, 1968). But Fried (1965b) found that a temperature-sensitive mutant of polyoma virus produced transformation when the cells were placed at the permissive temperature immediately after adding virus, but not when they were placed at the nonpermissive temperature. Once established, however, the transformed state was maintained at the nonpermissive temperature. This experiment is difficult to interpret, since it is not known which of the genes contained the mutation. One gene, perhaps the one that is mutated, may be important in the early stages; whereas another gene, not mutated in the virus used in these experiments, may be necessary for maintaining transformation.

If there is any validity in the lysogeny analogy, it could be predicted that the viral DNA becomes integrated into the cellular DNA. There is no reason to believe that Campbell's model would apply to transformation (Campbell, 1962); but if it does, it would predict that the viral DNA would circularize before integrating. It has already been mentioned (see Chapter 9) that in the infectious state the DNA of the viruses of the polyoma-papilloma group are normally circular. Dulbecco (1963b) suggested that the circularity might be relevant to integration, and Crawford *et al.* (1964) demonstrated that either the intact, supercoiled rings or the "nicked," open circles of polyoma DNA could produce plaques or transformed foci. The DNA of the adenoviruses, however, is not circular; and terminal redundancy cannot be demonstrated. Thus, it would seem difficult or impossible for adenoviral DNA to circularize.

According to Campbell's model, integration of temperate phage DNA into the host-cell genome occurs by mutual recombination. No evidence for such an event has been found with either the polyoma-papilloma viruses or with oncogenic adenoviruses. However, polyoma virus, SV40, and adenoviruses induce cellular DNA synthesis (see Chapter 9) after infection. This might represent a process that is analogous in some respects.

Transformation seems to be a two-stage process; if cells undergo the first stage only, they appear to be transformed, but revert to normal. Transformed properties persist only if the cells enter the second stage. This could be analogous to abortive lysogenization. In the first stage, the viral genome, although not integrated, could be expressing its genetic information for the transformation properties. Because it is not integrated, it perhaps would not replicate and would be diluted out by cell division. The integrated genome could also express the information for transformation, and it perhaps could be replicated. The fact that abortive transformation occurs in a high proportion of cells, and permanent transformation occurs in only a low proportion of cells, is consistent with this interpretation (Stoker, 1968). It is necessary for the cells to divide for SV40 (Todaro and Green, 1966) or for adenoviruses (Casto, 1968a) to cause transformation. Perhaps the division is necessary for integration. Much more experimental evidence will have to be obtained, however, to establish this point.

It has been shown that a region of homology (the b_2 region) exists between the cellular and λ viral attachment sites. Initial reports (Axelrod *et al.*, 1964; Reich *et al.*, 1966b) described homology between SV40 and polyoma viral DNA and DNA extracted from normal cells. This homology has been shown to be due to incorporation of some cellular DNA into the virion (Winocour *et al.*, 1965; Kaye and Winocour, 1967; Michel *et al.*, 1967; Winocour, 1967). Whether this phenomenon is analogous to specialized or generalized transduction is unknown, but no homology between viral DNA and host-cell DNA has been convincingly demonstrated.

Association of labeled adenoviral DNA with chromosomes

(Nichols *et al.*, 1968; zur Hausen, 1968) is suggestive but not conclusive evidence for integration.

Better evidence for integration, although still indirect and inconclusive, comes from studies of interferon sensitivity of 3T3 mouse cells to transformation by SV40 (Oxman and Black, 1966; Oxman *et al.*, 1967). The virus does not replicate in these cells. However, when the cells are infected at a high multiplicity, nearly all synthesize the intranuclear T antigen, and up to 50 per cent become transformed.

Transformation, being sensitive to interferon (Todaro and Baron, 1965; Todaro and Green, 1967), must require the translation of viral-specific proteins. At least one of these proteins seems to be the T antigen, because Oxman and Black (1966) found that pretreatment of the cells with interferon stops the production of T antigen at about the same rate as it stops transformation. The sensitivity to interferon is lost after about 4 hours. It seems, therefore, that some early function of the viral genome is necessary for transformation.

When the T antigen and its sensitivity to interferon were studied for longer periods, two kinds of effects were found. In nontransformed infected cells, the sensitivity of the T antigen to interferon persisted; however, the capacity to synthesize the T antigen was lost as the cells divided, apparently because the SV40 genome was not replicating and was "diluted out" by the cell division. But the ability to synthesize T antigen was perpetuated to daughter cells in the transformed cells without loss by dilution. In these cells, the synthesis of T antigen was insensitive to interferon. These results were interpreted to mean that the viral genome is integrated into the cell's genome during transformation; and, as a result, the sensitivity to interferon inhibition is lost.

Perhaps a next step in unraveling the processes leading to transformation will involve genetic analysis. Ample evidence is available to support the working hypothesis that the malignant change brought about by viruses involves function of one or more viral genes. Whether this occurs by direct expression of viral genes or by indirect effect of viral function in control of cellular genetic expression is unknown. Isolation and study of mutants that differ in their oncogenic capacity may well prove useful. Such studies have begun in several laboratories. For instance, Takemoto *et al.* (1966) and Koch and Eggers (1967) are working on SV40 mutants with varying oncogenicity.

TUMOR INDUCTION IN ANIMALS

The mechanism by which a virus causes malignant change in tissue culture is unknown. The evidence strongly suggests that the changed characteristics of the cell are due to expression of viral genes, perhaps only the "early" genes. The changed characteristics concern the cell's relationship to its neighbors. No longer contact inhibited, the cells freely migrate over one another. They also acquire a capacity for division that is not limited to the available space. Moreover, they produce at least two new antigens, apparently directed to do so by the viral genome.

It seems likely that similar changes occur in animals injected with these viruses (see Fig. 18-1). A virion enters a cell and causes the cell to become transformed. In an adult animal, one that is immunologically competent, the transplantation antigen that develops on the cell is recognized as "foreign" and the transformed cell is rejected before it has a chance to grow into a tumor. That animal is then immune to challenge with even a large number of tumor cells if they contain the same transplantation antigen.

However, if the virus is injected into an immunologically incompetent animal, such as a newborn, the transplantation antigen is not recognized as "foreign"; the tumor cell is not rejected, and it can continue to grow into a tumor. Because its movement is not inhibited by contact with other cells, it tends to invade adjacent tissues. It may migrate through blood vessel walls, and it can be carried by the blood to distant sites where it grows into a metastasis.

This explains why it is necessary to inject virus into newborn hamsters to obtain tumors (Law and Ting, 1965). Injection of animals of increasing age results in a lowered incidence of tumor formation; and in adult animals it is very difficult to induce tumors, even with large amounts of virus (Allison et al., 1967b; Yabe et al., 1962).

Suppressing an animal's immune rejection mechanism, such as by removing the thymus at an early age, makes the animal more susceptible to the formation of tumors. Because it is thus made immunologically incompetent, a thymectomized animal loses its age resistance to tumor formation (Allison et al., 1967a; Kirschstein et al., 1964; Malmgren et al., 1964; Miller et al., 1964).

VIRUSES AND HUMAN CANCER

As we have seen in this chapter, the tumor cell does not necessarily contain detectable infectious virus particles. Once transformed, the cell may contain only a part of the viral genome. This property may explain why it has been so difficult to isolate viruses from human cancers. Another possibility, of course, is that human cancers may not be virus induced. Viruses isolated from human tumors, such as adenovirus type I (McAllister et al., 1964a) may be only "passenger" viruses. However, with the large number of cancers of lower animals that are known to be viral induced, and with the belief that uniformity exists among organisms, it would be surprising if at least some human tumors were not viral induced.

Tumorigenesis by the DNA-containing viruses has some superficial resemblances to lysogenization, but more concrete evidence is required for the analogy to stand. As with lysogeny, however, transformation could be an adaptive mechanism for dealing with certain viral infections. In undergoing transformation, a cell removes virus from the organism, eliminating its infective potential by incorporating the viral genome into the cell's genome, and subsequent immunological rejection of the transformed cell completes the process.

But once the viral genome is integrated or otherwise incorporated into the transformed cell, is it still a virus? A similar question arises with the prophage, but at least the prophage is able to detach and undergo subsequent virulent infection. Just what is a virus?

Further Reading

Black, P. H.: Recent Advances in the Study of Oncogenic Viruses. New England Journal of Medicine, 275:377-383, 1966.

Dulbecco, R.: Transformation of Cells in Vitro by DNA-Containing Viruses. Journal of the American Medical Association, 190:721-726, 1964.

Dulbecco, R.: The Induction of Cancer by Viruses. Scientific American, 216(April):28-37, 1967.

Habel, K.: Virus Tumor Antigens; Specific Fingerprints? Cancer Research, 26:2018-2024, 1966.

Luria, S. E.: Viruses, Cancer Cells, and the Genetic Concept of Virus Infection. Cancer Research, 20:677-688, 1960.

19

WHAT IS A VIRUS?

In Chapter 1 the question, What are viruses? was asked but was not satisfactorily answered. Many properties of viruses have been discussed in the intervening chapters. Now, in this concluding chapter, it seems appropriate to reconsider the question in the light of the information that has been presented about viruses. In doing so, it will be useful first to discuss some organisms that once were called viruses but now are known not to be.

THE "NO-LONGER VIRUSES"

The pleuropneumonia-like organisms or mycoplasma clearly are not viruses but are bacteria. They are small cells (Morowitz and Tourtellotte, 1962) that can grow by binary fission (Fig. 19-1) extracellularly on appropriate media. Therefore, they contain all the requisite enzymatic machinery for utilizing the nutrients in the media.

At one time some of the mycoplasmata were considered to be viruses. Their true nature quickly became apparent, but they temporarily received the virus label because they are small enough to pass through filters that retain bacteria. Although they can be grown on specialized media, the fact that many are found to grow much more readily in tissue cultures may indicate that present media are deficient. Some investigators, however, believe that some mycoplasmata or related organisms may have such strict growth needs that they grow only in or on living cells. The facts that mycoplasmata are small enough to be filterable and have strict cultural requirements are not sufficient reasons to call them viruses.

The rickettsiae are also quite clearly cells. Most have a coccoid or

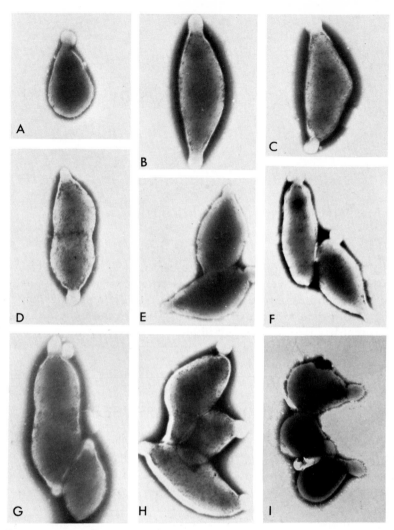

Figure 19-1. Cells of *Mycoplasma gallisepticum* showing binary fission. The cells were grown directly on the electron microscope grids; at various times, the cells were fixed with glutaraldehyde and were negatively stained. *A*, At zero time: a single teardrop-shaped cell having one bleb. At 30 minutes (*B*) and 60 minutes (*C*): cells having two blebs. *D*, At 90 minutes, a constriction has begun midway between the blebs. At 120 minutes (*E*) and 150 minutes (*F*): two-cell microcolonies. *G*, At 180 minutes, one cell of the two-cell microcolony has begun to form a constriction midway between the two blebs. At 210 minutes (*H*) and 240 minutes (*I*): three-cell microcolonies. Although some mycoplasmata clearly undergo binary fission, others may also replicate by other methods, such as by a kind of budding process. (Magnification ×36,400.) (Morowitz and Maniloff, 1966. By permission of the authors and the editors of the Journal of Bacteriology.)

bacillary form, are 0.3 to 0.5 μ long and 0.3 μ wide, and are obligate intracellular parasites. They are barely visible by light microscopy, and they are at the borderline of filterability by bacteriologic filters.

The rickettsiae apparently have not developed any specialized properties that enhance their ability to grow intracellularly, but they seem to have lost many enzyme systems necessary for independent existence and therefore require the kind of rich medium that can be supplied only by a cell. Yet, in the cell they retain their identity as discrete organisms with a limiting membrane. When they grow to a certain size, they divide by binary fission; and, when the organisms in a host cell increase to the point that the nutrients are used faster than the cell can make more, the host cell dies. Consequently, the rickett-siae are best considered as highly specialized bacteria with fastidious requirements for growth.

Another group of agents, however, cannot so easily be disqualified as viruses. These are the agents of the psittacosis group. For an extended period they were generally accepted as viruses, because their properties have many features in common with the properties of viruses. Many virologists still consider them to be viruses.

Nevertheless, because these agents have many properties that are so completely different from those of any of the known viruses, it now seems proper to classify them as bacteria. They are highly specialized in many respects, perhaps; but nevertheless, they are bacteria. S. S. Cohen (1963) aptly called this group of agents the "no-longer viruses."

The psittacosis group, or chlamydiae, includes the psittacosis agent itself, the type species, which commonly infects parrots (Latin: *psittacus*), as well as other birds. Other agents in the group are listed in Table 19-1. The various members of the group resemble each other morphologically and have similar growth cycles and common group antigens. They are distinguished from one another by biological

TABLE 19-1. IMPORTANT MEMBERS OF THE PSITTACOSIS GROUP OF MICROORGANISMS*

Human Agents	
Lymphogranuloma venereum	Inclusion conjunctivitis
Trachoma	Pneumonitis

Other Mammalian Agents	
Meningopneumonitis	Bovine enteritis
Mouse pneumonitis	Bovine encephalitis
Feline pneumonitis	Enzootic abortion of ewes
Sheep pneumonitis	

Avian Agents	
Psittacosis	Ornithosis

*After Moulder, 1964.

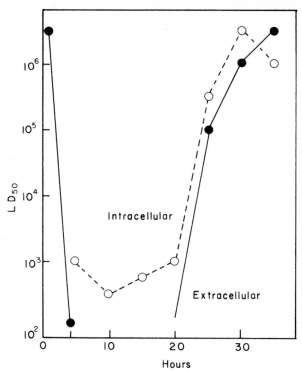

Figure 19-2. Growth curve of feline pneumonitis agent in the chorioallantoic ectoderm of the chick embryo. The agent ($10^{6.5}$ LD$_{50}$) was inoculated onto the chorioallantoic membrane of 9 day old chick embryos. Samples taken at the indicated times were assayed in the yolk sac of other embryos for the content of infective agent, expressed in units of LD$_{50}$. (Redrawn from Moulder, 1964.)

characteristics: the hosts in which they grow, the nature of the disease they produce, and the presence of certain type-specific antigens.

Moulder (1964, 1966) has described the properties of the chlamydiae. All, like viruses, are obligate intracellular parasites and are filterable; their size, 200 to 300 mμ in diameter, is more variable than that of viruses. It will be recalled that this is only slightly larger than the poxviruses and the T phages.

The chlamydiae undergo a growth cycle (Fig. 19-2) similar in some respects to that of the viruses. After the agent is inoculated onto the chorioallantoic membrane of embryonated chicken eggs, the titer of agent in the extracellular fluid decreases, indicating that the agent has either become intracellular or lost its infectivity. However, the decrease is not accompanied by an equal increase in intracellular agent, indicating that the agent has undergone some kind of change.

The change that viruses undergo when they become intracellular results from the dissociation of capsid and nucleic acid—a loss of identity of the virus as such. But the chlamydiae undergo a different kind of change. The extracellular particle is relatively small and has a dense central body. During the first 5 hours or so after entry into a cell, the small particle becomes larger and the central body becomes unapparent.

Thus, the small particle changes to the large form. In so doing, it loses its ability to infect other cells when artificially released; and, in addition, it becomes sensitive to freezing. The large particle is the form for replication, and it replicates by successive binary fissions (Higashi, 1965; Anderson *et al.*, 1965) (Fig. 19-3). About 20 hours after infection, after many of the large particles have accumulated, some of the progeny large particles change into small particles. These are the extracellular form, able to withstand freezing and to infect other cells.

The replicative cycle of the chlamydiae therefore has some of the rudiments of the viral replicative cycle, with a suggestion of an eclipse phase. It also resembles bacterial cycles that include sporulation. Furthermore, replication of the meningopneumonitis agent inhibits cellular nucleic acid syntheses (Schechter *et al.*, 1964). But the change

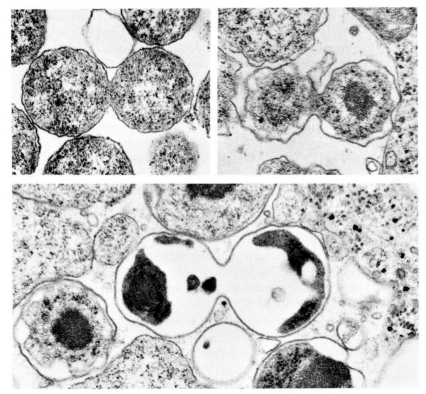

Figure 19-3. Dumbbell-shaped bodies of ornithosis agent in electron micrographs of thinly sectioned infected cells. The shape of the organisms suggests that they are undergoing division by binary fission. The organism in the bottom picture seems more "mature" than the other organisms. (Magnification ×45,000.) (Anderson *et al.*, 1965. By permission of the authors and the editors of the Journal of Bacteriology.)

TABLE 19-2. PHOSPHORUS CONTENTS OF FRACTIONS OF LARGE AND SMALL PARTICLES OF MENINGOPNEUMONITIS AGENT[°]

	PER CENT OF TOTAL PHOSPHORUS	
FRACTION	LARGE PARTICLE	SMALL PARTICLE
Acid-soluble	10.8	7.2
Lipid	34.9	31.5
RNA	31.3	27.4
DNA	22.5	26.6
Residue	2.7	4.1

[°]From Moulder, 1964.

from the small particle to the noninfectious, large particle of the chlamydiae is hardly comparable to the drastic change that occurs to a virion when its nucleic acid separates from its protein capsid and actually becomes part of the cell during eclipse.

The composition of the agent particles is quite unlike that found in viruses. All known viruses have either RNA or DNA as the nucleic acid, and probably only a single molecule of that nucleic acid. When purified preparations of the large particles and small particles of meningopneumonitis agent were fractionated so that the amount of phosphorus could be determined (Table 19-2), the acid-soluble fraction was found to contain materials of small molecular weight. The agent particles were found to contain phospholipid in rather large amount. Of most significance, however, is the fact that both large and small particles were found to contain both kinds of nucleic acids—a finding that clearly sets the meningopneumonitis agent apart from any virus.

Furthermore, the RNA from trachoma agent has been fractionated by centrifuging through sucrose gradients (Tamura, 1967; Sarov and Becker, 1968). Not only are several RNA species present, but they correspond to ribosomal subunits and RNA. The implication is that the chlamydiae have the ability to synthesize proteins, rather than relying on the host cell's synthetic machinery. Ribosomes have been seen in electron micrographs of chlamydiae (Tamura *et al.*, 1967; Anderson *et al.*, 1965) (Fig. 19-4).

The chlamydiae can also carry out certain energy metabolic steps. For instance, they can convert glucose into carbon dioxide or pyruvate (Weiss *et al.*, 1964), even when the organisms have been purified so that no host cellular material is present (Ormsbee and Weiss, 1963). It will be recalled that no virus carries metabolic enzymes, but several carry other enzymes. These include sialidase (myxoviruses), nucleotide phosphohydrolase (vaccinia; see Munyon *et al.*, 1968), phage lysozyme, and adenosine triphosphatase; the last, found in the avian leukosis viruses and a few other enveloped viruses, is apparently carried only by chance, because of the fact that the cellular material that supplies the viral envelope contains the enzyme.

The last characteristic to be discussed here that helps distinguish the chlamydiae from viruses is that the former have a rudimentary cell wall that contains muramic acid (Perkins and Allison, 1963; Armstrong and Reed, 1964). No virus has either a cell wall or muramic acid, which is characteristically a constituent of bacterial cell walls. The cell wall surrounds both the large and the small particles and is probably complete during all stages of the growth cycle, both intracellular and extracellular.

Much more evidence, detailed by Moulder (1966), convincingly removes the chlamydiae from the realm of viruses. Since this book is

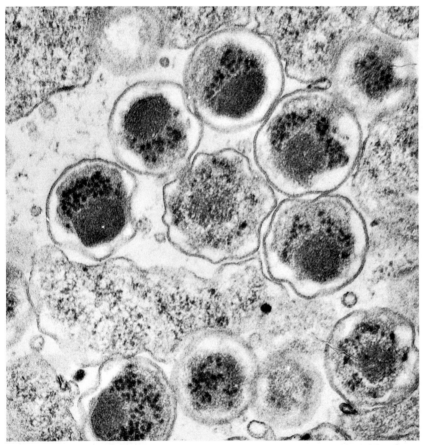

Figure 19-4. "Elementary bodies" of ornithosis agent in an electron micrograph of thinly sectioned infected cells. The organisms show a double-layered membrane surrounding a mass of dense, homogeneous material. Adjacent to the dense material are clusters of ribosomes that appear quite dense to the electron beam. (Magnification ×70,000.) (Anderson *et al.*, 1965. By permission of the authors and the editors of the Journal of Bacteriology.)

concerned with viruses, that evidence will not be discussed in greater detail here. The chlamydiae are clearly highly specialized and simplified bacteria.

Could chlamydiae represent an intermediate form? If viruses arose from cells, such as bacteria, by successive loss of enzyme systems with consequently increasing dependence on the metabolic machinery of the host cell, could viruses have evolved from the chlamydiae? It hardly seems likely, because the number of mutational events required to complete the transition seems very large. The chlamydiae have very little in common with any of the viruses. However, there is no other known organism that can qualify as the transitional form. Unfortunately, there is no fossil record to search for such forms that may have existed in former times.

THE "ALMOST VIRUSES"

The distinction between viruses and small bacteria is clear. What about agents that might be simpler than viruses? Are there any, and if so, can they be distinguished from viruses? Or, to word these questions differently, are there independent entities smaller than viruses that are able to reproduce?

One such entity is the group of materials, called bacteriocins, that are released by certain bacteria (Bradley and Dewar, 1966) and that kill other bacteria. Bacteriocins, reviewed by Bradley (1967), are of two basic types. One type is small, does not sediment easily in the ultracentrifuge, and has not been resolved by electron microscopy. The other type, which will be discussed briefly here, is much larger, is sedimentable, and by electron microscopy appears to consist of phage parts, usually the tail.

The bacteriocins attach to specific receptors on the cell walls of certain bacteria (Coetzee et al., 1968); they do so in a way that is completely analogous to the attachment of bacteriophages. One bacteriocin particle is sufficient to kill a bacterium. Cell death results from the bacteriocin-induced cessation of synthesis of RNA, DNA, and protein in the cell, but how this is caused is unknown.

Agents that induce lysogenic cells to produce temperate phage can also induce cells to lyse and release bacteriocins. It is not difficult, therefore, to draw a parallel with lysogeny. The bacterial cell that produces a bacteriocin could contain a defective prophage-like genome, in turn containing only the genetic information for synthesis of the tail parts of a phage. The tail parts are sufficient to cause death of other cells. The bacteriocins themselves are not infective — the ability of a bacterium to produce bacteriocins is passed from one generation to the next by division or from one cell to another by conjugation.

It seems likely, then, that bacteriocins are the product of a cell lysogenized by a defective prophage. Therefore, perhaps the bacteriocins should be considered defective viruses. Because they contain no nucleic acid, or at least not a complete genome, they are unable to infect another cell.

Another interesting agent is the potato spindle tuber virus. This virus also seems to be incomplete. Aqueous extracts of infected plant tissues yield an infectious agent that is relatively resistant to ribonuclease and that sediments through a sucrose gradient at approximately the same rate as double-stranded RNA (Diener and Raymer, 1967). Therefore, this virus seems to lack a normal protein coat. But when it is remembered that the protein coat of a virus serves only to protect the nucleic acid and aid in infection, it is easy to see how a virus could dispense with its capsid. This is especially true for a virus with double-stranded RNA, for this molecule is exceptionally resistant to ribonuclease.

Further precedent has been obtained in experiments in which viral nucleic acids, extracted by phenol, have been shown to be infective. Here again, the concept of a virus needs only slight modification to include infectious nucleic acids, both naturally occurring and experimentally produced.

But another group of agents presents more difficult problems of classification. One of these is associated with scrapie, a disease of sheep. The disease is transmitted by a filterable agent with an extremely long incubation period, as long as 1 to 3 years. Other diseases are clinically similar to scrapie, may also be transmitted by filterable agents, and have long incubation periods. These include Aleutian disease of mink and a human disease, kuru. Other diseases with some characteristics in common to these are amyotrophic lateral sclerosis, multiple sclerosis, subacute sclerosing leukoencephalitis, and others. This group of diseases, and the causative agents, were the subject of a symposium (Gajdusek et al., 1965).

Of these agents, the scrapie agent has been studied the most extensively, but information is still incomplete. This is not surprising when it is remembered that up to 3 years are required to obtain the result of an assay. Progress will be accelerated when a tissue culture assay becomes available. Some work has been done by injecting the sheep agent into mice; although this type of assay is much more rapid, it is not clear that the mouse agent is the same as the sheep agent.

Nevertheless, the mouse agent is small: Filtration experiments indicate that its size is 17 to 27 mμ (Gibbs et al., 1965). Although small, it could be a virus by this criterion. If it is a virus, it is extremely resistant to heat (infectivity remains after boiling for up to 1 hour) and to ultraviolet irradiation (Gibbons and Hunter, 1967), suggesting that it may not contain nucleic acid.

For these and other reasons, it has been proposed that the scrapie agent is a protein (Gibbons and Hunter, 1967). There is no known mechanism by which proteins convey the information for their own synthesis, but Griffith (1967) proposed three possible mechanisms for the self-replication of proteins. It seems premature to make such speculations.

The difficulties inherent in investigating such an agent have prevented the collection of biochemical analytical data on the agent; until this is done, the possibility that the scrapie agent is viral cannot be ruled out. However, if it proves true that the agent, containing no nucleic acid, is a self-replicating protein, the agent will have to be placed in a category of subviral entities, or the definition of viruses will have to be changed.

WHAT IS A VIRUS?

Lwoff (1959) proposed that all true viruses have four characteristics: They contain one and only one type of nucleic acid; they are reproduced from their genetic material and in the form of their genetic material; they do not grow, and they do not undergo binary fission; and they possess no enzyme systems for energy production. This definition easily includes infectious nucleic acids and the potato spindle tuber virus, as well as viruses in the provirus, vegetative, and extracellular infectious state.

We have seen in this book that viruses have many other characteristics that justify their inclusion in the realm of biology. All the individual particles of any one "species" of virus are constant with respect to size and morphology, with the exception, of course, of the faultily made defective individuals that are always present in small proportion.

Although there is no completely satisfactory taxonomy of viruses, it is possible to arrange the known viruses into a hierarchical grouping which may have some phylogenetic meaning. Without a fossil record, however, it will be difficult to arrive at a classification based on evolutionary relationships. It is possible to speculate on the origin of viruses — whether they are "degenerate" cells or whether they are cell organelles that have acquired autonomy — but it will probably be very difficult to devise an experimental test for the origin of viruses.

Not only are all the individual viruses of a genetically pure population similar with respect to size and morphology, but they are also alike with respect to inactivation by various physical and chemical agents. Their proteinaceous capsids are similar, as evidenced by their reactions to specific antibodies.

But one of the most important biological characteristics is also constant: the growth cycle. This is true for viruses taken together: They all undergo an eclipse, with separation of the nucleic acid from the protecting protein capsid, which serves no further purpose; then the nucleic acid directs the host cell along a new course. The eventual outcome varies, but almost all viruses, in one host or another, can direct the cell to produce more virions.

During the latent period the viral nucleic acid is, in reality, a part of the cell. By directing the synthesis of various macromolecules, the viral nucleic acid may (1) cause the cell's nucleic acid to cease functioning or even to disintegrate; (2) cause the production of materials that help other viruses to replicate, or that cause the production of inhibiting materials; (3) interact directly with the nucleic acid of another virus, giving rise to new forms by recombination; (4) undergo changes in its sequence of bases, resulting in mutations; or (5) interact directly with the cell's nucleic acid, becoming incorporated and forming a lysogenic cell or perhaps a malignant cell.

Viruses incorporate, in a minute, elegantly constructed package, the essence of biological entities—the reproduction of progeny that are like the parent, but perhaps even better able to cope with changed environmental conditions. Is this characteristic sufficient to establish viruses as living? This question cannot be answered; it cannot be tested experimentally, and the answer depends on an individual's concept of life. It can be said that viruses are not cells; and if cells are the smallest unit of life, then viruses are not alive. But reproduction as discrete units seems an overriding criterion; it is this property that has made viruses of such great interest to biologists who continually strive to study life processes in simplest terms.

Further Reading

Jawetz, E.: Agents of Trachoma and Inclusion Conjunctivitis. Annual Reviews of Microbiology, 18:301-334, 1964.

Lwoff, A.: The Concept of Virus. Journal of General Microbiology, 17:239-253, 1957.

Moulder, J. W.: The Psittacosis Group as Bacteria. New York, John Wiley & Sons, Inc., 1964.

REFERENCES

Adams, M. H. (1959): Bacteriophages. New York, Interscience Publishers, Inc.

Adams, W. R. (1966): Cellular Origin of the Slowly Sedimenting Ribonucleic Acid (RNA) Fraction Associated with Partially Purified Newcastle Disease Virus (NDV). Fed. Proc., 25(1):422.

Adler, J., and B. Templeton (1963): The Amount of Galactose Genetic Material in λdg Bacteriophage with Different Densities. J. Mol. Biol., 7:710-720.

Ahlström, C. G., and N. Forsby (1962): Sarcomas in Hamsters after Injection with Rous Chicken Tumor Material. J. Exptl. Med., 115:839-852.

Ahlström, C. G., R. Kato, and A. Levan (1964): Rous Sarcoma in Chinese Hamsters. Science, 144:1232-1233.

Alexander, P. A., and K. A. Stacey (1956): Production of "Hidden" Breaks in DNA by the Direct Action of Ionising Radiation. In Mitchell, J. S., B. E. Holmes, and C. L. Smith (eds.): Progress in Radiobiology; Proceedings of the Fourth International Conference on Radiobiology. Springfield, Illinois, Charles C Thomas, pp. 105-113.

Allen, E. H., and R. S. Schweet (1962): Synthesis of Hemoglobin in a Cell-free System; I, Properties of the Complete System. J. Biol. Chem., 237:760-767.

Allison, A. C., L. D. Berman, and R. H. Levey (1967a): Increased Tumour Induction by Adenovirus Type 12 in Thymectomized Mice and Mice Treated with Anti-Lymphocyte Serum. Nature, 215:185-187.

Allison, A. C., F. C. Chesterman, and S. Baron (1967b): Induction of Tumors in Adult Hamsters with Simian Virus 40. J. Natl. Cancer Inst., 38:567-572.

Almeida, J. D., F. Brown, and A. P. Waterson (1967): The Morphologic Characteristics of 19S Antibody. J. Immunol., 98:186-193.

Almeida, J., B. Cinader, and A. Howatson (1963): The Structure of Antigen-Antibody Complexes; a Study by Electron Microscopy. J. Exptl. Med., 118:327-340.

Almeida, J. D., A. F. Howatson, and M. G. Williams (1962): Morphology of Varicella (Chicken Pox) Virus. Virology, 16:353-355.

Altstein, A. D., G. I. Deichman, and N. N. Dodonova (1966): Induction of Specific Antitumor Immunity in Hamsters with Hydroxylamine-Inactivated SV40 Virus. Virology, 30:747-749.

366

Altstein, A. D., G. I. Deichman, O. F. Sarycheva, N. N. Dodonova, E. M. Tsetlin, and N. N. Vassilieva (1967a): Oncogenic and Transforming Activity of Hydroxylamine-Inactivated SV40 Virus. Virology, 33:746-748.

Altstein, A. D., O. F. Sarycheva, and N. N. Dodonova (1967b): Transforming Activity of Green Monkey SA7 (C8) Adenovirus in Tissue Culture. Science, 158:1455-1457.

Altstein, A. D., O. F. Sarycheva, and N. N. Dodonova (1967c): Detection of Defective (T-Antigen Inducing, but Noninfectious) Particles in Preparations of SV40 Virus. Virology, 33:744-746.

Ames, B. N., and D. T. Dubin (1960): The Role of Polyamines in the Neutralization of Bacteriophage Deoxyribonucleic Acid. J. Biol. Chem., 235:769-775.

Anderson, D. R., H. E. Hopps, M. F. Barile, and B. C. Bernheim (1965): Comparison of the Ultrastructure of Several Rickettsiae, Ornithosis Virus, and *Mycoplasma* in Tissue Culture. J. Bacteriol., 90:1387-1404.

Anderson, T. F. (1951): Techniques for the Preservation of Three-Dimensional Structure in Preparing Specimens for the Electron Microscope. Trans. N.Y. Acad. Sci., 13:130-134.

Anderson, T. F. (1963): Structure and Genetic Properties of Bacterial Viruses. *In* Viruses, Nucleic Acids, and Cancer. Baltimore, The Williams and Wilkins Co., pp. 122-140.

Andrewes, C. (1964a): Viruses of Vertebrates. Baltimore, The Williams and Wilkins Co.

Andrewes, C. H. (1964b): Tumour-viruses and Virus-tumours. British Med. J., 1:653-658.

Andrewes, C. H. (1965): Viruses and Noah's Ark. Bacteriol. Rev., 29:1-8.

Andrewes, C. H., A. C. Allison, J. A. Armstrong, G. Bearcroft, J. S. F. Niven, and H. G. Pereira (1959): A Virus Disease of Monkeys Causing Large Superficial Growths. Acta Un. Int. Cancr., 15:760-763.

Anraku, N., and J. Tomizawa (1965): Molecular Mechanisms of Genetic Recombination of Bacteriophage; V, Two Kinds of Joining of Parental DNA Molecules. J. Mol. Biol., 12:805-815.

Apelgot, S., and R. Latarjet (1966): Comparaison des "Suicides" d'une Bactérie Marquée par les Phosphores Radioactifs 32 et 33. Int. J. Rad. Biol., 10:165-175.

Aposhian, H. V., and A. Kornberg (1962): Enzymatic Synthesis of Deoxyribonucleic Acid; IX, The Polymerase Formed after T2 Bacteriophage Infection of *Escherichia coli*: A New Enzyme. J. Biol. Chem., 237:519-525.

Appleyard, G. (1967): The Photosensitivity of Semliki Forest and Other Viruses. J. Gen. Virol., 1:143-152.

Arber, W. (1965): Host-Controlled Modification of Bacteriophage. Ann. Rev. Microbiol., 19:365-378.

Arber, W., and D. Dussoix (1962): Host-Specificity of DNA Produced by *Escherichia coli*; I, Host-Controlled Modification of Bacteriophage λ. J. Mol. Biol., 5:18-36.

Archetti, I., E. Bereczky, and D. Steve-Bocciarelli (1966): A Small Virus Associated with the Simian Adenovirus SV11. Virology, 29:671-673.

Archetti, I. and D. Steve-Bocciarelli (1965): Struttura e Caratteristiche Biologiche di un Piccolo Virus. Ann. Ist. Super. Sanita, 1:103-105.

Arhelger, R. B., and C. C. Randall (1964): Electron Microscopic Observations on the Development of Fowlpox Virus in Chorioallantoic Membrane. Virology, 22:59-66.

Armstrong, J. A., and S. E. Reed (1964): Nature and Origin of Initial Bodies in Lymphogranuloma Venereum. Nature, 201:371-373.

Ashe, W. K., and H. W. Scherp (1963): Antigenic Analysis of Herpes Simplex Virus by Neutralization Kinetics. J. Immunol., 91:658-665.

Ashkenazi, A., and J. L. Melnick (1962): Induced Latent Infection of Monkeys with Vacuolating SV-40 Papova Virus; Virus in Kidneys and Urine. Proc. Soc. Exptl. Biol. Med., 111:367-372.

Astrachan, L., and E. Volkin (1958): Properties of Ribonucleic Acid Turnover in T2-Infected *Escherichia coli*. Biochim. Biophys. Acta, 29:536-544.

Atchison, R. W., B. C. Casto, and W. McD. Hammon (1965): Adenovirus-Associated Defective Virus Particles. Science, 149:754-756.

Atchison, R. W., B. C. Casto, and W. McD. Hammon (1966): Electron Microscopy of Adenovirus-Associated Virus (AAV) in Cell Cultures. Virology, 29:353-357.

Attardi, G., S. Naono, J. Rouviére, F. Jacob, and F. Gros (1963): Production of Messenger RNA and Regulation of Protein Synthesis. Cold Spring Harbor Symposia Quant. Biol., 28:363-372.

Attardi, G., and J. Smith (1962): Virus Specific Protein and a Ribonucleic Acid Associated with Ribosomes in Poliovirus Infected HeLa Cells. Cold Spring Harbor Symposia Quant. Biol., 27:271-292.

Axelrod, D., K. Habel, and E. T. Bolton (1964): Polyoma Virus Genetic Material in a Virus-Free Polyoma-Induced Tumor. Science, 146:1466-1469.

Bachrach, H. L. (1961): Thermal Degradation of Foot-and-Mouth Disease Virus into Infectious Ribonucleic Acid. Proc. Soc. Exptl. Biol. Med., 107:610-613.

Bachrach, H. L., and J. Polatnick (1967): Amino Acid Composition of Three Immunological Types of Foot-and-Mouth Disease Virus. Proc. Soc. Exptl. Biol. Med., 124: 465-469.

Bader, J. P. (1964): The Role of Deoxyribonucleic Acid in the Synthesis of Rous Sarcoma Virus. Virology, 22:462-468.

Bader, J. P. (1965a): The Requirement for DNA Synthesis in the Growth of Rous Sarcoma and Rous-Associated Viruses. Virology, 26:253-261.

Bader, J. P. (1965b): Transformation by Rous Sarcoma Virus; a Requirement for DNA Synthesis. Science, 149:757-758.

Bader, J. P. (1967): Metabolic Requirements in Rous Sarcoma Virus Replication. In Colter, J. S., and W. Paranchych (eds.): The Molecular Biology of Viruses. New York, Academic Press Inc., pp. 697-708.

Baker, R., and I. Tessman (1967): The Circular Genetic Map of Phage S13. Proc. Natl. Acad. Sci., 58:1438-1445.

Balandin, I. G., and R. M. Franklin (1964): The Effect of Mengovirus Infection on the Activity of the DNA-Dependent RNA Polymerase of L-Cells; II, Preliminary Data on the Inhibitory Factor. Biochem. Biophys. Res. Commun., 15:27-32.

Baldwin, R. L., P. Barrand, A. Fritsch, D. A. Goldthwait, and F. Jacob (1966): Cohesive Sites on the Deoxyribonucleic Acids from Several Temperate Coliphages. J. Mol. Biol., 17:343-357.

Baltimore, D., Y. Becker, and J. E. Darnell (1964): Virus-Specific Double-Stranded RNA in Poliovirus-Infected Cells. Science, 143:1034-1036.

Baltimore, D., and R. M. Franklin (1962a): The Effect of Mengovirus Infection on the Activity of the DNA-Dependent RNA Polymerase of L-Cells. Proc. Natl. Acad. Sci., 48:1383-1390.

Baltimore, D., and R. M. Franklin (1962b): Preliminary Data on a Virus-Specific Enzyme System Responsible for the Synthesis of Viral RNA. Biochem. Biophys. Res. Commun., 9:388-392.

Baltimore, D., and R. M. Franklin (1963): A New Ribonucleic Acid Polymerase Appearing after Mengovirus Infection of L-Cells. J. Biol. Chem., 238:3395-3400.

Baltimore, D., R. M. Franklin, and J. Callender (1963): Mengovirus-Induced Inhibition of Host Ribonucleic Acid and Protein Synthesis. Biochim. Biophys. Acta, 76:425-430.

Baltimore, D., and M. Girard (1966): An Intermediate in the Synthesis of Poliovirus RNA. Proc. Natl. Acad. Sci., 56:741-748.

Baluda, M. A. (1957): Homologous Interference by Ultraviolet-Inactivated Newcastle Disease Virus. Virology, 4:72-96.

Baluda, M. A., I. E. Goetz, and S. Ohno (1963): Induction of Differentiation in Certain Target Cells by Avian Myeloblastosis Virus; an in Vitro Study. In Viruses, Nucleic Acids, and Cancer. Baltimore, The Williams and Wilkins Co., pp. 387-400.

Baluda, M. A., and P. P. Jamieson (1961): In Vivo Infectivity Studies with Avian Myeloblastosis Virus. Virology, 14:33-45.

Bancroft, J. B., G. J. Hills, and R. Markham (1967): A Study of the Self-Assembly Process in a Small Spherical Virus; Formation of Organized Structures from Protein Subunits in Vitro. Virology, 31:354-379.

Barksdale, L. (1959): Symposium on the Biology of Cells Modified by Viruses or Antigens; I, Lysogenic Conversions in Bacteria. Bacteriol. Rev., 23:202-212.

Barksdale, W. L., and A. M. Pappenheimer, Jr. (1954): Phage-Host Relationships in Nontoxigenic and Toxigenic Diphtheria Bacilli. J. Bacteriol., 67:220-232.

Barner, H. D., and S. S. Cohen (1954): The Induction of Thymine Synthesis by T2

Infection of a Thymine Requiring Mutant of *Escherichia coli.* J. Bacteriol., 68:80-88.

Barner, H. D., and S. S. Cohen (1959): Virus-Induced Acquisition of Metabolic Function; IV, Thymidylate Synthetase in Thymine-Requiring *Escherichia coli* Infected by T2 and T5 Bacteriophages. J. Biol. Chem., 234:2987-2991.

Baron, S. (1966): The Biological Significance of the Interferon System. *In* Finter, N. B. (ed.): Interferons. Philadelphia, W. B. Saunders Co., pp. 268-293.

Baron, S., S. Barban, and C. E. Buckler (1964): Host Cell Species Specificity of Mouse and Chicken Interferons. Science, 145:814.

Baron, S., and C. E. Buckler (1963): Circulating Interferon in Mice after Intravenous Injection of Virus. Science, 141:1061-1063.

Baron, S., C. E. Buckler, R. M. Friedman, and R. V. McCloskey (1966a): Role of Interferon During Viremia; II, Protective Action of Circulating Interferon. J. Immunol., 96:17-24.

Baron, S., C. E. Buckler, H. B. Levy, and R. M. Friedman (1967): Some Factors Affecting the Interferon-Induced Antiviral State. Proc. Soc. Exptl. Biol. Med., 125:1320-1326.

Baron, S., C. E. Buckler, R. V. McCloskey, and R. L. Kirschstein (1966b): Role of Interferon During Viremia; I, Production of Circulating Interferon. J. Immunol., 96:12-16.

Baron, S., and H. B. Levy (1966): Interferon. Ann. Rev. Microbiol., 20:291-318.

Baron, S., T. C. Merigan, and M. L. McKerlie (1966c): Effect of Crude and Purified Interferons on the Growth of Uninfected Cells in Culture. Proc. Soc. Exptl. Biol. Med., 121:50-52.

Barrera-Oro, J. G., K. O. Smith, and J. L. Melnick (1962): Quantitation of Papova Virus Particles in Human Warts. J. Natl. Cancer Inst., 29:583-595.

Barrington, L. F., and L. M. Kozloff (1954): Action of T2r^+ Bacteriophage on Host-Cell Membranes. Science, 120:110-111.

Barry, R. D. (1961): The Multiplication of Influenza Virus; II, Multiplicity Reactivation of Ultraviolet Irradiated Virus. Virology, 14:398-405.

Barry, R. D., D. R. Ives, and J. G. Cruickshank (1962): Participation of Deoxyribonucleic Acid in the Multiplication of Influenza Virus. Nature, 194:1139-1140.

Bases, R. E., and A. S. King (1967): Inhibition of Rauscher Murine Leukemia Virus Growth *in Vitro* by Actinomycin D. Virology, 32:175-183.

Basilico, C., and G. Di Mayorca (1965): Radiation Target Size of the Lytic and the Transforming Ability of Polyoma Virus. Proc. Natl. Acad. Sci., 54:125-127.

Basilico, C., G. Marin, and G. Di Mayorca (1966): Requirement for the Integrity of the Viral Genome for the Induction of Host DNA Synthesis by Polyoma Virus. Proc. Natl. Acad. Sci., 56:208-215.

Baum, S. G., P. R. Reich, C. J. Hybner, W. P. Rowe, and S. M. Weissman (1966): Biophysical Evidence for Linkage of Adenovirus and SV40 DNA's in Adenovirus 7-SV40 Hybrid Particles. Proc. Natl. Acad. Sci., 56:1509-1515.

Bautz, E. K. F. (1962): The Role of Phage Specific RNA as Messenger. Biochem. Biophys. Res. Commun., 9:192-197.

Bautz, E. K. F., and B. D. Hall (1962): The Isolation of T4-Specific RNA on a DNA-Cellulose Column. Proc. Natl. Acad. Sci., 48:400-408.

Bautz, E. K. F., T. Kasai, E. Reilly, and F. A. Bautz (1966): Gene-Specific MRNA; II, Regulation of MRNA Synthesis in *E. coli* after Infection with Bacteriophage T4. Proc. Natl. Acad. Sci., 55:1081-1088.

Bayne-Jones, S., and L. A. Sandholzer (1933): Changes in the Shape and Size of Bacterium Coli and Bacillus Megatherium under the Influence of Bacteriophage—A Motion Photomicrographic Analysis of the Mechanism of Lysis. J. Exptl. Med., 57:279-304.

Bearcroft, W. G. C., and M. F. Jamieson (1958): An Outbreak of Subcutaneous Tumours in Rhesus Monkeys. Nature, 182:195-196.

Beard, J. W., R. A. Bonar, U. Heine, G. de Thé, and D. Beard (1963): Studies on the Biological, Biochemical, and Biophysical Properties of Avian Tumor Viruses. *In* Viruses, Nucleic Acids, and Cancer. Baltimore, The Williams and Wilkins Co., pp. 344-373.

Beaudreau, G. S., C. Becker, R. A. Bonar, A. M. Wallbank, D. Beard, and J. W. Beard

(1960): Virus of Avian Myeloblastosis; XIV, Neoplastic Response of Normal Chicken Bone Marrow Treated with the Virus in Tissue Culture. J. Natl. Cancer Inst., 24:395-415.

Becker, A., G. Lyn, M. Gefter, and J. Hurwitz (1967): The Enzymatic Repair of DNA; II, Characterization of Phage-Induced Sealase. Proc. Natl. Acad. Sci., 58:1996-2003.

Becker, Y. (1966): An Approach to the Organization and Classification of Vertebrate Viruses. Nature, 210:1019-1021.

Becker, Y., and W. K. Joklik (1964): Messenger RNA in Cells Infected with Vaccinia Virus. Proc. Natl. Acad. Sci., 51:577-585.

Becker, Y., U. Olshevsky, and J. Levitt (1967): The Role of Arginine in the Replication of Herpes Simplex Virus. J. Gen. Virol., 1:471-478.

Becker, Y., S. Penman, and J. E. Darnell (1963): A Cytoplasmic Particulate Involved in Poliovirus Synthesis. Virology, 21:274-276.

Beckwith, J. R. (1967): Regulation of the Lac Operon. Science, 156:597-604.

Beijerinck, M. W. (1898): Concerning a *Contagium Vivum Fluidum* as Cause of the Spot Disease of Tobacco Leaves. Verhandelingen der Koninklyke akademie van Wettenshappen te Amsterdam, 65:3-21. Reprinted in abridged translation. Hahon, N. (1964): Selected Papers on Virology. Englewood Cliffs, New Jersey, Prentice-Hall, Inc., pp. 52-63.

Bellamy, A. R., and W. K. Joklik (1967): Studies on the A-Rich RNA of Reovirus. Proc. Natl. Acad. Sci., 58:1389-1395.

Bellett, A. J. D. (1967): Preliminary Classification of Viruses Based on Quantitative Comparisons of Viral Nucleic Acids. J. Virol., 1:245-259.

Bello, L. J., and H. S. Ginsberg (1967): Inhibition of Host Protein Synthesis in Type 5 Adenovirus-Infected Cells. J. Virol., 1:843-850.

Bello, L. J., M. J. Van Bibber, and M. J. Bessman (1961): The Enzymology of Virus-Infected Bacteria; I, Demonstration of Two Forms of Deoxyguanylate Kinase in Infected *Escherichia coli*. J. Biol. Chem., 236:1467-1470.

Bendich, A. (1967): Discussion following Benjamin, T. L. (1967): Radiobiological and Biochemical Investigations of Polyoma Virus-Cell Interactions. *In* Ito, Y. (ed.): Subviral Carcinogenesis. Kyoto, Japan, The Editorial Committee for the 1st International Symposium on Tumor Viruses, pp. 62-81.

Benjamin, T. L. (1965): Relative Target Sizes for the Inactivation of the Transforming and Reproductive Abilities of Polyoma Virus. Proc. Natl. Acad. Sci., 54:121-124.

Benjamin, T. L. (1966): Virus-Specific RNA in Cells Productively Infected or Transformed by Polyoma Virus. J. Mol. Biol., 16:359-373.

Benjamin, T. L. (1967): Radiobiological and Biochemical Investigations of Polyoma Virus-Cell Interactions. *In* Ito, Y. (ed.): Subviral Carcinogenesis. Kyoto, Japan, The Editorial Committee for the 1st International Symposium on Tumor Viruses, pp. 62-81.

Ben-Porat, T., C. Coto, and A. S. Kaplan (1966): Unstable DNA Synthesized by Polyoma Virus-Infected Cells. Virology, 30:74-81.

Ben-Porat, T., and A. S. Kaplan (1962): The Chemical Composition of Herpes Simplex and Pseudorabies Viruses. Virology, 16:261-266.

Benzer, S. (1955): Fine Structure of a Genetic Region in Bacteriophage. Proc. Natl. Acad. Sci., 41:344-354.

Benzer, S. (1957): The Elementary Units of Heredity. *In* McElroy, W. D., and B. Glass (eds.): The Chemical Basis of Heredity. Baltimore, The Johns Hopkins Press, pp. 70-93.

Benzer, S. (1959): On the Topology of the Genetic Fine Structure. Proc. Natl. Acad. Sci., 45:1607-1620.

Benzer, S. (1962): The Fine Structure of the Gene. Sci. Amer., 206(Jan.):70-84.

Benzer, S., and E. Freese (1958): Induction of Specific Mutations with 5-Bromouracil. Proc. Natl. Acad. Sci., 44:112-119.

Benzinger, R., and P. H. Hofschneider (1963): Biological Melting Curves for the "Replicative Form" of ϕX174 DNA. Z. Vererbungslehre, 94:316-321.

Berman, L. D. (1967): Comparative Morphologic Study of the Virus-Induced Solid Tumors of Syrian Hamsters. J. Natl. Cancer Inst., 39:847-901.

Bernal, J. D., and I. Fankuchen (1941): X-ray and Crystallographic Studies of Plant Virus Preparations; I, Introduction and Preparation of Specimens; II, Modes of

Aggregation of the Virus Particles; III, The Structure of Particles and Biological Implications. J. Gen. Physiol., 25:111-165.

Bernhard, W. (1960): The Detection and Study of Tumor Viruses with the Electron Microscope. Cancer Res., 20:712-727.

Bertani, G. (1953): Lysogenic Versus Lytic Cycle of Phage Multiplication. Cold Spring Harbor Symposia Quant. Biol., 18:65-70.

Bertani, L. E., A. Häggmark, and P. Reichard (1963): Enzymatic Synthesis of Deoxyribonucleotides; II, Formation and Interconversion of Deoxyuridine Phosphates. J. Biol. Chem., 238:3407-3413.

Bessman, M. J. (1959): Deoxyribonucleotide Kinases in Normal and Virus-Infected *Escherichia coli.* J. Biol. Chem., 234:2735-2740.

Bessman, M. J., and M. J. Van Bibber (1959): A Change in the Properties of Deoxyguanlylate Kinase of *E. coli* caused by Viral Infection. Biochem. Biophys. Res. Commun., 1:101-104.

Billeter, M. A., M. Libonati, E. Viñuela, and C. Weissmann (1966): Replication of Viral Ribonucleic Acid; X, Turnover of Virus-Specific Double-Stranded Ribonucleic Acid During Replication of Phage MS2 in *Escherichia coli.* J. Biol. Chem., 241:4750-4757.

Bishop, D. H. L. (1966a): Physical Properties of Single- and Double-Stranded Coliphage Ribonucleic Acid. Biochem. J., 100:321-329.

Bishop, D. H. L. (1966b): Ribonucleic Acid Synthesis by *Escherichia coli* C 3000/L after Infection by the Ribonucleic Acid Coliphage ZIK/1, and Properties of the Coliphage-Induced Double-Stranded Ribonucleic Acid. Biochem. J., 100:601-613.

Bishop, D. H. L., J. R. Claybrook, N. R. Pace, and S. Spiegelman (1967): An Analysis by Gel Electrophoresis of Qβ-RNA Complexes Formed During the Latent Period of an *in Vitro* Synthesis. Proc. Natl. Acad. Sci., 57:1474-1481.

Bishop, J. M., and G. Koch (1967): Purification and Characterization of Poliovirus-Induced Infectious Double-Stranded Ribonucleic Acid. J. Biol. Chem., 242:1736-1743.

Bishop, J. M., D. F. Summers, and L. Levintow (1965): Characterization of Ribonuclease-Resistant RNA from Poliovirus-Infected HeLa Cells. Proc. Natl. Acad. Sci., 54:1273-1281.

Bittner, J. J. (1936): Some Possible Effects of Nursing on the Mammary Gland Tumor Incidence in Mice. Science, 84:162.

Black, P. H. (1966a): An Analysis of SV40-Induced Transformation of Hamster Kidney Tissue *in Vitro*; III, Persistence of SV40 Viral Genome in Clones of Transformed Hamster Cells. J. Natl. Cancer Inst., 37:487-493.

Black, P. H. (1966b): Recent Advances in the Study of Oncogenic Viruses. New Eng. J. Med., 275:377-383.

Black, P. H., A. M. Lewis, Jr., N. R. Blacklow, J. B. Austin, and W. P. Rowe (1967): The Presence of Adenovirus-Specific Antigens in Hamster Cells Rendered Neoplastic by Adenovirus 1-SV40 and Adenovirus 2-SV40 Hybrid Viruses. Proc. Natl. Acad. Sci., 57:1324-1330.

Black, P. H., and W. P. Rowe (1965): Increase of Malignant Potential of BHK-21 Cells by SV40 DNA Without Persistent New Antigen. Proc. Natl. Acad. Sci., 54:1126-1133.

Blacklow, N. R., M. D. Hoggan, and W. P. Rowe (1967): Isolation of Adenovirus-Associated Viruses from Man. Proc. Natl. Acad. Sci., 58:1410-1415.

Blacklow, N. R., M. D. Hoggan, and W. P. Rowe (1968): Serologic Evidence for Human Infection with Adenovirus-Associated Viruses. J. Natl. Cancer Inst., 40:319-327.

Bloomfield, V. A. (1966): Twisted Circular DNA; Sedimentation Coefficients and the Number of Twists. Proc. Natl. Acad. Sci., 55:717-720.

Bode, V., and A. D. Kaiser (1965): Changes in the Structure and Activity of λ DNA in a Superinfected Immune Bacterium. J. Mol. Biol., 14:399-417.

Boeyé, A. (1959): Induction of a Mutation in Poliovirus by Nitrous Acid. Virology, 9:691-700.

Boiron, M., J. P. Lévy, and J. Périès (1967): *In Vitro* Investigations on Murine Leukemia Viruses. Progr. Med. Virol., 9:341-391.

Boiron, M., J. P. Lévy, M. Thomas, J. C. Friedman, and J. Bernard (1964): Some Properties of Bovine Papilloma Virus. Nature, 201:423-424.

Borecký, L. (1968): Interferon Induction by Nonviral Agents. *In* Sanders, M., and E. H. Lennette (eds.): St. Louis, Warren H. Green, Inc., pp. 181-189.

Borman, G. S., and B. Roizman (1965): The Inhibition of Herpes Simplex Virus Multiplication by Nucleosides. Biochim. Biophys. Acta, 103:50-59.

Borrell, A. (1903): Epithélioses Infectieuses et Epithéliomas. Ann. Inst. Pasteur, 17:81-122.

Bose, S. K., and R. J. Warren (1967): On the Stability of Phage Messenger RNA. Biochem. Biophys. Res. Commun., 26:385-391.

Boyce, R. P., and P. Howard-Flanders (1964): Release of Ultraviolet Light-Induced Thymine Dimers from DNA in *E. coli* K-12. Proc. Natl. Acad. Sci., 51:293-300.

Boyce, R. P., and M. Tepper (1968): X-ray-Induced Single-Strand Breaks and Joining of Broken Strands in Superinfecting λ DNA in *Escherichia coli* Lysogenic for λ. Virology, 34:344-351.

Boyer, G. S., F. W. Denny, Jr., and H. S. Ginsberg (1959): Sequential Cellular Changes Produced by Types 5 and 7 Adenoviruses in HeLa Cells and in Human Amniotic Cells. Cytological Studies Aided by Fluorescein-Labelled Antibody. J. Exptl. Med., 110:827-844.

Boyer, G. S., C. Leuchtenberger, and H. S. Ginsberg (1957): Cytological and Cytochemical Studies of HeLa Cells Infected with Adenoviruses. J. Exptl. Med., 105:195-216.

Bradley, D. E. (1963): Structure of Some Staphylococcus and Pseudomonas Phages. J. Ultrastructure Res., 8:552-565.

Bradley, D. E. (1967): Ultrastructure of Bacteriophages and Bacteriocins. Bacteriol. Rev., 31:230-314.

Bradley, D. E., and C. A. Dewar (1966): The Structure of Phage-Like Objects Associated with Non-Induced Bacteriocinogenic Bacteria. J. Gen. Microbiol., 45:399-408.

Bradley, D. E., and C. A. Dewar (1967): Intracellular Changes in Cells of *Escherichia coli* Infected with a Filamentous Bacteriophage. J. Gen. Virol., 1:179-188.

Braun, W. (1965): Bacterial Genetics. Philadelphia, W. B. Saunders Co.

Bray, D., and P. W. Robbins (1967): Mechanism of ϵ^{15} Conversion Studied with Bacteriophage Mutants. J. Mol. Biol., 30:457-475.

Breedis, C., L. Berwick, and T. F. Anderson (1962): Fractionation of Shope Papilloma Virus in Cesium Chloride Density Gradients. Virology, 17:84-94.

Breese, S. S., Jr., R. Trautman, and H. L. Bachrach (1965): Rotational Symmetry in Foot-and-Mouth Disease Virus and Models. Science, 150:1303-1305.

Breeze, D. C., and H. Subak-Sharpe (1967): The Mutability of Small-Plaque-Forming Encephalomyocarditis Virus. J. Gen. Virol., 1:81-88.

Brenner, S., L. Barnett, F. H. C. Crick, and A. Orgel (1961a): The Theory of Mutagenesis. J. Mol. Biol., 3:121-124.

Brenner, S., L. Barnett, E. R. Katz, and F. H. C. Crick (1967): UGA; a Third Nonsense Triplet in the Genetic Code. Nature, 213:449-450.

Brenner, S., and J. R. Beckwith (1965): *Ochre* Mutants, a New Class of Suppressible Nonsense Mutants. J. Mol. Biol., 13:629-637.

Brenner, S., S. P. Champe, G. Streisinger, and L. Barnett (1962): On the Interaction of Adsorption Cofactors with Bacteriophages T2 and T4. Virology, 17:30-39.

Brenner, S., and R. W. Horne (1959): A Negative Staining Method for High Resolution Electron Microscopy of Viruses. Biochim. Biophys. Acta, 34:103-110.

Brenner, S., F. Jacob, and M. Meselson (1961b): An Unstable Intermediate Carrying Information from Genes to Ribosomes for Protein Synthesis. Nature, 190:576-581.

Brenner, S., and C. Milstein (1966): Origin of Antibody Variation. Nature, 211:242-243.

Brenner, S., G. Streisinger, R. W. Horne, S. P. Champe, L. Barnett, S. Benzer, and M. W. Rees (1959): Structural Components of Bacteriophage. J. Mol. Biol., 1:281-292.

Brenner, S., and A. O. W. Stretton (1964): The *Amber* Mutation. J. Cell. Comp. Physiol., 64(Supp. 1):43-49.

Bretscher, M. S. (1968): How Repressor Molecules Function. Nature, 217:509-511.

Brinton, C. C. (1965): The Structure, Function, Synthesis and Genetic Control of Bacterial Pili and a Molecular Model for DNA and RNA Transport in Gram-Negative Bacteria. Trans. N.Y. Acad. Sci., 27:1003-1054.

Brown, F., and T. F. Wild (1966): The Effect of Heat on the Structure of Foot-and-Mouth Disease Virus and the Viral Ribonucleic Acid. Biochim. Biophys. Acta, 119:301-308.

Brunner, K. T., and R. Ward (1959): Differences in Stability of Antigen-Antibody Complexes Formed with Poliovirus and Acute and Convalescent Phase Human Sera. J. Immunol., 83:405-410.

Bryan, W. R. (1962): The Search for Causative Viruses in Human Cancer; a Discussion of the Problem. J. Natl. Cancer Inst., 29:1027-1034.

Buckler, C. E., and S. Baron (1966): Antiviral Action of Mouse Interferon in Heterologous Cells. J. Bacteriol., 91:231-235.

Buckler, C. E., S. Baron, and H. B. Levy (1966): Interferon; Lack of Detectable Uptake by Cells. Science, 152:80-82.

Bucknall, R. A. (1967): "Species Specificity" of Interferons; a Misnomer? Nature, 216:1022-1023.

Bujard, H. (1967): Studies on Circular Deoxyribonucleic Acid; I, Isolation of Bovine Papilloma Virus and Characterization of Its Deoxyribonucleic Acid. J. Virol., 1:1135-1138.

Burdon, R. H., M. A. Billeter, C. Weissmann, R. C. Warner, S. Ochoa, and C. A. Knight (1964): Replication of Viral RNA; V, Presence of a Virus-Specific Double-Stranded RNA in Leaves Infected with Tobacco Mosaic Virus. Proc. Natl. Acad. Sci., 52:768-775.

Burge, B. W., and E. R. Pfefferkorn (1965): Conditional-Lethal Mutants of an Animal Virus; Identification of Two Cistrons. Science, 148:959-960.

Burge, B. W., and E. R. Pfefferkorn (1967): Temperature-Sensitive Mutants of Sindbis Virus; Biochemical Correlates of Complementation. J. Virol., 1:956-962.

Burke, D. C., and J. Ross (1965): Molecular Weight of Chick Interferon. Nature, 208:1297-1299.

Burkitt, D. (1963): A Children's Cancer Dependent on Environment. In Viruses, Nucleic Acids, and Cancer. Baltimore, The Williams and Wilkins Co., pp. 615-629.

Burkitt, D., and D. Wright (1966): Geographical and Tribal Distribution of the African Lymphoma in Uganda. British Med. J., 1:569-573.

Burness, A. T. H. (1967): Separation of Plaque-Type Variants of Encephalomyocarditis Virus by Chromatography on Calcium Phosphate. J. Virol., 1:308-316.

Burnet, F. M. (1932): Lysogenicity as a Normal Function of Certain Salmonella Strains. J. Path. Bacteriol., 35:851-863.

Burnet, F. M. (1933): A Specific Soluble Substance from Bacteriophages. Brit. J. Exp. Path., 14:100-108.

Burnet, F. M. (1945): Virus as Organism. Cambridge, Harvard University Press.

Burnet, F. M. (1959): The Scope and Limitations of Immunological Methods in the Characterization and Functional Study of Viruses. In Burnet, F. M., and W. M. Stanley (eds.): The Viruses, Vol. 1. New York, Academic Press, Inc., pp. 525-548.

Burnet, F. M. (1960): Principles of Animal Virology, Ed. 2. New York, Academic Press, Inc.

Burnet, F. M. (1966): A Possible Genetic Basis for Specific Pattern in Antibody. Nature, 210:1308-1310.

Burnet, F. M., and M. McKie (1929): Observations on a Permanently Lysogenic Strain of B. enteritidis Gaertner. Austral. J. Exptl. Biol. Med. Sci., 6:277-284.

Burton, A., and R. L. Sinsheimer (1963): Process of Infection with φX174; Effect of Exonucleases on the Replicative Form. Science, 142:962-963.

Burton, A., and R. L. Sinsheimer (1965): The Process of Infection with Bacteriophage φX174; VII, Ultracentrifugal Analysis of the Replicative Form. J. Mol. Biol., 14:327-347.

Butel, J. S. (1967): Characterization of the Strain of Adenovirus Type 7 Carrying the Defective Monkey Cell-Adapting Component. J. Virol., 1:876-882.

Butel, J. S., J. L. Melnick, and F. Rapp (1966a): Detection of Biologically Active Adenovirions Unable to Plaque in Human Cells. J. Bacteriol., 92:433-438.

Butel, J. S., F. Rapp, J. L. Melnick, and B. A. Rubin (1966b): Replication of Adenovirus Type 7 in Monkey Cells; a New Determinant and Its Transfer to Adenovirus Type 2. Science, 154:671-673.

Cairns, J. (1960): The Initiation of Vaccinia Infection. Virology, 11:603-623.

Cairns, J. (1961): An Estimate of the Length of the DNA Molecule of T2 Bacteriophage by Autoradiography. J. Mol. Biol., 3:756-761.

Cairns, J., G. S. Stent, and J. D. Watson (eds.) (1966): Phage and the Origins of Molecular Biology. Cold Spring Harbor Laboratory of Quantitative Biology.

Calef, E., and G. Licciardello (1960): Recombination Experiments on Prophage Host Relationships. Virology, 12:81-103.

Calef, E., C. Marchelli, and F. Guerrini (1965): The Formation of Superinfection-Double Lysogens of Phage λ in *Escherichia coli* K12. Virology, 27:1-10.

Campbell, A. (1959): Ordering of Genetic Sites in Bacteriophage λ by the Use of Galactose-Transducing Defective Phages. Virology, 9:293-305.

Campbell, A. (1962): Episomes. Adv. Genetics, 11:101-145.

Campbell, A. (1965a): The Steric Effect in Lysogenization by Bacteriophage Lambda; I, Lysogenization of a Partially Diploid Strain of *Escherichia coli* K12. Virology, 27:329-339.

Campbell, A. (1965b): The Steric Effect in Lysogenization by Bacteriophage Lambda; II, Chromosomal Attachment of the b_2 Mutant. Virology, 27:340-345.

Campbell, A., and K. Killen (1967): Effect of Temperature on Prophage Attachment and Detachment During Heteroimmune Superinfection. Virology, 33:749-752.

Cantell, K. (1961): Mumps Virus. Adv. Virus Res., 8:123-164.

Cardiff, R. D., P. B. Blair, and P. Nakayama (1968): *In Vitro* Cultivation of Mouse Mammary Tumor Virus; Detection of MTV Production by Radioisotope Labeling and Identification by Immune Precipitation. Proc. Natl. Acad. Sci., 59:895-902.

Caro, L. G., and M. Schnös (1966): The Attachment of the Male-Specific Bacteriophage F1 to Sensitive Strains of *Escherichia coli*. Proc. Natl. Acad. Sci., 56:126-132.

Carp, R. I. (1967): Thymidine Kinase from Normal, Simian Virus 40-Transformed and Simian Virus 40-Lytically Infected Cells. J. Virol., 1:912-919.

Carter, W. A., and H. B. Levy (1967): Ribosomes; Effect of Interferon on Their Interaction with Rapidly Labeled Cellular and Viral RNA's. Science, 155:1254-1257.

Carusi, E. A., and R. L. Sinsheimer (1963): The Physical Properties of a Protein Isolated from Bacteriophage φX174. J. Mol. Biol., 7:388-400.

Caspar, D. L. D. (1963): Assembly and Stability of the Tobacco Mosaic Virus Particle. Adv. Protein Chem., 18:37-121.

Caspar, D. L. D. (1965): Design Principles in Virus Particle Construction. *In* Horsfall, F. L., Jr., and I. Tamm (eds.): Viral and Rickettsial Infections of Man. Philadelphia, J. B. Lippincott Co., pp. 51-93.

Caspar, D. L. D., R. Dulbecco, A. Klug, A. Lwoff, M. G. P. Stoker, P. Tournier, and P. Wildy (1962): Proposals. Cold Spring Harbor Symposia Quant. Biol., 27:49-50.

Caspar, D. L. D., and A. Klug (1962): Physical Principles in the Construction of Regular Viruses. Cold Spring Harbor Symposia Quant. Biol., 27:1-24.

Caspar, D. L. D., and A. Klug (1963): Structure and Assembly of Regular Virus Particles. *In* Viruses, Nucleic Acids, and Cancer. Baltimore, The Williams and Wilkins Co., pp. 27-39.

Casto, B. C. (1968a): Adenovirus Transformation of Hamster Embryo Cells. J. Virol., 2:376-383.

Casto, B. C. (1968b): Effects of Ultraviolet Irradiation on the Transforming and Plaque Forming Capacities of Simian Adenovirus, SA7. J. Virol., 2:641-642.

Casto, B. C., J. A. Armstrong, R. W. Atchison, and W. McD. Hammon (1967a): Studies on the Relationship Between Adeno-Associated Virus Type 1 (AAV-1) and Adenoviruses; II, Inhibition of Adenovirus Plaques by AAV; Its Nature and Specificity. Virology, 33:452-458.

Casto, B. C., R. W. Atchison, and W. McD. Hammon (1967b): Studies on the Relationship Between Adeno-Associated Virus Type 1 (AAV-1) and Adenoviruses; I, Replication of AAV-1 in Certain Cell Cultures and Its Effect on Helper Adenovirus. Virology, 32:52-59.

Champe, S. P. (1963): Bacteriophage Reproduction. Ann. Rev. Microbiol., 17:87-114.

Chamsy, H. M., and P. D. Cooper (1963): Indirect Evidence for the Presence of Ribonucleic Acid in Vesicular Stomatitis Virions. Virology, 20:14-19.

Chandler, B., M. Hayashi, M. N. Hayashi, and S. Spiegelman (1964): Circularity of the Replicating Form of a Single-Stranded DNA Virus. Science, 143:47-49.

Chang, L. M. S., and M. E. Hodes (1967): Induction of DNA Nucleotidyl-transferase by the Shope Fibroma Virus. Virology, 32:258-266.

Clark, A. J., and A. D. Margulies (1965): Isolation and Characterization of Recombination-Deficient Mutants of *Escherichia coli* K12. Proc. Natl. Acad. Sci., 53:451-459.

Clark, J. M., Jr., A. Y. Chang, S. Spiegelman, and M. E. Reichmann (1965): The *in Vitro* Translation of a Monocistronic Message. Proc. Natl. Acad. Sci., 54:1193-1197.

Coetzee, H. L., H. C. deKlerk, and J. N. Coetzee (1968): Bacteriophage-Tail-Like Particles Associated with Intra-species Killing of *Proteus vulgaris*. J. Gen. Virol., 2:29-36.

Cohen, A. (1963): Mechanisms of Cell Infection; I, Virus Attachment and Penetration. *In* Smith, W. (ed.): Mechanisms of Virus Infection. New York, Academic Press Inc., pp. 153-190.

Cohen, J. A. (1967): Chemistry and Structure of Nucleic Acids of Bacteriophages. Science, 158:343-351.

Cohen, S., and C. Milstein (1967): Structure of Antibody Molecules. Nature, 214:449-452.

Cohen, S. S. (1947): The Synthesis of Bacterial Viruses in Infected Cells. Cold Spring Harbor Symposia Quant. Biol., 12:35-49.

Cohen, S. S. (1948a): The Synthesis of Bacterial Viruses; I, The Synthesis of Nucleic Acid and Protein in *Escherichia coli* B Infected with T2r$^+$ Bacteriophage. J. Biol. Chem., 174:281-293.

Cohen, S. S. (1948b): The Synthesis of Bacterial Viruses; II, The Origin of the Phosphorus Found in the Desoxyribonucleic Acids of the T_2 and T_4 Bacteriophages. J. Biol. Chem., 174:295-303.

Cohen, S. S. (1961): Virus-Induced Acquisition of Metabolic Function. Fed. Proc., 20:641-649.

Cohen, S. S. (1963): The Biochemistry of Viruses. Ann. Rev. Biochem., 32:83-154.

Cohen, S. S., J. G. Flaks, H. D. Barner, M. R. Loeb, and J. Lichtenstein (1958): The Mode of Action of 5-Fluorouracil and Its Derivatives. Proc. Natl. Acad. Sci., 44:1004-1012.

Compans, R. W., and P. W. Choppin (1967): Isolation and Properties of the Helical Nucleocapsid of the Parainfluenza Virus SV5. Proc. Natl. Acad. Sci., 57:949-956.

Cooper, P. D. (1961a): A Chemical Basis for the Classification of Animal Viruses. Nature, 190:302-305.

Cooper, P. D. (1961b): The Plaque Assay of Animal Viruses. Adv. Virus Res., 8:319-378.

Cooper, S., and N. D. Zinder (1962): The Growth of an RNA Bacteriophage; The Role of DNA Synthesis. Virology, 18:405-411.

Cords, C. E., and J. J. Holland (1964): Interference Between Enteroviruses and Conditions Effecting Its Reversal. Virology, 22:226-234.

Courington, D., and P. K. Vogt (1967): Electron Microscopy of Chick Fibroblasts Infected by Defective Rous Sarcoma Virus and Its Helper. J. Virol., 1:400-414.

Cowie, D. B., and B. J. McCarthy (1963): Homology Between Bacteriophage λ DNA and *E. coli* DNA. Proc. Natl. Acad. Sci., 50:537-543.

Crawford, L. V. (1962): The Adsorption of Polyoma Virus. Virology, 18:177-181.

Crawford, L. V. (1964a): A Study of Shope Papilloma Virus DNA. J. Mol. Biol., 8:489-495.

Crawford, L. V. (1964b): The Physical Characteristics of Polyoma Virus; IV, The Size of the DNA. Virology, 22:149-152.

Crawford, L. V. (1966): A Minute Virus of Mice. Virology, 29:605-612.

Crawford, L. V., and E. M. Crawford (1963): A Comparative Study of Polyoma and Papilloma Viruses. Virology, 21:258-263.

Crawford, L. V., E. M. Crawford, J. P. Richardson, and H. S. Slayter (1965): The Binding of RNA Polymerase to Polyoma and Papilloma DNA. J. Mol. Biol., 14:593-597.

Crawford, L. V., E. M. Crawford, and D. H. Watson (1962): The Physical Characteristics of Polyoma Virus; I, Two Types of Particle. Virology, 18:170-176.

Crawford, L. V., R. Dulbecco, M. Fried, L. Montagnier, and M. Stoker (1964): Cell Transformation by Different Forms of Polyoma Virus DNA. Proc. Natl. Acad. Sci., 52:148-152.

Crawford, L. V., and M. J. Waring (1967): The Supercoiling of Papilloma Virus DNA. J. Gen. Virol., 1:387-390.

Crick, F. H. C. (1962): The Genetic Code. Sci. Amer., 207(Oct.):66-74.

Crick, F. H. C., L. Barnett, S. Brenner, and R. J. Watts-Tobin (1961): General Nature of the Genetic Code for Proteins. Nature, 192:1227-1232.

Crick, F. H. C., and J. D. Watson (1956): The Structure of Small Viruses. Nature, 177:473-475.

Crocker, T., E. Pfendt, and R. Spendlove (1964): Poliovirus; Growth in Non-Nucleate Cytoplasm. Science, 145:401-403.

Cromack, A. S. (1968): An Electron Microscope Study of Virus-like Particles in Chick Embryo and L Cell Cultures. J. Gen. Virol., 2:195-198.

Cruickshank, J. G., D. M. Berry, and B. Hay (1963): The Fine Structure of Infectious Laryngotracheitis Virus. Virology, 20:376-378.

Dales, S. (1962a): Attachment and Uptake of Animal Viruses as Studied by Electron Microscopy. Cold Spring Harbor Symposia Quant. Biol., 27:132-136.

Dales, S. (1962b): An Electron Microscope Study of the Early Association Between Two Mammalian Viruses and Their Hosts. J. Cell Biol., 13:303-322.

Dales, S. (1963a): The Uptake and Development of Vaccinia Virus in Strain L Cells Followed with Labeled Viral Deoxyribonucleic Acid. J. Cell Biol., 18:51-72.

Dales, S. (1963b): Association Between the Spindle Apparatus and Reovirus. Proc. Natl. Acad. Sci., 50:268-275.

Dales, S. (1965a): Penetration of Animal Viruses into Cells. Progr. Med. Virol., 7:1-43.

Dales, S. (1965b): Effects of Streptovitacin A on the Initial Events in the Replication of Vaccinia and Reovirus. Proc. Natl. Acad. Sci., 54:462-468.

Dales, S., P. J. Gomatos, and K. C. Hsu (1965): The Uptake and Development of Reovirus in Strain L Cells Followed with Labeled Viral Ribonucleic Acid and Ferritin-Antibody Conjugates. Virology, 25:193-211.

Dales, S., and R. Kajioka (1964): The Cycle of Multiplication of Vaccinia Virus in Earle's Strain L Cells; I, Uptake and Penetration. Virology, 24:278-294.

Dales, S., and L. Siminovitch (1961): The Development of Vaccinia Virus in Earle's L Strain Cells as Examined by Electron Microscopy. J. Biophys. Biochem. Cyto., 10:475-503.

Dalgarno, L., R. A. Cox, and E. M. Martin (1967): Polyribosomes in Normal Krebs 2 Ascites Tumor Cells and in Cells Infected with Encephalomyocarditis Virus. Biochim. Biophys. Acta, 138:316-328.

Dalldorf, G., C. A. Linsell, F. E. Barnhart, and R. Martyn (1964): An Epidemiologic Approach to the Lymphomas of African Children and Burkitt's Sarcoma of the Jaws. Pers. Biol. Med., 7:435-449.

Dalton, A. J., et al. (1966): Suggestions for the Classification of Oncogenic RNA Viruses. J. Natl. Cancer Inst., 37:395-397.

Dann-Markert, A., H. F. Deutsch, and W. Zillig (1966): Studies on the Coat Protein of Bacteriophage ϕX174. Virology, 29:126-132.

Darbyshire, J. H. (1966): Oncogenicity of Bovine Adenovirus Type 3 in Hamsters. Nature, 211:102.

Darken, M. A. (1964): Puromycin Inhibition of Protein Synthesis. Pharm. Rev., 16:223-243.

Darlington, R. W., A. Granoff, and D. C. Breeze (1966): Viruses and Renal Carcinoma of Rana pipiens; II, Ultrastructural Studies and Sequential Development of Virus Isolated from Normal and Tumor Tissue. Virology, 29:149-156.

Darlington, R. W., and L. H. Moss, III (1968): Herpesvirus Envelopment. J. Virol., 2:48-55.

Darnell, J. E., M. Girard, D. Baltimore, D. F. Summers, and J. V. Maizel (1967): The Synthesis and Translation of Poliovirus RNA. In Colter, J. S:, and W. Paranchych (eds.): The Molecular Biology of Viruses. New York, Academic Press Inc., pp. 375-401.

Davies, M. C., M. E. Englert, M. R. Stebbins, and V. J. Cabasso (1961): Electron Microscopic Structure of Infectious Canine Hepatitis (ICH) Virus—A Canine Adenovirus. Virology, 15:87-88.

Davies, W. L., R. R. Grunert, R. F. Haff, J. W. McGahen, E. M. Neumayer, M. Paulshock, J. C. Watts, T. R. Wood, E. C. Hermann, and C. E. Hoffman (1964): Antiviral Activity of 1-Adamantanamine (Amantadine). Science, 144:862-863.

Davis, J. E., and R. L. Sinsheimer (1963): The Replication of Bacteriophage MS2; I, Transfer of Parental Nucleic Acid to Progeny Phage. J. Mol. Biol., 6:203-207.

Defendi, V. (1967): Discussion following Rowe, W. P.: Virus-Specific Antigens in Viral Tumors. In Trentin, J. (ed.): Cross-Reacting Antigens and Neoantigens. Baltimore, The Williams and Wilkins Co., pp. 74-84.

Defendi, V., and G. Gasic (1963): Surface Mucopolysaccharides of Polyoma Virus Transformed Cells. J. Cell. Comp. Physiol., 62:23-32.

Defendi, V., and F. Jensen (1967): Oncogenicity by DNA Tumor Viruses; Enhancement after Ultraviolet and Cobalt-60 Radiations. Science, 157:703-705.

Defendi, V., F. Jensen, and G. Sauer (1967): Analysis of Some Viral Functions Related to Neoplastic Transformation. In Colter, J. S., and W. Paranchych (eds.): The Molecular Biology of Viruses. New York, Academic Press Inc., pp. 645-663.

de Harven, E., and C. Friend (1960): Further Electron Microscope Studies of a Mouse Leukemia Induced by Cell-Free Filtrates. J. Biophys. Biochem. Cyto., 7:747-752.

de Harven, E., and D. S. Yohn (1966): The Fine Structure of the Yaba Monkey Tumor Poxvirus. Cancer Res., 26:995-1008.

Deinhardt, F. (1966): Neoplasms Induced by Rous Sarcoma Virus in New World Monkeys. Nature, 210:443.

Delamore, I. W., and W. H. Prusoff (1962): Effect of 5-Iodo-2'-deoxyuridine on the Biosynthesis of Phosphorylated Derivatives of Thymidine. Biochem. Pharm., 11:101-112.

Delbrück, M. (1940): The Growth of Bacteriophage and Lysis of the Host. J. Gen. Physiol., 23:643-660. Reprinted in Stent, G. S. (1960): Papers on Bacterial Viruses. Boston, Little, Brown and Co., pp. 57-74.

Delbrück, M. (1945): Effects of Specific Antisera on the Growth of Bacterial Viruses (Bacteriophages). J. Bacteriol., 50:137-150.

Delbrück, M., and W. T. Bailey, Jr. (1946): Induced Mutations in Bacterial Viruses. Cold Spring Harbor Symposia Quant. Biol., 11:33-37.

De Maeyer, E. (1962): Organ Cultures of Newborn Rabbit Skin Affected by Rabbit Papilloma Virus. Science, 136:985-986.

De Mars, R. I. (1955): The Production of Phage-Related Materials when Bacteriophage Development Is Interrupted by Proflavine. Virology, 1:83-99.

Denhardt, D. T., D. H. Dressler, and A. Hathaway (1967): The Abortive Replication of ϕX174 DNA in a Recombination-Deficient Mutant of Escherichia coli. Proc. Natl. Acad. Sci., 57:813-820.

Denhardt, D. T., and R. B. Silver (1966): An Analysis of the Clone Size Distribution of ϕX174 Mutants and Recombinants. Virology, 30:10-19.

Denhardt, D. T., and R. L. Sinsheimer (1965a): The Process of Infection with Bacteriophage ϕX174; III, Phage Maturation and Lysis after Synchronized Infection. J. Mol. Biol., 12:641-646.

Denhardt, D. T., and R. L. Sinsheimer (1965b): The Process of Infection with Bacteriophage ϕX174; IV, Replication of the Viral DNA in a Synchronized Infection. J. Mol. Biol., 12:647-662.

Denhardt, D. T., and R. L. Sinsheimer (1965c): The Process of Infection with Bacteriophage ϕX174; V, Inactivation of the Phage-Bacterium Complex by Decay of ^{32}P Incorporated in the Infecting Particle. J. Mol. Biol., 12:663-673.

Denhardt, D. T., and R. L. Sinsheimer (1965d): The Process of Infection with Bacteriophage ϕX174; VI, Inactivation of Infected Complexes by Ultraviolet Irradiation. J. Mol. Biol., 12:674-694.

DeOme, K. B. (1963): The Role of the Mammary Tumor Virus in Mouse Mammary Noduligenesis and Tumorigenesis. In Viruses, Nucleic Acids, and Cancer. Baltimore, The Williams and Wilkins Co., pp. 498-507.

Desmyter, J., W. E. Rawls, and J. L. Melnick (1968): A Human Interferon That Crosses the Species Line. Proc. Natl. Acad. Sci., 59:69-76.

de Somer, P., A. Prinzie, P. Denys, Jr., and E. Schonne (1962): Mechanism of Action of Interferon; I, Relationship with Viral Ribonucleic Acid. Virology, 16:63-70.

de Somer, P., A. Prinzie, and E. Schonne (1959): Infectivity of Polio Virus Ribonucleic Acid for Embryonated Eggs and Unsusceptible Cell Lines. Nature, 184:652-653.

d'Herelle, F. (1922): Discussion on the Bacteriophage (Bacteriolysin): I, The Nature of Bacteriophage. British Med. J., 2:289-297. Reprinted in Stent, G. S. (1960): Papers on Bacterial Viruses. Boston, Little, Brown and Co., pp. 3-13.

Diener, T. O., and W. B. Raymer (1967): Potato Spindle Tuber Virus; a Plant Virus with Properties of a Free Nucleic Acid. Science, 158:378-381.

Di Mayorca, G. A., B. E. Eddy, S. E. Stewart, W. S. Hunter, C. Friend, and A. Bendich (1959): Isolation of Infectious Deoxyribonucleic Acid from S E Polyoma-Infected Tissue Cultures. Proc. Natl. Acad. Sci., 45:1805-1808.

Doermann, A. H. (1948): Lysis and Lysis Inhibition with *Escherichia coli* Bacteriophage. J. Bacteriol., 55:257-276.

Doermann, A. H. (1952): The Intracellular Growth of Bacteriophages; I, Liberation of Intracellular Bacteriophage T4 by Premature Lysis with Another Phage or with Cyanide. J. Gen. Physiol., 35:645-656. Reprinted in Stent, G. S. (1960): Papers on Bacterial Viruses. Boston, Little, Brown and Co., pp. 75-86.

Doermann, A. H. (1953): The Vegetative State in the Life Cycle of Bacteriophage; Evidence for Its Occurrence and Its Genetic Characterization. Cold Spring Harbor Symposia Quant. Biol., 18:3-11.

Doi, R. H., and S. Spiegelman (1962): Homology Test Between the Nucleic Acid of an RNA Virus and the DNA in the Host Cell. Science, 138:1270-1272.

Doi, R. H., and S. Spiegelman (1963): Conservation of a Viral RNA Genome During Replication and Translation. Proc. Natl. Acad. Sci., 49:353-360.

Doty, P., J. Marmur, J. Eigner, and C. Schildkraut (1960): Strand Separation and Specific Recombination in Deoxyribonucleic Acids; Physical Chemical Studies. Proc. Natl. Acad. Sci., 46:461-476.

Dove, W. F. (1966): Action of the Lambda Chromosome; I, Control of Functions Late in Bacteriophage Development. J. Mol. Biol., 19:187-201.

Dove, W. F., and J. J. Weigle (1965): Intracellular State of the Chromosome of Bacteriophage Lambda; I, The Eclipse of Infectivity of the Bacteriophage DNA. J. Mol. Biol., 12:620-629.

Dowell, C. E. (1967): Cold-Sensitive Mutants of Bacteriophage ϕX174; I, A Mutant Blocked in the Eclipse Function at Low Temperature. Proc. Natl. Acad. Sci., 58:958-961.

Drake, J. W. (1966a): Heteroduplex Heterozygotes in Bacteriophage T4 Involving Mutations of Various Dimensions. Proc. Natl. Acad. Sci., 55:506-512.

Drake, J. W. (1966b): Spontaneous Mutations Accumulating in Bacteriophage T4 in the Complete Absence of DNA Replication. Proc. Natl. Acad. Sci., 55:738-743.

Drake, J. W. (1967): The Length of the Homologous Pairing Region for Genetic Recombination in Bacteriophage T4. Proc. Natl. Acad. Sci., 58:962-966.

Drake, J. W., and P. A. Lay (1962): Host-Controlled Variation in NDV. Virology, 17:56-64.

Drzeniek, R., J. T. Seto, and R. Rott (1966): Characterization of Neuraminidases from Myxoviruses. Biochim. Biophys. Acta, 128:547-558.

Dubbs, D. R., and S. Kit (1964a): Isolation and Properties of Vaccinia Mutants Deficient in Thymidine Kinase-Inducing Activity. Virology, 22:214-225.

Dubbs, D. R., and S. Kit (1964b): Mutant Strains of Herpes Simplex Deficient in Thymidine Kinase-Inducing Activity. Virology, 22:493-502.

Dubbs, D. R., and S. Kit (1965): The Effect of Temperature on Induction of Deoxythymidine Kinase Activity by Herpes Simplex Mutants. Virology, 25:256-270.

Dubbs, D. R., S. Kit, R. A. de Torres, and M. Anken (1967): Virogenic Properties of Bromodeoxyuridine-Sensitive and Bromodeoxyuridine-Resistant Simian Virus 40-Transformed Mouse Kidney Cells. J. Virol., 1:968-979.

Dulbecco, R. (1949): Reactivation of Ultra-Violet-Inactivated Bacteriophage by Visible Light. Nature, 163:949-950.

Dulbecco, R. (1950): Experiments on Photoreactivation of Bacteriophages Inactivated with Ultraviolet Radiation. J. Bacteriol., 59:329-347. Reprinted in Stent, G. S. (1960): Papers on Bacterial Viruses. Boston, Little, Brown and Co., pp. 228-246.

Dulbecco, R. (1952): Production of Plaques in Monolayer Tissue Cultures by Single Particles of an Animal Virus. Proc. Natl. Acad. Sci., 38:747-752.

Dulbecco, R. (1957): Clonal Derivation of Viruses. Ann. N. Y. Acad. Sci., 68:245-249.

Dulbecco, R. (1963a): Properties of the DNA of Polyoma Virus. *In* Viruses, Nucleic Acids, and Cancer. Baltimore, The Williams and Wilkins Co., pp. 271-281.

Dulbecco, R. (1963b): Transformation of Cells in Vitro by Viruses. Science, 142:932-936.

Dulbecco, R. (1964): Transformation of Cells in Vitro by DNA-Containing Viruses. J.A.M.A., 190:721-726.

Dulbecco, R. (1965): Characteristics of Virus-Cell Complexes. Amer. J. Med., 38:669-677.

Dulbecco, R. (1967): The Induction of Cancer by Viruses. Sci. Amer., 216(April):28-37.

Dulbecco, R., L. H. Hartwell, and M. Vogt (1965): Induction of Cellular DNA Synthesis by Polyoma Virus. Proc. Natl. Acad. Sci., 53:403-410.

Dulbecco, R., and M. Vogt (1954): Plaque Formation and Isolation of Pure Lines with Poliomyelitis Viruses. J. Exptl. Med., 99:167-182.

Dulbecco, R., and M. Vogt (1958): Study of the Mutability of d Lines of Polioviruses. Virology, 5:220-235.

Dulbecco, R., and M. Vogt (1960): Significance of Continued Virus Production in Tissue Cultures Rendered Neoplastic by Polyoma Virus. Proc. Natl. Acad. Sci., 46:1617-1623.

Dulbecco, R., and M. Vogt (1963): Evidence for a Ring Structure of Polyoma Virus DNA. Proc. Natl. Acad. Sci., 50:236-243.

Dulbecco, R., M. Vogt, and A. G. R. Strickland (1956): A Study of the Basic Aspects of Neutralization of Two Animal Viruses, Western Equine Encephalitis Virus and Poliomyelitis Virus. Virology, 2:162-205.

Dunnebacke, T. A. (1962): Amounts of Polio and Coxsackie Viruses Within the Separate Portions of Bisected Cultured Cells. Virology, 16:392-397.

Dunnill, P. (1967): Sequence Similarities Between Hen Egg-white and T4 Phage Lysozymes. Nature, 215:621-622.

Duryee, W. R., M. E. Long, H. C. Taylor, Jr., W. P. McKelway, and R. L. Ehrmann (1960): Human and Amphibian Neoplasms Compared. Science, 131:276-280.

Eason, R., M. J. Cline, and R. M. S. Smellie (1963): Ribonucleic Acid-Primed Synthesis of RNA Following Viral Infection. Nature, 198:479-481.

Easterbrook, K. B. (1963): Conservation of Vaccinial DNA during an Abortive Cycle of Multiplication. Virology, 21:508-510.

Easterbrook, K. B. (1966): Controlled Degradation of Vaccinia Virions *in Vitro*; an Electron Microscopic Study. J. Ultrastructure Res., 14:484-496.

Easterbrook, K. B. (1967): Morphology of Deoxyribonucleic Acid Extracted from Cores of Vaccinia Virus. J. Virol., 1:643-645.

Easton, J. M., and C. W. Hiatt (1965): Possible Incorporation of SV40 Genome Within Capsid Proteins of Adenovirus 4. Proc. Natl. Acad. Sci., 54:1100-1104.

Easton, J. M., and C. W. Hiatt (1966): Simian Virus 40; Replication in the Presence of Specific Antiserum and Adenovirus 4. Science, 151:582-583.

Echols, H., L. Pilarski, and P. Y. Cheng (1968): *In Vitro* Repression of Phage λ DNA Transcription by a Partially Purified Repressor from Lysogenic Cells. Proc. Natl. Acad. Sci., 59:1016-1023.

Eddy, B. E., G. S. Borman, W. H. Berkeley, and R. D. Young (1961): Tumors Induced in Hamsters by Injection of Rhesus Monkey Kidney Cell Extracts. Proc. Soc. Exptl. Biol. Med., 107:191-197.

Eddy, B. E., G. S. Borman, G. E. Grubbs, and R. D. Young (1962): Identification of the Oncogenic Substance in Rhesus Monkey Kidney Cell Cultures as Simian Virus 40. Virology, 17:65-75.

Edelman, G. M., and J. A. Gally (1964): A Model for the 7S Antibody Molecule. Proc. Natl. Acad. Sci., 51:846-853.

Edelman, G. M., and J. A. Gally (1967): Somatic Recombination of Duplicated Genes; an Hypothesis on the Origin of Antibody Diversity. Proc. Natl. Acad. Sci., 57:353-358.

Edgar, R. S., and R. H. Epstein (1965): The Genetics of a Bacterial Virus. Sci. Amer., 212(Feb.):71-78.

Edgar, R. S., and W. B. Wood (1966): Morphogenesis of Bacteriophage T4 in Extracts of Mutant-Infected Cells. Proc. Natl. Acad. Sci., 55:498-505.

Eggen, K., M. P. Oeschger, and D. Nathans (1967): Cell-Free Protein Synthesis Directed by Coliphage MS2 RNA; Sequential Synthesis of Specific Phage Proteins. Biochem. Biophys. Res. Commun., 28:587-597.

Eggers, H. J., D. Baltimore, and I. Tamm (1963): The Relation of Protein Synthesis to Formation of Poliovirus RNA Polymerase. Virology, 21:281-283.

Eidinoff, M. L., B. Bates, M. Steinglass, and J. R. Haddad (1965): Subcutaneous Sarcomata in Hamsters Induced by Rous Sarcoma Virus (Bryan). Nature, 208:336-338.

Elford, W. J. (1938): The Sizes of Viruses and Bacteriophages and Methods for Their Determination. *In* Doer, R., and C. Hallauer (eds.): Handbuch der Virusforschung. Vienna, Springer, pp. 126-231.

Ellermann, V., and O. Bang (1908): Experimentelle Leukämie bei Hühnern. Centr. Bakteriol. Parasitenk., Abt. I (Orig), 46:595-609.

Ellis, E. L., and M. Delbrück (1939): The Growth of Bacteriophage. J. Gen. Physiol., 22:365-384. Reprinted in Stent, G. S. (1960): Papers on Bacterial Viruses. Boston, Little, Brown and Co., pp. 37-56.

Enders, J. F., A. Holloway, and E. A. Grogan (1967): Replication of Poliovirus I in Chick Embryo and Hamster Cells Exposed to Sendai Virus. Proc. Natl. Acad. Sci., 57:637-644.

Epstein, M. A., G. Henle, B. G. Achong, and Y. M. Barr (1965): Morphological and Biological Studies on a Virus in Cultured Lymphoblasts from Burkitt's Lymphoma. J. Exptl. Med., 121:761-770.

Epstein, M. A., K. Hummeler, and A. Berkaloff (1964): The Entry and Distribution of Herpes Virus and Colloidal Gold in HeLa Cells after Contact in Suspension. J. Exptl. Med., 119:291-302.

Epstein, R. H., A. Bolle, C. M. Steinberg, E. Kellenberger, E. Boy de la Tour, R. Chevalley, R. S. Edgar, M. Susman, G. H. Denhardt, and A. Lielausis (1963): Physiological Studies of Conditional Lethal Mutants of Bacteriophage T4D. Cold Spring Harbor Symposia Quant. Biol., 28:375-394.

Erikson, R. L., and E. Erikson (1967): Structure and Function of Bacteriophage R17 Replicative Intermediate Ribonucleic Acid; II, Properties of the Parental Labeled Molecule. J. Virol., 1:523-528.

Erikson, R. L., M. L. Fenwick, and R. M. Franklin (1964): Replication of Bacteriophage RNA; Studies on the Fate of Parental RNA. J. Mol. Biol., 10:519-529.

Erikson, R. L., and R. M. Franklin (1966): Symposium on Replication of Viral Nucleic Acids; I, Formation and Properties of a Replicative Intermediate in the Biosynthesis of Viral Ribonucleic Acid. Bacteriol. Rev., 30:267-278.

Fantes, K. H. (1966): Purification, Concentration and Physico-Chemical Properties of Interferons. *In* Finter, N. B. (ed.): Interferons. Philadelphia, W. B. Saunders Co., pp. 119-180.

Fazekas de St. Groth, S. (1948): Viropexis, the Mechanism of Influenza Virus Infection. Nature, 162:294-295.

Fazekas de St. Groth, S. (1962): The Neutralization of Viruses. Adv. Virus Res., 9:1-125.

Fazekas de St. Groth, S., and A. F. Reid (1958): The Neutralization of Animal Viruses; II, A Critical Comparison of Hypotheses. J. Immunol., 80:225-235.

Fazekas de St. Groth, S., G. S. Watson, and A. F. Reid (1958): The Neutralization of Animal Viruses; I, A Model of Virus-Antibody Interaction. J. Immunol., 80:215-224.

Feix G., R. Pollet, and C. Weissmann (1968): Replication of Viral RNA; XVI, Enzymatic Synthesis of Infectious Viral RNA with Noninfectious Qβ Minus Strands as Template. Proc. Natl. Acad. Sci., 59:145-152.

Feix, G., M. C. Schneider, C. Weissmann, and S. Ochoa (1967a): Replication of Viral RNA; RNA Synthetase from *Escherichia coli* Infected with Phage MS2 or Qβ. Science, 157:701-703.

Feix, G., H. Slor, and C. Weissmann (1967b): Replication of Viral RNA; XIII, The Early Product of Phage RNA Synthesis *in Vitro*. Proc. Natl. Acad. Sci., 57:1401-1408.

Fenner, F. (1959): Myxomatosis. British Med. Bull., 15:240-245.

Fenner, F. (1965a): Immune Mechanisms in Viral Infections. *In* Horsfall, F. L., Jr., and I. Tamm (eds.): Viral and Rickettsial Infections of Man. Philadelphia, J. B. Lippincott Co., pp. 356-384.

Fenner, F. (1965b): Conditional Lethal Mutants in the Study of the Genetics of Animal Viruses. *In* Pollard, M. (ed.): Perspectives in Virology, Vol. 4. New York, Harper & Row, pp. 34-46.

Fenner, F., and J. F. Sambrook (1964): The Genetics of Animal Viruses. Ann. Rev. Microbiol., 18:47-94.

Fenwick, M. L. (1963): The Influence of Poliovirus Infection on RNA Synthesis in Mammalian Cells. Virology, 19:241-249.

Fenwick, M. L., and P. D. Cooper (1962): Early Interactions Between Poliovirus and ERK Cells; Some Observations on the Nature and Significance of the Rejected Particles. Virology, 18:212-223.

Fenwick, M. L., R. L. Erikson, and R. M. Franklin (1964): Replication of the RNA of Bacteriophage R17. Science, 146:527-530.

Field, A. K., G. P. Lampson, A. A. Tytell, M. M. Nemes, and M. R. Hilleman (1967a): Inducers of Interferon and Host Resistance; IV, Double-Stranded Replicative Form RNA (MS2-RF-RNA) from E. coli Infected with MS2 Coliphage. Proc. Natl. Acad. Sci., 58:2102-2108.

Field, A. K., A. A. Tytell, G. P. Lampson, and M. R. Hilleman (1967b): Inducers of Interferon and Host Resistance; II, Multistranded Synthetic Polynucleotide Complexes. Proc. Natl. Acad. Sci., 58:1004-1010.

Fiers, W., and R. L. Sinsheimer (1962a): The Structure of the DNA of Bacteriophage ϕX174; I, The Action of Exopolynucleotidases. J. Mol. Biol., 5:408-419.

Fiers, W., and R. L. Sinsheimer (1962b): The Structure of the DNA of Bacteriophage ϕX174; II, Thermal Inactivation. J. Mol. Biol., 5:420-423.

Fiers, W., and R. L. Sinsheimer (1962c): The Structure of the DNA of Bacteriophage ϕX174; III, Ultracentrifugal Evidence for a Ring Structure. J. Mol. Biol., 5:424-434.

Finch, J. T., and A. Klug (1965): The Structure of Viruses of the Papilloma-Polyoma Type; III, Structure of Rabbit Papilloma Virus, J. Mol. Biol., 13:1-12.

Finch, J. T., and A. Klug (1966): Arrangement of Protein Subunits and the Distribution of Nucleic Acid in Turnip Yellow Mosaic Virus; II, Electron Microscopic Studies. J. Mol. Biol., 15:344-364.

Finney, D. J. (1952): Probit Analysis. Cambridge, The University Press.

Finter, N. B. (1966): Interferons in Animals and Man. In Finter, N. B. (ed.): Interferons. Philadelphia, W. B. Saunders Co., pp. 232-267.

Finter, N. B. (1967): Interferon in Mice; Protection against Small Doses of Virus. J. Gen. Virol., 1:395-397.

Finter, N. B. (1968): Interferon as a Potential Antiviral Drug. In Sanders, M., and E. H. Lennette (eds.): Medical and Applied Virology. St. Louis, Warren H. Green, Inc., pp. 190-198.

Fischer, D. S. (1964): Theories of Antibody Formation; a Review. Yale J. Biol. Med., 37:1-30.

Flaks, J. G., and S. S. Cohen (1957): The Enzymic Synthesis of 5-hydroxymethyldeoxy-cytidylic Acid. Biochim. Biophys. Acta, 25:667-668.

Flaks, J. G., and S. S. Cohen (1959a): Virus-Induced Acquisition of Metabolic Function; I, Enzymatic Formation of 5-Hydroxymethyldeoxyctidylate. J. Biol. Chem., 234:1501-1506.

Flaks, J. G., and S. S. Cohen (1959b): Virus-Induced Acquisition of Metabolic Function; III, Formation and Some Properties of Thymidylate Synthetase of Bacteriophage-Infected Escherichia coli. J. Biol. Chem., 234:2981-2986.

Flaks, J. G., J. Lichtenstein, and S. S. Cohen (1959): Virus-Induced Acquisition of Metabolic Function; II, Studies on the Origin of the Deoxycytidylate Hydroxymethylase of Bacteriophage-Infected E. coli. J. Biol. Chem., 234:1507-1511.

Flanagan, J. F. (1967): Virus-Specific Ribonucleic Acid Synthesis in KB Cells Infected with Herpes Simplex Virus. J. Virol., 1:583-590.

Flanagan, J. F., and H. S. Ginsberg (1964): Role of Ribonucleic Acid Biosynthesis in Multiplication of Type 5 Adenovirus. J. Bacteriol., 87:977-987.

Follett, E. A. C., and L. V. Crawford (1967a): Electron Microscope Study of the Denaturation of Human Papilloma Virus DNA; I, Loss and Reversal of Supercoiling Turns. J. Mol. Biol., 28:455-459.

Follett, E. A. C., and L. V. Crawford (1967b): Electron Microscope Study of the Denaturation of Human Papilloma Virus DNA; II, The Specific Location of Denatured Regions. J. Mol. Biol., 28:461-467.

Fraenkel-Conrat, H. (1964): The Genetic Code of a Virus. Sci. Amer., 211(Oct.):46-54.

Fraenkel-Conrat, H., and R. C. Williams (1955): Reconstitution of Active Tobacco Mosaic Virus from Its Inactive Protein and Nucleic Acid Components. Proc. Natl. Acad. Sci., 41:690-698.

Francke, B., and P. H. Hofschneider (1966a): Infectious Nucleic Acids of E. coli Bacteriophages; IX, Sedimentation Constants and Strand Integrity of Infectious M12 Phage Replicative-Form RNA. Proc. Natl. Acad. Sci., 56:1883-1890.

Francke, B., and P. H. Hofschneider (1966b): Über infektiöse Substrukturen aus *Escherichia coli* Bakteriophagen; VII, Formation of a Biologically Intact Replicative Form in Ribonucleic Acid Bacteriophage (M12)-infected Cells. J. Mol. Biol., 16:544-552.

Franklin, N. C. (1961): Serological Study of Tail Structure and Function in Coliphages T2 and T4. Virology, 14:417-429.

Franklin, R. M. (1966): Purification and Properties of the Replicative Intermediate of the RNA Bacteriophage R17. Proc. Natl. Acad. Sci., 55:1504-1511.

Franklin, R. M. (1967): Replication of Bacteriophage Ribonucleic Acid; Some Properties of Native and Denatured Replicative Intermediate. J. Virol., 1:514-522.

Franklin, R. M., and D. Baltimore (1962): Patterns of Macromolecular Synthesis in Normal and Virus-Infected Mammalian Cells. Cold Spring Harbor Symposia Quant. Biol., 27:175-198.

Franklin, R. M., and J. Rosner (1962): Localization of Ribonucleic Acid Synthesis in Mengovirus-Infected L-Cells. Biochim. Biophys. Acta, 55:240-241.

Frearson, P. M., S. Kit, and D. R. Dubbs (1965): Deoxythymidylate Synthetase and Deoxythymidine Kinase Activities of Virus-Infected Animal Cells. Cancer Res., 25:737-744.

Frearson, P. M., S. Kit, and D. R. Dubbs (1966): Induction of Dihydrofolate Reductase Activity by SV40 and Polyoma Virus. Cancer Res., 26:1653-1660.

Freeman, A. E., P. H. Black, E. A. Vanderpool, P. H. Henry, J. B. Austin, and R. J. Huebner (1967a): Transformation of Primary Rat Embryo Cells by Adenovirus Type 2. Proc. Natl. Acad. Sci., 58:1205-1212.

Freeman, A. E., P. H. Black, R. Wolford, and R. J. Huebner (1967b): Adenovirus Type 12-Rat Embryo Transformation System. J. Virol., 1:362-367.

Freeman, A. E., S. Hollinger, P. J. Price, and C. H. Calisher (1965): The Effect of Calcium on Cell Lines Derived from Adenovirus Type 12-Induced Hamster Tumors. Exptl. Cell Res., 39:259-264.

Freeman, A. E., E. A. Vanderpool, P. H. Black, C. Turner, and R. J. Huebner (1967c): Transformation of Primary Rat Embryo Cells by a Weakly Oncogenic Adenovirus-Type 3. Nature, 216:171-173.

Freeman, V. J. (1951): Studies on the Virulence of Bacteriophage-Infected Strains of Corynebacterium Diphtheriae. J. Bacteriol., 61:675-688.

Freese, E. (1963): The Molecular Mechanisms of Mutations. *In* Engelhardt, V. A. (ed.): Proc. Fifth Intern. Congr. Biochem., Vol. 1. New York, Pergamon Press, pp. 204-229.

Freifelder, D. (1965): Mechanism of Inactivation of Coliphage T7 by X Rays. Proc. Natl. Acad. Sci., 54:128-134.

Freifelder, D. (1966): DNA Strand Breakage by X-irradiation. Radiation Res., 29:329-338.

Freifelder, D., A. K. Kleinschmidt, and R. L. Sinsheimer (1964): Electron Microscopy of Single-Stranded DNA; Circularity of DNA of Bacteriophage ϕX174. Science, 146:254-255.

Freitag, J. H. (1964): Interaction and Mutual Suppression Among Three Strains of Aster Yellow Virus. Virology, 24:401-413.

Fried, M. (1965a): Isolation of Temperature-Sensitive Mutants of Polyoma Virus. Virology, 25:669-671.

Fried, M. (1965b): Cell-Transforming Ability of a Temperature-Sensitive Mutant of Polyoma Virus. Proc. Natl. Acad. Sci., 53:486-491.

Friedman, R. M., and I. K. Berezesky (1967): Cytoplasmic Fractions Associated with Semliki Forest Virus Ribonucleic Acid Replication. J. Virol., 1:374-383.

Friedman, R. M., K. H. Fantes, H. B. Levy, and W. B. Carter (1967): Interferon Action on Parental Semliki Forest Virus Ribonucleic Acid. J. Virol., 1:1168-1173.

Friedman, R. M., H. B. Levy, and W. B. Carter (1966): Replication of Semliki Forest Virus; Three Forms of Viral RNA Produced During Infection. Proc. Natl. Acad. Sci., 56:440-446.

Friedman, R. M., and A. S. Rabson (1964): Polyoma Virus Strains of Differing Oncogenicity; Transplantation Immunity in Mice. Virology, 23:273-274.

Friedman, R. M., and J. A. Sonnabend (1964): Inhibition of Interferon Action by *p*-Fluorophenylalanine. Nature, 203:366-367.

Friedman-Kien, A. E., W. P. Rowe, and W. G. Banfield (1963): Milker's Nodules; Isolation of a Poxvirus from a Human Case. Science, 140:1335-1336.

Friedman-Kien, A. E., and J. Vilcek (1967): Induction of Interference and Interferon Synthesis by Non-Replicating Molluscum Contagiosum Virus. J. Immunol., 99: 1092-1098.

Friend, C. (1959): Immunological Relationships of a Filterable Agent Causing a Leukemia in Adult Mice; I, The Neutralization of Infectivity by Specific Antiserum. J. Exptl. Med., 109:217-228.

Fujinaga, K., and M. Green (1966): The Mechanism of Viral Carcinogenesis by DNA Mammalian Viruses; Viral-Specific RNA in Polyribosomes of Adenovirus Tumor and Transformed Cells. Proc. Natl. Acad. Sci., 55:1567-1574.

Fujinaga, K., and M. Green (1967a): Mechanism of Viral Carcinogenesis by DNA Mammalian Viruses; II, Viral-Specific RNA in Tumor Cells Induced by "Weakly" Oncogenic Human Adenoviruses. Proc. Natl. Acad. Sci., 57:806-812.

Fujinaga, K., and M. Green (1967b); Mechanism of Viral Carcinogenesis by Deoxyribonucleic Acid Mammalian Viruses; IV, Related Virus-Specific Ribonucleic Acids in Tumor Cells Induced by "Highly" Oncogenic Adenovirus Types 12, 18, and 31. J. Virol., 1:576-582.

Furumoto, W. A., and R. Mickey (1967a): A Mathematical Model for the Infectivity-Dilution Curve of Tobacco Mosaic Virus: Theoretical Considerations. Virology, 32:216-223.

Furumoto, W. A., and R. Mickey (1967b): A Mathematical Model for the Infectivity-Dilution Curve of Tobacco Mosaic Virus: Experimental Tests. Virology, 32:224-233.

Gafford, L. G., and C. C. Randall (1967): The High Molecular Weight of the Fowlpox Virus Genome. J. Mol. Biol., 26:303-310.

Gajdusek, D. C., C. J. Gibbs, Jr., and M. Alpers (eds.) (1965): Slow, Latent, and Temperate Virus Infections. Washington, D.C., U. S. Government Printing Office.

Galasso, G. J., and D. G. Sharp (1964): Relative Plaque-Forming, Cell-Infecting, and Interfering Qualities of Vaccinia Virus. J. Bacteriol., 88:433-439.

Gard, S., and O. Maaløe (1959): Inactivation of Viruses. In Burnet, F. M., and W. M. Stanley (eds.): The Viruses, Vol. 1. New York, Academic Press, Inc., pp. 359-427.

Garen, A. (1968): Sense and Nonsense in the Genetic Code. Science, 160:149-159.

Gefter, M. L., A. Becker, and J. Hurwitz (1967): The Enzymatic Repair of DNA; I, Formation of Circular λDNA. Proc. Natl. Acad. Sci., 58:240-247.

Gelbard, A. S., S. H. Kim, and M. L. Eidinoff (1966): Nucleoside Kinase Activities in Tissues Infected with Rous Sarcoma Virus. Cancer Res., 26:748-751.

Gellert, M. (1967): Formation of Covalent Circles of Lambda DNA by E. coli Extracts. Proc. Natl. Acad. Sci., 57:148-155.

Gemmell, A., and F. Fenner (1960): Genetic Studies with Mammalian Poxviruses; III, White (u) Mutants of Rabbitpox Virus. Virology, 11:219-235.

Gerber, P. (1962): An Infectious Deoxyribonucleic Acid Derived from Vacuolating Virus (SV40). Virology, 16:96-98.

Gerber, P. (1963): Tumors Induced in Hamsters by Simian Virus 40: Persistent Subviral Infection. Science, 140:889-890.

Gerber, P. (1964): Virogenic Hamster Tumor Cells: Induction of Virus Synthesis. Science, 145:833.

Gerber, P. (1966): Studies on the Transfer of Subviral Infectivity from SV40-Induced Hamster Tumor Cells to Indicator Cells. Virology, 28:501-509.

Gerber, P., and S. M. Birch (1967): Complement-Fixing Antibodies in Sera of Human and Nonhuman Primates to Viral Antigens Derived from Burkitt's Lymphoma Cells. Proc. Natl. Acad. Sci., 58:478-484.

Gershon, D., and L. Sachs (1964): The Temporal Relationships of Protein and DNA Synthesis in Polyoma Virus Development. Virology, 24:604-609.

Gesteland, R. F., W. Salsar, and A. Bolle (1967): In Vitro Synthesis of T4 Lysozyme by Suppression of Amber Mutations. Proc. Natl. Acad. Sci., 58:2036-2042.

Gibbons, R. A., and G. D. Hunter (1967): Nature of the Scrapie Agent. Nature, 215:1041-1043.

Gibbs, A. J., B. D. Harrison, D. H. Watson, and P. Wildy (1966): What's in a Virus Name? Nature, 209:450-454.

Gibbs, C. J., Jr., D. C. Gajdusek, and J. A. Morris (1965): Viral Characteristics of the Scrapie Agent in Mice. *In* Gajdusek, D. C., C. J. Gibbs, Jr., and M. Alpers (eds.): Slow, Latent, and Temperate Virus Infections. Washington, D.C., U. S. Government Printing Office, pp. 195-202.

Gierer, A., and K. W. Mundry (1958): Production of Mutants of Tobacco Mosaic Virus by Chemical Alteration of Its Ribonucleic Acid *in Vitro*. Nature, 182:1457-1458.

Gilead, Z., and H. S. Ginsberg (1966): Comparison of the Rates of Ultraviolet Inactivation of the Capacity of Type 12 Adenovirus to Infect Cells and to Induce T Antigen Formation. J. Bacteriol., 92:1853-1854.

Gilead, Z., and H. S. Ginsberg (1968a): Characterization of the Tumorlike (T) Antigen Induced by Type 12 Adenovirus; I, Purification of the Antigen from Infected KB Cells and a Hamster Tumor Cell Line. J. Virol., 2:7-14.

Gilead, Z., and H. S. Ginsberg (1968b): Characterization of the Tumorlike (T) Antigen Induced by Type 12 Adenovirus; II, Physical and Chemical Properties. J. Virol., 2:15-20.

Gingery, R., and H. Echols (1967): Mutants of Bacteriophage λ Unable to Integrate into the Host Chromosome. Proc. Natl. Acad. Sci., 58:1507-1514.

Ginsberg, H. S. (1961): Biological and Biochemical Basis for Cell Injury by Animal Viruses. Fed. Proc., 20:656-660.

Ginsberg, H. S., H. G. Pereira, R. C. Valentine, and W. C. Wilcox (1966): A Proposed Terminology for the Adenovirus Antigens and Virion Morphological Subunits. Virology, 28:782-783.

Girardi, A. J., M. R. Hilleman, and R. E. Zwickey (1964): Tests in Hamsters for Oncogenic Quality of Ordinary Viruses Including Adenovirus Type 7. Proc. Soc. Exptl. Biol. Med., 115:1141-1150.

Girardi, A. J., B. H. Sweet, and M. R. Hilleman (1963): Factors Influencing Tumor Induction in Hamsters by Vacuolating Virus, SV40. Proc. Soc. Exptl. Biol. Med., 112:662-667.

Girardi, A. J., B. H. Sweet, V. B. Slotnick, and M. R. Hilleman (1962): Development of Tumors in Hamsters Inoculated in the Neonatal Period with Vacuolating Virus, SV40. Proc. Soc. Exptl. Biol. Med., 109:649-660.

Godson, G. N., and R. L. Sinsheimer (1967): The Replication of Bacteriophage MS2; VI, Interaction Between Bacteriophage RNA and Cellular Components in MS2-Infected *Escherichia coli*. J. Mol. Biol., 23:495-521.

Goldberg, E. B. (1966): The Amount of DNA Between Genetic Markers in Phage T4. Proc. Natl. Acad. Sci., 56:1457-1463.

Gomatos, P. J. (1967): RNA Synthesis in Reovirus-Infected L929 Mouse Fibroblasts. Proc. Natl. Acad. Sci., 58:1798-1805.

Gomatos, P. J., R. M. Krug, and I. Tamm (1964): Enzymic Synthesis of RNA with Reovirus RNA as Template. I. Characteristics of the Reaction Catalysed by the RNA Polymerase from *Escherichia coli*. J. Mol. Biol., 9:193-207.

Gomatos, P. J., and I. Tamm (1963): The Secondary Structure of Reovirus RNA. Proc. Natl. Acad. Sci., 49:707-714.

Gomatos, P. J., I. Tamm, S. Dales, and R. M. Franklin (1962): Reovirus Type 3: Physical Characteristics and Interaction with L Cells. Virology, 17:441-454.

Goodheart, C. R. (1965): A Density Mutant of Encephalomyocarditis Virus. Virology, 26:466-477.

Goodheart, C. R. (1967): Non-Transfer of RNA from Parent to Progeny of Encephalomyocarditis Virus. J. Mol. Biol., 23:183-190.

Goodheart, C. R., J. E. Filbert, and R. M. McAllister (1963): Human Cytomegalovirus; Effects of 5-Fluorodeoxyuridine on Viral Synthesis and Cytopathology. Virology, 21:530-532.

Goodheart, C. R., R. M. McAllister, and J. E. Filbert (1964): Human Cytomegalovirus; DNA Synthesis and Migration in Infected Cells Studied Autoradiographically. Virology, 23:603-608.

Gordon, I., S.S. Chenault, D. Stevenson, and J. D. Acton (1966): Effect of Interferon on Polymerization of Single-Stranded and Double-Stranded Mengovirus Ribonucleic Acid. J. Bacteriol., 91:1230-1238.

Gottschalk, A. (1959): Chemistry of Virus Receptors. *In* Burnet, F. M., and W. M. Stanley (eds.): The Viruses, Vol. 3. New York, Academic Press, Inc., pp. 51-61.

Goulian, M., A. Kornberg, and R. L. Sinsheimer (1967): Enzymatic Synthesis of DNA; XXIV, Synthesis of Infectious Phage φX174 DNA. Proc. Natl. Acad. Sci., 58:2321-2328.

Granboulan, N., and R. M. Franklin (1966): Electron Microscopy of Viral RNA, Replicative Form and Replicative Intermediate of the Bacteriophage R17. J. Mol. Biol., 22:173-177.

Granboulan, N., and R. M. Franklin (1968): Replication of Bacteriophage Ribonucleic Acid; Analysis of the Ultrastructure of the Replicative Form and the Replicative Intermediate of Bacteriophage R17. J. Virol., 2:129-148.

Granoff, A. (1961): Induction of Newcastle Disease Virus Mutants with Nitrous Acid. Virology, 13:402-408.

Gratia, A. (1922): Discussion on the Bacteriophage (Bacteriolysin); IV, Concerning the Theories of the So-Called "Bacteriophage." British Med. J., 2:289-297. Reprinted in Stent, G. S. (1960): Papers on Bacterial Viruses. Boston, Little, Brown and Co., pp. 23-25.

Green, M. (1962a): Studies on the Biosynthesis of Viral DNA. Cold Spring Harbor Symposia Quant. Biol., 27:219-235.

Green, M. (1962b): Biochemical Studies on Adenovirus Multiplication; III, Requirement for DNA Synthesis. Virology, 18:601-613.

Green, M. (1966): Biosynthetic Modifications Induced by DNA Animal Viruses. Ann. Rev. Microbiol., 20:189-222.

Green, M., and M. Piña (1962): Stimulation of the DNA-Synthesizing Enzymes of Cultured Human Cells by Vaccinia Virus Infection. Virology, 17:603-604.

Green, M., and M. Piña (1964): Biochemical Studies on Adenovirus Multiplication; VI, Properties of Highly Purified Tumorigenic Human Adenoviruses and Their DNA's. Proc. Natl. Acad. Sci., 51:1251-1259.

Green, M., M. Piña, and V. Chagoya (1964): Biochemical Studies on Adenovirus Multiplication; V, Enzymes of Deoxyribonucleic Acid Synthesis in Cells Infected by Adenovirus and Vaccinia Virus. J. Biol. Chem., 239:1188-1197.

Green, M., M. Piña, and R. C. Kimes (1967a): Biochemical Studies on Adenovirus Multiplication; XII, Plaquing Efficiencies of Purified Human Adenoviruses. Virology, 31:562-565.

Green, M., M. Piña, R. Kimes, P. C. Wensink, L. A. MacHattie, and C. A. Thomas, Jr. (1967b): Adenovirus DNA; I, Molecular Weight and Conformation. Proc. Natl. Acad. Sci., 57:1302-1309.

Green, M. H. (1966): Inactivation of the Prophage Lambda Repressor Without Induction. J. Mol. Biol., 16:134-148.

Green, M. H. (1967): Regulation of the Development of the Temperate Phage Lambda. In Colter, J. S., and W. Paranchych (eds.): The Molecular Biology of Viruses. New York, Academic Press Inc., pp. 139-158.

Green, M. H., B. Gotchel, J. Hendershott, and S. Kennel (1967): Regulation of Bacteriophage Lambda DNA Replication. Proc. Natl. Acad. Sci., 58:2343-2350.

Greenberg, G. R. (1966): New dUTPase and dUDPase Activities after Infection of Escherichia coli by T2 Bacteriophage. Proc. Natl. Acad. Sci., 56:1226-1232.

Greenberg, G. R., and R. L. Somerville (1962): Deoxyuridylate Kinase Activity and Deoxyuridinetriphosphatase in Escherichia coli. Proc. Natl. Acad. Sci., 48:247-257.

Greenberg, G. R., R. L. Somerville, and S. DeWolf (1962): Resolution of Phage-Initiated and Normal Host Thymidylate Synthetases of Escherichia coli. Proc. Natl. Acad. Sci., 48:242-247.

Griffith, J. S. (1967): Self-Replication and Scrapie. Nature, 215:1043-1044.

Groman, N. B. (1953): Evidence for the Induced Nature of the Change from Nontoxigenicity to Toxigenicity in Corynebacterium diphtheriae as a Result of Exposure to Specific Bacteriophage. J. Bacteriol., 66:184-191.

Groman, N. B. (1955): Evidence for the Active Role of Bacteriophage in the Conversion of Nontoxigenic Corynebacterium diphtheriae to Toxin Production. J. Bacteriol., 69:9-15.

Groman, N. B., M. Eaton, and Z. K. Booher (1958): Studies of Mono- and Polylysogenic Corynebacterium diphtheriae. J. Bacteriol., 75:320-325.

Gross, L. (1951a): "Spontaneous" Leukemia Developing in C3H Mice Following Inoculation, in Infancy, with AK-Leukemic Extracts, or AK-Embryos. Proc. Soc. Exptl. Biol. Med., 76:27-32.

Gross, L. (1951b): Pathogenic Properties, and "Vertical" Transmission of the Mouse Leukemia Agent. Proc. Soc. Exptl. Biol. Med., 78:342-348.

Gross, L. (1952): Mouse Leukemia. Ann. N.Y. Acad. Sci., 54:1184-1196.

Gross, L. (1961): "Vertical" Transmission of Passage A Leukemia Virus from Inoculated C3H Mice to Their Untreated Offspring. Proc. Soc. Exptl. Biol. Med., 107:90-93.

Gross, L. (1962a): Transmission of Mouse Leukemia Virus Through Milk of Virus-Injected C3H Female Mice. Proc. Soc. Exptl. Biol. Med., 109:830-836.

Gross, L. (1962b): Viral Etiology of Leukemia. Blut, 8:321-325.

Gross, L. (1963): Oncogenic Viruses. Ann. Roy. Coll. Surg. Eng., 33:67-78.

Gross, L. (1965a): Neutralization *in Vitro* of Mouse Leukemia Virus by Specific Immune Serum; Importance of Virus Titration. Proc. Soc. Exptl. Biol. Med., 119:420-427.

Gross, L. (1965b): Viral Etiology of Leukemia and Lymphomas. Blood, 25:377-381.

Gross, L. (1965c): Recent Studies on the Mouse Leukemia Virus. *In* Polland, M. (ed.): Perspectives in Virology, Vol. 4. New York, Harper & Row, pp. 226-256.

Guthrie, G. D., and R. L. Sinsheimer (1963): Observations on the Infection of Bacterial Protoplasts with the Deoxyribonucleic Acid of Bacteriophage ϕX174. Biochim. Biophys. Acta, 72:290-297.

Habel, K. (1961): Resistance of Polyoma Virus Immune Animals to Transplanted Polyoma Tumors. Proc. Soc. Exptl. Biol. Med., 106:722-725.

Habel, K. (1962a): Antigenic Properties of Cells Transformed by Polyoma Virus. Cold Spring Harbor Symposia Quant. Biol., 27:433-439.

Habel, K. (1962b): Immunological Determinants of Polyoma Virus Oncogenesis. J. Exptl. Med., 115:181-193.

Habel, K. (1966): Virus Tumor Antigens; Specific Fingerprints? Cancer Res., 26:2018-2024.

Habel, K., and B. E. Eddy (1963): Specificity of Resistance to Tumor Challenge of Polyoma and SV40 Virus-Immune Hamsters. Proc. Soc. Exptl. Biol. Med., 113:1-4.

Hackett, A. J. (1964): A Possible Morphological Basis for the Auto-Interference Phenomenon in Vesicular Stomatitis Virus. Virology, 24:51-59.

Haguenau, F., and H. Hanafusa (1968): A Quantitative Electron Microscopic Study of the Virus Particles Found in Cells Infected with Rous Sarcoma Virus. Virology, 34:275-281.

Hakomori, S., and W. T. Murakami (1968): Glycolipids of Hamster Fibroblasts and Derived Malignant-Transformed Cell Lines. Proc. Natl. Acad. Sci., 59:254-261.

Hall, B. D., A. P. Nygaard and M. H. Green (1964): Control of T2-Specific RNA Synthesis. J. Mol. Biol., 9:143-153.

Hall, B. D., and S. Spiegelman (1961): Sequence Complementarity of T2-DNA and T2-Specific RNA. Proc. Natl. Acad. Sci., 47:137-146.

Hall, W. T., W. F. Andresen, K. K. Sanford, and V. J. Evans (1967): Virus Particles and Murine Leukemia Virus Complement-Fixing Antigen in Neoplastic and Nonneoplastic Cell Lines. Science, 156:85-88.

Hall, W. T., and D. H. Moore (1966): Effects of Estrogenic Hormones on the Mammary Tissue of Agent-Free and Agent-Bearing Male Mice. J. Natl. Cancer Inst., 36:181-188.

Hallum, J. V., J. S. Youngner, and W. R. Stinebring (1965): Interferon Activity Associated with High Molecular Weight Proteins in the Circulation of Mice Injected with Endotoxin or Bacteria. Virology, 27:429-431.

Hamada, C., T. Kamiya, and A. S. Kaplan (1966): Serological Analysis of Some Enzymes Present in Pseudorabies Virus-Infected and Noninfected Cells. Virology, 28:271-281.

Hamparian, V. V., M. R. Hilleman, and A. Ketler (1963): Contributions to Characterization and Classification of Animal Viruses. Proc. Soc. Exptl. Biol. Med. 112:1040-1050.

Hanafusa, H. (1965): Analysis of the Defectiveness of Rous Sarcoma Virus; III, Determining Influence of a New Helper Virus on the Host Range and Susceptibility to Interference of RSV. Virology, 25:248-255.

Hanafusa, H., T. Hanafusa, and H. Rubin (1963): The Defectiveness of Rous Sarcoma Virus. Proc. Natl. Acad. Sci., 49:572-580.

Hanafusa, H., T. Hanafusa, and H. Rubin (1964): Analysis of the Defectiveness of Rous Sarcoma Virus; II, Specification of RSV Antigenicity by Helper Virus. Proc. Natl. Acad. Sci., 51:41-48.

Hanafusa, T. (1961): Enzymatic Synthesis and Breakdown of Deoxyribonucleic Acid by Extracts of L Cells Infected with Vaccinia Virus. Biken's J., 4:97-110.

Hanafusa, T., and H. Hanafusa (1967): Interaction Among Avian Tumor Viruses Giving Enhanced Infectivity. Proc. Natl. Acad. Sci., 58:818-825.

Hanawalt, P. C., and R. H. Haynes (1967): The Repair of DNA. Sci. Amer., 216(Feb.):36.

Hare, J. D. (1964): Transplant Immunity to Polyoma Virus Induced Tumors; I, Correlations with Biological Properties of Virus Strains. Proc. Soc. Exptl. Biol. Med., 115:805-810.

Hare, J. D. (1967): Analysis of Hamster Tumor Cell Lines Isolated from Single Colonies Soon After Induction by Polyoma Strains Differing in Transplant Antigen Production. J. Virol., 1:905-911.

Hare, J. D. and T. Godal (1965): Transplant Immunity to Polyoma Virus Induced Tumors; III, Evidence for Heterogeneity Among Transplant Antigens *in Vivo*. Proc. Soc. Exptl. Biol. Med., 118:632-636.

Harrison, B. D., and N. C. Crowley (1965): Properties and Structure of Lettuce Necrotic Yellows Virus. Virology, 26:297-310.

Hartley, J. W., and W. P. Rowe (1966): Production of Altered Cell Foci in Tissue Culture by Defective Moloney Sarcoma Virus Particles. Proc. Natl. Acad. Sci., 55:780-786.

Hartwell, L. H., M. Vogt, and R. Dulbecco (1965): Induction of Cellular DNA Synthesis by Polyoma Virus; II, Increase in the Rate of Enzyme Synthesis After Infection with Polyoma Virus in Mouse Kidney Cells. Virology, 27:262-272.

Haruna, I., K. Nozu, Y. Ohtaka, and S. Spiegelman (1963): An RNA "Replicase" Induced by and Selective for a Viral RNA; Isolation and Properties. Proc. Natl. Acad. Sci., 50:905-911.

Haruna, I., and S. Spiegelman (1965a): Specific Template Requirements of RNA Replicases. Proc. Nat. Acad. Sci., 54:579-587.

Haruna, I., and S. Spiegelman (1965b): Autocatalytic Synthesis of a Viral RNA *in Vitro*. Science, 150:884-886.

Haruna, I., and S. Spiegelman (1966): A Search for an Intermediate Involving a Complement During Synchronous Synthesis by a Purified RNA Replicase. Proc. Natl. Acad. Sci., 55:1256-1263.

Harvey, J. J. (1964): An Unidentified Virus Which Causes the Rapid Production of Tumours in Mice. Nature, 204:1104-1105.

Hasegawa, T. (1964): Effects of Electron Staining on Molluscum Contagiosum Virus. J. Invest. Dermatology, 42:281-283.

Haselkorn, R., V. A. Fried, and J. E. Dahlberg (1963): Cell-Free Protein Synthesis; the Association of Viral RNA and *E. coli* Ribosomes. Proc. Natl. Acad. Sci., 49:511-517.

Hashimoto, K., T. Sugiyama, and S. Sasaki (1966): An Adenovirus Isolated from the Feces of Mice; I, Isolation and Identification. Japan. J. Microbiol., 10:115-125.

Hatanaka, M., and R. Dulbecco (1967): SV40-Specific Thymidine Kinase. Proc. Natl. Acad. Sci., 58:1888-1894.

Hausen, P., and D. W. Verwoerd (1963): Studies on the Multiplication of a Member of the Columbia SK Group (Me Virus) in L Cells; III, Alteration of RNA and Protein Synthetic Patterns in Virus-Infected Cells. Virology, 21:617-627.

Hay, J., G. J. Köteles, H. M. Keir, and H. Subak-Sharpe (1966): Herpes Virus Specified Ribonucleic Acids. Nature, 210:387-390.

Hayashi, M., M. N. Hayashi, and S. Spiegelman (1963a): Replicating Form of a Single-Stranded DNA Virus; Isolation and Properties. Science, 140:1313-1316.

Hayashi, M., M. N. Hayashi, and S. Spiegelman (1963b): Restriction of *in Vivo* Genetic Transcription to One of the Complementary Strands of DNA. Proc. Natl. Acad. Sci., 50:664-672.

Hayashi, M., M. N. Hayashi, and S. Spiegelman (1964): DNA Circularity and the Mechanism of Strand Selection in the Generation of Genetic Messages. Proc. Natl. Acad. Sci., 51:351-359.

Hayashi, K., and W. C. Russell (1968): A Study of the Development of Adenovirus Antigens by the Immunofluorescent Technique. Virology, 34:470-480.

Hayflick, L. (1968): Human Cells and Aging. Sci. Amer., 218(March):32-37.

Helgeland, K. (1966): Polyoma Virus 3; on the Nature of the Viral Receptors on the Mouse Embryo Cells. Arch. Path. Microbiol. Scandinav., 68:439-444.

Heller, E. (1963): Enhancement of Chikungunya Virus Replication and Inhibition of Interferon Production by Actinomycin D. Virology, 21:652-656.

Henle, G., and W. Henle (1965): Evidence for a Persistent Viral Infection in a Cell Line Derived from Burkitt's Lymphoma. J. Bacteriol., 89:252-258.

Henle, G., W. Henle, and V. Diehl (1968): Relation of Burkitt's Tumor-Associated Herpes-Type Virus to Infectious Mononucleosis. Proc. Natl. Acad. Sci., 59:94-101.

Henry, C., and J. S. Youngner (1963): Studies on the Structure and Replication of the Nucleic Acid of Poliovirus. Virology, 21:162-173.

Henson, D., and H. Pinkerton (1964): Effect of Aminopterin on the Replication of the Murine Salivary Gland Virus. Nature, 202:419-420.

Herold, F., and K. Munz (1967): Morphological Studies of Maize Mosaic Virus I. J. Gen. Virol., 1:227-234.

Herriott, R. M. (1951): Nucleic-Acid-Free T2 Virus "Ghosts" with Specific Biological Action. J. Bacteriol., 61:752-754.

Hershey, A. D. (1946): Mutation of Bacteriophage with Respect to Type of Plaque. Genetics, 31:620-640.

Hershey, A. D. (1953): Nucleic Acid Economy in Bacteria Infected with Bacteriophage T2; II, Phage Precursor Nucleic Acid. J. Gen. Physiol., 37:1-23.

Hershey, A. D., and E. Burgi (1965): Complementary Structure of Interacting Sites at the Ends of Lambda DNA Molecules. Proc. Natl. Acad. Sci., 53:325-328.

Hershey, A. D., E. Burgi, and L. Ingraham (1963): Cohesion of DNA Molecules Isolated from Phage Lambda. Proc. Natl. Acad. Sci., 49:748-755.

Hershey, A. D., and M. Chase (1952): Independent Functions of Viral Protein and Nucleic Acid in Growth of Bacteriophage. J. Gen. Physiol., 36:39-56. Reprinted in Stent, G. S. (1960): Papers on Bacterial Viruses. Boston, Little, Brown and Co., pp. 87-104.

Hershey, A. D., J. Dixon, and M. Chase (1953a): Nucleic Acid Economy in Bacteria Infected with Bacteriophage T2; I, Purine and Pyrimidine Composition. J. Gen. Physiol., 36:777-789.

Hershey, A. D., A. Garen, D. K. Fraser, and J. D. Hudis (1953b): Growth and Inheritance in Bacteriophage. Carnegie Institution of Washington Yearbook, 53:210-225.

Hershey, A. D., M. D. Kamen, J. W. Kennedy, and H. Gest (1951): The Mortality of Bacteriophage Containing Assimilated Radioactive Phosphorus. J. Gen. Physiol., 34:305-319.

Hershey, A. D., and R. Rotman (1949): Genetic Recombination Between Host-Range and Plaque-Type Mutants of Bacteriophage in Single Bacterial Cells. Genetics, 34:44-71.

Hiatt, C. W. (1964): Kinetics of the Inactivation of Viruses. Bacteriol. Rev., 28:150-163.

Higashi, N. (1965): Electron Microscope Studies on the Mode of Reproduction of Trachoma Virus and Psittacosis Virus in Cell Cultures. Exptl. Mol. Path., 4:24-39.

Hilleman, M. R. (1966): Immunologic Attack on Neoplasia. In Kirsten, W. H. (ed.): Malignant Transformation by Viruses. New York, Springer-Verlag, Inc., pp. 137-148.

Hinuma, Y., M. Konn, J. Yamaguchi, and J. T. Grace, Jr. (1967): Replication of Herpes-Type Virus in a Burkitt Lymphoma Cell Line. J. Virol., 1:1203-1206.

Hirst, G. K. (1941): The Agglutination of Red Cells by Allantoic Fluid of Chick Embryos Infected with Influenza Virus. Science, 94:22-23.

Hirst, G. K. (1962): Genetic Recombination with Newcastle Disease Virus, Polio-viruses, and Influenza. Cold Spring Harbor Symposia Quant. Biol., 27:303-309.

Hirst, G. K. (1965): Cell-Virus Attachment and the Action of Antibodies on Viruses. In Horsfall, F. L., Jr., and I. Tamm (eds.): Viral and Rickettsial Infections of Man, Ed. 4. Philadelphia, J. B. Lippincott Co., pp. 216-232.

Hirt, B. (1966): Evidence for Semiconservative Replication of Circular Polyoma DNA. Proc. Natl. Acad. Sci., 55:997-1004.

Hitchborn, J. H., G. J. Hill, and R. Hull (1966): Electron Microscopy of Virus-Like Particles Found in Diseased Plantago lanceolata in Britain. Virology, 28:768-772.

Hlozanek, I., L. Donner, and J. Svoboda (1966): Malignant Transformation in Vitro of Chinese Hamster Embryonic Fibroblasts with the Schmidt-Ruppin Strain of Rous

Sarcoma Virus and Karyological Analysis of This Process. J. Cell. Physiol., 68:221-235.

Ho, M.(1961): Inhibition of the Infectivity of Poliovirus Ribonucleic Acid by an Interferon. Proc. Soc. Exptl. Biol. Med., 107:639-644.

Ho, M. (1962): Interferons. New Eng. J. Med., 266:1258-1264, 1313-1318, 1367-1371.

Ho, M. (1964a): Interferon-Like Viral Inhibitor in Rabbits after Intravenous Administration of Endotoxin. Science, 146:1472-1474.

Ho, M. (1964b): Identification and "Induction" of Interferon. Bacteriol. Rev., 28:367-381.

Ho, M. (1966): The Production of Interferons. *In* Finter, N. B. (ed.): Interferons. Philadelphia, W. B. Saunders Co., pp. 21-54.

Ho, M., and J. F. Enders (1959a): An Inhibitor of Viral Activity Appearing in Infected Cell Cultures. Proc. Natl. Acad. Sci., 45:385-389.

Ho, M., and J. F. Enders (1959b): Further Studies on an Inhibitor of Viral Activity Appearing in Infected Cell Cultures and Its Role in Chronic Viral Infections. Virology, 9:446-477.

Ho, M., K. H. Fantes, D. C. Burke, and N. B. Finter (1966): Interferons or Interferon-Like Inhibitors Induced by Non-Viral Substances. *In* Finter, N. B. (ed.): Interferons. Philadelphia, W. B. Saunders Co., pp. 181-201.

Ho, M., and Y. Kono (1965): Effect of Actinomycin D on Virus and Endotoxin-Induced Interferon-Like Inhibitors in Rabbits. Proc. Natl. Acad. Sci., 53:220-224.

Hoffman, C. E., E. M. Neumayer, R. F. Haff, and R. A. Goldsby (1965): Mode of Action of the Antiviral Activity of Amantadine in Tissue Culture. J. Bacteriol., 90:623-628.

Hoffmann-Berling, H., H. Dürwald, and I. Beulke (1963): Ein fädiger DNS-Phage (fd) und ein spärischer RNS-Phage (fr) wirtsspezifisch für männliche Stämme von E. *coli*; III, Biologisches Verhalten von fd und fr. Z. Naturforsch., 18B:893-898.

Hoffmann-Berling, H., H. C. Kaerner, and R. Knippers (1966): Small Bacteriophages. Adv. Virus Res., 12:329-370.

Hoffmann-Berling, H., and R. Mazé (1964): Release of Male-Specific Bacteriophages from Surviving Host Bacteria. Virology, 22:305-313.

Hofschneider, P. H. (1963): Untersuchungen über "kleine" E. *coli* K12 Bakteriophagen. Z. Naturforsch., 18B:203-210.

Hofschneider, P. H., and A. Preuss (1963): M13 Bacteriophage Liberation from Intact Bacteria as Revealed by Electron Microscopy. J. Mol. Biol., 7:450-451.

Hoggan, M. D., N. R. Blacklow, and W. P. Rowe (1966): Studies of Small DNA Viruses Found in Various Adenovirus Preparations; Physical, Biological, and Immunological Characteristics. Proc. Natl. Acad. Sci., 55:1467-1474.

Hogness, D. S. (1966): The Structure and Function of the DNA from Bacteriophage Lambda. *In* Macromolecular Metabolism. Boston, Little, Brown and Co., pp. 29-57.

Hogness, D. S., W. Doerfler, J. B. Egan, and L. W. Black (1967): The Position and Orientation of Genes in λ and λdg DNA. *In* Colter, J. S., and W. Paranchych (eds.): The Molecular Biology of Viruses. New York, Academic Press Inc., pp. 91-110.

Holland, J. J. (1961): Receptor Affinities as Major Determinants of Enterovirus Tissue Tropisms in Humans. Virology, 15:312-326.

Holland, J. J. (1962): Inhibition of DNA-Primed RNA Synthesis During Poliovirus Infection of Human Cells. Biochem. Biophys. Res. Commun., 9:556-562.

Holland, J. J. (1964a): Enterovirus Entrance into Specific Host Cells, and Subsequent Alterations of Cell Protein and Nucleic Acid Synthesis. Bacteriol. Rev., 28:3-13.

Holland, J. J. (1964b): Inhibition of Host Cell Macromolecular Synthesis by High Multiplicities of Poliovirus Under Conditions Preventing Virus Synthesis. J. Mol. Biol., 8:574-581.

Holland, J. J., and D. W. Bassett (1964): Evidence for Cytoplasmic Replication of Poliovirus Ribonucleic Acid. Virology, 23:164-172.

Holland, J. J., and L. C. McLaren (1961): The Location and Nature of Enterovirus Receptors in Susceptible Cells. J. Exptl. Med., 114:161-171.

Holland, J. J., L. C. McLaren, and J. T. Syverton (1959): The Mammalian Cell Virus Relationship; IV, Infection of Naturally Insusceptible Cells with Enterovirus Ribonucleic Acid. J. Exptl. Med., 110:65-80.

Holland, J. J., and J. A. Peterson (1964): Nucleic Acid and Protein Synthesis During Poliovirus Infection of Human Cells. J. Mol. Biol., 8:556-573.

Hollinshead, A. C., T. C. Alford, S. Oroszlan, H. C. Turner, and R. J. Huebner (1968): Separation and Description of Adenovirus 12-Induced Cellular Antigens Which React with Hamster Tumor Antisera. Proc. Natl. Acad. Sci., 59:385-392.

Hollinshead, A. C., B. Bunnag, and T. C. Alford (1967): Relationship Between the Subunits and "T" Antigens of Adenovirus Type 12. Nature, 215:397-399.

Holmes, I. H., and D. H. Watson (1963): An Electron Microscope Study of the Attachment and Penetration of Herpes Virus in BHK21 Cells. Virology, 21:112-123.

Holowczak, J. A., and W. K. Joklik (1967a): Studies on the Structural Proteins of Vaccinia Virus; I, Structural Proteins of Virions and Cores. Virology, 33:717-725.

Holowczak, J. A., and W. K. Joklik (1967b): Studies on the Structural Proteins of Vaccinia Virus; II, Kinetics of the Synthesis of Individual Groups of Structural Proteins. Virology, 33:726-739.

Homma, M., and A. F. Graham (1965): Intracellular Fate of Mengo Virus Ribonucleic Acid. J. Bacteriol., 89:64-73.

Horiuchi, K., and N. D. Zinder (1967): Azure Mutants; a Type of Host-Dependent Mutant of the Bacteriophage f2. Science, 156:1618-1623.

Horne, R. W. (1963): The Structure of Viruses. Sci. Amer., 208(Jan.):48-56.

Horne, R. W., S. Brenner, A. P. Waterson, and P. Wildy (1959): The Icosahedral Form of an Adenovirus. J. Mol. Biol., 1:84-86.

Horne, R. W., and J. Nagington (1959): Electron Microscope Studies of the Development and Structure of Poliomyelitis Virus. J. Mol. Biol., 1:333-338.

Horne, R. W., and A. P. Waterson (1960): A Helical Structure in Mumps, Newcastle Disease and Sendai Viruses. J. Mol. Biol., 2:75-77.

Horne, R. W., and P. Wildy (1961): Symmetry in Virus Architecture. Virology, 15:348-373.

Horton, E., S.-L. Liu, L. Dalgarno, E. M. Martin, and T. S. Work (1964): Development of Ribonucleic Acid Polymerase in Cells Infected with Encephalomyocarditis Virus and the Synthesis of Single- and Double-Stranded RNA by the Isolated Polymerase. Nature, 204:247-250.

Howatson, A. F., and L. V. Crawford (1963): Direct Counting of the Capsomeres in Polyoma and Papilloma Viruses. Virology, 21:1-6.

Howatson, A. F., and G. F. Whitmore (1962): The Development and Structure of Vesicular Stomatitis Virus. Virology, 16:466-478.

Hoyer, B. H., B. J. McCarthy, and E. T. Bolton (1964): A Molecular Approach in the Systematics of Higher Organisms. Science, 144:959-967.

Hoyle, L., R. W. Horne, and A. P. Waterson (1961): The Structure and Composition of the Myxoviruses; II, Components Released from the Influenza Virus Particle by Ether. Virology, 13:448-459.

Hsiung, G.-D., and W. H. Gaylord, Jr. (1961): The Vacuolating Virus of Monkeys; I, Isolation, Growth Characteristics, and Inclusion Body Formation. J. Exptl. Med., 114:975-986.

Huang, A. S., and R. R. Wagner (1966): Defective T Particles of Vesicular Stomatitis Virus; II, Biologic Role in Homologous Interference. Virology, 30:173-181.

Hudson, J. B., and W. Paranchych (1967): Effect of Bacteriophage R17 Infection on Host-Directed Synthesis of Ribosomal Ribonucleates. J. Virol., 1:529-537.

Huebner, R. J. (1967): The Murine Leukemia-Sarcoma Virus Complex. Proc. Natl. Acad. Sci., 58:835-842.

Huebner, R. J., R. M. Chanock, B. A. Rubin, and M. J. Casey (1964): Induction by Adenovirus Type 7 of Tumors in Hamsters Having the Antigenic Characteristics of SV40 Virus. Proc. Natl. Acad. Sci., 52:1333-1340.

Huebner, R. J., J. W. Hartley, W. P. Rowe, W. T. Lane, and W. I. Capps (1966): Rescue of the Defective Genome of Moloney Sarcoma Virus from a Noninfectious Hamster Tumor and the Production of Pseudotype Sarcoma Viruses with Various Murine Leukemia Viruses. Proc. Natl. Acad. Sci., 56:1164-1169.

Huebner, R. J., W. P. Rowe, and W. T. Lane (1962): Oncogenic Effects in Hamsters of Human Adenovirus Types 12 and 18. Proc. Natl. Acad. Sci., 48:2051-2058.

Hull, R. N., I. S. Johnson, C. G. Culbertson, C. B. Reimer, and H. F. Wright (1965): Oncogenicity of the Simian Adenoviruses. Science, 150:1044-1046.

Hummeler, K., T. F. Anderson, and R. A. Brown (1962): Identification of Poliovirus

Particles of Different Antigenicity by Specific Agglutination as Seen in the Electron Microscope. Virology, 16:84-90.

Hummeler, K., G. Henle, and W. Henle (1966): Fine Structure of a Virus in Cultured Lymphoblasts from Burkitt Lymphoma. J. Bacteriol., 91:1366-1368.

Hummeler, K., H. Koprowski, and T. J. Wiktor (1967): Structure and Development of Rabies Virus in Tissue Culture. J. Virol., 1:152-170.

Hurwitz, J., J. J. Furth, M. Malamy, and M. Alexander (1962): The Role of Deoxyribonucleic Acid in Ribonucleic Acid Synthesis; III, The Inhibition of the Enzymatic Synthesis of Ribonucleic Acid and Deoxyribonucleic Acid by Actinomycin D and Proflavin. Proc. Natl. Acad. Sci., 48:1222-1230.

Hutchison, C. A., III, and R. L. Sinsheimer (1963): Kinetics of Bacteriophage Release by Single Cells of ϕX174-Infected E. coli. J. Mol. Biol., 7:206-208.

Hutchison, C. A., III, and R. L. Sinsheimer (1966): The Process of Infection with Bacteriophage ϕX174; X, Mutations in a ϕX Lysis Gene. J. Mol. Biol., 18:429-447.

Hyde, J. M., L. G. Gafford, and C. C. Randall (1965): Fine Structure of the Coat and Nucleoid Material of Fowlpox Virus. J. Bacteriol., 89:1557-1569.

Hyde, J. M., L. G. Gafford, and C. C. Randall (1967): Molecular Weight Determination of Fowlpox Virus DNA by Electron Microscopy. Virology, 33:112-120.

Hyde, J. M., and C. C. Randall (1966): Demonstration of Deoxyribonucleic Acid Release from Fowlpox Virus. J. Bacteriol., 91:1363-1365.

Ida, N., J. B. Moloney, and G. Taylor (1965): Vertical Transmission of Moloney Leukemia Virus in A/LN and BALB/c Strains of Mice. Gann, 56:239-249.

Igel, H. J., and P. H. Black (1967): In Vitro Transformation by the Adenovirus-SV40 Hybrid Viruses; III, Morphology of Tumors Induced with Transformed Cells. J. Exptl. Med., 125:647-655.

Ikeda, H., and J.-I. Tomizawa (1965): Transducing Fragments in Generalized Transduction by Phage P1; I, Molecular Origin of the Fragments. J. Mol. Biol., 14:85-109.

Inoue, Y. K., and Y. Nishibe (1967): Induction of T Antigen in HeLa Cells by Adeno-tumor Extracts and Differential Inactivation of the T Antigen Inducibility and the Infectivity of Type 12 Adenovirus. Virology, 31:186-188.

Inouye, M., E. Akaboshi, A. Tsugita, G. Streisinger, and Y. Okada (1967): A Frame-Shift Mutation Resulting in the Deletion of Two Base Pairs in the Lysozyme Gene of Bacteriophage T4. J. Mol. Biol., 30:39-47.

Ioachim, H. L. (1967): Neoplastic Transformation of Rat Thymic Cells Induced in Vitro by Gross Leukemia Virus. Science, 155:585-587.

Isaacs, A., and J. Lindenmann (1957): Virus Interference; I, The Interferon. Proc. Roy. Soc., Series B, 147:258-267.

Isaacs, A., J. Lindenmann, and R. C. Valentine (1957): Virus Interference; II, Some Properties of Interferon. Proc. Roy. Soc., Series B, 147:268-273.

Ishimoto, N., H. M. Temin, and J. L. Strominger (1966): Studies of Carcinogenesis by Avian Sarcoma Viruses; II, Virus-Induced Increase in Hyaluronic Acid Synthetase in Chicken Fibroblasts. J. Biol. Chem., 241:2052-2057.

Israel, J. V., T. F. Anderson, and M. Levine (1967): In Vitro Morphogenesis of Phage P22 from Heads and Base-Plate Parts. Proc. Natl. Acad. Sci., 57:284-291.

Ito, M., J. L. Melnick, and H. D. Mayor (1967): An Immunofluorescence Assay for Studying Replication of Adeno-Satellite Virus. J. Gen. Virol., 1:199-209.

Ito, Y. (1960): A Tumor-Producing Factor Extracted by Phenol from Papillomatous Tissue (Shope) of Cottontail Rabbits. Virology, 12:596-601.

Ito, Y. (1961): Heat-Resistance of the Tumorigenic Nucleic Acid of Shope Papillomatosis. Proc. Natl. Acad. Sci., 47:1897-1900.

Ito, Y., and C. A. Evans (1961): Induction of Tumors in Domestic Rabbits with Nucleic Acid Preparations from Partially Purified Shope Papilloma Virus and From Extracts of the Papillomas of Domestic and Cottontail Rabbits. J. Exptl. Med., 114:485-500.

Ito, Y., and C. A. Evans (1965): Tumorigenic Nucleic Acid Extracts from Tissues of a Transplantable Carcinoma, Vx7. J. Natl. Cancer Inst., 34:431-437.

Jacob, F. (1955): Transduction of Lysogeny in Escherichia coli. Virology, 1:207-220.

Jacob, F. (1966): Genetics of the Bacterial Cell. Science, 152:1470-1478.

Jacob, F., and C. R. Fuerst (1958): The Mechanism of Lysis by Phage Studied with Defective Lysogenic Bacteria. J. Gen. Microbiol., 18:518-526.

Jacob, F., and J. Monod (1961): Genetic Regulatory Mechanisms in the Synthesis of Proteins. J. Mol. Biol., 3:318-356.

Jacob, F., and E. L. Wollman (1953): Induction of Phage Development in Lysogenic Bacteria. Cold Spring Harbor Symposia Quant. Biol., 18:101-121.

Jacob, F., and E. L. Wollman (1957): Genetic Aspects of Lysogeny. In McElroy, W. D., and B. Glass (eds.): The Chemical Basis of Heredity. Baltimore, The Johns Hopkins Press, pp. 468-499.

Jacob, F., and E. L. Wollman (1959): Lysogeny. In Burnet, F. M., and W. M. Stanley (eds.): The Viruses, Vol. 2. New York, Academic Press Inc., pp. 319-351.

Jacob, F. and E. L. Wollman (1961): Viruses and Genes. Sci. Amer., 204(June):93-107.

Jaenisch, R., P. H. Hofschneider and A. Preuss (1966): Über infektiöse Substrukturen aus *Escherichia coli* Bakteriophagen; VIII, On the Tertiary Structure and Biological Properties of φX174 Replicative Form. J. Mol. Biol., 21:501-516.

Jawetz, E. (1964): Agents of Trachoma and Inclusion Conjunctivitis. Ann. Rev. Microbiol., 18:301-334.

Jenner, E. (1798): An Inquiry into the Causes and Effects of the Variolae Vaccinae, A Disease Discovered in Some of the Western Counties of England, Particularly Gloucestershire, and Known by the Name of the Cow Pox. London, Sampson Low. Reprinted in abridged form. Hahon, N. (1964): Selected Papers on Virology. Englewood Cliffs, New Jersey, Prentice-Hall, Inc., pp. 1-29.

Jensen, F., and V. Defendi (1968): Transformation of African Green Monkey Kidney Cells by Irradiated Adenovirus 7-Simian Virus 40 Hybrid. J. Virol., 2:173-177.

Jensen, F. C., A. J. Girardi, R. V. Gilden, and H. Koprowski (1964): Infection of Human and Simian Tissue Cultures with Rous Sarcoma Virus. Proc. Natl. Acad. Sci., 52:53-59.

Jensen, K. E., A. L. Neal, R. E. Owens, and J. Warren (1963): Interferon Responses of Chick Embryo Fibroblasts to Nucleic Acids and Related Compounds. Nature, 200:433-434.

Jerne, N. K. (1956): The Presence in Normal Serum of Specific Antibody Against Bacteriophage T4 and Its Increase During the Earliest Stages of Immunization. J. Immunol., 76:209-216.

Jerne, N. K., and P. Avegno (1956): The Development of the Phage-Inactivating Properties of Serum During the Course of Specific Immunization of an Animal; Reversible and Irreversible Inactivation. J. Immunol., 76:200-208.

Johnson, R. H., and J. G. Cruickshank (1966): Problems in Classification of Feline Panleucopaenia Virus. Nature, 212:622-623.

Joklik, W. K. (1962): Some Properties of Poxvirus Deoxyribonucleic Acid. J. Mol. Biol., 5:265-274.

Joklik, W. K. (1964a): The Intracellular Uncoating of Poxvirus DNA; I, The Fate of Radioactively-Labeled Rabbitpox Virus. J. Mol. Biol., 8:263-276.

Joklik, W. K. (1964b): The Intracellular Uncoating of Poxvirus DNA; II, The Molecular Basis of the Uncoating Process. J. Mol. Biol., 8:277-288.

Joklik, W. K. (1964c): The Intracellular Fate of Rabbitpox Virus Rendered Noninfectious by Various Reagents. Virology, 22:620-633.

Joklik, W. K. (1965): The Molecular Basis of the Viral Eclipse Phase. Progr. Med. Virol., 7:44-96.

Joklik, W. K. (1966): The Poxviruses. Bacteriol. Rev., 30:33-66.

Joklik, W. K., and Y. Becker (1964): The Replication and Coating of Vaccinia DNA. J. Mol. Biol., 10:452-474.

Joklik, W. K., and J. E. Darnell, Jr. (1961): The Adsorption and Early Fate of Purified Poliovirus in HeLa Cells. Virology, 13:439-447.

Joklik, W. K., C. Jungwirth, K. Oda, and B. Woodson (1967): Early and Late Functions During the Vaccinia Virus Multiplication Cycle. In Colter, J. S., and W. Paranchych (eds.): The Molecular Biology of Viruses. New York, Academic Press Inc., pp. 473-494.

Joklik, W. K., and T. C. Merigan (1966): Concerning the Mechanism of Action of Interferon. Proc. Natl. Acad. Sci., 56:558-565.

Jordan, L. E., and H. D. Mayor (1962): The Fine Structure of Reovirus, a New Member of the Icosahedral Series. Virology, 17:597-599.

Joyner, A., L. N. Isaacs, and H. Echols (1966): DNA Replication and Messenger RNA Production after Induction of Wild-Type λ Bacteriophage and λ Mutants. J. Mol. Biol., 19:174-186.

Kaiser, A. D. (1957): Mutations in a Temperate Bacteriophage Affecting Its Ability to Lysogenize Escherichia coli. Virology, 3:42-61.

Kaiser, A. D., and R. D. Inman (1965): Cohesion and the Biological Activity of Bacteriophage Lambda DNA. J. Mol. Biol., 13:78-91.

Kaiser, A. D., and F. Jacob (1957): Recombination Between Related Temperate Bacteriophages and the Genetic Control of Immunity and Prophage Localization. Virology, 4:509-521.

Kajioka, R., L. Siminovitch, and S. Dales (1964): The Cycle of Multiplication of Vaccinia Virus in Earle's Strain L Cells; II, Initiation of DNA Synthesis and Morphogenesis. Virology, 24:295-309.

Kallenbach, N. R., and D. M. Crothers (1966): Theory of Thermal Transitions in Cohered DNA from Phage Lambda. Proc. Natl. Acad. Sci., 56:1018-1025.

Kalnins, V. I., H. F. Stich, C. Gregory, and D. S. Yohn (1967): Localization of Tumor Antigens in Adenovirus-12-Induced Tumor Cells and in Adenovirus-12-Infected Human and Hamster Cells by Ferritin-Labeled Antibodies. Cancer Res., 27:1874-1886.

Kano-Sueoka, T., and S. Spiegelman (1962): Evidence for a Nonrandom Reading of the Genome. Proc. Natl. Acad. Sci., 48:1942-1949.

Kano-Sueoka, T., and N. Sueoka (1966): Modification of Leucyl-sRNA after Bacteriophage Infection. J. Mol. Biol., 20:183-209.

Kaplan, A. S., and T. Ben-Porat (1964): Mode of Replication of Pseudorabies Virus DNA. Virology, 23:90-95.

Kaplan, S., A. O. W. Stretton, and S. Brenner (1965): Amber Suppressors; Efficiency of Chain Propagation and Suppressor Specific Amino Acids. J. Mol. Biol., 14:528-533.

Kára, J., and R. Weil (1967): Specific Activation of the DNA-Synthesizing Apparatus in Contact-Inhibited Mouse Kidney Cells by Polyoma Virus. Proc. Natl. Acad. Sci., 57:63-70.

Kärber, G. (1931): Beitrag zur kollektiven Behandlung pharmakologischer Reihenversuche. Arch. Exptl. Path. Pharmakol., 162:480-483.

Kassanis, B. (1962): Properties and Behaviour of a Virus Depending for Its Multiplication on Another. J. Gen. Microbiol., 27:477-488.

Kassanis, B., and H. L. Nixon (1961): Activation of One Tobacco Necrosis Virus by Another. J. Gen. Microbiol., 25:459-471.

Kates, J. R., and B. R. McAuslan (1967a): Poxvirus DNA-Dependent RNA Polymerase. Proc. Natl. Acad. Sci., 58:134-141.

Kates, J. R., and B. R. McAuslan (1967b): Messenger RNA Synthesis by a "Coated" Viral Genome. Proc. Natl. Acad. Sci., 57:314-320.

Katz, L., and S. Penman (1966): The Solvent Denaturation of Double-Stranded RNA from Poliovirus Infected HeLa Cells. Biochem. Biophys. Res. Commun., 23:557-560.

Kawakami, T. G., G. H. Theilen, D. L. Dungworth, R. J. Munn, and S. G. Beall (1967): "C"-Type Viral Particles in Plasma of Cats with Feline Leukemia. Science, 158:1049-1050.

Kay, D. (1963): A Comparative Study of the Structures of a Variety of Bacteriophage Particles with Some Observations on the Mechanism of Nucleic Acid Injection. In Viruses, Nucleic Acids, and Cancer. (A Collection of Papers Presented at the Seventeenth Annual Symposium on Fundamental Cancer Research, 1963). Baltimore, The Williams and Wilkins Co., pp. 7-26.

Kayajanian, G., and A. Campbell (1966): The Relationship Between Heritable Physical and Genetic Properties of Selected gal⁻ and gal⁺ Transducing λdg. Virology, 30:482-492.

Kaye, A. M., and E. Winocour (1967): On the 5-Methylcytosine Found in the DNA Extracted from Polyoma Virus. J. Mol. Biol, 24:475-478.

Keck, K., H. R. Mahler, and D. Fraser (1960): Synthesis of Deoxycytidine-5'-Phosphate Deaminase in Escherichia coli Infected by T2 Bacteriophage. Arch. Biochem. Biophys., 86:85-88.

Keir, H. M., and E. Gold (1963): Deoxyribonucleic Acid Nucleotidyltransferase and Deoxyribonuclease from Cultured Cells Infected with Herpes Simplex Virus. Biochim. Biophys. Acta, 72:263-276.

Keir, H. M., J. Hay, J. M. Morrison, and H. Subak-Sharpe (1966a): Altered Properties of Deoxyribonucleic Acid Nucleotidyltransferase after Infection of Mammalian Cells with Herpes Simplex Virus. Nature, 210:369-371.

Keir, H. M., H. Subak-Sharpe, W. I. H. Shedden, D. H. Watson, and P. Wildy (1966b): Immunological Evidence for a Specific DNA Polymerase Produced after Infection by Herpes Simplex Virus. Virology, 30:154-157.

Kellenberger, E. (1961): Vegetative Bacteriophage and the Maturation of the Virus Particles. Adv. Virus Res., 8:1-61.

Kellenberger, E. (1966): The Genetic Control of the Shape of a Virus. Sci. Amer., 215 (Dec.):32-39.

Kellenberger, G., M. L. Zichichi, and J. J. Weigle (1961a): Exchange of DNA in the Recombination of Bacteriophage λ. Proc. Natl. Acad. Sci., 47:869-878.

Kellenberger, G., M. L. Zichichi, and J. J. Weigle (1961b): A Mutation Affecting the DNA Content of Bacteriophage Lambda and Its Lysogenizing Properties. J. Mol. Biol., 3:399-408.

Kelly, R. B., and R. L. Sinsheimer (1964): A New RNA Component in MS2-Infected Cells. J. Mol. Biol., 8:602-605.

Kelly, R. B., and R. L. Sinsheimer (1967a): The Replication of Bacteriophage MS2; VII, Non-Conservative Replication of Double-Stranded RNA. J. Mol. Biol., 26:169-179.

Kelly, R. B., and R. L. Sinsheimer (1967b): The Replication of Bacteriophage MS2; VIII, Fractionation of the "Replicative Intermediate" Using a BNC Column. J. Mol. Biol., 29:229-236.

Kelly, R. B., and R. L. Sinsheimer (1967c): The Replication of Bacteriophage MS2; IX, Structure and Replication of the Replicative Intermediate. J. Mol. Biol., 29:237-249.

Khoobyarian, N., and P. J. Fischinger (1965): Role of Heated Adenovirus 2 in Viral Interference. Proc. Soc. Exptl. Biol. Med., 120:533-538.

Kilbourne, E. D. (1963): Influenza Virus Genetics. Progr. Med. Virol., 5:79-126.

Kilbourne, E. D. (1968): Recombination of Influenza A Viruses of Human and Animal Origin. Science, 160:74-76.

Kilham, L., and H. W. Murphy (1953): A Pneumotropic Virus Isolated from C_3H Mice Carrying the Bittner Milk Agent. Proc. Soc. Exptl. Biol. Med., 82:133-137.

Kilham, L., and L. J. Olivier (1959): A Latent Virus of Rats Isolated in Tissue Culture. Virology, 7:428-437.

Kindig, D. A., and W. H. Kirsten (1967): Virus-Like Particles in Established Murine Cell Lines; Electron-Microscopic Observations. Science, 155:1543-1545.

Kirschstein, R. L., A. S. Rabson, and E. A. Peters (1964): Oncogenic Activity of Adenovirus 12 in Thymectomized BALB/c and C_3H/HeN Mice. Proc. Soc. Exptl. Biol. Med., 117:198-200.

Kirsten, W. H., L. A. Mayer, R. L. Wollmann, and M. I. Pierce (1967): Studies on a Murine Erythroblastosis Virus. J. Natl. Cancer Inst., 38:117-139.

Kit, S., R. A. de Torres, and D. R. Dubbs (1967a): Deoxycytidylate Deaminase Activity of Simian Virus 40-Infected Cell Cultures. Cancer Res., 27:1907-1914.

Kit, S., and D. R. Dubbs (1963a): Acquisition of Thymidine Kinase Activity by Herpes Simplex Infected Mouse Fibroblast Cells. Biochem. Biophys. Res. Commun., 11:55-59.

Kit, S., and D. R. Dubbs (1963b): Non-Functional Thymidine Kinase Cistron in Bromodeoxyuridine Resistant Strains of Herpes Simplex Virus. Biochem. Biophys. Res. Commun., 13:500-504.

Kit, S., and D. R. Dubbs (1965): Properties of Deoxythymidine Kinase Partially Purified from Noninfected and Virus-Infected Mouse Fibroblast Cells. Virology, 26:16-27.

Kit, S., D. R. Dubbs, R. A. de Torres, and J. L. Melnick (1965a): Enhanced Thymidine Kinase Activity Following Infection of Green Monkey Kidney Cells by Simian Adenoviruses, Simian Papovavirus SV40, and an Adenovirus-SV40 "Hybrid." Virology, 27:453-457.

Kit, S., D. R. Dubbs, and P. M. Frearson (1965b): Decline of Thymidine Kinase Activity in Stationary Phase Mouse Fibroblast Cells. J. Biol. Chem., 240:2565-2573.

Kit, S., D. R. Dubbs, and P. M. Frearson (1966a): Enzymes of Nucleic Acid Metabolism in Cells Infected with Polyoma Virus. Cancer Res., 26:638-646.

Kit, S., D. R. Dubbs, P. M. Frearson, and J. L. Melnick (1966b): Enzyme Induction in SV40-Infected Green Monkey Kidney Cultures. Virology, 29:69-83.

Kit, S., D. R. Dubbs, and L. J. Piekarski (1962): Enhanced Thymidine Phosphorylating Activity of Mouse Fibroblasts (Strain LM) Following Vaccinia Infection. Biochem. Biophys. Res. Commun., 8:72-75.

Kit, S., D. R. Dubbs, and L. J. Piekarski (1963a): Inhibitory Effects of Puromycin and Fluorophenylalanine on Induction of Thymidine Kinase by Vaccinia Infected L-Cells. Biochem. Biophys. Res. Commun., 11:176-181.

Kit, S., D. R. Dubbs, L. J. Piekarski, R. A. de Torres, and J. L. Melnick (1966c): Acquisition of Enzyme Function by Mouse Kidney Cells Abortively Infected with Papovavirus SV40. Proc. Natl. Acad. Sci., 56:463-470.

Kit, S., J. L. Melnick, M. Anken, D. R. Dubbs, R. A. de Torres, and T. Kitahara (1967b): Nonidentity of Some Simian Virus 40-Induced Enzymes with Tumor Antigen. J. Virol., 1:684-692.

Kit, S., L. J. Piekarski, and D. R. Dubbs (1963b): Induction of Thymidine Kinase by Vaccinia-Infected Mouse Fibroblasts. J. Mol. Biol., 6:22-33.

Kit, S., L. J. Piekarski, and D. R. Dubbs (1963c): Effects of 5-Fluorouracil, Actinomycin D and Mitomycin C on the Induction of Thymidine Kinase by Vaccinia-Infected L-Cells. J. Mol. Biol., 7:497-510.

Kit, S., L. J. Piekarski, and D. R. Dubbs (1967c): DNA Polymerase Induced by Simian Virus 40. J. Gen. Virol., 1:163-173.

Klein, G., and E. Klein (1962): Antigenic Properties of Other Experimental Tumors. Cold Spring Harbor Symposia Quant. Biol., 27:463-470.

Kleinschmidt, A. K., A. Burton, and R. L. Sinsheimer (1963): Electron Microscopy of the Replicative Form of the DNA of the Bacteriophage ϕX174. Science, 142:961.

Kleinschmidt, W. J., and L. F. Ellis (1967): Statolon, as an Inducer of Interferon. In Wolstenholme, G. E. W., and M. O'Connor (eds.): Interferon. Boston, Little, Brown and Co., pp. 39-49.

Kleinschmidt, W. J., and E. B. Murphy (1967): Interferon Induction with Statolon in the Intact Animal. Bacteriol. Rev., 31:132-137.

Klemperer, H. G., G. R. Haynes, W. I. H. Shedden, and D. H. Watson (1967): A Virus-Specific Thymidine Kinase in BHK21 Cells Infected with Herpes Simplex Virus. Virology, 31:120-128.

Klug, A. (1965): Structure of the Viruses of the Papilloma-Polyoma Type; II, Comments on Other Work. J. Mol. Biol., 11:424-431.

Klug, A., and D. L. D. Caspar (1960): The Structure of Small Viruses. Adv. Virus Res., 7:225-325.

Klug, A., and J. T. Finch (1960): The Symmetries of the Protein and Nucleic Acid in Turnip Yellow Mosaic Virus; X-ray Diffraction Studies. J. Mol. Biol., 2:201-215.

Klug, A., and J. T. Finch (1965): Structure of Viruses of the Papilloma-Polyoma Type; I, Human Wart Virus. J. Mol. Biol., 11:403-423.

Klug, A., W. Longley, and R. Leberman (1966): Arrangement of Protein Subunits and the Distribution of Nucleic Acid in Turnip Yellow Mosaic Virus; I, X-ray Diffraction Studies. J. Mol. Biol., 15:315-343.

Knippers, R., and H. Hoffmann-Berling (1966a): A Coat Protein from Bacteriophage fd; I, Hydrodynamic Measurements and Biological Characterization. J. Mol. Biol., 21:281-292.

Knippers, R., and H. Hoffmann-Berling (1966b): A Coat Protein from Bacteriophage fd; II, Interaction of the Protein with DNA in Vitro. J. Mol. Biol., 21:293-304.

Knippers, R., and H. Hoffmann-Berling (1966c): A Coat Protein from Bacteriophage fd; III, Specificity of Protein-DNA Association in Vivo. J. Mol. Biol., 21:305-312.

Knolle, P. (1967): Evidence for the Identity of the Mating-Specific Site of Male Cells of Escherichia coli with the Receptor Site of an RNA Phage. Biochem. Biophys. Res. Commun., 27:81-87.

Knudson, A. G., Jr., A. M. Brodetsky, and M. A. Baluda (1967): Transient Inhibition of Avian Myeloblastosis Virus Reproduction by Amethopterin and Fluorodeoxyuridine. J. Virol., 1:1150-1157.

Koch, G., and W. J. Dreyer (1958): Characterization of an Enzyme of Phage T2 as a Lysozyme. Virology, 6:291-293.

Koch, G., and A. D. Hershey (1959): Synthesis of Phage-Precursor Protein in Bacteria Infected with T2. J. Mol. Biol., 1:260-276.

Koch, M. A., and H. J. Eggers (1967): Mutants of Simian Virus 40 Which Differ in Cell-Transforming Activity. Nature, 214:178.

Koch, M. A., and A. B. Sabin (1963): Specificity of Virus-Induced Resistance to Transplantation of Polyoma and SV40 Tumors in Adult Hamsters. Proc. Soc. Exptl. Biol. Med., 113:4-12.

Koerner, J. F., M. S. Smith, and J. M. Buchanan (1959): A Deoxycytidine Triphosphate Splitting Enzyme and the Synthesis of the Deoxyribosenucleic Acid of T2 Bacteriophage. J. Amer. Chem. Soc., 81:2594-2595.

Koerner, J. F., M. S. Smith, and J. M. Buchanan (1960): Deoxycytidine Triphosphatase, an Enzyme Induced by Bacteriophage Infection. J. Biol. Chem., 235:2691-2697.

Konrad, M. W. (1968): Dependence of "Early" λ Bacteriophage RNA Synthesis on Bacteriophage-Directed Protein Synthesis. Proc. Natl. Acad. Sci., 59:171-178.

Koprowski, H., F. C. Jensen, and Z. Steplewski (1967): Activation of Production of Infectious Tumor Virus SV40 in Heterokaryon Cultures. Proc. Natl. Acad. Sci., 58:127-133.

Koprowski, H., J. A. Ponten, F. Jensen, R. G. Ravdin, R. Moorhead, and E. Saksela (1962): Transformation of Cultures of Human Tissue Infected with Simian Virus SV40. J. Cell. Comp. Physiol., 59:281-292.

Korn, D., and A. Weissbach(1963): The Effect of Lysogenic Induction on the Deoxyribonucleases of *Escherichia coli* K12λ. J. Biol. Chem., 238:3390-3394.

Kornberg, A. (1960): Biologic Synthesis of Deoxyribonucleic Acid. Science, 131:1503-1508.

Kornberg, A., S. B. Zimmerman, S. R. Kornberg, and J. Josse (1959): Enzymatic Synthesis of Deoxyribonucleic Acid; VI, Influence of Bacteriophage T2 on the Synthetic Pathway in Host Cells. Proc. Natl. Acad. Sci., 45:772-785.

Kornberg, S. R., S. B. Zimmerman, and A. Kornberg (1961): Glucosylation of Deoxyribonucleic Acid by Enzymes from Bacteriophage-Infected *Escherichia coli*. J. Biol. Chem., 236:1487-1493.

Kozinski, A. W. (1961a): Fragmentary Transfer of P^{32}-Labeled Parental DNA to Progeny Phage. Virology, 13:124-134.

Kozinski, A. W. (1961b): Uniform Sensitivity to P^{32} Decay Among Progeny of P^{32}-Free Phage φX174 Grown on P^{32}-Labeled Bacteria. Virology, 13:377-378.

Kozinski, A. W., and Z. Z. Felgenhauer (1967): Molecular Recombination in T4 Bacteriophage Deoxyribonucleic Acid; II, Single-Strand Breaks and Exposure of Uncomplemented Areas as a Prerequisite for Recombination. J. Virol., 1:1193-1202.

Kozinski, A. W., and P. B. Kozinski (1963): Fragmentary Transfer of P^{32}-Labeled Parental DNA to Progeny Phage; II, The Average Size of the Transferred Parental Fragment; Two-Cycle Transfer; Repair of the Polynucleotide Chain after Fragmentation. Virology, 20:213-229.

Kozloff, L. M., K. Knowlton, F. W. Putnam, and E. A. Evans, Jr. (1951): Biochemical Studies of Virus Reproduction; V, The Origin of Bacteriophage Nitrogen. J. Biol. Chem., 188:101-116.

Kozloff, L. M., M. Lute, and K. Henderson (1957): Viral Invasion; I, Rupture of Thiol Ester Bonds in the Bacteriophage Tail. J. Biol. Chem., 228:511-528.

Kreuz, L. E., and A. H. Levy (1963): Density Homogeneity and Estimated Molecular Weight of Interferon. Nature, 200:883-884.

Krimm, S., and T. F. Anderson (1967): Structure of Normal and Contracted Tail Sheaths of T4 Bacteriophage. J. Mol. Biol., 27:197-202.

Krugman, R. D., and C. R. Goodheart (1964): Human Cytomegalovirus; Thermal Inactivation. Virology, 23:290-291.

Kudo, H., and A. F. Graham (1965): Synthesis of Reovirus Ribonucleic Acid in L Cells. J. Bacteriol., 90:936-945.

Kudo, H., and A. F. Graham (1966): Selective Inhibition of Reovirus Induced RNA in L Cells. Biochem. Biophys. Res. Commun., 24:150-155.

Kunkee, R. E., and A. B. Pardee (1956): Studies on the Role of Deoxyribonuclease in T2 Bacteriophage Development. Biochim. Biophys. Acta, 19:236-246.

Kusano, T., and I. Yamane (1967a): Transformation *in Vitro* of the Embryonal Hamster Brain Cells by Human Adenovirus Type 12. Tohoku J. Exptl. Med., 92:141-150.

Kusano, T., and I. Yamane (1967b): General Characteristics of the Cells Transformed *in Vitro* by Human Adenovirus Type 12. Tohoku J. Exptl. Med., 92:151-160.

Lacy, S., and M. Green (1964): Biochemical Studies on Adenovirus Multiplication; VII, Homology Between DNA's of Tumorigenic and Nontumorigenic Human Adenoviruses. Proc. Natl. Acad. Sci., 52:1053-1059.

Lampson, G. P., A. A. Tytell, A. K. Field, M. M. Nemes, and M. R. Hilleman (1967): Inducers of Interferon and Host Resistance; I, Double-Stranded RNA from Extracts of *Penicillium funiculosum*. Proc. Natl. Acad. Sci., 58:782-789.

Lampson, G. P., A. A. Tytell, M. M. Nemes, and M. R. Hilleman (1965): Characterization of Chick Embryo Interferon Induced by a DNA Virus. Proc. Soc. Exptl. Biol. Med., 118:441-448.

Landau, B. J., V. M. Larson, G. A. Devers, and M. R. Hilleman (1966): Studies on Induction of Virus from Adenovirus and SV40 Hamster Tumors; I, Chemical and Physical Agents. Proc. Soc. Exptl. Biol. Med., 122:1174-1182.

Langridge, R., and P. J. Gomatos (1963): The Structure of RNA. Science, 141:694-698.

Larson, V. M., P. A. Gosnell, and M. R. Hilleman (1966): Studies on Induction from Adenovirus and SV40 Hamster Tumors 2; "Helper" Viruses. Proc. Soc. Exptl. Biol. Med., 122:1182-1191.

Lasfargues, E. Y., and D. H. Moore (1966): Cell Transformation by the Mammary Tumor Virus *in Vitro*. *In* Kirsten, W. H. (ed.): Malignant Transformation by Viruses. New York, Springer-Verlag, Inc., pp. 44-59.

Lasfargues, E. Y., D. H. Moore, M. R. Murray, C. D. Haagensen, and E. C. Pollard (1959): Production of the Milk Agent in Cultures of Mouse Mammary Carcinoma. J. Biophys. Biochem. Cyto., 5:93-96.

Latarjet, R., R. Cramer, and L. Montagnier (1967): Inactivation by UV-, X-, and γ-Radiations of the Infecting and Transforming Capacities of Polyoma Virus. Virology, 33:104-111.

Lauffer, M. A., D. Trkula, and A. Buzzell (1956): Mechanism of Inactivation of Tobacco Mosaic Virus by X-rays. Nature, 177:890.

Law, L. W., and R. C. Ting (1965): Immunologic Competence and Induction of Neoplasms by Polyoma Virus. Proc. Soc. Exptl. Biol. Med., 119:823-830.

Lawrence, W. C., and H. S. Ginsberg (1967): Intracellular Uncoating of Type 5 Adenovirus Deoxyribonucleic Acid. J. Virol., 1:851-867.

Lea, D. E. (1947): Actions of Radiations on Living Cells. New York, The Macmillan Co.

Le Bouvier, G. L., M. Sussman, and L. V. Crawford (1966): Antigenic Diversity of Mammalian Papillomaviruses. J. Gen. Microbiol., 45:497-501.

Lederberg, E. M. (1951): Lysogenicity in *E. coli* K-12. Genetics, 36:560.

Lederberg, E. M., and J. Lederberg (1953): Genetic Studies of Lysogenicity in *Escherichia coli*. Genetics, 38:51-64.

Lederberg, J., and E. L. Tatum (1946): Novel Genotypes in Mixed Cultures of Biochemical Mutants of Bacteria. Cold Spring Harbor Symposia Quant. Biol., 11:113-114.

Ledinko, N. (1963): Genetic Recombination with Poliovirus Type I; Studies of Crosses Between a Normal Horse Serum-Resistant Mutant and Several Guanidine-Resistant Mutants of the Same Strain. Virology, 20:107-119.

Ledinko, N. (1966): Changes in Metabolic and Enzymatic Activities of Monkey Kidney Cells after Infection with Adenovirus 2. Virology, 28:679-692.

Ledinko, N. (1967): Stimulation of DNA Synthesis and Thymidine Kinase Activity in Human Embryonic Kidney Cells Infected by Adenovirus 2 or 12. Cancer Res., 27:1459-1469.

Ledinko, N., and H. W. Toolan (1968): Human Adenovirus Type 12 as a "Helper" for Growth of H-1 Virus. J. Virol., 2:155-156.

Lehman, I. R., and E. A. Pratt (1960): On the Structure of the Glucosylated Hydroxymethylcytosine Nucleotides of Coliphages T2, T4, and T6. J. Biol. Chem., 235:3254-3259.

Lennette, E. H., and N. J. Schmidt (1964): Diagnostic Procedures for Viral and Rickettsial Diseases. New York, Amer. Pub. Health Assn.

Lennox, E. S. (1955): Transduction of Linked Genetic Characters of the Host by Bacteriophage P1. Virology, 1:190-206.

Lerman, L. S. (1961): Structural Considerations in the Interaction of DNA and Acridines. J. Mol. Biol., 3:18-30.

Levine, A. J., and H. S. Ginsberg (1967): Mechanism by Which Fiber Antigen Inhibits Multiplication of Type 5 Adenovirus. J. Virol., 1:747-757.

Levine, L., J. L. Barlow, and H. Van Vunakis (1958): An Internal Protein in T2 and T4 Bacteriophages. Virology, 6:702-717.

Levine, M. (1957): Mutations in the Temperate Phage P22 and Lysogeny in *Salmonella*. Virology, 3:22-41.

Levine, M., and H. O. Smith (1964): Sequential Gene Action in the Establishment of Lysogeny. Science, 146:1581-1582.

Levine, S. (1964): Effect of Actinomycin D and Puromycin Dihydrochloride on Action of Interferon. Virology, 24:586-588.

Levine, S., W. E. Magee, R. D. Hamilton, and O. V. Miller (1967): Effect of Interferon on Early Enzyme and Viral DNA Synthesis in Vaccinia Virus Infection. Virology, 32:33-40.

Levine, S., T. T. Puck, and B. P. Sagik (1953): An Absolute Method for Assay of Virus Hemagglutinins. J. Exptl. Med., 98:521-531.

Levitt, N. H., and R. L. Crowell (1967): Comparative Studies of the Regeneration of HeLa Cell Receptors for Poliovirus T1 and Coxsackievirus B3. J. Virol., 1:693-700.

Levy, H. B., and T. C. Merigan (1966): Interferon and Uninfected Cells. Proc. Soc. Exptl. Biol. Med., 121:53-55.

Lewis, A. M., Jr., K. O. Prigge, and W. P. Rowe (1966): Studies of Adenovirus-SV40 Hybrid Viruses; IV, An Adenovirus Type 2 Strain Carrying the Infectious SV40 Genome. Proc. Natl. Acad. Sci., 55:526-531.

Lieb, M. (1964): Ultraviolet Sensitivity of *Escherichia coli* Containing Heat-Inducible λ Prophages. Science, 145:175-176.

Lieb, M. (1966): Studies of Heat-Inducible Lambda Bacteriophage; I, Order of Genetic Sites and Properties of Mutant Prophages. J. Mol. Biol., 16:149-163.

Liebhaber, H., and K. K. Takemoto (1961): Alteration of Plaque Morphology of EMC Virus with Polycations. Virology, 14:502-504.

Liebhaber, H., and K. K. Takemoto (1963): The Basis for the Size Differences in Plaques Produced by Variants of Encephalomyocarditis (EMC) Virus. Virology, 20:559-566.

Lindenmann, J., D. C. Burke, and A. Isaacs (1957): Studies on the Production, Mode of Action and Properties of Interferon. Brit. J. Exp. Path., 38:551-562.

Lindqvist, B. H., and R. L. Sinsheimer (1967): Process of Infection with Bacteriophage φX174; XIV, Studies on Macromolecular Synthesis During Infection with a Lysis-Defective Mutant. J. Mol. Biol., 28:87-94.

Lipton, A., and A. Weissbach (1966a): The Appearance of Circular DNA after Lysogenic Induction in *Escherichia coli* CR34 (λ). J. Mol. Biol., 21:517-525.

Lipton, A., and A. Weissbach (1966b): The Formation of Circular DNA after Lysogenic Induction. Biochem. Biophys. Res. Commun., 23:436-441.

Litman, R. M., and A. B. Pardee (1956): Production of Bacteriophage Mutants by a Disturbance of Deoxyribonucleic Acid Metabolism. Nature, 178:529-531.

Little, J. W., S. B. Zimmerman, C. K. Oshinsky, and M. Gellert (1967): Enzymatic Joining of DNA Strands; II, An Enzyme-Adenylate Intermediate in the DPN-Dependent DNA Ligase Reaction. Proc. Natl. Acad. Sci., 58:2004-2011.

Littlefield, J. W., and C. Basilico (1966): Infection of Thymidine Kinase-Deficient *BHK* Cells with Polyoma Virus. Nature, 211:250-252.

Lockart, R. Z., Jr. (1964): The Necessity for Cellular RNA and Protein Synthesis for Viral Inhibition Resulting from Interferon. Biochem. Biophys. Res. Commun., 15:513-518.

Lockart, R. Z., Jr. (1967): Recent Progress in Research on Interferons. Progr. Med. Virol., 9:451-475.

Lockart, R. Z., Jr., and T. Sreevalsan (1963): The Effect of Interferon on the Synthesis of Viral Nucleic Acid. *In* Viruses, Nucleic Acids, and Cancer. Baltimore, The Williams and Wilkins Co., pp. 447-461.

Lockart, R. Z., Jr., T. Sreevalsan, and B. Horn (1962): Inhibition of Viral RNA Synthesis by Interferon. Virology, 18:493-494.

Lodish, H. F., and N. D. Zinder (1966a): Replication of the RNA of Bacteriophage f2. Science, 152:372-377.

Lodish, H. F., and N. D. Zinder (1966b): Semi-Conservative Replication of Bacteriophage f2 RNA. J. Mol. Biol., 21:207-209.

Loeb, T., and N. D. Zinder (1961): A Bacteriophage Containing RNA. Proc. Natl. Acad. Sci., 47:282-289.

Loeffler, F., and P. Frosch (1898): Report of the Commission for Rearch on the Foot-and-Mouth Disease. Centralbl. f. Bakt., Parasit. Infekt., Part 1, 23:371-391. Reprinted in Translation. Hahon, N. (1964): Selected Papers on Virology. Englewood Cliffs, New Jersey, Prentice-Hall, Inc., pp. 64-68.

Loh, P. C. (1964): Demonstration of Rapidly Labelled RNA Fractions in Virus-Infected HeLa Cells. Proc. Soc. Exptl. Biol. Med., 117:192-195.

Loh, P. C., and J. L. Riggs (1961): Demonstration of the Sequential Development of Vaccinial Antigens and Virus in Infected Cells; Observations with Cytochemical and Differential Fluorescent Procedures. J. Exptl. Med., 114:149-160.

Loh, P. C., and M. Soergel (1965): Growth Characteristics of Reovirus Type 2; Actinomycin D and the Synthesis of Viral RNA. Proc. Natl. Acad. Sci., 54:857-863.

Loh, P. C., and M. Soergel (1966): Growth Characteristics of Reovirus Type 2; Actinomycin D and the Preferential Synthesis of Viral RNA. Proc. Soc. Exptl. Biol. Med., 122:1248-1250.

Lorenz, R. J. (1962): Zur Statistik des Plaque-Testes. Arch. Virusforschung, 12:108-137.

Lorenz, R. J., and B. Zoeth (1966): An Estimation of the Overlap Bias in Plaque Assay. Virology, 28:379-385.

Losick, R., and P. W. Robbins (1967): Mechanism of ϵ^{15} Conversion Studied with a Bacterial Mutant. J. Mol. Biol., 30:445-455.

Lucké, B. (1934): A Neoplastic Disease of the Kidney of the Frog *Rana pipiens*. Amer. J. Cancer, 20:352-379.

Lucké, B. (1938): Carcinoma in the Leopard Frog; Its Probable Causation by a Virus. J. Exptl. Med., 68:457-468.

Lucké, B. (1939): Characteristics of Frog Carcinoma in Tissue Culture. J. Exptl. Med., 70:269-276.

Luria, S. E. (1945): Genetics of Bacterium-Bacterial Virus Relationship. Ann. Missouri Botanical Garden, 33:235-242.

Luria, S. E. (1947): Reactivation of Irradiated Bacteriophage by Transfer of Self-Replicating Units. Proc. Natl. Acad. Sci., 33:253-264.

Luria, S. E. (1951): The Frequency Distribution of Spontaneous Bacteriophage Mutants as Evidence for the Exponential Rate of Phage Reproduction. Cold Spring Harbor Symposia Quant. Biol. 16:463-470. Reprinted in Stent, G. S. (1960): Papers on Bacterial Viruses. Boston, Little, Brown and Co., pp. 139-150.

Luria, S. E. (1960): Viruses, Cancer Cells, and the Genetic Concept of Virus Infection. Cancer Res., 20:677-688.

Luria, S. E. (1962a): Bacteriophage Genes and Bacterial Functions. Science, 136:685-692.

Luria, S. E. (1962b): Genetics of Bacteriophage. Ann. Rev. Microbiol., 16:205-240.

Luria, S. E., and M. Delbrück (1943): Mutations of Bacteria from Virus Sensitivity to Virus Resistance. Genetics, 28:491-511. Reprinted in Adelberg, E. A. (1960): Papers on Bacterial Genetics. Boston, Little, Brown and Co., pp. 3-23.

Luria, S. E., and R. Dulbecco (1949): Genetic Recombination Leading to Production of Active Bacteriophage from Ultraviolet Inactivated Bacteriophage Particles. Genetics, 34:93-125.

Luria, S. E., R. C. Williams, and R. C. Backus (1951): Electron Micrographic Counts of Bacteriophage Particles. J. Bacteriol., 61:179-187.

Lwoff, A. (1953): Lysogeny. Bacteriol. Rev., 17:269-337.

Lwoff, A. (1957): The Concept of Virus. J. Gen. Microbiol., 17:239-253.

Lwoff, A. (1959): Bacteriophage as a Model of Host-Virus Relationship. *In* Burnet, F. M., and W. M. Stanley (eds.): The Viruses, Vol. 2. New York, Academic Press Inc., pp. 187-201.

Lwoff, A. (1966): Interaction Among Virus, Cell, and Organism. Science, 152:1216-1220.

Lwoff, A. (1967): Principles of Classification and Nomenclature of Viruses. Nature, 215:13-14.

Lwoff, A., T. F. Anderson, and F. Jacob (1959): Remarques sur les Caracteristiques de la Particule Virale Infectieuse. Ann. Inst. Pasteur, 97:281-289.

Lwoff, A., and A. Gutmann (1950): Recherches sur un *Bacillus Megatherium* Lysogene. Ann. Inst. Pasteur, 78:711-739. Reprinted in abridged translation. Stent, G. S. (1960): Papers on Bacterial Viruses. Boston, Little, Brown and Co., pp. 312-331.

Lwoff, A., R. Horne, and P. Tournier (1962): A System of Viruses. Cold Spring Harbor Symposia Quant. Biol., 27:51-55.

Lwoff, A., L. Siminovitch, and N. Kjeldgaard (1950): Induction of Bacteriophage Lysis of an Entire Population of Lysogenic Bacteria. C. R. Acad. Sci. 231:190-191. Reprinted in translation. Stent, G. S. (1960): Papers on Bacterial Viruses. Boston, Little, Brown and Co., pp. 332-333.

Lwoff, A., and P. Tournier (1966): The Classification of Viruses. Ann. Rev. Microbiol., 20:45-74.

Lyons, M. J., and D. H. Moore (1962): Purification of the Mouse Mammary Tumour Virus. Nature, 194:1141-1142.

Lyons, M. J., and D. H. Moore (1965): Isolation of the Mouse Mammary Tumor Virus; Chemical and Morphological Studies. J. Natl. Cancer Inst., 35:549-565.

Maaløe, O., and J. D. Watson (1951): The Transfer of Radioactive Phosphorus from Parental to Progeny Phage. Proc. Natl. Acad. Sci., 37:507-513.

McAllister, R. M., J. E. Filbert, and C. R. Goodheart (1967): Human Cytomegalovirus; Studies on the Mechanism of Viral Cytopathology and Inclusion Body Formation. Proc. Soc. Exptl. Biol. Med., 124:932-937.

McAllister, R. M., B. H. Landing, and C. R. Goodheart (1964a): Isolation of Adenoviruses from Neoplastic and Non-Neoplastic Tissues of Children. Lab. Invest., 13:894-901.

McAllister, R. M., and I. MacPherson (1968): Transformation of a Hamster Cell Line by Adenovirus Type 12. J. Gen. Virol., 2:99-106.

McAllister, R. M., R. M. Straw, J. E. Filbert, and C. R. Goodheart (1963): Human Cytomegalovirus; Cytochemical Observations of Intracellular Lesion Development Correlated with Viral Synthesis and Release. Virology, 19:521-531.

McAllister, R. M., H. T. Wright, Jr., and W. M. Tasem (1964b): Cytomegalic Inclusion Disease in Newborn Twins. J. Pediatrics, 64:278-281.

McAuslan, B. R. (1963a): Control of Induced Thymidine Kinase Activity in the Poxvirus-Infected Cell. Virology, 20:162-168.

McAuslan, B. R. (1963b): The Induction and Repression of Thymidine Kinase in the Poxvirus-Infected HeLa Cell. Virology, 21:383-389.

McAuslan, B. R., P. Herde, D. Pett, and J. Ross (1965): Nucleases of Virus-Infected Animal Cells. Biochem. Biophys. Res. Commun., 20:586-591.

McAuslan, B. R., and J. R. Kates (1966): Regulation of Virus-Induced Deoxyribonucleases. Proc. Natl. Acad. Sci., 55:1581-1587.

McAuslan, B. R., and J. R. Kates (1967): Poxvirus-Induced Acid Deoxyribonuclease; Regulation of Synthesis; Control of Activity *in Vivo*; Purification and Properties of the Enzyme. Virology, 33:709-716.

McBride, W. D., and A. Wiener (1964): *In Vitro* Transformation of Hamster Kidney Cells by Human Adenovirus Type 12. Proc. Soc. Exptl. Biol. Med., 115:870-874.

McCarthy, B. J., and E. T. Bolton (1964): Interaction of Complementary RNA and DNA. J. Mol. Biol., 8:184-200.

McClain, M. E., and R. S. Spendlove (1966): Multiplicity Reactivation of Reovirus Particles after Exposure to Ultraviolet Light. J. Bacteriol., 92:1422-1429.

McCrea, J. F., and M. B. Lipman (1967): Strand-Length Measurements of Normal and 5-Iodo-2'-Deoxyuridine-Treated Vaccinia Virus Deoxyribonucleic Acid Released by the Kleinschmidt Method. J. Virol., 1:1037-1044.

MacHattie, L. A., and C. A. Thomas, Jr. (1964): DNA from Bacteriophage Lambda; Molecular Length and Conformation. Science, 144:1142-1144.

McLeod, D. L., and A. W. Ham (1963): Search for Oncogenic Properties in Various Viruses Found in Man; Positive Results with Adenovirus Types 12 and 18. Canadian Med. Assoc. J., 89:799-805.

MacLeod, R., G. J. Hills, and R. Markham (1963): Formation of True Three-Dimensional Crystals of the Tobacco Mosaic Virus Protein. Nature, 200:932-934.

MacPherson, I. (1965): Reversion in Hamster Cells Transformed by Rous Sarcoma Virus. Science, 148:1731-1733.

Maes, R., and A. Granoff (1967): Viruses and Renal Carcinoma of *Rana pipiens*; IV,

Nucleic Acid Synthesis in Frog Virus 3-Infected BHK 21/13 Cells. Virology, 33: 491-502.

Maes, R., A. Granoff, and W. R. Smith (1967): Viruses and Renal Carcinoma of *Rana pipiens*; III, The Relationship Between Input Multiplicity of Infection and Inclusion Body Formation in Frog Virus 3-Infected Cells. Virology, 33:137-144.

Magee, W. E. (1962): DNA Polymerase and Deoxyribonucleotide Kinase Activities in Cells Infected with Vaccinia Virus. Virology, 17:604-607.

Magee, W. E., and O. V. Miller (1967): Immunological Evidence for the Appearance of a New DNA-Polymerase in Cells Infected with Vaccinia Virus. Virology, 31:64-69.

Maley, G. F., and F. Maley (1966): The Significance of the Substrate Specificity of $T2r^+$ Induced Deoxycytidylate Deaminase. J. Biol. Chem., 241:2176-2177.

Malmgren, R. A., K. K. Takemoto, and P. G. Carney (1968): Immunofluorescent Studies of Mouse and Hamster Cell Surface Antigens Induced by Polyoma Virus. J. Natl. Cancer Inst. 40:263-268.

Malmgren, R. A., A. S. Rabson, and P. G. Carney (1964): Immunity and Viral Carcinogenesis; Effect of Thymectomy on Polyoma Virus Carcinogenesis in Mice. J. Natl. Cancer Inst., 33:101-104.

Manaker, R. A., and V. Groupé (1956): Discrete Foci of Altered Chicken Embryo Cells Associated with Rous Sarcoma Virus in Tissue Culture. Virology, 2:838-840.

Mandel, B. (1960): Neutralization of Viral Infectivity; Characterization of the Virus-Antibody Complex, Including Association, Dissociation, and Host-Cell Interaction. Ann. N. Y. Acad. Sci., 83:515-527.

Mandel, B. (1961): Reversibility of the Reaction Between Poliovirus and Neutralizing Antibody of Rabbit Origin. Virology, 14:316-328.

Mandel, B. (1967a): The Interaction of Neutralized Poliovirus with HeLa Cells; I, Adsorption. Virology, 31:238-247.

Mandel, B. (1967b): The Interaction of Neutralized Poliovirus with HeLa Cells; II, Elution, Penetration, Uncoating. Virology, 31:248-259.

Mandel, H. G., R. E. F. Matthews, A. Matus, and R. K. Ralph (1964): Replication Form of Plant Viral RNA. Biochem. Biophys. Res. Commun., 16:604-609.

Manson, L. A. (1953): The Metabolism of Ribonucleic Acid in Normal and Bacteriophage Infected *Escherichia coli*. J. Bacteriol., 66:703-711.

Marcovich, H., and H. S. Kaplan (1963): Induction by 5-Fluorouracil of Bacteriophage Development in Lysogenic *E. coli* K12(λ). Nature, 200:487-488.

Marcus, P. I., and D. H. Carver (1965): Hemadsorption-Negative Plaque Test; New Assay for Rubella Virus Revealing a Unique Interference. Science, 149:983-986.

Marcus, P. I., and D. H. Carver (1967): Intrinsic Interference; a New Type of Viral Interference. J. Virol., 1:334-343.

Marcus, P. I., and J. M. Salb (1966): Molecular Basis of Interferon Action; Inhibition of Viral RNA Translation. Virology, 30:502-516.

Marin, G., and J. W. Littlefield (1968): Selection of Morphologically Normal Cell Lines from Polyoma-Transformed BHK21/13 Hamster Fibroblasts. J. Virol., 2:69-77.

Marinkovich, V. A., and M. A. Baluda (1966): *In Vitro* Synthesis of γM-Like Globulin by Various Chick Embryonic Cells. Immunology, 10:383-397.

Markert, A., and W. Zillig (1965): Studies on the Lysis of *Escherichia coli* C by Bacteriophage φX174. Virology, 25:88-97.

Markham, R. (1962): Cited in Mora, P. T. (1962): Directiveness in Biology on the Molecular Level? Amer. Scientist, 50:570-575.

Marmur, J., and P. Doty (1962): Determination of the Base Composition of Deoxyribonucleic Acid from Its Thermal Denaturation Temperature. J. Mol. Biol., 5:109-118.

Marmur, J., and D. Lane (1960): Strand Separation and Specific Recombination in Deoxyribonucleic Acids; Biological Studies. Proc. Natl. Acad. Sci., 46:453-461.

Marti, A., J. D. Connor, and M. M. Sigel (1968): Recovery of Infectious Virus from Adenovirus Type-12 Tumor Cells. J. Natl. Cancer Inst., 40:243-247.

Martin, E. M. (1967): Replication of Small RNA Viruses. British Med. Bull., 23:192-197.

Martin, E. M., J. Malec, S. Sved, and T. S. Work (1961): Studies on Protein and Nucleic Acid Metabolism in Virus-Infected Mammalian Cells; I, Encephalomyocarditis Virus in Krebs II Mouse-Ascites-Tumour Cells. Biochem. J., 80:585-597.

Marvin, D. A. (1966): X-ray Diffraction and Electron Microscope Studies on the Structure of the Small Filamentous Bacteriophage fd. J. Mol. Biol., 15:8-17.

Marvin, D. A., and H. Hoffmann-Berling (1963): Physical and Chemical Properties of Two New Small Bacteriophages. Nature, 197:517-518.

Marvin, D. A., and H. Schaller (1966): The Topology of DNA from the Small Filamentous Bacteriophage fd. J. Mol. Biol., 15:1-7.

Mathews, C. K. (1966): On the Metabolic Role of T6 Phage-Induced Dihydrofolate Reductase. J. Biol. Chem., 241:5008-5012.

Matsubara, K., K. Shimada, and Y. Takagi (1967): Replication Process of Single-Stranded DNA of Bacteriophage ϕX174; V, Production of Replicative Form in *Escherichia coli* Cells Irradiated by Ultraviolet Light. J. Mol. Biol., 29:297-306.

Matsubara, K., M. Takai, and Y. Takagi (1963): The Replication Process of Single-Stranded DNA of Bacteriophage ϕX174; II, The Non-Intermediation of the Double-Stranded DNA as a Material Precursor. Biochem. Biophys. Res. Commun., 11:372-377.

Matsuda, M., and L. Barksdale (1966): Phage-Directed Synthesis of Diphtherial Toxin in Non-Toxinogenic *Corynebacterium diphtheriae*. Nature, 210:911-913.

Matsuda, M., and L. Barksdale (1967): System for the Investigation of the Bacteriophage-Directed Synthesis of Diphtherial Toxin. J. Bacteriol., 93:722-730.

Mattern, C. F. T. (1962): Polyoma and Papilloma Viruses; Do They Have 42 or 92 Subunits? Science, 137:612-613.

Mayor, H. D. (1964): Picornavirus Symmetry. Virology, 22:156-160.

Mayor, H. D., and M. Ito (1967): Distribution of Antibodies to Type 4 Adeno-Associated Satellite Virus in Simian and Human Sera. Proc. Soc. Exptl. Biol. Med., 126:723-725.

Mayor, H. D., M. Ito, L. E. Jordan, and J. L. Melnick (1967): Morphological Studies on the Replication of a Defective Satellite Virus and Its Helper Adenovirus. J. Natl. Cancer Inst., 38:805-820.

Mayor, H. D., R. M. Jamison, L. E. Jordan, and J. L. Melnick (1965): Structure and Composition of a Small Particle Prepared from a Simian Adenovirus. J. Bacteriol., 90:235-242.

Mayor, H. D., and J. L. Melnick (1962): Icosahedral Models and Viruses; a Critical Evaluation. Science, 137:613-615.

Mayor, H. D., and J. L. Melnick (1966): Small Deoxyribonucleic Acid-Containing Viruses (Picodnavirus Group). Nature, 210:331-332.

Mécs, E., J. A. Sonnabend, and E. M. Martin (1967): The Effect of Interferon on the Synthesis of RNA in Chick Cells Infected with Semliki Forest Virus. J. Gen. Virol., 1:25-40.

Medill-Brown, M., and B. A. Broidy (1955): Mutation and Selection Pressure During Adaption of Influenza Virus to Mice. Virology, 1:301-312.

Melechen, N. E., and P. D. Skaar (1962): The Provocation of an Early Step of Induction by Thymine Deprivation. Virology, 16:21-29.

Melnick, J. L. (1962): Papova Virus Group. Science, 135:1128-1130.

Melnick, J. L., H. D. Mayor, K. O. Smith, and F. Rapp (1965): Association of 20-Millimicron Particles with Adenoviruses. J. Bacteriol., 90:271-274.

Merigan, T. C. (1964): Purified Interferons; Physical Properties and Species Specificity. Science, 145:811-813.

Merigan, T. C. (1967): Various Molecular Species of Interferon Induced by Viral and Nonviral Agents. Bacteriol. Rev., 31:138-144.

Merigan, T. C., and W. Regelson (1967): Interferon Induction in Man by a Synthetic Polyanion of Defined Composition. New Eng. J. Med., 277:1283-1287.

Merigan, T. C., C. A. Winget, and C. B. Dixon (1965): Purification and Characterization of Vertebrate Interferons. J. Mol. Biol., 13:679-691.

Merriam, V., and M. P. Gordon (1965): Photoreactivation of Tobacco Mosaic Virus Ribonucleic Acid Following Near Ultraviolet Irradiation. Proc. Natl. Acad. Sci., 54:1261-1268.

Meselson, M., and F. W. Stahl (1958): The Replication of DNA in *Escherichia coli*. Proc. Natl. Acad. Sci., 44:671-682.

Meselson, M., and J. J. Weigle (1961): Chromosome Breakage Accompanying Genetic Recombination in Bacteriophage. Proc. Natl. Acad. Sci., 47:857-868.

Michel, M. R., B. Hirt, and R. Weil (1967): Mouse Cellular DNA Enclosed in Polyoma Viral Capsids (Pseudovirions). Proc. Natl. Acad. Sci., 58:1381-1388.

Middelkamp, J., and B. L. Munger (1964): The Ultrastructure and Histogenesis of Molluscum Contagiosum. J. Pediatrics, 64:888-905.

Miller, E. M., and W. F. Goebel (1954): The Nature of Prophage in Lysogenic *Bacillus megatherium*. J. Exptl. Med., 100:525-540.

Miller, J. F. A. P. (1964): The Thymus and the Development of Immunologic Responsiveness. Science, 144:1544-1551.

Miller, J. F. A. P., R. C. Ting, and L. W. Law (1964): Influence of Thymectomy on Tumor Induction by Polyoma Virus in C57Bl Mice. Proc. Soc. Exptl. Biol. Med., 116:323-327.

Mills, D. R., R. L. Peterson, and S. Spiegelman (1967): An Extracellular Darwinian Experiment with a Self-Duplicating Nucleic Acid Molecule. Proc. Natl. Acad. Sci., 58:217-224.

Miner, N., W. J. Ray, Jr., and E. H. Simon (1966): Effect of Interferon on the Production and Action of Viral RNA Polymerase. Biochem. Biophys. Res. Commun., 24:264-268.

Mizell, M., and J. Zambernard (1965): Viral Particles of the Frog Renal Adenocarcinoma; Causative Agent or Passenger Virus? II, A Promising Model System for the Demonstration of a "Lysogenic" State in a Metazoan Tumor. Ann. N. Y. Acad. Sci., 126:146-169.

Moloney, J. B. (1966): A Virus-Induced Rhabdomyosarcoma of Mice. *In* Rich, M. A., and J. B. Moloney (eds.): Conference on Murine Leukemia, National Cancer Institute Monograph 22. Washington, D.C., U.S. Gov. Printing Office, pp. 139-142.

Montagnier, L., and F. K. Sanders (1963): Replicative Form of Encephalomyocarditis Virus Ribonucleic Acid. Nature, 199:664-667.

Moody, M. F. (1967a): Structure of the Sheath of Bacteriophage T4; I, Structure of the Contracted Sheath and Polysheath. J. Mol. Biol., 25:167-200.

Moody, M. F. (1967b): Structure of the Sheath of Bacteriophage T4; II, Rearrangement of the Sheath Subunits During Contraction. J. Mol. Biol., 25:201-208.

Moore, A. E. (1962): Characteristics of Certain Viruses Isolated from Transplantable Tumors. Virology, 18:182-191.

Moore, D. H. (1967): Comments on Mouse Mammary Tumor Viruses. *In* Carcinogenesis: A Broad Critique. Baltimore, The Williams and Wilkins Co., pp. 287-293.

Moore, D. H., E. Y. Lasfargues, M. R. Murray, C. D. Haagensen, and E. C. Pollard (1959): Correlation of Physical and Biological Properties of Mouse Mammary Tumor Agent. J. Biophys. Biochem. Cyto., 5:85-92.

Morgan, C., G. C. Godman, H. M. Rose, C. Howe, and J. S. Huang (1957): Electron Microscopic and Histochemical Studies of an Unusual Crystalline Protein Occurring in Cells Infected by Type 5 Adenovirus; Preliminary Observations. J. Biophys. Biochem. Cyto., 3:505-507.

Morgan, C., C. Howe, H. M. Rose, and D. H. Moore (1956): Structure and Development of Viruses Observed in the Electron Microscope; IV, Viruses of the RI-APC Group. J. Biophys. Biochem. Cyto., 2:351-359.

Morgan, C., R. A. Rifkind, and H. M. Rose (1962): The Use of Ferritin-Conjugated Antibodies in Electron Microscopic Studies of Influenza and Vaccinia Viruses. Cold Spring Harbor Symposia Quant. Biol., 27:57-65.

Morowitz, H. J., and J. Maniloff (1966): Analysis of the Life Cycle of *Mycoplasma gallisepticum*. J. Bacteriol., 91:1638-1644.

Morowitz, H. J., and M. E. Tourtellotte (1962): The Smallest Living Cells. Sci. Amer., 206(March):117-126.

Morris, A., S. Favelukes, R. Arlinghaus, and R. Schweet (1962): Mechanism of Puromycin Inhibition of Hemoglobin Synthesis. Biochem. Biophys. Res. Commun., 7:326-330.

Morris, V. L., P. G. Spear, and B. Roizman (1966): Some Biophysical Properties of Frog Viruses and Their DNA. Proc. Natl. Acad. Sci., 56:1155-1157.

Moscovici, C. (1967): A Quantitative Assay for Avian Myeloblastosis Virus. Proc. Soc. Exptl. Biol. Med., 125:1213-1215.

Mosig, G. (1963): Genetic Recombination in Bacteriophage T4 During Replication of DNA Fragments. Cold Spring Harbor Symposia Quant. Biol., 28:35-42.

Mosig, G. (1966): Distances Separating Genetic Markers in T4 DNA. Proc. Natl. Acad. Sci., 56:1177-1183.

Moulder, J. W. (1964): The Psittacosis Group as Bacteria. New York, John Wiley & Sons, Inc.

Moulder, J. W. (1966): The Relation of the Psittacosis Group (Chlamydiae) to Bacteria and Viruses. Ann. Rev. Microbiol., 20:107-130.

Mountain, I. M., and H. E. Alexander (1959): Infectivity of Ribonucleic Acid (RNA) from Type I Poliovirus in Embryonated Egg. Proc. Soc. Exptl. Biol. Med., 101:527-532.

Munk, K., and G. Sauer (1964): Relationship Between Cell DNA Metabolism and Nucleocytoplasmic Alterations in Herpes Virus-Infected Cells. Virology, 22:153-154.

Munroe, J. S. and W. F. Windle (1963): Tumors Induced in Primates by Chicken Sarcoma Virus. Science, 140:1415-1416.

Munyon, W., E. Paoletti, and J. T. Grace, Jr. (1967): RNA Polymerase Activity in Purified Infectious Vaccinia Virus. Proc. Natl. Acad. Sci., 58:2280-2287.

Munyon, W., E. Paoletti, J. Ospina, and J. T. Grace, Jr. (1968): Nucleotide Phosphohydrolase in Purified Vaccinia Virus. J. Virol., 2:167-172.

Naegele, R. F., and F. Rapp (1967): Enhancement of the Replication of Human Adenoviruses in Simian Cells by Simian Adenovirus SV15. J. Virol., 1:838-840.

Nagata, T. (1963): The Molecular Synchrony and Sequential Replication of DNA in *Escherichia coli*. Proc. Natl. Acad. Sci., 49:551-559.

Nagington, J., and R. W. Horne (1962): Morphological Studies of Orf and Vaccinia Viruses. Virology, 16:248-260.

Naono, S., and F. Gros (1967): On the Mechanism of Transcription of the Lambda Genome During Induction of Lysogenic Bacteria. J. Mol. Biol., 25:517-536.

Nathans, D., G. Notani, J. H. Schwartz, and N. D. Zinder (1962): Biosynthesis of the Coat Protein of Coliphage f2 by *E. coli* Extracts. Proc. Natl. Acad. Sci., 48:1424-1431.

Nayak, D. P., and M. A. Baluda (1967): Isolation and Partial Characterization of Nucleic Acid of Influenza Virus. J. Virol., 1:1217-1223.

Nayak, D. P., and M. A. Baluda (1968a): An Intermediate in the Replication of Influenza Virus RNA. Proc. Natl. Acad. Sci., 59:184-191.

Nayak, D. P., and M. A. Baluda (1968b): Ribonucleic Acid Synthesis in Cells Infected with Influenza Virus. J. Virol., 2:99-109.

Nichols, W. W. (1966a): The Role of Viruses in the Etiology of Chromosomal Abnormalities. Amer. J. Human Genet., 18:81-92.

Nichols, W. W. (1966b): Studies on the Role of Viruses in Somatic Mutation. Hereditas, 55:1-27.

Nichols, W. W., A. Levan, L. L. Coriell, H. Goldner, and C. G. Ahlström (1964): Chromosome Abnormalities *in Vitro* in Human Leukocytes Associated with Schmidt-Ruppin Rous Sarcoma Virus. Science, 146:248-250.

Nichols, W. W., M. Peluse, C. R. Goodheart, R. McAllister, and C. Bradt (1968): Autoradiographic Studies on Nuclei and Chromosomes of Cultured Leukocytes after Infection with Tritium-Labeled Adenovirus Type 12. Virology, 34:303-311.

Nirenberg, M. W. (1963): The Genetic Code; II, Sci. Amer., 208(March):80-94.

Nirenberg, M. W., and J. H. Matthaei (1961): The Dependence of Cell-Free Protein Synthesis in *E. coli* upon Naturally Occurring or Synthetic Polyribonucleotides. Proc. Natl. Acad. Sci., 47:1588-1602.

Niven, J. S. F., J. A. Armstrong, C. H. Andrewes, H. G. Pereira, and R. C. Valentine (1961): Subcutaneous "Growths" in Monkeys Produced by a Poxvirus. J. Path. Bacteriol., 81:1-14.

Nixon, H. L., and R. D. Woods (1960): The Structure of Tobacco Mosaic Virus Protein. Virology, 10:157-159.

Nohara, H., and A. S. Kaplan (1963): Induction of a New Enzyme in Rabbit Kidney Cells by Pseudorabies Virus. Biochem. Biophys. Res. Commun., 12:189-193.

Noll, H., T. Aoyagi, and J. Orlando (1962): The Structural Relationship of Sialidase to the Influenza Virus Surface. Virology, 18:154-157.

Nomura, M., B. D. Hall, and S. Spiegelman (1960): Characterization of RNA Synthesized in *Escherichia coli* after Bacteriophage T2 Infection. J. Mol. Biol., 2:306-326.

Norrby, E. (1966): The Relationship Between the Soluble Antigens and the Virion of Adenovirus Type 3; I, Morphological Characteristics. Virology, 28:236-248.

Norrby, E., P. Magnusson, B. Friding, and S. Gard (1963): A Note on the Morphology of Rubella Virus. Arch. Gesamte Virusforsch., 13:421-424.

Notani, G. W., D. L. Engelhardt, W. Konigsberg, and N. D. Zinder (1965): Suppression of a Coat Protein Mutant of the Bacteriophage f2. J. Mol. Biol., 12:439-447.

Novick, A., and L. Szilard (1951): Virus Strains of Identical Phenotype but Different Genotype. Science, 113:34-35.

Nowinski, R. C., L. J. Old, D. H. Moore, G. Geering, and E. A. Boyse (1967): A Soluble Antigen of the Mammary Tumor Virus. Virology, 31:1-14.

O'Connor, T. E., and P. J. Fischinger (1968): Titration Patterns of a Murine Sarcoma-Leukemia Virus Complex; Evidence for Existence of Competent Sarcoma Virions. Science, 159:325-329.

O'Conor, G. T., A. S. Rabson, I. K. Berezesky, and F. J. Paul (1963): Mixed Infection with Simian Virus 40 and Adenovirus 12. J. Natl. Cancer Inst., 31:903-917.

O'Conor, G. T., A. S. Rabson, R. A. Malmgren, I. K. Berezesky, and F. J. Paul (1965): Morphologic Observations of Green Monkey Kidney Cells after Single and Double Infection with Adenovirus 12 and Simian Virus 40. J. Natl. Cancer Inst., 34:679-693.

Oda, K.-I., and W. K. Joklik (1967): Hybridization and Sedimentation Studies on "Early" and "Late" Vaccinia Messenger RNA. J. Mol. Biol., 27:395-419.

Ofengand, J., and R. Haselkorn (1961): Viral RNA-Dependent Incorporation of Amino Acids into Protein by Cell-Free Extracts of E. coli. Biochem. Biophys. Res. Commun., 6:469-474.

Offord, R. E. (1966): Electron Microscopic Observations on the Substructure of Tobacco Rattle Virus. J. Mol. Biol., 17:370-375.

Ogawa, H., and J.-I. Tomizawa (1967): Bacteriophage Lambda DNA with Different Structures Found in Infected Cells. J. Mol. Biol., 23:265-276.

Ohtaka, Y., and S. Spiegelman (1963): Translational Control of Protein Synthesis in a Cell-Free System Directed by a Polycistronic Viral RNA. Science, 142:493-497.

Okada, Y., E. Terzaghi, G. Streisinger, J. Emrich, M. Inouye, and A. Tsugita (1966): A Frame-Shift Mutation Involving the Addition of Two Base Pairs in the Lysozyme Gene of Phage T4. Proc. Natl. Acad. Sci., 56:1692-1698.

Old, L. J., E. A. Boyse, H. F. Oettgen, E. de Harven, G. Geering, B. Williamson, and P. Clifford (1966): Precipitating Antibody in Human Serum to an Antigen Present in Cultured Burkitt's Lymphoma Cells. Proc. Natl. Acad. Sci., 56:1699-1704.

Olivera, B. M., and I. R. Lehman (1967): Linkage of Polynucleotides Through Phosphodiester Bonds by an Enzyme from Escherichia coli. Proc. Natl. Acad. Sci., 57:1426-1433.

Olson, C. (1963): Cutaneous Papillomatosis in Cattle and Other Animals. Ann. N.Y. Acad. Sci., 108:1042-1056.

Opler, S. R. (1967a): Observations on a New Virus Associated with Guinea Pig Leukemia; Preliminary Note. J. Natl. Cancer Inst., 38:797-800.

Opler, S. E. (1967b): Animal Model of Viral Oncogenesis. Nature, 215:184.

Ormsbee, R. A., and E. Weiss (1963): Trachoma Agent; Glucose Utilization by Purified Suspensions. Science, 142:1077-1078.

Oroszlan, S., and M. A. Rich (1964): Human Wart Virus; in Vitro Cultivation. Science, 146:531-533.

Oxman, M. N., and P. H. Black (1966): Inhibition of SV40 T Antigen Formation by Interferon. Proc. Natl. Acad. Sci., 55:1133-1140.

Oxman, M. N., W. P. Rowe, and P. H. Black (1967): Studies of Adenovirus-SV40 Hybrid Viruses; VI, Differential Effects of Interferon on SV40 and Adenovirus T Antigen Formation in Cells Infected with SV40 Virus, Adenoviruses, and Adenovirus-SV40 Hybrid Viruses. Proc. Natl. Acad. Sci., 57:941-948.

Ozaki, Y., A. R. Diwan, W. D. McBride, and J. L. Melnick (1963): Antigenic Characterization of Oral Poliovaccine Progeny by Neutralization Kinetics. J. Immunol., 90:288-296.

Pace, N. R., D. H. L. Bishop, and S. Spiegelman (1967): Examination of the $Q\beta$-Replicase Reaction by Sucrose Gradient and Gel Electrophoresis. J. Virol., 1:771-778.

Pace, N. R., D. H. L. Bishop, and S. Spiegelman (1968): The Immediate Precursor of Viral RNA in the $Q\beta$-Replicase Reaction. Proc. Natl. Acad. Sci., 59:139-144.

Pace, N. R., and S. Spiegelman (1966a): The Synthesis of Infectious RNA with a Replicase Purified According to Its Size and Density. Proc. Natl. Acad. Sci., 55:1608-1615.

Pace, N. R., and S. Spiegelman (1966b): *In Vitro* Synthesis of an Infectious Mutant RNA with a Normal RNA Replicase. Science, 153:64-67.

Padgett, B. L., M. S. Moore, and D. L. Walker (1962): Plaque Assays for Myxoma and Fibroma Viruses and Differentiation of the Viruses by Plaque Form. Virology, 17:462-469.

Pardee, A. B., and I. Williams (1952): The Increase in Deoxyribonuclease of Virus-Infected *E. coli*. Arch. Biochem. Biophys., 40:222-223.

Parkman, P. D., E. L. Buescher, M. S. Artenstein, J. M. McCown, F. K. Mundon, and A. D. Druzd (1964): Studies of Rubella I; Properties of the Virus. J. Immunol., 93:595-607.

Parks, W. P., A. M. Casazza, J. Alcott, and J. L. Melnick (1968): Adeno-Associated Satellite Virus Interference with the Replication of Its Helper Adenovirus. J. Exptl. Med., 127:91-108.

Parks, W. P., M. Green, M. Piña, and J. L. Melnick (1967a): Physicochemical Characterization of Adeno-Associated Satellite Virus Type 4 and Its Nucleic Acid. J. Virol., 1:980-987.

Parks, W. P., J. L. Melnick, R. Rongey, and H. D. Mayor (1967b): Physical Assay and Growth Cycle Studies of a Defective Adeno-Satellite Virus. J. Virol., 1:171-180.

Parsons, D. F. (1963): Structure of the Gross Leukemia Virus. J. Natl. Cancer Inst. 30:569-583.

Pasteur, L. (1884): A New Communication on Rabies. C. R. Acad. Sci., 98:457-463. Reprinted in translation. Hahon, N. (1964): Selected Papers on Virology. Englewood Cliffs, New Jersey, Prentice-Hall, Inc., pp. 30-36.

Paucker, K., and K. Cantell (1962): Neutralization of Interferon by Specific Antibody. Virology, 18:145-147.

Pauling, C., and P. Hanawalt (1965): Nonconservative DNA Replication in Bacteria after Thymine Starvation. Proc. Natl. Acad. Sci., 54:1728-1735.

Payne, F. E., T. F. Beals, and R. E. Preston (1964): Morphology of a Small DNA Virus. Virology, 23:109-113.

Penman, S., Y. Becker, and J. E. Darnell (1964): A Cytoplasmic Structure Involved in the Synthesis and Assembly of Poliovirus Components. J. Mol. Biol., 8:541-555.

Penman, S., K. Scherrer, Y. Becker, and J. E. Darnell (1963): Polyribosomes in Normal and Poliovirus-Infected HeLa Cells and Their Relationship to Messenger-RNA. Proc. Natl. Acad. Sci., 49:654-662.

Pereira, H. G. (1960): A Virus Inhibitor Produced in HeLa Cells Infected with Adenovirus. Virology, 11:590-602.

Pereira, M. S., Pereira, H. G., and S. K. R. Clarke (1965): Human Adenovirus Type 31; A New Serotype with Oncogenic Properties. Lancet, 1:21-23.

Pereira da Silva, L. H., and F. Jacob (1967): Induction of C_{II} and O Functions in Early Defective Lambda Prophages. Virology, 33:618-624.

Perk, K., and J. B. Moloney (1966): Pathogenesis of a Virus-Induced Rhabdomyosarcoma in Mice. J. Natl. Cancer Inst., 37:581-599.

Perkins, H. R., and A. C. Allison (1963): Cell-Wall Constituents of Rickettsiae and Psittacosis-Lymphogranuloma Organisms. J. Gen. Microbiol., 30:469-480.

Pettijohn, D., and P. Hanawalt (1964): Evidence for Repair-Replication of Ultraviolet Damaged DNA in Bacteria. J. Mol. Biol., 9:395-410.

Pettijohn, D., and T. Kamiya (1967): Interaction of RNA Polymerase with Polyoma DNA. J. Mol. Biol., 29:275-295.

Pfefferkorn, E. R., and B. W. Burge (1967): Genetics and Biochemistry of Arbovirus Temperature-Sensitive Mutants. *In* Colter, J. S., and W. Paranchych (eds.): The Molecular Biology of Viruses. New York, Academic Press Inc., pp. 403-426.

Pfefferkorn, E. R., B. W. Burge, and H. M. Coady (1966): Characteristics of the Photoreactivation of Pseudorabies Virus. J. Bacteriol., 92:856-861.

Pfefferkorn, E. R., and R. L. Clifford (1964): The Origin of the Protein of Sindbis Virus. Virology, 23:217-223.

Pfefferkorn, E. R., and H. S. Hunter (1963): The Source of the Ribonucleic Acid and Phospholipid of Sindbis Virus. Virology, 20:446-456.

Philipson, L. (1963): The Early Interaction of Animal Viruses and Cells. Progr. Med. Virol., 5:43-78.

Philipson, L. (1967): Attachment and Eclipse of Adenovirus. J. Virol., 1:868-875.

Pienta, R. J., and V. Groupé (1967): Growth Curve and Distribution of Rous Sarcoma Virus (Bryan) in Japanese Quail. J. Virol., 1:1122-1129.

Pirie, N. W. (1962): Prerequisites for Virus Classification. Symp. Soc. Gen. Microbiol., 12:374-393.

Plagemann, P. G. W., and H. E. Swim (1966): Replication of Mengovirus; II, General Properties of the Viral-Induced Ribonucleic Acid Polymerase. J. Bacteriol., 91:2327-2332.

Pollard, E., and J. Setlow (1953): Action of Heat on the Serological Affinity of T1 Bacteriophage. Arch. Biochem. Biophys., 43:136-142.

Pons, M. (1964): Infectious Double-Stranded Poliovirus RNA. Virology, 24:467-473.

Pons, M. (1967): Effect of Actinomycin D on the Replication of Influenza Virus and Influenza Virus RNA. Virology, 33:150-154.

Pontecorvo, G. (1963): Microbial Genetics; Retrospect and Prospect. Proc. Roy. Soc., Series B., 158:1-23.

Pope, J. H., and W. P. Rowe (1964): Immunofluorescent Studies of Adenovirus 12 Tumors and of Cells Transformed or Infected by Adenoviruses. J. Exptl. Med., 120:577-588.

Pouwels, P. H., H. S. Jansz, J. Van Rotterdam, and J. A. Cohen (1966): Structure of the Replicative Form of Bacteriophage φX174; Physico-Chemical Studies. Biochim. Biophys Acta, 119:289-300.

Powers, E. L. (1962): Considerations of Survival Curves and Target Theory. Physics Med. Biol., 7:3-28.

Pringle, C. R. (1968): Recombination Between Conditional Lethal Mutants Within a Strain of Foot-and-Mouth Disease Virus. J. Gen. Virol., 2:199-202.

Provisional Committee for the Nomenclature of Viruses (1965): Proposals and Recommendations. Ann. Inst. Pasteur, 109:625-637.

Prusoff, W. H., Y. S. Bakhle, and L. Sekely (1965): Cellular and Antiviral Effects of Halogenated Deoxyribonucleosides. Ann. N.Y. Acad. Sci., 130:135-150.

Ptashne, M. (1965): The Detachment and Maturation of Conserved Lambda Prophage DNA. J. Mol. Biol., 11:90-96.

Ptashne, M. (1967a): Isolation of the λ Phage Repressor. Proc. Natl. Acad. Sci., 57:306-313.

Ptashne, M. (1967b): Specific Binding of the λ Phage Repressor to λ DNA. Nature, 214:232-234.

Putnam, F. W., and L. M. Kozloff (1950): Biochemical Studies of Virus Reproduction; IV, The Fate of the Infecting Virus Particle. J. Biol. Chem., 182:243-250.

Rabotti, G. F., W. A. Raine, and R. L. Sellers (1965): Brain Tumors (Gliomas) Induced in Hamsters by Bryan's Strain of Rous Sarcoma Virus. Science, 147:504-506.

Rabson, A. S., and R. L. Kirschstein (1962): Induction of Malignancy in Vitro in Newborn Hamster Kidney Tissue Infected with Simian Vacuolating Virus (SV40). Proc. Soc. Exptl. Biol. Med., 111:323-328.

Rabson, A. S., G. T. O'Conor, I. K. Berezesky, and F. J. Paul (1964): Enhancement of Adenovirus Growth in African Green Monkey Kidney Cell Cultures by SV40. Proc. Soc. Exptl. Biol. Med., 116:187-190.

Rafajko, R. R. (1967): Routine Establishment of Serial Lines of Hamster Embryo Cells Transformed by Adenovirus Type 12. J. Natl. Cancer Inst., 38:581-591.

Rafferty, K. A., Jr. (1963): Effect of Injected Frog-Kidney Tumor Extracts on Development of Tumors under Promoting Conditions. J. Natl. Cancer Inst., 30:1103-1113.

Rafferty, K. A., Jr. (1964): Kidney Tumors of the Leopard Frog; a Review. Cancer Res., 24:169-186.

Ralph, R. K., and S. J. Wojcik (1966): Synthesis of Double-Stranded Viral RNA by Cell-Free Extracts from Turnip Yellow Mosaic Virus-Infected Leaves. Biochim. Biophys. Acta, 119:347-361.

Randall, C. C., L. G. Gafford, and R. B. Arhelger (1961): Electron Microscopic Examination of Isolated Fowlpox Inclusions. Virology, 14:380-382.

Rapoza, N. P., and R. W. Atchison (1967): Association of AAV-1 with Simian Adenoviruses. Nature, 215:1186-1187.

Rapoza, N. P., L. P. Merkow, and M. Slifkin (1967): Tumor Production *in Vivo* and Cell Transformation *in Vitro* by Two SV20 Strains. Cancer Res., 27:1887-1894.

Rapp, F. (1966): Complementation Between Defective Oncogenic Viruses. *In* Kirsten, W. H. (ed.): Malignant Transformation by Viruses. New York, Springer-Verlag, Inc., pp. 77-94.

Rapp, F., J. S. Butel, L. A. Feldman, T. Kitahara, and J. L. Melnick (1965a): Differential Effects of Inhibitors on the Steps Leading to the Formation of SV40 Tumor and Virus Antigens. J. Exptl. Med., 121:935-944.

Rapp, F., M. Jerkofsky, and D. Vanderslice (1967): Characterization of Defectiveness of Human Adenoviruses in Green Monkey Kidney Cells. Proc. Soc. Exptl. Biol. Med., 126:782-786.

Rapp, F., and J. L. Melnick (1966): Papovavirus SV40, Adenovirus and Their Hybrids; Transformation, Complementation, and Transcapsidation. Progr. Med. Virol., 8:349-399.

Rapp, F., J. L. Melnick, J. S. Butel, and T. Kitahara (1964): The Incorporation of SV40 Genetic Material into Adenovirus 7 as Measured by Intranuclear Synthesis of SV40 Tumor Antigen. Proc. Natl. Acad. Sci., 52:1348-1352.

Rapp, F., J. L. Melnick, and T. Kitahara (1965b): Tumor and Virus Antigens of Simian Virus 40; Differential Inhibition of Synthesis by Cytosine Arabinoside. Science, 147:625-627.

Ray, D. S., H.-P. Bscheider, and P. H. Hofschneider (1966a): Replication of the Single-Stranded DNA of the Male-Specific Bacteriophage M13; Isolation of Intracellular Forms of Phage-Specific DNA. J. Mol. Biol., 21:473-483.

Ray, D. S., A. Preuss, and P. H. Hofschneider (1966b): Replication of the Single-Stranded DNA of the Male-Specific Bacteriophage M13; Circular Forms of the Replicative DNA. J. Mol. Biol., 21:485-491.

Reed, L. J., and H. Muench (1938): A Simple Method of Estimating Fifty Per Cent Endpoints. Amer. J. Hyg., 27:493-497.

Reed, S. E. (1967): Transformation of Hamster Cells *in Vitro* by Adenovirus Type 12. J. Gen. Virol., 1:405-412.

Reich, E., R. M. Franklin, A. J. Shatkin, and E. L. Tatum (1961): Effect of Actinomycin D on Cellular Nucleic Acid Synthesis and Virus Production. Science, 134:556-557.

Reich, E., R. M. Franklin, A. J. Shatkin, and E. L. Tatum (1962): Action of Actinomycin D on Animal Cells and Viruses. Proc. Natl. Acad. Sci., 48:1238-1245.

Reich, P. R., S. G. Baum, J. A. Rose, W. P. Rowe, and S. M. Weissman (1966a): Nucleic Acid Homology Studies of Adenovirus Type 7-SV40 Interactions. Proc. Natl. Acad. Sci., 55:336-341.

Reich, P. R., P. H. Black, and S. M. Weissman (1966b): Nucleic Acid Homology Studies of SV40 Virus-Transformed and Normal Hamster Cells. Proc. Natl. Acad. Sci., 56:78-85.

Reichmann, M. E. (1964): The Satellite Tobacco Necrosis Virus; a Single Protein and Its Genetic Code. Proc. Natl. Acad. Sci., 52:1009-1017.

Reissig, M., and A. S. Kaplan (1962): The Morphology of Noninfective Pseudorabies Virus Produced by Cells Treated with 5-Fluorouracil. Virology, 16:1-8.

Rich, A., S. Penman, Y. Becker, J. Darnell, and C. Hall (1963): Polyribosomes; Size in Normal and Polio-Infected HeLa Cells. Science, 142:1658-1663.

Riggs, J. L., and E. H. Lennette (1967): *In Vitro* Transformation of Newborn-Hamster Kidney Cells by Simian Adenoviruses. Proc. Soc. Exptl. Biol. Med., 126:802-806.

Ris, H., and B. L. Chandler (1963): The Ultrastructure of Genetic Systems in Prokaryotes and Eukaryotes. Cold Spring Harbor Symposia Quant. Biol., 28:1-8.

Robbins, P. W., J. M. Keller, A. Wright, and R. L. Bernstein (1965): Enzymatic and Kinetic Studies on the Mechanism of O-Antigen Conversion by Bacteriophage ϵ^{15}. J. Biol. Chem., 240:384-390.

Roberts, J. W., and J. E. A. Steitz (1967): The Reconstitution of Infective Bacteriophage R17. Proc. Natl. Acad. Sci., 58:1416-1421.

Robinson, H. L. (1967): Isolation of Noninfectious Particles Containing Rous Sarcoma Virus RNA from the Medium of Rous Sarcoma Virus-Transformed Nonproducer Cells. Proc. Natl. Acad. Sci., 57:1655-1662.

Roizman, B. (1962): Polykaryocytosis. Cold Spring Harbor Symposia Quant. Biol., 27:327-342.

Roizman, B. (1963): The Programing of Herpes Virus Multiplication in Mammalian Cells. *In* Viruses, Nucleic Acids, and Cancer. Baltimore, The Williams and Wilkins Co., pp. 205-223.

Roizman, B. (1965): Abortive Infection of Canine Cells by Herpes Simplex Virus; III, The Interference of Conditional Lethal Virus with an Extended Host Range Mutant. Virology, 27:113-117.

Roizman, B., L. Aurelian, and P. R. Roane, Jr. (1963): The Multiplication of Herpes Simplex Virus; I, The Programing of Viral DNA Duplication in HEp-2 Cells. Virology, 21:482-498.

Roizman, B., and P. R. Roane, Jr. (1964): The Multiplication of Herpes Simplex Virus; II, The Relation Between Protein Synthesis and the Duplication of Viral DNA in Infected HEp-2 Cells. Virology, 22:262-269.

Rolfe, U., and R. L. Sinsheimer (1965): Antigens of Bacteriophage φX174. J. Immunol., 94:18-21.

Rose, J. A., M. D. Hoggan, and A. J. Shatkin (1966): Nucleic Acid from an Adeno-Associated Virus; Chemical and Physical Studies. Proc. Natl. Acad. Sci., 56:86-92.

Roth, T. F., and M. Hayashi (1966): Allomorphic Forms of Bacteriophage φX174 Replicative DNA. Science, 154:658-660.

Rountree, P. M. (1949): The Phenomenon of Lysogenicity in Staphylococci. J. Gen. Microbiol., 3:153-163.

Rous, P. (1911): Transmission of a Malignant New Growth by Means of a Cell-Free Filtrate. J.A.M.A., 56:198.

Rous, P. (1965): Viruses and Tumour Causation; an Appraisal of Present Knowledge. Nature, 207:457-463.

Rous, P. (1967): The Challenge to Man of the Neoplastic Cell. Science, 157:24-28.

Rouse, H. C., and R. W. Schlesinger (1967): An Arginine-Dependent Step in the Maturation of Type 2 Adenovirus. Virology, 33:513-522.

Rowe, W. P. (1961): The Epidemiology of Mouse Polyoma Virus Infection. Bacteriol. Rev., 25:18-31.

Rowe, W. P. (1965): Studies of Adenovirus-SV40 Hybrid Viruses; III, Transfer of SV40 Gene Between Adenovirus Types. Proc. Natl. Acad. Sci., 54:711-717.

Rowe, W. P., and S. G. Baum (1964): Evidence for a Possible Genetic Hybrid Between Adenovirus Type 7 and SV40 Viruses. Proc. Natl. Acad. Sci., 52:1340-1347.

Rowe, W. P., and S. G. Baum (1965): Studies of Adenovirus SV40 Hybrid Viruses; II, Defectiveness of the Hybrid Particles. J. Exptl. Med., 122:955-966.

Rowe, W. P., S. G. Baum, W. R. Pugh, and M. D. Hoggan (1965): Studies of Adenovirus SV40 Hybrid Viruses; I, Assay System and Further Evidence for Hybridization. J. Exptl. Med., 122:943-954.

Rowe, W. P., and I. Brodsky (1959): A Graded-Response Assay for the Friend Leukemia Virus. J. Natl. Cancer Inst. 23:1239-1248.

Rowson, K. E. K., and B. W. J. Mahy (1967): Human Papova (Wart) Virus. Bacteriol. Rev., 31:110-131.

Rubenstein, I., C. A. Thomas, Jr., and A. D. Hershey (1961): The Molecular Weights of T2 Bacteriophage DNA and Its First and Second Breakage Products. Proc. Natl. Acad. Sci., 47:1113-1122.

Rubin, H. (1961): The Nature of a Virus-Induced Cellular Resistance to Rous Sarcoma Virus. Virology, 13:200-206.

Rubin, H. (1962a): Conditions for Establishing Immunological Tolerance to a Tumour Virus. Nature, 195:342-345.

Rubin, H. (1962b): Response of Cell and Organism to Infection with Avian Tumor Viruses. Bacteriol. Rev., 26:1-13.

Rubin, H. (1964a): Carcinogenic Interactions Between Virus, Cell, and Organism. J. A.M.A., 190:727-731.

Rubin, H. (1964b): A Defective Cancer Virus. Sci. Amer., 210 (June):46-52.

Rubin, H. (1965): Discussion following Stewart, S. E., and J. C. Landon: Virus Latency in Hamster Tumors. *In* Pollard, M. (ed.): Perspectives in Virology, Vol. 4. New York, Harper & Row, pp. 217-225.

Rubin, H., A. Cornelius, and L. Fanshier (1961): The Pattern of Congenital Transmission of an Avian Leukosis Virus. Proc. Natl. Acad. Sci., 47:1058-1060.

Rubin, H., L. Fanshier, A. Cornelius, and W. F. Hughes (1962): Tolerance and Immunity in Chickens after Congenital and Contact Infection with an Avian Leukosis Virus. Virology, 17:143-156.

Rubin, H., R. M. Franklin, and M. Baluda (1957): Infection and Growth of Newcastle Disease Virus (NDV) in Cultures of Chick Embryo Lung Epithelium. Virology, 3:587-600.

Rubin, H., and P. K. Vogt (1962): An Avian Leukosis Virus Associated with Stocks of Rous Sarcoma Virus. Virology, 17:184-194.

Rueckert, R. R., and W. Zillig (1962): Biosynthesis of Virus Protein in *Escherichia coli* C *In Vivo* Following Infection with Bacteriophage ϕX174. J. Mol. Biol., 5:1-9.

Rush, M. G., A. K. Kleinschmidt, W. Hellmann, and R. C. Warner (1967): Multiple-Length Rings in Preparations of ϕX174 Replicative Form. Proc. Natl. Acad. Sci., 58:1676-1683.

Rush, M. G., and R. C. Warner (1967): Multiple-Length Rings of ϕX174 Replicative Form; II, Infectivity. Proc. Natl. Acad. Sci., 58:2372-2376.

Russell, W. C., and L. V. Crawford (1963): Some Characteristics of the Deoxyribonucleic Acid from Herpes Simplex Virus. Virology, 21:353-361.

Russell, W. C., and L. V. Crawford (1964): Properties of the Nucleic Acids from Some Herpes Group Viruses. Virology, 22:288-292.

Rüst, P., and R. L. Sinsheimer (1967): The Process of Infection with Bacteriophage ϕX174; XI, Infectivity of the Complementary Strand of the Replicative Form. J. Mol. Biol., 23:545-552.

Sabin, A. (1963): Discussion following Rubin, H., and H. Hanafusa: Significance of the Absence of Infectious Virus in Virus-Induced Tumors. *In* Viruses, Nucleic Acids, and Cancer. Baltimore, The Williams and Wilkins Co., pp. 508-525.

Sabin, A. B., and M. A. Koch (1963): Behavior of Noninfectious SV40 Viral Genome in Hamster Tumor Cells; Induction of Synthesis of Infectious Virus. Proc. Natl. Acad. Sci., 50:407-417.

Sachs, L., and D. Medina (1961): *In Vitro* Transformation of Normal Cells by Polyoma Virus. Nature, 189:457-458.

Sachs, L., D. Medina, and Y. Berwald (1962): Cell Transformation by Polyoma Virus in Clones of Hamster and Mouse Cells. Virology, 17:491-493.

Salzman, L. A., and A. Weissbach (1967a): Studies on the Formation of Circular λ DNA. Virology, 31:70-77.

Salzman, L. A., and A. Weissbach (1967b): Formation of Intermediates in the Replication of Phage Lambda DNA. J. Mol. Biol., 28:53-70.

Salzman, L. A., and A. Weissbach (1968): Deoxyribonucleic Acid Replication in λ Bacteriophage Mutants. J. Virol., 2:118-123.

Salzman, N. P., A. J. Shatkin, and E. D. Sebring (1963): Viral Protein and DNA Synthesis in Vaccinia Virus-Infected HeLa Cell Cultures. Virology, 19:542-550.

Salzman, N. P., A. J. Shatkin, and E. D. Sebring (1964): The Synthesis of a DNA-Like RNA in the Cytoplasm of HeLa Cells Infected with Vaccinia Virus. J. Mol. Biol., 8:405-416.

Sambrook, J. F., D. P. Fan, and S. Brenner (1967): A Strong Suppressor Specific for UGA. Nature, 214:452-453.

Sarabhai, A. S., A. O. W. Stretton, S. Brenner, and A. Bolle (1964): Co-Linearity of the Gene with the Polypeptide Chain. Nature, 201:13-17.

Sarma, P. S., R. J. Huebner, and W. T. Lane (1965): Induction of Tumors in Hamsters with an Avian Adenovirus (CELO). Science, 149:1108.

Sarma, P. S., W. Vass, and R. J. Huebner (1966): Evidence for the *in Vitro* Transfer of Defective Rous Sarcoma Virus Genome from Hamster Tumor Cells to Chick Cells. Proc. Natl. Acad. Sci., 55:1435-1442.

Sarma, P. S., W. Vass, R. J. Huebner, H. Igel, W. T. Lane, and H. C. Turner (1967): Induction of Tumours in Hamsters with Infectious Canine Hepatitis Virus. Nature, 215:293-294.

Sarov, I., and Y. Becker (1967): Studies on Vaccinia Virus DNA. Virology, 33:369-375.

Sarov, I., and Y. Becker (1968): RNA in the Elementary Bodies of Trachoma Agent. Nature, 217:849-852.

Sauer, G., H. Koprowski, and V. Defendi (1967): The Genetic Heterogeneity of Simian Virus 40. Proc. Natl. Acad. Sci., 58:599-606.

Scharff, M. D., A. J. Shatkin, and L. Levintow (1963): Association of Newly Formed Viral Protein with Specific Polyribosomes. Proc. Natl. Acad. Sci., 50:686-694.

Schechter, E. M., I. I. E. Tribby, and J. W. Moulder (1964): Nucleic Acid Metabolism in L Cells Infected with a Member of the Psittacosis Group. Science, 145:819-821.

Schell, K., W. T. Lane, M. J. Casey, and R. J. Huebner (1966): Potentiation of Oncogenicity of Adenovirus Type 12 Grown in African Green Monkey Kidney Cell Cultures Preinfected with SV40 Virus; Persistence of Both T Antigens in the Tumors and Evidence for Possible Hybridization. Proc. Natl. Acad. Sci., 55:81-88.

Schildkraut, C. L., K. L. Wierzchowski, J. Marmur, D. M. Green, and P. Doty (1962): A Study of the Base Sequence Homology among the T Series of Bacteriophages. Virology, 18:43-55.

Schlesinger, M. (1932): Adsorption of Bacteriophages to Homologous Bacteria; II, Quantitative Investigations of Adsorption Velocity and Saturation; Estimation of the Particle Size of the Bacteriophage. Z. Hyg. Immunit., 114:149-160. Reprinted in translation. Stent, G. S. (1960): Papers on Bacterial Viruses. Boston, Little, Brown, and Co., pp. 26-36.

Schlesinger, R. W. (1959): Interference Between Animal Viruses. In Burnet, F. M., and W. M. Stanley (eds.): The Viruses, Vol. 3. New York, Academic Press Inc., pp. 157-194.

Schrödinger, E. (1944): What Is Life? Cambridge, The University Press.

Schwerdt, C. E. (1959): Quantitative Relationships Between Virus Particles and Their Functional Activity. In Burnet, F. M., and W. M. Stanley (eds.): The Viruses, Vol. 1. New York, Academic Press Inc., pp. 329-358.

Sebring, E. D.,and N. P. Salzman (1967): Metabolic Properties of Early and Late Vaccinia Virus Messenger Ribonucleic Acid. J. Virol., 1:550-558.

Séchaud, J., G. Streisinger, J. Emrich, J. Newton, H. Lanford, H. Reinhold, and M. M. Stahl (1965): Chromosome Structure in Phage T4; II, Terminal Redundancy and Heterozygosis. Proc. Natl. Acad. Sci., 54:1333-1339.

Seligman, S. J., and M. R. Mickey (1964): Estimation of the Number of Infectious Bacterial or Viral Particles by the Dilution Method. J. Bacteriol., 88:31-36.

Setlow, R. B. (1966): Cyclobutane-Type Pyrimidine Dimers in Polynucleotides. Science, 153:379-386.

Setlow, R. B., and W. L. Carrier (1964): The Disappearance of Thymine Dimers from DNA; an Error-Correcting Mechanism. Proc. Natl. Acad. Sci., 51:226-231.

Shatkin, A. J. (1963a): Actinomycin D and Vaccinia Virus Infection of HeLa Cells. Nature, 199:357-358.

Shatkin, A. J. (1963b): The Formation of Vaccinia Virus Protein in the Presence of 5-Fluorodeoxyuridine. Virology, 20:292-301.

Shatkin, A. J. (1965): Inactivity of Purified Reovirus RNA as a Template for *E. coli* Polymerases *in Vitro*. Proc. Natl. Acad. Sci., 54:1721-1728.

Shatkin, A. J., and B. Rada (1967): Studies on the Replication of Reovirus. In Colter, J. S., and W. Paranchych (eds.): The Molecular Biology of Viruses. New York, Academic Press Inc., pp. 427-447.

Shatkin, A. J., E. D. Sebring, and N. P. Salzman (1965): Vaccinia Virus Directed RNA; Its Fate in the Presence of Actinomycin. Science, 148:87-90.

Shatkin, A. J., and J. D. Sipe (1968): Single-Stranded, Adenine-Rich RNA from Purified Reoviruses. Proc. Natl. Acad. Sci., 59:246-253.

Shein, H. M., and J. F. Enders (1962): Multiplication and Cytopathogenicity of Simian Vacuolating Virus 40 in Cultures of Human Tissues. Proc. Soc. Exptl. Biol. Med., 109:495-500.

Sheinin, R. (1966): Studies on the Thymidine Kinase Activity of Mouse Embryo Cells Infected with Polyoma Virus. Virology, 28:47-55.

Shipp, W., and R. Haselkorn (1964): Double-Stranded RNA from Tobacco Leaves Infected with TMV. Proc. Natl. Acad. Sci., 52:401-408.

Shope, R. E. (1932a): A Transmissible Tumor-Like Condition in Rabbits. J. Exptl. Med., 56:793-802.

Shope, R. E. (1932b): A Filtrable Virus Causing a Tumor-Like Condition in Rabbits and Its Relationship to Virus Myxomatosum. J. Exptl. Med., 56:803-822.

Siegel, J. E. D., and M. Hayashi (1967): Complementary Strand Infectivity in ϕX174 Replicative Form DNA. J. Mol. Biol., 27:443-451.

Siddiqi, M. S. H., L. M. Kozloff, F. W. Putnam, and E. A. Evans, Jr. (1952): Biochemical Studies of Virus Reproduction; IX, Nature of the Host Cell Contributions. J. Biol. Chem., 199:165-176.

Signer, E. R., and J. R. Beckwith (1966): Transposition of the *Lac* Region of *Escherichia coli*; III, The Mechanism of Attachment of Bacteriophage φ80 to the Bacterial Chromosome. J. Mol. Biol., 22:33-51.

Silverstein, A. M. (1964): Ontogeny of the Immune Response. Science, 144:1423-1428.

Simon, E. (1965): Recombination in Bacteriophage T4; a Mechanism. Science, 150:760-763.

Simon, E. H. (1961): Evidence for the Nonparticipation of DNA in Viral RNA Synthesis. Virology, 13:105-118.

Simon, L. D., and T. F. Anderson (1967): The Infection of *Escherichia coli* by T2 and T4 Bacteriophages as Seen in the Electron Microscope; I, Attachment and Penetration. Virology, 32:279-297.

Simons, P. J., R. H. Bassin, and J. J. Harvey (1967a): Transformation of Hamster Embryo Cells *in Vitro* by Murine Sarcoma Virus (Harvey). Proc. Soc. Exptl. Biol. Med., 125:1242-1246.

Simons, P. J., R. R. Dourmashkin, A. Turano, D. E. H. Phillips, and F. C. Chesterman (1967b): Morphological Transformation of Mouse Embryo Cells *in Vitro* by Murine Sarcoma Virus (Harvey). Nature, 214:897-898.

Simpson, R. W., and G. K. Hirst (1961): Genetic Recombination Among Influenza Viruses; I, Cross Reactivation of Plaque-Forming Capacity as a Method for Selecting Recombinants from the Progeny of Crosses Between Influenza A Strains. Virology, 15:436-451.

Sinsheimer, R. L. (1959a): Purification and Properties of Bacteriophage φX174. J. Mol. Biol., 1:37-42.

Sinsheimer, R. L. (1959b): A Single-Stranded Deoxyribonucleic Acid from Bacteriophage φX174. J. Mol. Biol., 1:43-53.

Sinsheimer, R. L. (1960): The Nucleic Acids of the Bacterial Viruses. *In* Chargaff, E., and J. N. Davidson (eds.): The Nucleic Acids, Vol. 3. New York, Academic Press Inc., pp. 187-244.

Sinsheimer, R. L. (1962): Single-Stranded DNA. Sci. Amer., 207(July):109-116.

Sinsheimer, R. L., C. A. Hutchison, III, and B. H. Lindqvist (1967): Bacteriophage φX174; Viral Functions. *In* Colter, J. S., and W. Paranchych (eds.): The Molecular Biology of Viruses. New York, Academic Press Inc., pp. 175-192.

Sinsheimer, R. L., and M. Lawrence (1964): *In Vitro* Synthesis and Properties of a φX DNA-RNA Hybrid. J. Mol. Biol., 8:289-296.

Sinsheimer, R. L., B. Starman, C. Nagler, and S. Guthrie (1962): The Process of Infection with Bacteriophage φX174; I, Evidence for a "Replicative Form." J. Mol. Biol., 4:142-160.

Sjögren, H. O. (1964a): Studies on Specific Transplantation Resistance to Polyoma-Virus-Induced Tumors; I, Transplantation Resistance Induced by Polyoma Virus Infection. J. Natl. Cancer Inst., 32:361-374.

Sjögren, H. O. (1964b): Studies on Specific Transplantation Resistance to Polyoma-Virus-Induced Tumors; II, Mechanism of Resistance Induced by Polyoma Virus Infection. J. Natl. Cancer Inst., 32:375-393.

Sjögren, H. O. (1964c): Studies on Specific Transplantation Resistance to Polyoma-Virus-Induced Tumors; III, Transplantation Resistance to Genetically Compatible Polyoma Tumors Induced by Polyoma Tumor Homografts. J. Natl. Cancer Inst., 32:645-659.

Sjögren, H. O. (1964d): Studies on Specific Transplantation Resistance to Polyoma-Virus-Induced Tumors; IV, Stability of the Polyoma Cell Antigen. J. Natl. Cancer Inst., 32:661-666.

Sjögren, H. O., I. Hellström, and G. Klein (1961): Transplantation of Polyoma Virus-Induced Tumors in Mice. Cancer Res., 21:329-337.

Sjögren, H. O., J. Minowada, and J. Ankerst (1967): Specific Transplantation Antigens of Mouse Sarcomas Induced by Adenovirus Type 12. J. Exptl. Med., 125:689-701.

Skalka, A., B. Butler, and H. Echols (1967): Genetic Control of Transcription During Development of Phage λ. Proc. Natl. Acad. Sci., 58:576-583.

Smadel, J. E., T. M. Rivers, and E. G. Pickels (1939): Estimation of the Purity of Preparations of Elementary Bodies of Vaccinia. J. Exptl. Med., 70:379-385.

Smith, D. W., and P. C. Hanawalt (1967): Properties of the Growing Point Region in the Bacterial Chromosome. Biochem. Biophys. Acta, 149:519-531.

Smith, H. O., and M. Levine (1964): Two Sequential Repressions of DNA Synthesis in the Establishment of Lysogeny by Phage P22 and Its Mutants. Proc. Natl. Acad. Sci., 52:356-363.

Smith, H. O., and M. Levine (1965): The Synthesis of Phage and Host DNA in the Establishment of Lysogeny. Virology, 25:585-590.

Smith, K. M. (1963): The Arthropod Viruses. In Viruses, Nucleic Acids, and Cancer. Baltimore, The Williams and Wilkins Co., pp. 72-84.

Smith, K. M., and R. C. Williams (1958): Insect Viruses and Their Structure. Endeavor, 17:12-21.

Smith, K. O., and W. D. Gehle (1967): Replication of an Adeno-Associated Virus in Canine and Human Cells with Infectious Canine Hepatitis Virus as a "Helper." J. Virol., 1:648-649.

Smith, K. O., W. D. Gehle, and J. F. Thiel (1966): Properties of a Small Virus Associated with Adenovirus Type 4. J. Immunol., 97:754-766.

Smith, K. O., and J. L. Melnick (1964): Adenovirus-Like Particles from Cancers Induced by Adenovirus-12 but Free of Infectious Virus. Science, 145:1190-1192.

Smith, K. O., and L. Rasmussen (1963): Morphology of Cytomegalovirus (Salivary Gland Virus). J. Bacteriol., 85:1319-1325.

Smithies, O. (1967): Antibody Variability. Science, 157:267-273.

Soehner, R. L., G. A. Gentry, and C. C. Randall (1965): Some Physicochemical Characteristics of Equine Abortion Virus Nucleic Acid. Virology, 26:394-405.

Somerville, R., K. Ebisuzaki, and G. R. Greenberg (1959): Hydroxymethyldeoxycytidylate Kinase Formation after Bacteriophage Infection of Escherichia coli. Proc. Natl. Acad. Sci., 45:1240-1245.

Sonnabend, J. A., E. M. Martin, and E. Mécs (1967a): Viral Specific RNAs in Infected Cells. Nature, 213:365-367.

Sonnabend, J. A., E. M. Martin, and E. Mécs (1967b): The Effect of Interferon on the Synthesis and Activity of an RNA Polymerase Isolated from Chick Cells Infected with Semliki Forest Virus. J. Gen. Virol., 1:41-48.

Spencer, H. J., and V. Groupé (1962): Pathogenesis of Virus-Induced Rous Sarcoma; I, Distribution of Virus and Tumor Foci in Chicks and Turkeys. J. Natl. Cancer Inst., 29:397-419.

Spendlove, R. S., E. H. Lennette, and A. C. John (1963): The Role of the Mitotic Apparatus in the Intracellular Location of Reovirus Antigen. J. Immunol., 90:554-560.

Spiegelman, S. (1967): An in Vitro Analysis of a Replicating Molecule. Amer. Scientist, 55:221-264.

Spiegelman, S., and I. Haruna (1966a): A Rationale for an Analysis of RNA Replication. Proc. Natl. Acad. Sci., 55:1539-1554.

Spiegelman, S., and I. Haruna (1966b): Problems of an RNA Genome Operating in a DNA-Dominated Biological Universe. In Macromolecular Metabolism. Boston, Little, Brown, and Co., pp. 263-304.

Spiegelman, S., I. Haruna, I. B. Holland, G. Beaudreau, and D. Mills (1965): The Synthesis of a Self-Propagating and Infectious Nucleic Acid with a Purified Enzyme. Proc. Natl. Acad. Sci., 54:919-927.

Sproul, E. E., R. S. Metzgar, and J. T. Grace, Jr. (1963): The Pathogenesis of Yaba Virus Induced Histiocytomas in Primates. Cancer Res., 23:671-675.

Sreevalsan, T., and R. Z. Lockart, Jr. (1966a): Heterogeneous RNA's Occurring During the Replication of Western Equine Encephalomyelitis Virus. Proc. Natl. Acad. Sci., 55:974-981.

Sreevalsan, T., and R. Z. Lockart, Jr. (1966b): Interference Not Mediated by Interferon. Nature, 212:540.

Stanley, E. D., R. E. Muldoon, L. W. Akers, and G. G. Jackson (1965): Evaluation of Antiviral Drugs; the Effect of Amantadine on Influenza in Volunteers. Ann. N. Y. Acad. Sci., 130:44-51.

Stanley, W. M. (1935): Isolation of a Crystalline Protein Possessing the Properties of Tobacco-Mosaic Virus. Science, 81:644-645.

Steinberg, C., and F. Stahl (1961): The Clone-Size Distribution of Mutants Arising from a Steady-State Pool of Vegetative Phage. J. Theoret. Biol., 1:488-497.

Stenback, W. A., and D. P. Durand (1963): Host Influence on the Density of Newcastle Disease Virus (NDV). Virology, 20:545-551.

Stent, G. S., and C. R. Fuerst (1955): Inactivation of Bacteriophages by Decay of Incorporated Radioactive Phosphorus. J. Gen. Physiol., 38:441-458. Reprinted in Stent, G. S. (1960): Papers on Bacterial Viruses. Boston, Little, Brown and Co., pp. 280-297.

Stent, G. S., and C. R. Fuerst (1960): Genetic and Physiological Effects of the Decay of Incorporated Radioactive Phosphorus in Bacterial Viruses and Bacteria. Adv. Biol. Med. Physics, 7:1-75.

Stent, G. S., C. R. Fuerst, and F. Jacob (1957): Inactivation d'un Prophage par la Désintégration du Radiophosphore C. R. Acad. Sci., 244:1840-1842.

Stent, G. S., G. H. Sato, and N. K. Jerne (1959): Dispersal of the Parental Nucleic Acid of Bacteriophage T4 Among Its Progeny, J. Mol. Biol., 1:134-146.

Stewart, S. E. (1960): The Polyoma Virus. Sci. Amer., 203(Nov.):63-71.

Stewart, S. E., B. E. Eddy, A. M. Gochenour, N. G. Borgese, and G. E. Grubbs (1957): The Induction of Neoplasms with a Substance Released from Mouse Tumors by Tissue Culture. Virology, 3:380-400.

Stewart, S. E., D. Glazer, T. Ben, and B. J. Lloyd (1968): Studies on the Hamster-Brain Passage Virus Recovered from Human Lymphoma Cultures. J. Natl. Cancer Inst., 40:423-428.

Stinebring, W. R., and J. S. Youngner (1964): Patterns of Interferon Appearance in Mice Injected with Bacteria or Bacterial Endotoxin. Nature, 204:712.

Stoker, M. (1968): Abortive Transformation by Polyoma Virus. Nature, 218:234-238.

Stoker, M., and I. MacPherson (1961): Studies on Transformation of Hamster Cells by Polyoma Virus in Vitro. Virology, 14:359-370.

Stoker, M. G. P., and H. Rubin (1967): Density Dependent Inhibition of Cell Growth in Culture. Nature, 215:171-172.

Stollar, V., R. W. Schlesinger, and T. M. Stevens (1967): Studies on the Nature of Dengue Viruses. Virology, 33:650-658.

Stone, A. B. (1967): Some Factors Which Influence the Replication of the Replicative Form of Bacteriophage ϕX174. Biochem. Biophys. Res. Commun., 26:247-254.

Stone, A. B., and K. Burton (1962): Studies on the Deoxyribonucleases of Bacteriophage-Infected Escherichia coli. Biochem. J., 85:600-606.

Strack, H. B., and A. D. Kaiser (1965): On the Structure of the Ends of Lambda DNA. J. Mol. Biol., 12:36-49.

Strauss, B., T. Searashi, and M. Robbins (1966): Repair of DNA Studied with a Nuclease Specific for UV-Induced Lesions. Proc. Natl. Acad. Sci., 56:932-939.

Strauss, J. H., Jr., and R. L. Sinsheimer (1963): Purification and Properties of Bacteriophage MS2 and of Its Ribonucleic Acid. J. Mol. Biol., 7:43-54.

Streisinger, G.(1956): Phenotypic Mixing of Host Range and Serological Specificities in Bacteriophages T2 and T4. Virology, 2:388-398.

Streisinger, G., and V. Bruce (1960): Linkage of Genetic Markers in Phages T2 and T4. Genetics, 45:1289-1296.

Streisinger, G., R. S. Edgar, and G. H. Denhardt (1964): Chromosome Structure in Phage T4; I, Circularity of the Linkage Map. Proc. Natl. Acad. Sci., 51:775-779.

Streisinger, G., J. Emrich, and M. M. Stahl (1967): Chromosome Structure in Phage T4; III, Terminal Redundancy and Length Determination. Proc. Natl. Acad. Sci., 57:292-295.

Streisinger, G., and N. C. Franklin (1956): Mutation and Recombination at the Host Range Genetic Region of Phage T2. Cold Spring Harbor Symposia Quant. Biol., 21:103-111.

Streisinger, G., F. Mukai, W. J. Dreyer, B. Miller, and S. Horiuchi (1961): Mutations Affecting the Lysozyme of Phage T4. Cold Spring Harbor Symposia Quant. Biol., 16:25-30.

Streissle, G., and K. Maramorosch (1963): Reovirus and Wound-Tumor Virus; Serological Cross Reactivity. Science, 140:996-997.

Strohl, W. A., A. S. Rabson, and H. Rouse (1967): Adenovirus Tumorigenesis; Role of the Viral Genome in Determining Tumor Morphology. Science, 156:1631-1633.

Stubbs, J. D., and P. Kaesberg (1967): Amino Acid Incorporation in an *Escherichia coli* Cell-Free System Directed by Bromegrass Mosaic Virus Ribonucleic Acid. Virology, 33:385-397.

Studdert, M. J., J. Pangborn, and R. B. Addison (1966): Bluetongue Virus Structure. Virology, 29:509-511.

Subak-Sharpe, H., and J. Hay (1965): An Animal Virus with DNA of High Guanine + Cytosine Content Which Codes for S-RNA. J. Mol. Biol., 12:924-928.

Sueoka, N., and T. Kano-Sueoka (1964): A Specific Modification of Leucyl-sRNA of *Escherichia coli* after Phage T2 Infection. Proc. Natl. Acad. Sci., 52:1535-1540.

Sugiyama, T., and D. Nakada (1967): Control of Translation of MS2 RNA Cistrons by MS2 Coat Protein. Proc. Natl. Acad. Sci., 57:1744-1750.

Summers, D. F. (1967): Biochemistry of Animal Virus Replication. New Eng. J. Med., 276:1016-1023, 1076-1081.

Summers, D. F., N. F. McElvain, M. M. Thorén, and L. Levintow (1964): Incorporation of Amino Acids into Polyribosome-Associated Protein in Cytoplasmic Extracts of Poliovirus-Infected HeLa Cells. Biochem. Biophys. Res. Commun., 15:290-295.

Summers, D. F., J. V. Maizel, Jr., and J. E. Darnell, Jr. (1965): Evidence for Virus-Specific Noncapsid Proteins in Poliovirus-Infected HeLa Cells. Proc. Natl. Acad. Sci., 54:505-513.

Summers, D. F., J. V. Maizel, Jr., and J. E. Darnell, Jr. (1967): The Decrease in Size and Synthetic Activity of Poliovirus Polysomes Late in the Infectious Cycle. Virology, 31:427-435.

Summers, W. C., and W. Szybalski (1967): Gamma-Irradiation of Deoxyribonucleic Acid in Dilute Solutions; II, Molecular Mechanisms Responsible for Inactivation of Phage, Its Transfecting DNA, and of Bacterial Transforming Activity. J. Mol. Biol., 26:227-235.

Sussenbach, J. S. (1967): Early Events in the Infection Process of Adenovirus Type 5 in HeLa Cells. Virology, 33:567-574.

Svehag, S., and B. Mandel (1964a): The Formation and Properties of Poliovirus-Neutralizing Antibody; I, 19S and 7S Antibody Formation; Differences in Kinetics and Antigen Dose Requirement for Induction. J. Exptl. Med., 119:1-19.

Svehag, S., and B. Mandel (1964b): The Formation and Properties of Poliovirus-Neutralizing Antibody; II, 19S and 7S Antibody Formation; Differences in Antigen Dose Requirement for Sustained Synthesis, Anamnesis, and Sensitivity to X-Irradiation. J. Exptl. Med., 119:21-39.

Svet-Moldavsky, G. J., and I. A. Svet-Moldavskaya (1964): Sarcomas in Cotton Rats Inoculated with Rous Virus. Science, 143:54-55.

Sweet, B. H., and M. R. Hilleman (1960): Detection of a "Non-Detectable" Simian Virus (Vacuolating Agent) Present in Rhesus and Cynomolgus Monkey-Kidney Cell Culture Material; a Preliminary Report. Second Internatl. Conf. on Live Poliovirus Vaccines, Washington, D.C., pp. 79-85.

Sydiskis, R. J., and B. Roizman (1966): Polysomes and Protein Synthesis in Cells Infected with a DNA Virus. Science, 153:76-78.

Sydiskis, R. J., and B. Roizman (1967): The Disaggregation of Host Polyribosomes in Productive and Abortive Infection with Herpes Simplex Virus. Virology, 32:678-686.

Symington, J., B. Commoner, and M. Yamada (1962): Linear Biosynthesis of Tobacco Mosaic Virus; Evidence that Short Virus Rods are Natural Products of TMV Biosynthesis. Proc. Natl. Acad. Sci., 48:1675-1683.

Takai, M. (1966): Complex-Formation by Protein and Nucleic Acid; I, Evidence for Specific Interaction Between ϕX174 Phage Protein and ϕX174 Phage Deoxyribonucleic Acid *in Vitro*. Biochim. Biophys. Acta, 119:20-28.

Takemori, N., and S. Nomura (1960): Mutation of Polioviruses with Respect to Size of Plaque; II, Reverse Mutation of Minute Plaque Mutant. Virology, 12:171-184.

Takemoto, K. K. (1966): Plaque Mutants of Animal Viruses. Progr. Med. Virol., 8:314-348.

Takemoto, K. K., R. L. Kirschstein, and K. Habel (1966): Mutants of Simian Virus 40 Differing in Plaque Size, Oncogenicity, and Heat Sensitivity. J. Bacteriol., 92:990-994.

Takemoto, K. K., and H. Liebhaber (1961): Virus-Polysaccharide Interactions; I, An Agar Polysaccharide Determining Plaque Morphology of EMC Virus. Virology, 14:456-462.

Takemoto, K. K., and H. Liebhaber (1962): Virus-Polysaccharide Interactions; II, Enhancement of Plaque Formation and the Detection of Variants of Poliovirus with Dextran Sulfate. Virology, 17:499-501.

Tamura, A. (1967): Isolation of Ribosome Particles from Meningopneumonitis Organisms. J. Bacteriol., 93:2009-2016.

Tamura, A., A. Matsumoto, and N. Higashi (1967): Purification and Chemical Composition of Reticulate Bodies of the Meningopneumonitis Organisms. J. Bacteriol., 93:2003-2008.

Tao, T.-W., and J. W. Uhr (1966): Primary-Type Antibody Response *in Vitro*. Science, 151:1096-1098.

Taylor, J. (1964): Inhibition of Interferon Action by Actinomycin. Biochem. Biophys. Res. Commun., 14:447-451.

Taylor, J. (1965): Studies on the Mechanism of Action of Interferon; I, Interferon Action and RNA Synthesis in Chick Embryo Fibroblasts Infected with Semliki Forest Virus. Virology, 25:340-349.

Temin, H. M. (1960): The Control of Cellular Morphology in Embryonic Cells Infected with Rous Sarcoma Virus *in Vitro*. Virology, 10:182-197.

Temin, H. M. (1961): Mixed Infection with Two Types of Rous Sarcoma Virus. Virology, 13:158-163.

Temin, H. M. (1963): The Effects of Actinomycin D on Growth of Rous Sarcoma Virus *in Vitro*. Virology, 20:577-582.

Temin, H. M. (1964a): The Participation of DNA in Rous Sarcoma Virus Production. Virology, 23:486-494.

Temin, H. M. (1964b): Homology Between RNA from Rous Sarcoma Virus and DNA from Rous Sarcoma Virus-Infected Cells. Proc. Natl. Acad. Sci., 52:323-329.

Temin, H. M. (1966a): Studies on Carcinogenesis by Avian Sarcoma Viruses; III, The Differential Effect of Serum and Polyanions on Multiplication of Uninfected and Converted Cells. J. Natl. Cancer Inst., 37:167-175.

Temin, H. M. (1966b): Malignant Conversion by Avian Sarcoma Virus. *In* Kirsten, W. H. (ed.): Malignant Transformation by Viruses. New York, Springer-Verlag, Inc., pp. 12-17.

Temin, H. M. (1966c): Genetic and Possible Biochemical Mechanisms in Viral Carcinogenesis. Cancer Res., 26:212-216.

Temin, H. M. (1967a): Studies on Carcinogenesis by Avian Sarcoma Viruses IV. *In* Colter, J. S., and W. Paranchych (eds.): The Molecular Biology of Viruses. New York, Academic Press Inc., pp. 709-715.

Temin, H. M. (1967b): Studies on Carcinogenesis by Avian Sarcoma Viruses; V, Requirement for New DNA Synthesis and for Cell Division. J. Cell. Physiol., 69:53-63.

Temin, H. M., and H. Rubin (1958): Characteristics of an Assay for Rous Sarcoma Virus and Rous Sarcoma Cells in Tissue Culture. Virology, 6:669-688.

Temin, H. M., and H. Rubin (1959): A Kinetic Study of Infection of Chick Embryo Cells *in Vitro* by Rous Sarcoma Virus. Virology, 8:209-222.

Tessman, E. S. (1966): Mutants of Bacteriophage S13 Blocked in Infectious DNA Synthesis. J. Mol. Biol., 17:218-236.

Tessman, I. (1959a): Some Unusual Properties of the Nucleic Acid in Bacteriophages S13 and φX174. Virology, 7:263-275.

Tessman, I. (1959b): Mutagenesis in Phages φX174 and T4 and Properties of the Genetic Material. Virology, 9:375-385.

Tessman, I., H. Ishiwa, S. Kumar, and R. Baker (1967a): Bacteriophage S13; a Seventh Gene. Science, 156:824-825.

Tessman, I., S. Kumar, and E. S. Tessman (1967b): Direction of Translation in Bacteriophage S13, Science, 158:267-268.

Tessman, I., and E. S. Tessman (1966): Functional Units of Phage S13; Identification of Two Genes That Determine the Structure of the Phage Coat. Proc. Natl. Acad. Sci., 55:1459-1462.

Tessman, I., E. S. Tessman, and G. S. Stent (1957): The Relative Radiosensitivity of Bacteriophages S13 and T2. Virology, 4:209-215.

Tevethia, S. S., M. Katz, and F. Rapp (1965): New Surface Antigen in Cells Transformed by Simian Papovavirus SV40. Proc. Soc. Exptl. Biol. Med., 119:896-901.

Tevethia, S. S., and F. Rapp (1965): Demonstration of New Surface Antigens in Cells Transformed by Papovavirus SV40 by Cytotoxic Tests. Proc. Soc. Exptl. Biol. Med., 120:455-458.

Thomas, C. A., Jr. (1966): The Arrangement of Information in DNA Molecules. In Macromolecular Metabolism. Boston, Little, Brown and Co., pp. 143-169.

Thomas, C. A., Jr., and I. Rubenstein (1964): The Arrangements of Nucleotide Sequences in T2 and T5 Bacteriophage DNA Molecules. Biophys. J., 4:93-106.

Thorne, H. V., and D. Warden (1967): Electrophoretic Evidence for a Single Protein Component in the Capsid of Polyoma Virus. J. Gen. Virol., 1:135-137.

Ting, R. C. (1966): In Vitro Transformation of Rat Embryo Cells by a Murine Sarcoma Virus. Virology, 28:783-785.

Tobey, R. A. (1964a): Mengovirus Replication; I, Conservation of Virus RNA. Virology, 23:10-22.

Tobey, R. A. (1964b): Mengovirus Replication; II, Isolation of Polyribosomes Containing the Infecting Viral Genome. Virology, 23:23-29.

Todaro, G. J., and S. Baron (1965): The Role of Interferon in the Inhibition of SV40 Transformation of Mouse Cell Line 3T3. Proc. Natl. Acad. Sci., 54:752-756.

Todaro, G. J., and H. Green (1964): An Assay for Cellular Transformation by SV40. Virology, 23:117-119.

Todaro, G. J., and H. Green (1966): Cell Growth and the Initiation of Transformation by SV40. Proc. Natl. Acad. Sci., 55:302-308.

Todaro, G. J., and H. Green (1967): Interferon Resistance of SV40 Induced DNA Synthesis. Virology, 33:752-754.

Todaro, G. J., K. Habel, and H. Green (1965): Antigenic and Cultural Properties of Cells Doubly Transformed by Polyoma Virus and SV40. Virology, 27:179-185.

Tomita, Y., and A. M. Prince (1963): Photodynamic Inactivation of Arbor Viruses by Neutral Red and Visible Light. Proc. Soc. Exptl. Biol. Med., 112:887-890.

Tomizawa, J.-I., and N. Anraku (1964): Molecular Mechanisms of Genetic Recombination in Bacteriophage; II, Joining of Parental DNA Molecules of Phage T4. J. Mol. Biol., 8:516-540.

Tomizawa, J.-I., and T. Ogawa (1967): Inhibition of Growth of rII Mutants of Bacteriophage T4 by Immunity Substance of Bacteriophage Lambda. J. Mol. Biol., 23:277-280.

Tonegawa, S., and M. Hayashi (1966): The Direction of in Vitro Genetic Transcription on Circular DNA. Biochim. Biophys. Acta, 123:634-637.

Tooze, J., and K. Weber (1967): Isolation and Characterization of Amber Mutants of Bacteriophage R17. J. Mol. Biol., 28:311-330.

Toplin, I., and G. Schidlovsky (1966): Partial Purification and Electron Microscopy of Virus in the EB-3 Cell Line Derived from a Burkitt Lymphoma. Science, 152:1084-1085.

Trentin, J. J., Y. Yabe, and G. Taylor (1962): The Quest for Human Cancer Viruses. Science, 137:835-841.

Tromans, W. J., and R. W. Horne (1961): The Structure of Bacteriophage ϕX174. Virology, 15:1-7.

Tsugita, A. (1962): The Proteins of Mutants of TMV; Composition and Structure of Chemically Evoked Mutants of TMV RNA. J. Mol. Biol., 5:284-292.

Tsugita, A., and H. Fraenkel-Conrat (1960): The Amino Acid Composition and C-Terminal Sequence of a Chemically Evoked Mutant of TMV. Proc. Natl. Acad. Sci., 46:636-642.

Twort, F. W. (1915): An Investigation on the Nature of Ultra-Microscopic Viruses. Lancet, 2:1241-1243. Reprinted in Hahon, N. (1964): Selected Papers on Virology. Englewood Cliffs, New Jersey, Prentice-Hall, Inc., pp. 97-102.

Tyrrell, D. A. J., and R. M. Chanock (1963): Rhinoviruses; a Description. Science, 141:152-153.

Tyrrell, D. A. J., and R. C. Valentine (1957): The Assay of Influenza Virus Particles by Haemagglutination and Electron Microscopy. J. Gen. Microbiol., 16:668-675.

Tytell, A. A., G. P. Lampson, A. K. Field, and M. R. Hilleman (1967): Inducers of Interferon and Host Resistance; III, Double-Stranded RNA from Reovirus Type 3 Virions (REO 3-RNA). Proc. Natl. Acad. Sci., 58:1719-1722.

Uchida, S., K. Yoshiike, S. Watanabe, and A. Furuno (1968): Antigen-Forming Defective Viruses of Simian Virus 40. Virology, 34:1-8.

Uetake, H., S. E. Luria, and J. W. Burrous (1958): Conversion of Somatic Antigens in *Salmonella* by Phage Infection Leading to Lysis or Lysogeny. Virology, 5:68-91.

Uetake, H., T. Nakagawa, and T. Akiba (1955): The Relationship of Bacteriophage to Antigenic Changes in Group E Salmonellas. J. Bacteriol., 69:571-579.

Uetake, H., and T. Uchida (1959): Mutants of *Salmonella* Phage ϵ^{15} with Abnormal Conversion Properties. Virology, 9:495-505.

Uhr, J. W. (1964): The Heterogeneity of the Immune Response. Science, 145:457-464.

Uhr, J. W., J. Dancis, E. C. Franklin, M. S. Finkelstein, and E. W. Lewis (1962a): The Antibody Response to Bacteriophage ϕX174 in Newborn Premature Infants. J. Clin. Invest., 41:1509-1513.

Uhr, J. W., and M. S. Finkelstein (1963): Antibody Formation; IV, Formation of Rapidly and Slowly Sedimenting Antibodies and Immunological Memory to Bacteriophage ϕX174. J. Exptl. Med., 117:457-477.

Uhr, J. W., M. S. Finkelstein, and J. B. Baumann (1962b): Antibody Formation; III, The Primary and Secondary Antibody Response to Bacteriophage ϕX174 in Guinea Pigs. J. Exptl. Med., 115:655-670.

Valentine, A. F., and J. P. Bader (1968): Production of Virus by Mammalian Cells Transformed by Rous Sarcoma and Murine Sarcoma Viruses. J. Virol., 2:224-237.

Valentine, R. C., and H. G. Pereira (1965): Antigens and the Structure of the Adenovirus. J. Mol. Biol., 13:13-20.

Valentine, R. C., and H. Wedel (1965): The Extracellular Stages of RNA Bacteriophage Infection. Biochem. Biophys. Res. Commun., 21:106-112.

Van der Eb, A. J., and L. W. Van Kesteren (1966): Structure and Molecular Weight of the DNA of Adenovirus Type 5. Biochim. Biophys. Acta, 129:441-444.

Vasquez, C., N. Granboulan, and R. M. Franklin (1966): Structure of the Ribonucleic Acid Bacteriophage R17. J. Bacteriol., 92:1779-1786.

Vasquez, C., and P. Tournier (1962): The Morphology of Reovirus. Virology, 17:503-510.

Vielmetter, W., and C. M. Wieder (1959): Mutagene und inaktiviernede Wirkung salpetriger Säure auf freie Partikel des Phagen T2. Z. Naturforsch., 14B:312-317.

Vilček, J. (1960): An Interferon-Like Substance Released from Tick-Borne Encephalitis Virus-Infected Chick Embryo Fibroblast Cells. Nature, 187:73-74.

Vinograd, J., J. Lebowitz, R. Radloff, R. Watson, and P. Laipis (1965): The Twisted Circular Form of Polyoma Viral DNA. Proc. Natl. Acad. Sci., 53:1104-1111.

Viola, M. V., A. J. Dalton, E. Mitchell, and J. B. Moloney (1967): Virus-Like Particles in a Patient with Chronic Lymphocytic Leukemia. New Eng. J. Med., 277:503-506.

Visconti, N., and M. Delbrück (1953): The Mechanism of Genetic Recombination in Phage. Genetics, 38:5-33.

Vogt, M., and R. Dulbecco (1960): Virus-Cell Interaction with a Tumor-Producing Virus. Proc. Natl. Acad. Sci., 46:365-370.

Vogt, M., and R. Dulbecco (1962): Studies on Cells Rendered Neoplastic by Polyoma Virus; the Problem of the Presence of Virus-Related Materials. Virology, 16:41-51.

Vogt, P. K. (1963): The Cell Surface in Tumor Virus Infection. Cancer Res., 23:1519-1527.

Vogt, P. K. (1967a): A Virus Released by "Nonproducing" Rous Sarcoma Cells. Proc. Natl. Acad. Sci., 58:801-808.

Vogt, P. K. (1967b): Nonproducing State of Rous Sarcoma Cells; Its Contagiousness in Chicken Cell Cultures. J. Virol., 1:729-737.

Volkin, E. (1960): The Function of RNA in T2-Infected Bacteria. Proc. Natl. Acad. Sci., 46:1336-1349.

Volkin, E., and L. Astrachan (1956): Phosphorus Incorporation in *Escherichia coli* Ribonucleic Acid after Infection with Bacteriophage T2. Virology, 2:149-161.

Volkin, E., and L. Astrachan (1957): RNA Metabolism in T2-Infected *Escherichia coli*. *In* McElroy, W. D., and B. Glass (eds.): The Chemical Basis of Heredity. Baltimore, The Johns Hopkins Press, pp. 686-695.

Wagner, R. R. (1960): Viral Interference; Some Considerations of Basic Mechanisms and Their Potential Relationship to Host Resistance. Bacteriol. Rev., 24:151-166.

Wagner, R. R. (1961): Biological Studies of Interferon; I, Suppression of Cellular Infection with Eastern Equine Encephalomyelitis Virus. Virology, 13:323-337.

Wagner, R. R., and A. S. Huang (1965): Reversible Inhibition of Interferon Synthesis by Puromycin; Evidence for an Interferon-Specific Messenger RNA. Proc. Natl. Acad. Sci., 54:1112-1118.

Wahl, R., and L. M. Kozloff (1962): The Nucleoside Triphosphate Content of Various Bacteriophages. J. Biol. Chem., 237:1953-1960.

Wallbank, A. M., R. E. Matter, and N. G. Klinikowski (1966): 1-Adamantanamine Hydrochloride; Inhibition of Rous and Esh Sarcoma Viruses in Cell Culture. Science, 152:1760-1761.

Walters, S., D. C. Burke, and J. J. Skehel (1967): Interferon Production and RNA Inhibitors. J. Gen. Virol., 1:349-362.

Wang, J. C., D. Baumgarten, and B. M. Olivera (1967): On the Origin of Tertiary Turns in Covalently Closed Double-Stranded Cyclic DNA. Proc. Natl. Acad. Sci., 58:1852-1858.

Wang, J. C., and N. Davidson (1966a): Thermodynamic and Kinetic Studies on the Interconversion Between the Linear and Circular Forms of Phage Lambda DNA. J. Mol. Biol., 15:111-123.

Wang, J. C., and N. Davidson (1966b): On the Probability of Ring Closure of Lambda DNA. J. Mol. Biol., 19:469-482.

Wang, S. Y., M. H. Patrick, A. J. Varghese, and C. S. Rupert (1967): Concerning the Mechanism of Formation of UV-Induced Thymine Photo-Products in DNA. Proc. Natl. Acad. Sci., 57:465-472.

Ward, R., K. Shive, and R. Valentine (1967): Capsid Protein of f2 as Translational Repressor. Biochem. Biophys. Res. Commun., 29:8-13.

Warner, H. R., and J. E. Barnes (1966): Evidence for a Dual Role for the Bacteriophage T4-Induced Deoxycytidine Triphosphate Nucleotidohydrolase. Proc. Natl. Acad. Sci., 56:1233-1240.

Warner, J. R., A. Rich, and C. E. Hall (1962): Electron Microscope Studies of Ribosomal Clusters Synthesizing Hemoglobin. Science, 138:1399-1403.

Watanabe, Y. (1965): Double-Stranded RNA of Poliovirus-Infected HeLa Cells; Thermal Denaturation and Annealing. Biochim. Biophys. Acta. 95:515-518.

Watanabe, Y., K. Watanabe, N. Ishida, and Y. Hinuma (1965): A Poliovirus-Induced Double-Stranded RNA: Double-Helical Properties and Labeling Kinetics. J. Biochem., 58:322-333.

Waters, L. C., and G. D. Novelli (1967): A New Change in Leucine Transfer RNA Observed in *Escherichia coli* Infected with Bacteriophage T2. Proc. Natl. Acad. Sci., 57:979-985.

Watkins, J. F., and R. Dulbecco (1967): Production of SV40 Virus in Heterokaryons of Transformed and Susceptible Cells. Proc. Natl. Acad. Sci., 58:1396-1403.

Watson, D. H., W. C. Russell, and P. Wildy (1963): Electron Microscopic Particle Counts on Herpes Virus Using the Phosphotungstate Negative Staining Technique. Virology, 19:250-260.

Watson, D. H., and P. Wildy (1963): Some Serological Properties of Herpes Virus Particles Studied with the Electron Microscope. Virology, 21:100-111.

Watson, D. H., P. Wildy, and W. C. Russell (1964): Quantitative Electron Microscope Studies on the Growth of Herpes Virus Using the Techniques of Negative Staining and Ultramicrotomy. Virology, 24:523-538.

Watson, J. D. (1950): The Properties of X-ray-Inactivated Bacteriophage; I, Inactivation by Direct Effect. J. Bacteriol., 60:697-718.

Watson, J. D., and F. H. C. Crick (1953a): A Structure for Deoxyribose Nucleic Acid. Nature, 171:737-738.

Watson, J. D., and F. H. C. Crick (1953b): Genetical Implications of the Structure of Deoxyribonucleic Acid. Nature, 171:964-967.

Watson, J. D., and F. H. C. Crick (1953c): The Structure of DNA. Cold Spring Harbor Symposia Quant. Biol., 18:123-131.

Watson, J. D., and O. Maaløe (1953): Nucleic Acid Transfer from Parental to Progeny

Bacteriophage. Biochim. Biophys. Acta, 10:432-442. Reprinted in Stent, G. S. (1960): Papers on Bacterial Viruses. Boston, Little, Brown and Co., pp. 105-115.

Weidel, W., and E. Kellenberger (1955): The *E. coli* B-Receptor for the Phage T5; II, Electron Microscopic Studies. Biochim. Biophys. Acta, 17:1-9.

Weigert, M. G., E. Lanka, and A. Garen (1965): Amino Acid Substitutions Resulting from Suppression of Nonsense Mutations; II, Glutamine Insertion by the *Su*-2 Gene; Tyrosine Insertion by the *Su*-3 Gene. J. Mol. Biol., 14:522-527.

Weigle, J. (1961): Densities of Transducing Lambda Bacteriophages. J. Mol. Biol., 3:393-398.

Weigle, J. (1966): Assembly of Phage Lambda *in Vitro*. Proc. Natl. Acad. Sci., 55:1462-1466.

Weil, R. (1961): A Quantitative Assay for a Subviral Infective Agent Related to Polyoma Virus. Virology, 14:46-53.

Weil, R., and J. Vinograd (1963): The Cyclic Helix and Cyclic Coil Forms of Polyoma Viral DNA. Proc. Natl. Acad. Sci., 50:730-738.

Weinblum, D. (1967): Characterization of the Photodimers from DNA. Biochem. Biophys. Res. Commun., 27:384-390.

Weisberg, R. A. (1963): Delayed Appearance of Transformed Cells in Polyoma Virus-Infected Mouse Embryo Cultures. Virology, 21:669-671.

Weisberg, R. A., and J. A. Gallant (1967): Dual Function of the λ Prophage Repressor. J. Mol. Biol., 25:537-544.

Weiss, E., W. F. Myers, H. R. Dressler, and H. Chun-Hoon (1964): Glucose Metabolism by Agents of the Psittacosis-Trachoma Group. Virology, 22:551-562.

Weissbach, A., and L. A. Salzman (1967): The Biosynthesis of Phage Lambda DNA; the Structure of the First Intermediate. Proc. Natl. Acad. Sci., 58:1096-1101.

Weissmann, C., M. A. Billeter, M. C. Schneider, C. A. Knight, and S. Ochoa (1965): Replication of Viral RNA; VI, Nucleotide Composition of the Replicative Form of Tobacco Mosaic Virus RNA and of Its Component Strands. Proc. Natl. Acad. Sci., 53:653-656.

Weissmann, C., and P. Borst (1963): Double-Stranded Ribonucleic Acid Formation *in Vitro* by MS2 Phage-Induced RNA Synthetase. Science, 142:1188-1191.

Weissmann, C., P. Borst, R. H. Burdon, M. A. Billeter, and S. Ochoa (1964a): Replication of Viral RNA; III, Double-Stranded Replicative Form of MS2 Phage RNA. Proc. Natl. Acad. Sci., 51:682-690.

Weissmann, C., P. Borst, R. H. Burdon, M. A. Billeter, and S. Ochoa (1964b): Replication of Viral RNA; IV, Properties of RNA Synthetase and Enzymatic Synthesis of MS2 Phage RNA. Proc. Natl. Acad. Sci., 51:890-897.

Weissmann, C., and G. Feix (1966): Replication of Viral RNA; XI, Synthesis of Viral "Minus" Strands *in Vitro*. Proc. Natl. Acad. Sci., 55:1264-1268.

Wertz, R. K., C. C. O' Connor, A. S. Rabson, and G. T. O'Conor (1965): Mixed Infection of African Green Monkey Kidney Cells by Adenovirus 7 and SV40. Nature, 208:1350.

Whipple, H. E. (1965): Antiviral Substances. Ann. N. Y. Acad. Sci., 130(Art. 1):1-482.

Whitehouse, H. L. K. (1967): Crossover Model of Antibody Variability. Nature, 215:371-374.

Wiesmeyer, H. (1966): Prophage Repression as a Model for the Study of Gene Regulation; I, Titration of the λ Repressor. J. Bacteriol., 91:89-94.

Wilcox, W. C., and G. H. Cohen (1967): Soluble Antigens of Vaccinia-Infected Mammalian Cells; II, Time Course of Synthesis of Soluble Antigens and Virus Structural Proteins. J. Virol., 1:500-508.

Wilcox, W. C., H. S. Ginsberg, and T. F. Anderson (1963): Structure of Type 5 Adenovirus; II, Fine Structure of Virus Subunits; Morphologic Relationship of Structural Subunits to Virus-Specific Soluble Antigens from Infected Cells. J. Exptl. Med., 118:307-314.

Wildy, P., W. C. Russell, and R. W. Horne (1960a): The Morphology of Herpes Virus. Virology, 12:204-222.

Wildy, P., M. G. P. Stoker, I. A. MacPherson, and R. W. Horne (1960b): The Fine Structure of Polyoma Virus. Virology, 11:444-457.

Wildy, P., and D. H. Watson (1962): Electron Microscopic Studies on the Architecture of Animal Viruses. Cold Spring Harbor Symposia Quant. Biol., 27:25-47.

Williams, G. (1959): Virus Hunters. New York, Alfred A. Knopf, Inc.

Williams, R. C., S. J. Kass, and C. A. Knight (1960): Structure of Shope Papilloma Virus Particles. Virology, 12:48-58.

Williams, R. C., and R. W. G. Wyckoff (1946): Applications of Metallic Shadow-Casting to Microscopy. J. Appl. Physics, 17:23-33.

Williams Smith, H. (1948): Investigations on the Typing of Staphylococci by Means of Bacteriophage; I, The Origin and Nature of Lysogenic Strains. J. Hyg., 46:74-81.

Wilson, R. G., and J. P. Bader (1965): Viral Ribonucleic Acid Polymerase; Chick-Embryo Cells Infected with Vesicular Stomatitis Virus or Rous-Associated Virus. Biochim. Biophys. Acta, 103:549-557.

Winkler, U., H. E. Johns, and E. Kellenberger (1962): Comparative Study of Some Properties of Bacteriophage T4D Irradiated with Monochromatic Ultraviolet Light. Virology, 18:343-358.

Winocour, E. (1963): Purification of Polyoma Virus. Virology, 19:158-168.

Winocour, E. (1965): Attempts to Detect an Integrated Polyoma Genome by Nucleic Acid Hybridization; I, "Reconstruction" Experiments and Complementarity Tests Between Synthetic Polyoma RNA and Polyoma Tumor DNA. Virology, 25:276-288.

Winocour, E. (1967): On the Apparent Homology Between DNA from Polyoma Virus and Normal Mouse Synthetic RNA. Virology, 31:15-28.

Winocour, E., A. M. Kaye, and V. Stollar (1965): Synthesis and Transmethylation of DNA in Polyoma-Infected Cultures. Virology, 27:156-169.

Winocour, E., and L. Sachs (1960): Cell-Virus Interactions with the Polyoma Virus; I, Studies on the Lytic Interaction in the Mouse Embryo System. Virology, 11:699-721.

Witkin, E. M. (1966): Radiation-Induced Mutations and Their Repair. Science, 152:1345-1353.

Wittmann, H. G. (1963): Studies on the Nucleic Acid-Protein Correlation in Tobacco Mosaic Virus. In Engelhardt, V. A. (ed.): Proc. Fifth Intern. Congr. Biochem., Vol. 1. New York, Pergamon Press, pp. 240-254.

Wittmann, H. G., and C. Scholtissek (1966): Biochemistry of Viruses. Ann. Rev. Biochem., 35:299-334.

Wittmann, H. G., and B. Wittmann-Liebold (1963): Tobacco Mosaic Virus Mutants and the Genetic Coding Problem. Cold Spring Harbor Symposia Quant. Biol., 28:589-595.

Woese, C. (1960): Thermal Inactivation of Animal Viruses. Ann. N.Y. Acad. Sci., 83:741-751.

Wollman, E. L., and F. Jacob (1954): Lysogeny and Genetic Recombination in Escherichia coli K12. Reprinted in Stent, G. S. (1960): Papers on Bacterial Viruses. Boston, Little, Brown and Co., pp. 334-335.

Wood, T. R. (1965): Methods Useful in Evaluating 1-Adamantanamine Hydrochloride — a New Orally Active Synthetic Antiviral Agent. Ann. N.Y. Acad. Sci., 130:419-431.

Wood, W. B., and R. S. Edgar (1967): Building a Bacterial Virus. Sci. Amer., 217(July):60-74.

Woodson, B. (1967): Vaccinia mRNA Synthesis under Conditions Which Prevent Uncoating. Biochem. Biophys. Res. Commun., 27:169-175.

Woodson, B., and W. K. Joklik (1965): The Inhibition of Vaccinia Virus Multiplication by Isatin-β-Thiosemicarbazone. Proc. Natl. Acad. Sci., 54:946-953.

Wright, H. T., Jr., C. R. Goodheart, and A. Lielausis (1964): Human Cytomegalovirus; Morphology by Negative Staining. Virology, 23:419-424.

Wu, R., and A. D. Kaiser (1967): Mapping the 5'-Terminal Nucleotides of the DNA of Bacteriophage λ and Related Phages. Proc. Natl. Acad. Sci., 57:170-177.

Wulff, D. L. (1963): The Role of Thymine Dimer in the Photo-Inactivation of the Bacteriophage T4v_1. J. Mol. Biol., 7:431-441.

Wulff, D. L., and C. S. Rupert (1962): Disappearance of Thymine Photodimer in Ultraviolet Irradiated DNA Upon Treatment with a Photoreactivating Enzyme from Baker's Yeast. Biochem. Biophys. Res. Commun., 7:237-240.

Wyatt, G. R., and S. S. Cohen (1953): The Bases of the Nucleic Acids of Some Bacterial and Animal Viruses; the Occurrence of 5-Hydroxymethylcytosine. Biochem. J., 55:774-782.

Yabe, Y., L. Samper, E. Bryan, G. Taylor, and J. J. Trentin (1964): Oncogenic Effect of Human Adenovirus Type 12, in Mice. Science, 143:46-47.

Yabe, Y., L. Samper, G. Taylor, and J. J. Trentin (1963): Cancer Induction in Hamsters by Human Type 12 Adenovirus; Effect of Route of Injection. Proc. Soc. Exptl. Biol. Med., 113:221-224.

Yabe, Y., J. J. Trentin, and G. Taylor (1962): Cancer Induction in Hamsters by Human Type 12 Adenovirus; Effect of Age and of Virus Dose. Proc. Soc. Exptl. Biol. Med., 111:343-344.

Yamagishi, H., K. Nakamura, and H. Ozeki (1965): Cohesion Occurring Between DNA Molecules of Temperate Phages ϕ80 and Lambda or ϕ81. Biochem. Biophys. Res. Commun., 20:727-732.

Yamaguchi, J., Y. Hinuma, and J. T. Grace, Jr. (1967): Structure of Virus Particles Extracted from a Burkitt Lymphoma Cell Line. J. Virol., 1:640-642.

Yarmolinsky, M. B. (1963): Influence of Phages on the Synthesis of Host Enzymes of Bacteria. In Viruses, Nucleic Acids, and Cancer. Baltimore, The Williams and Wilkins Co., pp. 151-172.

Yarmolinsky, M. B., and H. Wiesmeyer (1960): Regulation by Coliphage Lambda of the Expression of the Capacity to Synthesize a Sequence of Host Enzymes. Proc. Natl. Acad. Sci., 46:1626-1645.

Yoshiike, K. (1968): Studies on DNA from Low-Density Particles of SV40; I, Heterogeneous Defective Virions Produced by Successive Undiluted Passages. Virology, 34:391-401.

Young, E. T., II, and R. L. Sinsheimer (1964): Novel Intracellular Forms of Lambda DNA. J. Mol. Biol., 10:562-564.

Youngner, J. S., and W. R. Stinebring (1964): Interferon Production in Chickens Injected with Brucella abortus. Science, 144:1022-1023.

Youngner, J. S., and W. R. Stinebring (1966): Comparison of Interferon Production in Mice by Bacterial Endotoxin and Statolon. Virology, 29:310-316.

Youngner, J. S., W. R. Stinebring, and S. E. Taube (1965): Influence of Inhibitors of Protein Synthesis on Interferon Formation in Mice. Virology, 27:541-550.

Zajac, I., and R. L. Crowell (1965): Location and Regeneration of Enterovirus Receptors of HeLa Cells. J. Bacteriol., 89:1097-1100.

Zelle, M. R., and A. Hollaender (1954): Monochromatic Ultraviolet Action Spectra and Quantum Yields for Inactivation of T1 and T2 Escherichia coli Bacteriophages. J. Bacteriol., 68:210-215.

Zimmerman, E. F., M. Heeter, and J. E. Darnell (1963): RNA Synthesis in Poliovirus-Infected Cells. Virology, 19:400-408.

Zimmerman, S. B., and A. Kornberg (1961): Deoxycytidine Di- and Triphosphate Cleavage by an Enzyme Formed in Bacteriophage-Infected Escherichia coli. J. Biol. Chem., 236:1480-1486.

Zinder, N. D., and J. Lederberg (1952): Genetic Exchange in Salmonella. J. Bacteriol., 64:679-699.

Zinder, N. D., and L. B. Lyons (1968): Cell Lysis; Another Function of the Coat Protein of the Bacteriophage f2. Science, 159:84-86.

Zinder, N. D., R. C. Valentine, M. Roger, and W. Stoeckenius (1963): f1, a Rod-Shaped Male-Specific Bacteriophage That Contains DNA. Virology, 20:638-640.

zur Hausen, H. (1968): Association of Adenovirus Type 12 Deoxyribonucleic Acid with Host Cell Chromosomes. J. Virol., 2:218-223.

INDEX

Page numbers in *italics* refer to illustrations. Page numbers in **boldface** refer to tables.

Absolute particle count, 76
Acridine, 266
Actinomycin D, *209*, 219, 220, 242, 245, 246, 251, *252*, 253
Action spectrum, 88, 89
Activation energy of inactivation, 84
Adeno-associated virus, 45, 229, *230*, 231
  human isolation, 231
Adenoviridae, 46
Adenovirion, DNA, 18
  number of proteins, 18
Adenovirus, *46*, 229, *230*
  capsomer, 18
  DNA, 287
    molecular weight, 160
  efficiency of plating, 76
  fiber antigen, 250
  growth cycle, *163*
  helper for adeno-associated virus, 232
  hybrid, 289
  inclusion body, 178, *179*
  inhibition by adeno-associated virus, 231, *232*
  interaction with SV40, 233, **234**
  messenger RNA, 169
  oncogenic, 337, *338*
  structure, 17, 18, *17*, *19*
  uncoating, 168
Adenylic kinase, *143*, 146
Adsorption
  cofactors, 121
  interference with, 251

Adsorption *(Continued)*
  phage, 117, *117*, 118
  rate of, 119
  reversible, 119
  sites, 120
Aleutian disease of mink, 363
"Almost viruses," 362
Amantadine, 251, *252*
Amber mutation, 263
Amyotrophic lateral sclerosis, 363
Androphagovirinae, 56
Animal virus, efficiency of plating, 76
Antibody, 100
  action on phage tail, 114
  complement fixing, 101
  development, 104-106, *105*, 113
  hemagglutination, inhibiting, 101
  in vitro synthesis, 105, 106
  neutralizing, 101
  persistence, 107
  precipitating, 100
  protection of host, 107
  response in disease, 108, 113
  synthesis, 103
Antibody molecule, structure, 104, *104*
Antigen, 99
  amino acid composition, 100
  cell protein, 100
  development, 100
  enzyme, 100
  group-specific, 101
Antiserum, reference, 101

Arboviridae, **52**, 57
Arginine, 185
Arrhenius equation, 84
Assay
  biochemical analysis, 60
  by electron microscopy, 62, *62*
  by optical density, 61
  hemagglutination, 63
  infectivity, 63
  particle counts, 61
  quantal, 64
  radioactivity, 61
Assembly, 222
  phage, 133, 134
  spontaneous, 13
Aster yellows virus, 250
Asymmetric semiconservative replication, 214, *215*
Attachment sites, 120
Autoclave, 80
Avian leukosis complex, 54, **318**, 320
Avian myeloblastosis virus, 320
Avidity, 113
Avipoxvirus, 44
Azure mutation, 263

B virus, 48
Bacteria, compared with viruses, 2
  phage attachment sites, 120
Bacteriocin, 362
Bacteriophage
  classification, 49, 50
  discovery, 6
  efficiency of plating, 76
  filamentous, 47
  growth of, 6
  male specific, 47
  T4, inactivation, 88, *90*
  T-even, *49*
    DNA, 35
    structure, 34, *35*
  T-odd, 50, *51*
  T-phages, 48
Binary fission, 355, *356,* 357, 359, *359*
Bittner virus, 55
Blue tongue disease, 56
Bovine papilloma virus, DNA, *158*
Bovine papular dermatitis virus, 43
Breakage-and-reunion, 276, *277, 278*
5-Bromodeoxyuridine, *253, 254*
5-Bromouracil, 265
Bronchovirus, 54
Browsing, 202
"Burkitt virus, " 335
Burst size, *117*

Cabbage mosaic virus, 50
Camel pox, 43
Campbell model, 303, *303*
Canary pox, 44
Capsid, 99
  defined, 13
Capsid protein, polioviral, *206*
Capsomer
  adenovirus, 18
  defined, 13
  herpesvirus, 21
  hexon, 18, *20*
  penton, 18, *20*
  polyoma virus, 24
Carcinoma, 316
Cardiovirus, 55
Cell-free synthesis, protein, 139
  φX174 DNA, 189
Chicken leukemia, discovery, 6
Chicken sarcoma virus, discovery, 6
Chickenpox virus, 48
Chikungunya virus, 59
Chitovirales, **42**
Chlamydia, 357, **357**, 358
  chemical composition, 360, *360*
    metabolism, 360
    ribosomes, 360, 361
5-Chlorodeoxyuridine, *253,* 254
Chloroform, 79
Chorioallantoic membrane, 73
Circular DNA, 158, *158, 159*
Circular permutation, 285, *286*
Cistron, 281
Classification of plants and animals, 37
Coat protein, 99
Colchicine, 222
Columbia SK virus, 56
Common cold virus, 54, 55
Competence, immune, 108
Complement fixation, 101
Complement-fixing antibody, 101
Complementation, 274
Complex symmetry, 32
Conditional-lethal mutant, 262
Conservative replication, 152, *152,* 214, 215
Contact inhibition, 331
Contagious pustular dermatitis virus, 43
Contagium vivum fluidum, 5
Conversion, 307
  antigenic, 345
Copy-choice, 276, 277
Core, tail, 126
Cowpea chlorotic mottle virus, assembly, 222
Cowpox virus, 43
  DNA, 33
Coxsackievirus, 55

CPE, 177
Crossreactivation, 93, *93*, 96
Croup, 46
Crystallization, tobacco mosaic virus, 7
Cubic symmetry, 12
Cyclic DNA, 158, *158*, *159*, 336
  φX174, 188, 189
Cytidine diphosphate reductase, 175
Cytomegalovirus, 48
  growth cycle, *163*
  human, *21*, *23*
  inclusion body, 180, 181
  thermal inactivation, *81*
Cytopathic effect, 177, 200, 235
Cytopathology, 235
  molecular mechanism, 180, 181
Cytosine arabinoside, 254

Dark repair, 92, *92*
Darwin, Charles, 38
Defective virus, 227, 350
Denaturation, DNA, 158, *158*, *159*
Dengue virus, 59, 212
Density gradient analysis, 138
Deoxybinala, **42**, 48
Deoxycubica, **42**, 44
Deoxycytidine triphosphatase, *143*, 144,
  145
Deoxycytidylate deaminase, 175
Deoxycytidylate hydroxymethylase, *143*,
  143, *144*
Deoxycytidylate kinase, *145*, 175
Deoxycytidylic deaminase, *143*, 145, *145*
Deoxyguanylic kinase, *143*, 146
Deoxyhelica, 42, **42**
Deoxyribonuclease, 98, 149
Deoxythymidylate kinase, *143*, 147
Deoxyuridine diphosphatase, *143*, 146
Deoxyuridine kinase, 174
Deoxyuridine triphosphatase, *143*, 146
Deoxyvira, 41, **42**
Dermovirus, 43
Dihydrofolate reductase, 149, 175
Dilution series, 64
Diphtheria, prophage, 308
Dispersive replication, 152, *152*
Distemper (canine) virus, 53
DNA
  base ratio, 188
  binding to RNA polymerase, 159
  cellular, induction of synthesis, 176
  condensation, 133
  cyclic, 28, 158, *158*, *159*
  denaturation, 158, *158*, *159*
  function, 142, *142*, 150
  glucosylated, 148, **149**

DNA *(Continued)*
  melting temperature, 188
  phage precursor pool, 131
  replication, 152, *152*
  single-stranded, criteria for, 188
  synthesis, phage, 130, *130*, 131, *132*
  transfer, fragmentary, 153, *155*
    from parent to progeny, 151
    phage, 130
DNA polymerase, *143*, 147, 175
DNA synthesis, inhibition, 129
DNA transcription, 93
Double-strand breaks, 86, *86*

"Early" genes, and transformation, 353
Early proteins, 142, 143
Eastern equine encephalitis virus, 58
Echovirus, 55
Eclipse, phage, 127, *127*, 128
ED_{50}, 66
Efficiency of planting, 76
EID_{50}, 66
EMC, 199, 207, 209, 212
  effect on host cell, 220
  efficiency of plating, 76
  plaque mutant, *260*, 261
Encephalitis viruses, 59
Encephalomyocarditis virus, 56
End point, 66
Endonuclease, 189
Enterovirus, 55
Enzymes, DNA-animal-virus induced,
  171-176
  phase induced, *143*, *144*, *145*, 146-150
EOP, 76
Equilibrium density gradient centrifuga-
  tion, 138
Equine abortion virus, DNA, *160*
  molecular weight, 160
Erythroblastosis virus, murine, 322
Ether, 79
Excision-and-repair enzyme, 92, *92*, 279
Exclusion, 149
Exopolynucleotidase, 188
Exponential decrease, 80
Evolution of viruses, 38

F pili, 197, 204
f1, 47, 199
f1 phage, 197
f2, *201*, 206-208
  lysis, 225
fd, *47*, 197
Feline leukemia virus, **318**

Feline panleukopenia virus, 45
Fiber antigen, 18, *20*
   adenoviral, 250
Fibroma virus, 334
Fibromavirus, 44
Filamentous phage, 197, 198
Filterability, 1
Filterable virus, 1
Filtration, 230
Filtration end point, 10, *11*
Flexiviridales, 50
Flow-through experiment, 129
5-Fluorodeoxyuridine, 235, *253,* 254
p-Fluorophenylalanine, 246, 254
Foot-and-mouth disease virus, 55
   discovery, 5
Formaldehyde, inactivation by, 98
Fowlpox, *43,* 44
Fowlpox virus, DNA, *161*
Frame-shift mutation, 266, *267*
Friend leukemia virus, 55, **318**
Fruit fly, 258
Fuller, Buckminster, 14

Gallivirus, 54
Gel electrophoresis, 217, *217*
Genetic code, *266*
Genetic continuity, 1
Genetic map, 279
   circular, 283, *284*
   correlated with nucleotide sequence,
      281
   λ, 297, *297*
   prophage, 302
Genotypic mixing, 290
Geodesic domes, 14
German measles, 53
Giant cell, 181, 220
Glucosyl transferase, *143,* 148, 149
Goat pox, 43
Gradacol membranes, 10
Graffi leukemia virus, 55, **318**
Gross leukemia virus, 55, **318**, 322, 336
Group-specific antigen, 101
Growth cycle, DNA-animal viruses, 162
   phage, 116, 117, *117*
Guinea pig leukemia virus, **318**, 322
Gymnovirales, **52**, 55

H1 virus, 45, 233
H3 virus, 45
Haplovirales, **42**, 44
Helical symmetry, 28
Helper virus, 227, 320, 326
Hemagglutination, 46, 200
   assay, 63

Hemagglutination-inhibiting antibody,
   101
Hepatitis virus, 64
Herpes simplex virus, 48
   differential counts, 62
   DNA, molecular weight, 160
Herpes zoster, 48
Herpes-like (Burkitt) virus, 335
Herpesviridae, 47
Herpesvirus
   attachment, 22
   chemical composition, 22, 23
   DNA, 22
   four kinds of particles, 22, *23*
   inclusion body, 180, *181*
   maturation, 184, 185
   messenger RNA, 170
   morphology and infectivity, 21, 22, 23
   penetration, 22
   peplos, 22
   structure, 18
   uncoating, 168
Hershey-Chase experiment, 124, *125*
Heteroduplex heterozygote, 283
Heterogenote, 313
Heterozygote, recombinational, 282, *282*
Hexon, *20*
Hit number, 83
Hit theory, 82
Horizontal transmission, 319
Horse pox, 43
Host cell, virus effects on, 220, *221*
Host-controlled variation, 270
Host-range mutant, *259,* 261
Human malignancy and viruses, 353
Human wart virus, 336
Hyaluronic acid synthetase, 330
Hybrid, 288
Hybridization, molecular, 139, 140
5-Hydroxymethylcytosine, 131, *131*
Hydroxymethyldeoxycytidylic kinase,
   143, 144 *145*

Icosahedral deltrahedra, classes, **25**
Icosahedron, *14*
   defined, 13
ID$_{50}$, 66
Immune competence, 108
Immune tolerance, 108
Immunity substance, 298, *298*
Inactivation, 78
   by antibody, mechanism, 113
Inactivation constant, 83
Inclusion body, 178
Indicator cells, 292
Induction, 308, *309*
   of SV40, 344
   zygotic, 309

Infectious canine hepatitis, 46
Infectious dose, 66
Infectious RNA, 204
Infective center, 118
Infectivity assay, 63
   error, 74
Influenza virus, 53, 64, 212
   actinomycin D and, *209*
   assembly, 222, *223*, *224*, 225
   external membrane, 31
   internal component, 31
   multiplicity reactivation, 94
   size, 31, 52
Injection, 126, *126*
Inoviridae, 47
Integration, 302
Interference
   between plant viruses, 250
   chemical, 251
   without interferon, 249
Interferon, 239
   antibody, 242
   disease and, 248
   effect on polysomes, 246, **247**
   induction, 241
   mechanism of action, 244, *247*
   mechanism of synthesis, 242, *243*
   properties, biological, 240
     chemical and physical, 241
   specificity, 240
   transformation and, 352
Intracellular parasites, 2
Intrinsic motility, 1
5-Iododeoxyuridine, *253*, 254
Iridoviridae, 46
Irreversible attachment, 121
Isatin-β-thiosemicarbazone, 254, 255, *255*

Japanese B encephalitis virus, 59
Jenner, Edward, 4

K virus, 46, 336
Kärber method, 68
Keratoconjunctivitis, 46
Kuru, 363

λ, 50
   circular DNA, *304*
Latent period, 117, *117*, 127, *127*
LD$_{50}$, 66
Lettuce necrotic yellows virus, 54
Leukemia viruses, **318**
   maturation, *323*
   mycoplasma and, 324

Leukoencephalitis, subacute sclerosing, 363
Ligase, 304
Light inactivation, 95
Linnaeus, 37
Lipid solvents, 79
Logarithmic decrease, 80
Lucké virus, 334
Lysis, 135, 225
Lysis-from-without, 123
Lysogenic cycle, *310*
Lysogeny
   abortive, 306
   conversion, 307
   curing, 294
   genetic control, *301*, 302
   genetic property of cells, 294
   immunity substance, 298, *298*
   integration, 302
   repressor, 297, 298, *298*
Lysozyme, 121

M13, 47, 197
Mad itch, 48
Maize mosaic virus, 54
Male-specific phage, 197
Maloney leukemia virus, **318**
Mammary tumor virus, 55, **318**, 319, 324, *325*
   transmission, 324
Marker rescue, 94
Mating, phage, 276
Maturation, 221
   leukemia virus, *323*
   phage, 127, *127*, 132
Measles virus, 53, 220
Melting temperature, 188
Mendel, Gregor, 257
Mengo, 56, *201*, 207, 222
Meselson-Stahl experiment, 153, *154*
Messenger RNA
   adenovirus, 169
   "early" and "late," 140
   phage, 137, *137*, 138
   turnover, 140, 170
   vaccinia, 169
Metabolic systems, 1
Microviridae, 44
Milker's nodule virus, 44, 334
Mitomycin C, 253
MM virus, 56
Molluscovirus, 44
Molluscum contagiosum virus, 44, 333
Moloney sarcoma virus, 55
Monkey cell adapting component, 290
MS2, 56, 199, 206, 207, 212
Multiple hit curves, *83*
Multiple sclerosis, 363
Multiplicity of infection, 120

Multiplicity reactivation, 93, *94*, 95, 96
Mumps virus, 53
  internal component, 31
Murine leukemia virus, **318**, 321
  maturation, *323*
Murine sarcoma virus, **318**, 324
Murivirus, 54
Murray Valley encephalitis virus, 59
Mutagenesis, 93
Mutants, plaque morphology, 74
Mutation, 1, 258
  mechanism, 264
Mutation rate, 264, **264**
Mycoplasma, 355, *356*
Myeloblastosis virus, 326
Myxoma virus, 334
Myxoviridae, 50
Myxovirus
  assembly, 222
  size, 31
  structure, 31

Napoviridae, **52**, 55
Napovirinae, 55
Necrotic lesion counts, 76
Negative stain, 12
Neovirus, 56
Neuraminidase, 164, 202
Neutralization
  early and late sera, 113
  kinetics, 102
  rate constant, 102
  reaction, 109, 110, *110*
  reactivation, 112, 114
  reversibility, 111, 112, *112*
  test, 102
Neutralizing antibody, 101
Newcastle disease virus, 53, *201*, 207
  actinomycin D and, *209*
  interference, 239
Nitrous acid, 265
  inactivation by, 97
"No-longer viruses," 355
Non-overlapping genetic code, *266*
Nucleases, 98
Nucleic acid, action of ultraviolet, 88
  arrangement in virion, 28
Nucleocapsid, defined, 13

Ochre mutation, 263
One-step growth, 116, 117, *117*
O'nyong-nyong fever virus, 59
Operon, 206
Orf virus, 43

P^{32}, inactivation, 95, *96*
  efficiency, 95, 97
  mechanism, 96, *97*
  suicide, 97
P^{33}, inactivation, 96
Papilloma and polyoma viruses, size difference, 27, *27*, **27**
Papilloma virus, 45, 336
Papilloviridae, 45
Papovavirus, 46
Parainfluenza virus, 53
  nucleocapsid, 32, *32*
  RNA, 32
Paramyxoviridae, 53
Paramyxovirus, 53
Parvoviridae, 45
Passage A virus, 55, 322
Pasteur, Louis, 4
Pea mosaic virus, 50
Penetration, 123
Penicillium stoloniferum, 241
Penton, 18, *20*
Peplomers, 13
Peplos, definition, 13
  herpesvirus, 22
Peplovirales, **42**, 47
Persistent fraction, 111, *111*
Phage
  host-controlled modification, 271
  protein, precursor, 129
    synthesis, 129, *130*
  synthesis, 136, 137, *137*
Phage-induced enzymes, 143-150
Phagoviridae, 48
Phenotypic mixing, 133, *134*, 274
ϕX174, 44, *44*
  capsid protein, 189
  DNA, 44, 188, 189
    cell-free synthesis, 189
    replication, 194, *194*, 195, *195*, 196, 269, **270**
  growth curve, 190, *190*, 191
  inactivation by P^{32}, 97
  induced enzymes, 190
  P^{32} suicide, 189
  structure, 44
Phosphodiesterase, pancreatic, 189
Phosphotungstic acid stain, 12
Photodynamic inactivation, 95
Photoproduct, 89
Photoreactivating enzyme, 91, 92
Photoreactivation, 91
  action spectrum, 91
  in pseudorabies virus, 92
  in tobacco mosaic virus, 92
Picornavirinae, 55
Pinocytosis, 164
Poisson distribution, 70, 80, 120
Poliomyelitis, 3
  vaccine, 4

Polioviral capsid protein, *206*
Polioviral RNA, *210*
Polioviral specific proteins, 206
Poliovirus, 55, 203, 207, 208, 212
  attenuated, 238
  effect on host cell, 220
  inactivation, by formaldehyde, 98
    by P³², 97
  infectious RNA, 222, 244
  replication in cytoplasm, 222
Plantain agent, 54, *54*
Plaque mutants, 74
Plaque purification of virus, 263
Plaque titration
  animal virus, 71, *72*
  linearity with dilution, 75, *75*
  number of virus particles per plaque,
    74, 75
  phage, 71
  sampling error, 74
Plaque-type mutation, 258, *259*, *260*
Polycistronic messenger RNA, 205
Polykaryocyte, 181
Polyoma and papilloma viruses, size dif-
    ference, 27, *27*, **27**
Polyoma virus, 45, 336
  assembly, 183
  capsomers, 24
  DNA, 158, *159*
    infectious, 164
    molecular weight, 159
  filamentous, 28
  growth cycle, *163*
  in transformed cells, 347, **348**
  inactivation by P³², 97
  messenger RNA, 170, *170*
  number of capsomers, 24
  temperature-sensitive mutant, 350
  uncoating, 168
Polysome, *142*, 170, 205, 220
Potato spindle tuber virus, 363
Potato virus X, 50
Poxviridae, 42, **42**
Poxvirus, 43
Poxvirus
  factory, 169, 178, *184*
  inclusion body, 178
  maturation, 182, *183*, 185
  size, 33
  structure, 33, *33*
  uncoating, 166, *167*, *168*
Precipitating antibody, 100
Primer, DNA, 147
Productive response, 294
Proflavine, 129
Prophage
  conversion, 307
  detachment, 311, *312*
  diphtherial toxin, 308
  function, 306

Prophage *(Continued)*
  genetic map, 302
  homology with host DNA, 305
  induction, 307, 308
  nature, 294
  number per cell, 295
  on bacterial chromosome, 295
  size, 295
Protein
  action of ultraviolet, 88, *90*
  "early," 142, 143, 255
  "early" and "late," 171
Provirus, 327
Pseudocowpox, 44
Pseudorabies virus, 48
  inhibition of DNA by FUdR, 21
Psittacosis agents, 357, **357**, 358
Pulse-chase experiment, 129
Puromycin, 219, 246, 254, *255*
Pustulovirus, 43
Putrescine, 35

Qβ, 207, 216, *216*
Quantal assay, 64, *65*, **65**
  Kärber method, 68
  sampling error, 74
  statistical methods, 68
Quantum yield, 87

R17, *56*, 199, 212, 213
  assembly, 222
Rabbit fibroma, 44
Rabbit myxoma, 44
Rabbitpox virus, DNA, 160
Rabies virus, 4, 54, *54*
Radioisotopes, 61
Radiophosphorus, inactivation by, 95, *96*
Rapid-lysis mutant, 259, *259*
Rauscher leukemia virus, 55, **318**, 326
Receptor, 164, 203
Receptor destroying enzyme, 202
Receptor gradient, 202
Receptor sites, 120, 123, *123*
Recombination, 93, 94
  animal virus, 288
  discovery, 7
  frequency, 276, 279
  phage, 275
Reductive response, 294
Reed-Muench method, 66
Regulation of transcription, 206
Renal carcinoma of frogs, 334
Reoviridae, **52**, 57
Reovirus, 57, *57*, 200, *201*
  multiplicity reactivation, 94
  replication in cytoplasm, 222

Replicase, 207
Replication of nucleic acid, 267, *268*, **270**
Replicative form, 212
 φX174, 192
Replicative intermediate, 213
Repressor, 309
 binding to DNA, *299*, *300*
 genetic control, *301*, 302
 in transformed cells, 344
 lysogeny, 297, 298, *298*
Respiratory syncytial virus, 54
Response to stimuli, 1
Rhabdovirales, 50, **52**
Rhinovirus, 55
Ribocubica, **52**, 55
Ribohelica, 50, **52**
Ribonuclease, 98
Ribosomes
 after infection, 141
 carrying genetic information, 138
 density labeled, 139
Ribovira, 50, **52**
Rickettsia, 357
Rigidoviridales, 50
Rinderpest virus, 53
Rise time, *117*
RNA
 cellular, inhibition of, by virus, 221
 double-stranded, 211, *211*, 212, 218
 during phage latent period, 137, *137*
 evolution in vitro, 218
 messenger. See *Messenger RNA.*
 self-replicating, 199, 207
 synthesis in vitro, 215, *216*, *217*, 218
 viral induced synthesis, 220, *221*
RNA polymerase, DNA-dependent, 207,
    219, 220, 253
 RNA-dependent, 207, 229, 253
Rous sarcoma virus, 54, **318**, 320
 defectiveness, 236, 326
 human chromosomes and, *321*
 provirus, 327
Rubella virus, 53

S13, 44
Sagovirales, 50, **52**
St. Louis encephalitis virus, 59
Salk vaccine, 98
Sarcoma, 316
Satellite tobacco necrosis virus, 228, *228*,
    229
Scrapie, 363
Sealase, 304
Semiconservative replication, 152, *152*,
    154
Semliki Forest virus, 58, 212
 inactivation by light, 95
Sendai virus, 53, 344

Serial dilution, 64
Serum blocking power, 128
Serum neutralization test, 102
Shadowing, in electron microscopy, 12
Sheath, contraction, 124, 125
 structure, 125
Sheep pox, 43
Shope fibroma virus, 334
Shope papilloma virus, 336
 DNA, 159
 levo, 26
Sialidase, 202
Siamese cat, temperature-sensitive mu-
    tant, 262
Sindbis virus, 58, 246
 assembly, 225
Single-burst experiment, 268
Single-strand breaks, 86, *86*
Skew class, 25
 dextro, 26
 levo, 26
Smallpox, 3
Smallpox vaccine, development, 4
Specific infectivity, 76
Specificity of interferon, 240
Spermidine, 35
Spleen weight, assay for leukemia virus,
    73
Spontaneous assembly, 13
Statistical estimate of end-point, 68
Statistics of titration, 70, 74
Statolon, 241, 248
Stomatoviridae, 54
Structural units, arrangement of, *16*
 number of, **15**
Structure
 bacteriophage tail, 35
 influenza virus, 31
 poxviruses, 33
 tobacco mosaic virus, 28, 29, *29*, *30*
 vesicular stomatitis virus, 33
Sucrose gradient analysis, 210, *210*, *211*
Supercoil, DNA, 158, *158*, *159*
 φX174 DNA, 193
Superinfection exclusion, 149, 239
Suppressor gene, 263
Survival, ultraviolet, 87, 88
SV5, nucleocapsid, 32, *32*
 RNA, 32
SV40, 45, 336
 enhancement of adenoviral oncogenic-
    ity, 235
 in transformed cells, 347, **348**
 infectious DNA, 165
 interaction with adenovirus, 233, **234**
Swine pox, 43
Symmetry
 axes, 14
 binal, 13
 complex, 13, 32

Symmetry *(Continued)*
  cubic, 12
  helical, 13, 28

T antigen, 345
Tadpole-shaped viruses, 34
Tail
  collar, 36
  core, 35, 126
  fibers, 36, 121, *121*
    action of antibody, 114
  sheath, 35
    contraction, 124, 125
    structure, 125
  spikes, 36
Target cell, myeloblastosis virus, 330
Target size, for plaque and focus forma-
    tion, 349, **349**
Target volume, 85
TCID$_{50}$, 66
Temperature-sensitive mutants, 262
Temperature-sensitive repressor, 310
Terminal redundancy, 283, *285*
Thermal inactivation, 79
  mechanism, 84
  theory, 80-82
Three-factor cross, 280
Thylaxoviridae, 54
Thymidine kinase, 171-174
  in transformed cells, 347
Thymidylate kinase, 174, 175
Thymidylate synthetase, *143*, 146, 147,
    148, 174
  inhibition, 254
Thymine dimer, 89, *91*
Thymus, in immune competence, 108
Tipula iridescent virus, *14*, 46
Tobacco mosaic virus, 50, 199, 207, 212
  assay, 73
    efficiency, 76
  assembly, 222
  crystallization, 7
  differential counts, *62*, 63
  disaggregation and reassembly, 30
  discovery, 5
  mutants, 29
  one-dimensional crystal, 30
  RNA, 30
  structure, 28, 29, *29*, *30*
Tobacco necrosis virus, 227, *228*
  infectious RNA, 227
Tobacco rattle mosaic virus, 50
Togavirales, **52**, 57
Tolerance, immune, 108
Transcription, interference with, 251, 253
  regulation, 206
Transduction, 311, *312*
  generalized, 313

Transduction *(Continued)*
  high frequency, 312
  low frequency, 311
  specialized, 313
Transfer, from parent to progeny, 208
Transfer experiment, 151
  DNA-animal-virus, 177
  phage, 130
  ϕX174, 192
Transfer RNA, 141
Transformation, 338, *339*, *340*
  by SV40, 337
  interferon and, 352
  lysogeny analogy, 342
  target size, 349, **349**
Transformed cells, compared with nor-
    mal, 340, *341*
  viral genome in, 347, **348**
Translation inhibition, 254
Translation inhibitory protein, 247
Transplant antigen, 344, *345*
  viral specificity, *346*
Triangulation number, 25, 41
Tumor cells, properties, 315
Tumor viruses, RNA, morphology, *319*
Turbidity, following phage infection, 122,
    122
Turnip yellow mosaic virus, 55, 207, 212
Two-factor cross, 280

Ultraviolet inactivation, 87
  mechanism, 88, *90*
Uncoating enzyme, poxviral, 166
Uracil, halogen derivatives, 253, *253*, 254
Urovirales, **42**, 48

Vaccine
  live, 5
  measles, 5
  poliomyelitis, 5
  rabies, 5
  smallpox, 4
  yellow fever, 5
Vaccinia virus, 43
  attachment, 164, *165*
  DNA, 161
  growth cycle, *163*
  messenger RNA, 167, 169, 170, 172
Vacuolating agent, 336
Varicella virus, 48
Variola, 43
Venezuelan equine encephalitis virus, 58
Vertical transmission, 319
Vesicular stomatitis virus, 54, *54*
  structure, 33, *34*
Vibrio cholera, 164, 202

Viral antigen, 99
Virion, defined, 13
Virogeny, 344
Virology, highlights in development of, 3
Viropexis, 164
Virus(es). See also names of specific viruses.
  "almost," 362
  classification of, by base composition, 39
    by base sequence, 40
    by chemical composition, 40
    by molecular weight, 40
    proposed by Provisional Committee for Nomenclature of Viruses, 41
  definition of, 2
  evolution of, 38
  helper, 227, 320, 326
  living nature of, 2
  "no-longer," 355
  origin of, as degenerate cells, 3
    as primitive life, 3
    from cell organelles, 3
  size determination, 9
    by electron microscopy, 10-12
    by filtration, 10
Virus-directed enzymes, 207

Wart virus, 45, 336
  dextro, 26
West Nile encephalitis virus, 59
Western equine encephalitis virus, 58
  inhibition by interferon, 245
White clover mosaic virus, 50
Wound tumor virus, 56, 200

X14 virus, 45
X-ray diffraction, 29
X-ray inactivation, 84
  effect of, direct, 85, 85
    indirect, 84
    on nucleic acid, 86
  mechanism, 86

Yaba virus, 43, 44, 333
Yellow fever virus, 59

ZIK/1, 212
Zygotic induction, 309, 344